# Applied Mathematics

## The Consortium for Foundation Mathematics

| | |
|---|---|
| Ralph Bertelle | *Columbia-Greene Community College* |
| Judith Bloch | *University of Rochester* |
| Roy Cameron | *SUNY Cobleskill* |
| Carolyn Curley | *Erie Community College–South Campus* |
| Ernie Danforth | *Corning Community College* |
| Brian Gray | *Howard Community College* |
| Arlene Kleinstein | *SUNY Farmingdale* |
| Kathleen Milligan | *Monroe Community College* |
| Patricia Pacitti | *SUNY Oswego* |
| Rick Patrick | *Adirondack Community College* |
| Renan Sezer | *LaGuardia Community College* |
| Patricia Shuart | *Polk Community College* |
| Sylvia Svitak | *Queensborough Community College* |
| Assad J. Thompson | *LaGuardia Community College* |

Taken from:

*Mathematical Models with Applications*
by The Consortium for Foundation Mathematics

*Mathematics in Action: Algebraic, Graphical, and Trigonometric Problem Solving*
by The Consortium for Foundation Mathematics

*Mathematics in Action: Algebraic, Graphical, and Numerical Problem Solving*
by The Consortium for Foundation Mathematics

**Custom Publishing**

New York   Boston   San Francisco
London   Toronto   Sydney   Tokyo   Singapore   Madrid
Mexico City   Munich   Paris   Cape Town   Hong Kong   Montreal

Cover Art: Courtesy of the National Park Service.

Excerpts taken from:

*Mathematical Models with Applications,* Texas Edition
by The Consortium for Foundation Mathematics
Copyright © 2008 by Pearson Education, Inc.
Published by Addison Wesley
Boston, Massachusetts 02116

*Mathematics in Action: Algebraic, Graphical, and Trigonometric Problem Solving*
by The Consortium for Foundation Mathematics
Copyright © 2008 by Pearson Education, Inc.
Published by Addison Wesley

*Mathematics in Action: Algebraic, Graphical, and Numerical Problem Solving*
by The Consortium for Foundation Mathematics
Copyright © 2008 by Pearson Education, Inc.
Published by Addison Wesley

Printed in the United States of America

10 9 8 7 6 5 4 3    V0ZN    14 13 12


2009360265

CF


**Pearson
Custom Publishing**
is a division of

www.pearsonhighered.com    ISBN 10: 0-558-20315-9
ISBN 13: 978-0-558-20315-3

# Contents

CHAPTER 1    INTRODUCTION TO PROBLEM SOLVING AND MATHEMATICAL MODELS        1

**Activity 1.1**    **Wild about Harry    1**

Objectives:    1. Practice communication skills.

2. Organize information.

3. Write a solution in sentences.

4. Develop problem-solving skills.

**Activity 1.2**    **The Classroom    3**

Objectives:    1. Organize information.

2. Develop problem-solving strategies.

• Draw a picture.

• Recognize a pattern.

• Do a simpler problem.

3. Communicate problem-solving ideas.

**Activity 1.3**    **Make Me an Offer    10**

Objectives:    1. Use the basic steps for problem-solving.

2. Translate verbal statements into algebraic equations.

3. Use the basic principles of algebra to solve real-world problems.

4. Use formulas to solve problems.

**Activity 1.4**    **Proportional Reasoning    20**

Objectives:    1. Use proportional reasoning as a problem-solving strategy.

2. Write a proportion and then solve the resulting proportion.

3. Determine the relative error in a measurement or prediction using a linear model.
4. Interpret the slope and $y$-intercept of linear functions in contextual situations.
5. Use the slope-intercept form of linear equations to solve problems.

Objectives:
1. Determine the equation for a linear function that includes two given points.
2. Interpret the slope and $y$-intercept of a linear function in contextual situations.
3. Use the point-slope form $y - k = m(x - h)$ of linear equations to solve problems.

Objectives:
1. Construct scatterplots from sets of data pairs.
2. Recognize when patterns of points in a scatterplot have a linear form.
3. Recognize when the pattern in the scatterplot shows that the two variables are positively related or negatively related.
4. Identify individual data points, called outliers, that fall outside the general pattern of the other data.
5. Estimate and draw a line of best fit through a set of points in a scatterplot.
6. Determine residuals between the actual value and the predicted value for each point in the data set.
7. Use a graphing calculator to determine a line of best fit by the least-squares method.
8. Measure the strength of the correlation (association) by a correlation coefficient.
9. Recognize that a strong correlation does not necessarily imply a linear or a cause-and-effect relationship.

Objective:
1. Understand the need to first make a scatterplot of the data before calculating a correlation coefficient and regression line.

Objectives:
1. Determine the equation of a regression line using a graphing calculator.
2. Use the regression equation to interpolate and extrapolate.

Objectives:
1. Collect and organize data in a table.
2. Plot data in a scatterplot.
3. Recognize linear patterns in paired data.
4. Determine a linear regression equation.

Objectives:
1. Graph a piecewise linear function.
2. Write a piecewise linear function to represent a given situation.
3. Determine if a piecewise function is continuous.
4. Graph a function defined by $y = |x - c|$.

# To the Teacher

## Our Vision

*Applied Mathematics* is intended to build on previous mathematics courses, including Algebra I, and to place emphasis on bringing about a deeper understanding of those mathematical relationships that will help students gain mathematical literacy in the real world, show the connection between algebra and statistics, and simultaneously help them build a strong foundation for future study in mathematics and other disciplines. The main goals for this textbook are to teach students how to **problem-solve**, **communicate** and **reason** mathematically, make **mathematical connections**, create and interpret mathematical **representations** and **models**, and make efficient and appropriate use of **technology** to solve problems. *Applied Mathematics* is based on the principle that students learn mathematics best by doing mathematics within a meaningful context. In keeping with this premise, students solve problems in a series of realistic situations, or investigations, from which the crucial need for mathematics arises. *Applied Mathematics* guides students toward developing a sense of independence and taking responsibility for their own learning. Students are encouraged to construct, reflect on, apply, and describe their own mathematical models, which they use to solve meaningful problems. We see this as the key to bridging the gap between abstraction and application and as the basis for transfer learning. Appropriate technology is integrated throughout the book, allowing students to interpret real-life data verbally, numerically, symbolically, and graphically.

We expect that by using the *Applied Mathematics* book all students will be able to achieve the following goals:

- Develop mathematical intuition and a relevant base of mathematical knowledge.
- Gain experiences that connect classroom learning with real-world applications.
- Learn to work in groups as well as independently.
- Increase knowledge of mathematics through explorations with appropriate technology.
- Develop a positive attitude about learning and using mathematics.
- Build techniques of reasoning for effective problem solving.
- Learn to apply, display, and communicate knowledge through alternative means of assessment, such as mathematical portfolios and journal writing.

Our vision for your students is to join the growing number of students using our approach who discover that mathematics is an essential and learnable survival skill for the 21st century.

## Pedagogical Features

The pedagogical core of *Applied Mathematics* is a series of guided-discovery activities in which students work in groups to discover mathematical principles embedded in realistic situations. The key principles of each activity or investigation are highlighted and summarized at the activity's conclusion. Each activity is followed by exercises that reinforce the concepts and skills revealed in the activity.

Each chapter contains regular activities along with project activities that relate to particular topics. The activities may require more than just paper, pencil, and calculator. They may also require measurements and data collection and are ideal for in-class group work. The project activities are designed to allow students to explore specific topics in greater depth, either individually or in groups. For specific suggestions on how to use the two types of activities, we strongly encourage you to refer to the *Teacher's Resource Guide* that accompanies this text.

Occurring naturally as summary and review are the What Have I Learned? and How Can I Practice? exercises. The What Have I Learned? exercises are designed to help students pull together the key concepts of the section. The How Can I Practice? exercises are designed primarily to provide additional practice with the numeric, graphical, and algebraic skills of the section. Taken as a whole, these exercises give students the tools they need to bridge the gaps between abstraction, skills, and application.

Additionally, each chapter ends with a summary that contains a brief description of the concepts and skills discussed in the chapter, plus examples illustrating these concepts and skills. The concepts and skills are also cross-referenced to the activity in which they appear, making the format easier to follow for those students who are unfamiliar with our approach. Each chapter also ends with a Gateway Review, providing students with an opportunity to check their understanding of the chapter's concepts and skills.

## Supplements

### Teacher Supplements

**Annotated Teacher's Edition ISBN 0-558-20316-7**
**ISBN 978-0-558-20316-0**

This special version of the student text provides answers to all exercises directly beneath each problem.

**Teacher's Resource Guide/Printed Test Bank ISBN 0-558-20318-3**
**ISBN 978-0-558-20318-4**

This valuable teaching resource includes the following materials:

* Teaching notes for each chapter. These notes are ideal for those using the *Applied Mathematics* approach for the first time.
* Extra practice skills worksheets for topics with which students typically have difficulty.
* Sample chapter tests and final exams for in-class and take-home use by individual students and groups.
* Sample journal topics for the students to write comments and observations about the course are included for each chapter.
* Transparency Masters of graphs, charts, and data used throughout the book.

- A section discussing learning in groups with questions and answers for teachers trying collaborative learning for the first time.
- Information about incorporating technology in the classroom, including sample graphing calculator assignments.
- Answers to the exercises contained in the *Student Extra Practive Workbook* calculator assignments.

### TestGen with QuizMaster ISBN 0-558-20738-3
### ISBN 978-0-558-20738-0

TestGen enables teachers to build, edit, print, and administer tests using a computerized bank of questions developed to cover all the objectives of the text. TestGen is algorithmically based so that multiple, yet equal, versions of the same question or test can be generated at the click of a button. Teachers can also modify test bank questions or add new questions by using the built-in question editor, which allows users to create graphs, import graphics, insert math notation, and insert variable numbers or text. Tests can be printed or administered online via the Web or other network. Many questions in TestGen can be expressed in a short-answer or multiple-choice form, giving teachers greater flexibility in their test preparation. TestGen comes packaged with QuizMaster, which allows students to take tests on a local area network. The software is available on a dual-platform Windows/Macintosh CD-ROM.

## Supplements for Teachers and Students
### MathXL Tutorials on CD ISBN 0-558-20819-3

This interactive tutorial CD-ROM provides algorithmically generated practice exercises that are correlated to the skills covered in the textbook. Every practice exercise is accompanied by an example and a guided solution designed to involve students in the solution process. The software provides helpful feedback for incorrect answers and can generate printed summaries of students' progress.

### MathXL www.MathXLforSchool.com

MathXL is a powerful online homework, tutorial, and assessment system. With MathXL, teachers can create, edit, and assign online homework and tests using algorithmically generated exercises correlated to the basic skills of the textbook. They can also create and assign their own online exercises and import TestGen tests for added flexibility. All student work is tracked in MathXL's online gradebook. Students can take chapter tests in MathXL and receive personalized study plans based on their test results. The study plan diagnoses weaknesses and links students directly to tutorial exercises for the basic skill they need to study and retest. For additional information, visit our web site at www.mathxl.com, or contact your Pearson Education sales representative.

### Student Extra Practice Workbook ISBN 0-558-20317-5
### ISBN 978-0-558-20317-7

The *Student Extra Practice Workbook* is designed to provide students with additional opportunities to practice the basic skills covered in the text. The workbook is made up of a series of worksheets that include skill maintenance exercises for concepts and skills that tend to be challenging for students. In addition, the workbook provides additional activities for teachers who want to challenge their students with related but new problem-solving situations. Answers to the extra practice worksheets and additional activities are provided in the Teacher's Resource Guide/Printed Test Bank.

# To the Student

The book in your hands is most likely very different from any mathematics textbook you have seen before. In this book, you will take an active role in developing the important ideas of mathematical modeling. It is the belief of the authors that students learn mathematics best when they are actively involved in solving problems that are meaningful to them.

**Problem-Solving and Mathematical Reasoning:** The text is primarily a collection of situations drawn from real life. Each situation leads to one or more problems. By answering a series of questions and solving each part of the problem, you will be using and learning one or more mathematical ideas. Sometimes, these will be basic skills that build on your knowledge of arithmetic and algebra. Other times, they will be new concepts that are more general and far-reaching. The important point is that you won't be asked to master a skill until you see a real need for that skill as part of solving a realistic application.

**Communication:** Another important aspect of this text and the course you are taking is the benefit gained by collaborating with your classmates. Much of your work in class will result from being a member of a team. Working in small groups, you will help each other work through a problem situation. While you may feel uncomfortable working this way at first, there are several reasons we believe it is appropriate in this course. First, it is part of the learning-by-doing philosophy. You will be talking about mathematics, needing to express your thoughts in words. This is a key to learning. Secondly, you will be developing skills that will be very valuable when you leave the classroom. Currently, many jobs and careers require the ability to collaborate within a team environment. Your teacher will provide you with more specific information about this collaboration.

**Representation and Technology:** One more fundamental part of this course is that you will have access to appropriate technology. You will have access to calculators and some form of graphics tool—either a calculator or computer. Technology is a part of our modern world, and learning to use technology and recognizing what the results of the technology represents goes hand in hand with learning mathematics. Your work in this course will help prepare you for whatever you pursue in your working life.

This course will help you develop both the mathematical and general skills necessary in today's workplace, such as organization, problem solving, communication, reasoning, representation, and collaborative skills. In addition, this book will help preprare you to be successful on your local exam. By keeping up with your work and following the suggested organization of the text, you will gain a valuable resource that will serve you well in the future. With hard work and dedication, you will be ready for the next step.

The Consortium for Foundation Mathematics

# Applied Mathematics Correlation

## APPLIED MATHEMATICS I

*Sample Course Based on P21 Sample Student Outcomes*
*http://www.21stcenturyskills.org/images/stories/matrices/ictmap_math.pdf*

Applied Mathematics I provides learners an opportunity to apply mathematical concepts and skills from earlier high school mathematics courses in practical situations while focusing on learning skills associated with information and communication technology.

**Strands:** Algebra, Data Analysis and Probability

COMPETENCY GOAL 1: **The learner will use graphs, tables, symbolic manipulation, and technology to communicate mathematically and solve problems.**

### Objectives

1.01  Use the language of mathematics to express mathematical ideas in content specific and applied settings.

SE/TE: 6, 9, 14, 21, 43, 45-46, 70, 78-80, 111-112, 166-168, 177-183, 219-220, 234-236, 300-302, 322-329, 411-415, 421-424, 440-441, 473, 501-502, 527-528, 530-531, 552-553, 589-590, 593-595, 628-630, 701-705, 713-715, 724-725, 738-739, 765-766, 815-818, 830-832, 837, 838-844, 850-853, 857-860, 865, 916-917

1.02  Use online bulletin boards or other web 2.0 tools to engage in discussions of math concepts with people (students and/or experts) from around the world.

Related material:

SE/TE: 38, 257, 460-461, 617, 672

1.03  Apply an appropriate strategy to solve problems both individually and in a group.

SE/TE: 1-2, 3-9, 10-14, 16-18, 23-27

1.04  Use a variety of problem-solving tools such as graphing calculators, probes, GPS, and geometry tool software to formulate, approach, and solve problems.

SE/TE: 61, 65, 69-70, 72, 78, 82-83, 86, 124-125, 195, 204-207, 210-211, 230, 238-242, 252-253, 263, 265-266, 269, 300-301, 306, 308-309, 323-324, 339, 341, 400, 402, 406-407, 410-420, 421-423, 425-426, 431-434, 435-439, 440, 443, 450, 452, 454-459, 474, 490-494, 498, 545, 549, 554-560, 363-565, 567-569, 572-580, 583-586, 588, 593-596, 601-602, 611-616, 635-639, 644-651, 655-660, 662, 666-667, 670, 673-674, 705, 807,

818-820, 836-837, 857-861, 878-883, 885-892, 916-919, 921, 926-928, 931, 937, 943, 949, 957

1.05 Employ more complex problem-solving methods to develop a deeper understanding of mathematics, such as simulating a construction project(within certain material and budget constraints).

SE/TE: 1-2, 258-261, 373-375, 610-617, 748-752, 753-756, 957

1.06 Use estimation to determine the reasonableness of an answer and use word-processing software to explain the process.

SE/TE: 105-106, 219-224, 236-242, 245-248, 252-257, 406, 455-461, 572, 580, 584-588, 611-616, 653-654, 666-667

COMPETENCY GOAL 2: **The learner will use graphs, tables, and technology to model relationships.**

## Objectives

2.01 Illustrate a mathematical concept, connection, or problem and its applicability to a real-world context.

SE/TE: 10-14, 16-18, 20-22, 24-27, 28-36, 43-49, 52-56, 57-61, 68-77, 78-86, 87-93, 94-97, 107-110, 112-116, 118-120, 122-123, 132-134, 165-174, 175-178, 180-181, 185-188, 190-192, 193-194, 197-200, 202-203, 218-224, 225, 227-229, 231-233, 234-248, 249-251, 252-257, 258-261, 262-270, 299-300, 302-303, 305-309, 310-314, 315, 322-324, 327-328, 330-331, 333-335, 336, 344-345, 349-352, 353-364, 365-368, 371-372, 373-375, 399-401, 405-406, 409-410, 412, 414, 421, 423, 426-427, 432-434, 435-436, 438-439, 440, 446, 447, 450-453, 454-461, 473-478, 480, 482, 486, 488, 493-496, 497, 502, 504-505, 508-509, 527, 529-530, 532-537, 538-542, 543-551, 552-554, 570-576, 578-580, 581-588, 589-597, 598-600, 604-609, 610-617, 626-627, 634, 643, 644-654, 655-657, 663-665, 666-672, 673-676, 701-712, 713-723, 724-737, 738-747, 748-752, 753-756, 757-763, 764-771, 789-791, 792-803, 804-814, 815-822, 830-837, 838-846, 847-849, 850-856,857-863, 864-873, 879-883, 884-892, 909-915, 916-923, 924-929, 930-935, 936-937, 942-947, 948-956, 957

2.02 Use physical and digital models to demonstrate mathematical concepts.

SE/TE: 69-70, 72, 78, 82-83, 86, 124-125, 195, 204-207, 210-211, 230, 238-242, 252-253, 263, 265-266, 269, 300-301, 306, 308-309, 323-324, 339, 341, 400, 402, 406-407, 410-420, 421-423, 425-426, 431-434, 435-439, 440, 443, 450, 452, 454-459, 474, 490-494, 498, 545, 549, 554-560, 363-565, 567-569, 572-580, 583-586, 588, 593-596, 601-602, 611-616, 635-639, 644-651, 655-660, 662, 666-667, 670, 673-674, 705, 807, 818-820, 836-837, 857-861, 878-883, 885-892, 916-919, 921, 926-928, 931, 937, 943, 949, 957

2.03  Demonstrate the development of a mathematical conjecture and create a convincing proof of its validity or disproof.

SE/TE: 3-5, 8-9

**Objectives**

3.01  Construct and interpret displays of data to solve problems.

SE/TE: 68-69, 165, 168-172, 235, 238-242, 245, 247-248, 249-251, 252, 254-256, 258-261, 461-461, 610, 614-615, 617, 653-654, 670, 789-791, 793-803, 804-813, 815, 817, 847-849, 850, 856, 860-861, 863, 864

3.02  Develop methods to collect univariate and bivariate data to describe trends within and between populations or local settings.

SE/TE: 258-261, 460-461, 617, 653-654, 670, 830-837, 838-846, 847-849, 850-856

3.03  Find and analyze data sets and collection processes with respect to the authenticity of the data and legitimacy of its use for various purposes.

SE/TE: 789-791, 803, 832, 838-839, 841-846, 850-856

3.04  Use graphing calculators and probes to collect and analyze environmental data (e.g. pH of streams) or contextual data (e.g. speed of cars in school zones).

SE/TE: 68-70, 610-616, 654, 670, 818-820, 836-837, 857-861, 878-883, 885-892

3.05  Identify a potential community issue that can be analyzed using a wide range of mathematical tools, develop an analysis plan, and develop a report presenting data and possible interventions.

SE/TE: 838-846, 847-849, 856

3.06  Develop an audience-appropriate presentation that uses analysis, interpretation and display of data and related inferences to describe the situation and possible solutions.

SE/TE: 259-261, 461, 617, 804-813, 848-849, 856

3.07  Analyze statistical techniques, sampling bias, and population parameters in published scientific or economic reports and evaluate the validity of the reports' findings.

SE/TE: 243, 249-251, 791, 822, 854-855

# Introduction to Problem Solving and Mathematical Models

**OBJECTIVES**

1. Practice communication skills.
2. Organize information.
3. Write a solution in sentences.
4. Develop problem-solving skills.

The last *Harry Potter* novel has just arrived and by 11:00 A.M., a line has formed outside the crowded bookstore. Knowing you have class at noon, you ask the guard at the door how long you can expect to wait. She provides you with the following information: She is permitted to let 6 people into the bookstore only after 6 people have left; customers are leaving at the rate of 2 customers per minute; and she has just let 6 new customers in. Also, each customer spends an average of 15 minutes browsing at books and 10 minutes waiting in line to check out.

Currently 38 people are ahead of you in line. You know that it is a 10-minute walk to your noon class. Can you buy your book and still expect to make it to your noon class on time? Use the following questions to guide you in solving this problem.

1. What was your initial reaction after reading the problem?

2. Have you ever worked on a problem such as this before?

3. Organizing the information will help you solve the problem.

   a. How many customers must leave the bookstore before the guard allows more to enter?

   b. How many customers per minute leave the bookstore?

   c. How many minutes are there between groups of customers entering the bookstore?

   d. How long will you stand in line outside the bookstore?

**e.** Now finish solving the problem and answer the question: How early or late for your noon class will you be?

**4.** In complete sentences, write what you did to solve this problem. Then, explain your solution to a classmate.

---

**SUMMARY**
Activity 1.1

**Steps in Problem Solving**

**1.** Sort out the relevant information and organize it.

**2.** Discuss the problem with others to increase your understanding of the problem.

**3.** Write your solution in complete sentences to review your steps and check your answer.

---

**EXERCISES**
Activity 1.1

**1.** Think about the various approaches you and your classmates used to solve Activity 1.1, Wild about Harry. Choose the approach that is best for you, and describe it in complete sentences.

**2.** What mathematical operations and skills did you use?

**ACTIVITY 1.2**
The Classroom

**OBJECTIVES**

1. Organize information.
2. Develop problem-solving strategies.
   • Draw a picture.
   • Recognize a pattern.
   • Do a simpler problem.
3. Communicate problem-solving ideas.

## The Handshake

This mathematics course involves working with other students in the class, so form a group of three, four, or five students. Introduce yourself to every other student in your group with a firm handshake. Share some information about yourself with the other members of your group.

**1.** How many people are in your group?

**2.** How many handshakes in all were there in your group?

**3.** Discuss how your group determined the number of handshakes. Be sure everyone understands and agrees with the method and the answer. Write the explanation of the method here.

### Put 'er There

| NUMBER OF STUDENTS IN GROUP | NUMBER OF HANDSHAKES |
|:---:|:---:|
| 2 | |
| 3 | |
| 4 | |
| 5 | |
| 6 | |
| 7 | |

**4.** Share your findings with the other groups, and fill in the chart.

**5. a.** Describe a rule for determining the number of handshakes in a group of seven students.

   **b.** Describe a rule for determining the number of handshakes in a class of $n$ students.

  **6.** If each student shakes hands with each other student, how many handshakes will be needed in your class?

  **7.** Is shaking hands during class time a practical way for students to introduce themselves? Explain.

> George Polya's book, *How to Solve It*, **outlines a four-step process for solving problems.**
> **1.** Understand the problem (determine what is involved).
> **2.** Devise a plan (look for connections to obtain the idea of a solution).
> **3.** Carry out the plan.
> **4.** Look back at the completed solution (review and discuss it).

  **8.** Describe how your experiences with the handshake problem correspond with Polya's suggestions.

## The Classroom

The tables in your classroom have square tops. Four students can comfortably sit at each table with ample working space. Putting tables together in clusters as shown will allow students to work in larger groups.

9. Construct a table of values for the number of tables and the corresponding total number of students.

| NUMBER OF SQUARE TABLES IN EACH CLUSTER | TOTAL NUMBER OF STUDENTS |
|---|---|
| 1 | 4 |
| 2 | 6 |
| | |
| | |
| | |

10. How many students can sit around a cluster of 7 square tables?

11. Describe the pattern that connects the number of square tables in a cluster and the total number of students that can be seated. Write a rule in sentences that will determine the total number of students that can sit in a cluster of a given number of square tables.

12. There are 24 students in a science course at your school.

    a. How many tables must be put together to seat a group of six students?

    b. How many clusters of tables are needed?

13. Discuss the best way to arrange the square tables into clusters given the number of students in your class.

## SUMMARY
### Activity 1.2

1. Problem-solving strategies include:
   - discussing the problem
   - organizing information
   - drawing a picture
   - recognizing patterns
   - doing a simpler problem

2. George Polya's book, *How to Solve It*, outlines **a four-step process for solving problems**.
   i. Understand the problem (determine what is involved).
   ii. Devise a plan (look for connections to obtain the idea of a solution).
   iii. Carry out the plan.
   iv. Look back at the completed solution (review and discuss it).

**EXERCISES**
**Activity 1.2**

1. At the opening session of the United States Supreme Court, each justice shakes hands with all the others.

   **a.** How many justices are there?

   **b.** How many handshakes do they make?

2. Identify how the numbers are generated in this triangular arrangement, known as Pascal's triangle. Fill in the missing numbers.

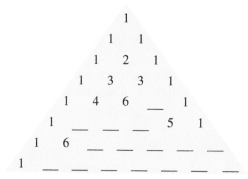

3. An **arithmetic sequence** is a list of numbers in which consecutive numbers share a common difference. Each number after the first is calculated by adding the common difference to the preceding number. For example, the arithmetic sequence 1, 4, 7, 10, . . . has 3 as its common difference. Identify the common difference in each arithmetic sequence that follows.

   **a.** 2, 4, 6, 8, 10, . . .

   **b.** 1, 3, 5, 7, 9, 11, . . .

   **c.** 26, 31, 36, 41, 46, . . .

4. A **geometric sequence** is a list of numbers in which consecutive numbers share a common ratio. Each number after the first is calculated by multiplying the preceding number by the common ratio. For example, 1, 3, 9, 27, . . . has 3 as its common ratio. Identify the common ratio in each geometric sequence that follows.

   **a.** 2, 4, 8, 16, 32, . . .

   **b.** 1, 5, 25, 125, 625, . . .

5. The operations needed to get from one number to the next in a sequence can be more complex. Describe a relationship shared by consecutive numbers in the following sequences.

   **a.** 2, 4, 16, 256, . . .

   **b.** 2, 5, 11, 23, 47, . . .

   **c.** 1, 2, 5, 14, 41, 122, . . .

6. In biology lab, you conduct the following experiment. You put two rabbits in a large caged area. In the first month, the pair produces no offspring (rabbits need a month to reach adulthood). At the end of the second month, the pair produces exactly one new pair of rabbits (one male and one female). The result makes you wonder how many male/female pairs you might have if you continue the experiment and each existing pair of rabbits produces a new pair each month, starting after their first month. The numbers for the first four months are calculated and recorded for you in the following table. The arrows in the table illustrate that the number of pairs produced in a given month equals the number of pairs that existed at the beginning of the preceding month. Continue the pattern and fill in the rest of the table.

### Hare Today

| MONTH | NUMBER OF PAIRS AT THE BEGINNING OF THE MONTH | NUMBER OF NEW PAIRS PRODUCED | TOTAL NUMBER OF PAIRS AT THE END OF THE MONTH |
|---|---|---|---|
| 1 | 1 | 0 | 1 |
| 2 | 1 | 1 | 2 |
| 3 | 2 | 1 | 3 |
| 4 | 3 | 2 | 5 |
| 5 | | | |
| 6 | | | |
| 7 | | | |
| 8 | | | |

The list of numbers in the second column is called the **Fibonacci sequence**. This problem on the reproduction of rabbits first appeared in 1202 in the mathematics text *Liber Abaci*, written by Leonardo of Pisa (nicknamed Fibonacci). Using the first two numbers, 1 and 1, as a starting point, describe how the next number is generated. Your rule should generate the rest of the numbers shown in the sequence in column two.

**7.** If you shift all the numbers in Pascal's triangle so that all the 1s are in the same column, you get the following triangle.

**a.** Add the numbers crossed by each arrow. Put the sums at the tip of the arrow.

```
1
1   1
1   2   1
1   3   3   1
1   4   6   4   1
1   5   10  10  5   1
1   6   15  20  15  6   1
1   7   21  35  35  21  7   1
```

**b.** What is the name of the sequence formed by these sums?

**8.** There are some interesting patterns within the Fibonacci sequence itself. Take any number in the sequence and multiply it by itself, and then subtract the product of the number immediately before it and the number immediately after it. What is the result? Pick another number and follow the same procedure. What result do you obtain? Try two more numbers in the sequence.

For example, choose 5.
$5 \cdot 5 = 25$
$3 \cdot 8 = 24$
$25 - 24 = 1$

For example, choose 3.
$3 \cdot 3 = 9$
$2 \cdot 5 = 10$
$9 - 10 = -1$

**9. a.** Complete the following table by performing the following sequence of operations on the original number: Multiply the number by 4, add 12 to the product, divide the sum by 2, and subtract 6 from the quotient.

| ORIGINAL NUMBER | RESULT OF SEQUENCE OF OPERATIONS |
|---|---|
| 2 | |
| 5 | |
| 10 | |
| 15 | |

**b.** There is a hidden pattern in the sequence of operations that causes the original number and the result of the sequence of operations to always have the same relationship. What relationship do you observe between the number and the result?

Based on the specific examples in part a, you might conclude that if you follow the given sequence of operations on *any* number, the result would always be twice the original number. Arriving at a general conclusion from specific examples is a type of reasoning called **inductive reasoning** or **induction**. However, this type of reasoning does not prove that the general conclusion is true for all numbers.

**c.** Generalize the situation in part a by choosing a variable to represent the original number. Use $x$ as your variable and perform the sequence of operations on the variable $x$. Simplify the resulting algebraic expression.

**d.** What general conclusion is proven in part c?

The type of reasoning used in parts c and d is called **deductive reasoning** or **deduction**. Deductive reasoning is used to prove conjectures true or false.

**ACTIVITY 1.3**
Make Me an
Offer

**OBJECTIVES**

1. Use the basic steps for problem-solving.

2. Translate verbal statements into algebraic equations.

3. Use the basic principles of algebra to solve real-world problems.

4. Use formulas to solve problems.

Many students believe "I can do math. I just can't do word problems." In reality, you learn mathematics so you can solve practical problems in everyday life, and in science, business, technology, medicine, and most other fields.

On a personal level, you solve problems every day, balancing your checkbook, remembering an anniversary, or figuring out how to get more exercise. Most everyday problems don't require algebra, or even arithmetic, to be solved. But the basic steps and methods for solving any problem can be discussed and understood. In the process you will, with practice, become a better problem solver.

Solve the following problem any way you can, making notes of your thinking as you work. In the space provided, record your work on the left side. On the right side jot down in a few sentences what you are thinking as you work on the problem.

## "Night Train" Henson's Contract

1. "Night Train" Henson is negotiating a new contract with his team. He wants $800,000 for the year with an additional $6000 for every game he starts. His team offered $10,000 for every game he starts, but only $700,000 for a base salary. How many games would he need to start in order to make more with the team's offer?

| SOLUTION TO THE PROBLEM | YOUR THINKING |
|---|---|
|  |  |
|  |  |
|  |  |

2. Talk about and compare your methods for solving the above problem with classmates or your group. As a group, write down the steps you all went through from the very beginning to the end of your problem solving.

**PROCEDURE: Basic Steps for Problem Solving**

Solving any problem generally requires the following four steps.

1. Understand the problem.

2. Develop a strategy for solving the problem (Devise a plan).

3. Execute your strategy to solve the problem (Carry out the plan).

4. Check your solution for correctness (Look back at the completed solution).

**3.** How do these four steps compare to your group's solutions? How do your group's answers compare with other groups' answers?

Let's consider each of the steps 1 through 4.

**Step 1. Understand the problem.** This step may seem obvious, but many times this is the most important step, and is the one that commonly leads to errors. Read the problem carefully, as many times as necessary. Draw some diagrams to help you visualize the situation. Get an explanation from available resources if you are unsure of any details.

**4.** List some strategies you could use to make sure you understand the "Night Train" Henson problem.

**Step 2. Develop a strategy for solving the problem.** Once you understand the problem, it may not be at all clear what strategy is required. Practice and experience is the best guide. Algebra is often useful for solving a math problem, but is not always required.

**5.** How many different strategies were tried in your group for solving the "Night Train" problem? Describe one or two of them.

**Step 3. Execute your strategy to solve the problem.** Once you have decided on a strategy, carrying it out is sometimes the easiest step in the process. If you really understand the problem, and are clear on your strategy, the solution should happen almost automatically.

**6.** When you decided on a strategy, how confident did you feel about your solution?

**Step 4. Check your solution for correctness.** This last step is *critically important*. Your solution must be reasonable, it must answer the question, and most importantly, it must be correct.

**7.** Are you absolutely confident your solution is correct? If so, how do you know?

## Solution: "Night Train" Henson's Contract

As beginning problem solvers, you may find it useful to develop a consistent strategy. Let's examine one possible way you can solve "Night Train's" problem by applying some algebra tools.

**Step 1. Understand the problem.** If you understand the problem, you will realize that "Night Train" needs to make $100,000 more with the team's offer (800,000 – 700,000) to make up for the difference in base salary. So he must start enough games to make up for this difference. Otherwise, he should not want the team's offer.

**Step 2. Develop a strategy for solving the problem.** Recall that a variable, usually represented by a letter, is a quantity or quality that may change in value from one particular instance to another. In this situation, you could let the variable $x$ represent the number of games "Night Train" needs to start to make the same amount of money with either offer. Then we note that he would make $4000 more for each game started with the team's offer. So $4000 for each game started times the number of games started must equal $100,000.

**Step 3. Execute your strategy for solving the problem.** You can translate the statement above into an equation, then apply the fundamental principle of solving equations to obtain the number of games.

$$4000x = 100,000$$
$$4000x \div 4000 = 100,000 \div 4000$$
$$x = 25$$

Your answer would be: "Night Train needs to start in more than 25 games to make more with the team's offer."

**Step 4. Check your solution for correctness.** This answer seems reasonable, but to check it you should refer back to the original statement of the problem. If "Night Train" starts in exactly 25 games his salary for the two offers can be calculated.

Night Train's demand:  $800,000 + $6000 × 25 = $950,000
Team's offer:  $700,000 + $10,000 × 25 = $950,000

If he starts in 26 games, the team's offer is $960,000 and "Night Train's" demand is $956,000.

This confirms our solution.

There are other ways to solve this problem. But this gives you an example of how algebra can be used. Use algebra in a similar way to solve the following problems. Be sure to follow the four steps of problem solving.

## Additional Problems to Solve

**8.** You need to open a checking account and decide to shop around for a bank. Acme Bank has an account with a $10 monthly charge, plus 25 cents per check. Farmer's Bank will charge you $12 per month, with a 20 cent charge per check. How many checks would you need to write each month to make Farmer's Bank the better deal?

**Step 1. Understand the problem.**

**Step 2. Develop a strategy for solving the problem.**

**Step 3. Execute your strategy to solve the problem.**

**Step 4. Check your solution for correctness.**

9. The perimeter of a rectangular pasture is 2400 feet. If the width is 800 feet, how long is the pasture?

   **Step 1. Understand the problem.**

   **Step 2. Develop a strategy for solving the problem.**

**Step 3. Execute your strategy to solve the problem.**

**Step 4. Check your solution for correctness.**

## Formulas

The solution to Problem 9 involved the relationship between a rectangle's perimeter and its length and width. Stated in words, the perimeter is the sum of twice the width and twice the length. This can be translated into an equation involving letters called a **formula**. If $P$ represents the perimeter, $w$ represents the width, and $l$ represents the length, the stated relationship can be written as

$$P = 2w + 2l$$

Formulas are useful in many business applications. For Problems 10–12,

   **a.** First, choose appropriate letters to represent each variable quantity and write what each letter represents.

   **b.** Use the letters to translate each stated relationship into a symbolic formula.

   **c.** Use the formula to solve the exercise.

**10.** Net income is equal to the total revenue from selling an item minus the cost of producing the item. Determine the net income if the revenue from a business is $400,000 and the cost is $156,800.

**11.** Net pay is the difference between a worker's gross income and his or her deductions. A person's gross income for the year was $65,000 and their total deductions were $12,860. What was their net pay for the year?

12. Annual depreciation equals the difference between the original cost of an item and its remaining value, divided by its estimated life in years. Determine the annual depreciation of a new car that costs $25,000, has an estimated life of ten years, and a remaining value of $2000.

Formulas are also found in the sciences. In Problems 13–15, use the given formulas to solve each problem.

13. In general, temperature is measured using either the Celsius (C) or Fahrenheit (F) scales. To convert from degrees Celsius to degrees Fahrenheit, use the following formula.

$$F = (9C \div 5) + 32$$

   a. Use the formula to convert 20°C into degrees F.

   b. 100°C is equal to how many degrees F?

14. To convert from degrees F to degrees C, use the following formula.

$$C = 5(F - 32) \div 9$$

   a. Use the formula to convert 86°F into degrees C.

   b. What is a temperature of 41 degrees F equal to in degrees C?

**15.** The distance an object travels is determined by how fast it goes and for how long it moves. If an object's speed remains constant, the formula is $d = r \cdot t$, where $d$ is the distance, $r$ is the speed, and $t$ is the time.

**a.** If you drive at 50 miles per hour for 5 hours, how far will you have traveled?

**b.** A satellite is orbiting the Earth at the rate of 25 kilometers per minute. How far will it travel in two hours?

Orbits at 25 km per minute

---

**SUMMARY**
**Activity 1.3**

**The Four Steps of Problem Solving**

**Step 1. Understand the problem.**

**a.** Read the problem completely and carefully.

**b.** Draw a sketch of the problem, if possible.

**Step 2. Develop a strategy for solving the problem.**

**a.** Identify and list everything you know about the problem, including relevant formulas. Add labels to the diagram if you have one.

**b.** Identify and list what you want to know.

**Step 3. Execute your strategy to solve the problem.**

**a.** Write an equation that relates the known quantities and the unknowns.

**b.** Solve the equation.

**Step 4. Check your solution for correctness.**

**a.** Is your answer reasonable?

**b.** Is your answer correct? (Does it answer the original question? Does it agree with all the given information?)

In Exercises 1–10, solve the following problems by applying the four steps of problem solving. Use the strategy of solving an algebra equation for each problem.

1. In preparing for a family trip, your assignment is to make the travel arrangements. You can rent a car for $75 per day with unlimited mileage. If you have budgeted $600 for car rental, how many days can you drive?

2. You need to drive 440 miles to get to your best friend's wedding. How fast must you drive to get there in 8 hours?

3. Your goal is to save $1200 to pay for next year's books and fees. How much must you save each month if you have 5 months to accomplish your goal?

4. You have enough wallpaper to cover 240 square feet. If your walls are 8 feet high, what wall length can you paper?

5. In your part-time job selling kitchen knives, you have two different sets available. The better set sells for $35, the cheaper set for $20. Last week you sold more of the cheaper set, in fact twice as many as the better sets. Your receipts for the week totaled $525. How many of the better sets did you sell?

**6.** A rectangle that has an area of 357 square inches is 17 inches wide. How long is the rectangle?

**7.** A rectangular field is five times longer than it is wide. If the perimeter is 540 feet, what are the dimensions (length and width) of the field?

$w$ ┌─────────────────────┐
     │                     │
     └─────────────────────┘
              $5w$

**8.** In your part-time job, your hours vary each week. Last month you worked 22 hours the first week, 25 hours the second week, 14 hours during week three and 19 hours in week four. Your gross pay for those four weeks was $960.

   **a.** Let $p$ represent your hourly pay rate. Write the equation for your gross pay over these four weeks.

   **b.** Solve the equation in part a to determine your hourly pay rate.

**9.** Over the first three months of the year you sold 12, 15, and 21 SuperPix digital cameras. The total in sales was $18,960.

   **a.** Let $p$ represent the price of one SuperPix digital camera. Write the equation for your total in sales over these three months.

**b.** Solve the equation in part a to find the retail price of the SuperPix digital camera.

**10.** Evaluate each formula for the given value(s).

    **a.** $d = r \cdot t$, where $r = 35$ and $t = 6$

    **b.** $F = ma$, where $m = 120$ and $a = 25$

    **c.** $V = lwh$, where $l = 100$, $w = 5$, and $h = 25$

    **d.** $F = \dfrac{mv^2}{r}$, where $m = 200$, $v = 25$, and $r = 125$

    **e.** $A = \dfrac{(t_1 + t_2 + t_3)}{3}$, where $t_1 = 76$, $t_2 = 83$, and $t_3 = 81$

**ACTIVITY 1.4**
Proportional
Reasoning

**OBJECTIVES**

1. Use proportional reasoning as a problem-solving strategy.

2. Write a proportion and then solve the resulting proportion.

The following table summarizes Michael Jordan's statistics during the six games of one of his National Basketball Association (NBA) championship series.

| GAME | POINTS | FIELD GOALS | FREE THROWS |
|------|--------|-------------|-------------|
| 1 | 28 | 9 out of 18 | 9 out of 10 |
| 2 | 29 | 9 out of 22 | 10 out of 16 |
| 3 | 36 | 11 out of 23 | 11 out of 11 |
| 4 | 23 | 6 out of 19 | 11 out of 13 |
| 5 | 26 | 11 out of 22 | 4 out of 5 |
| 6 | 22 | 5 out of 19 | 11 out of 12 |

1. What was his points-per-game average over the six-game series?

2. In which game did he score the most points?

3. In which game(s) did he score the most field goals? The most free throws?

Problem 3 focused on the *actual* number of Jordan's successful field goals and free throws in these six games. Another way of assessing Jordan's performance is to *compare* the number of successful shots to the total number of attempts for each game. This comparison gives you information on the *relative* success of his shooting. For example, in each of games 1 and 2, Jordan made 9 field goals. Relatively speaking, you could argue that he was more successful in game 1 because he made 9 out of 18 attempts; in game 2, he only made 9 out of 22 attempts.

4. Use the free-throw data from the six games to express Jordan's *relative* performance in the given comparison formats (verbal, fraction, division, and decimal). The data from the first game have been entered for you.

**Jordan's Relative Free-Throw Performance**

| | VERBAL | FRACTION | DIVISION | DECIMAL |
|---|--------|----------|----------|---------|
| **GAME 1** | 9 out of 10 | $\frac{9}{10}$ | $9 \div 10$ or $10\overline{)9}$ | 0.90 |
| **GAME 2** | | | | |
| **GAME 3** | | | | |
| **GAME 4** | | | | |
| **GAME 5** | | | | |
| **GAME 6** | | | | |

**5. a.** For which of the six games was his relative free-throw performance highest?

**b.** Which comparison format did you use to answer part a? Why?

**6.** For which of the six games was Jordan's *actual* free-throw performance the lowest?

**7.** For which of the six games was Jordan's *relative* free-throw performance the lowest?

When relative comparisons using quotients are made between different values or quantities of the same kind (e.g., number of baskets to number of baskets), the comparison is called a **ratio**. Ratios can be expressed in several forms—verbal, fraction, division, or decimal, as you saw in Problem 4.

**Proportional reasoning** is the ability to recognize when two ratios are equivalent, that is, when equivalent ratios represent the same relative performance level.

DEFINITION

Two ratios are said to be **equivalent** if the ratios have equal numerical (e.g., decimal or fraction) values. The mathematical statement that two ratios are equivalent is called a **proportion.** In fraction form, the proportion is written $\frac{a}{b} = \frac{c}{d}$.

You can determine *equivalent* ratios the same way you determine equivalent fractions. For example, 3 out of 4 is equivalent to 6 out of 8, because $\frac{3}{4} \cdot \frac{2}{2} = \frac{6}{8}$.

**8.** Fill in the blanks in each of the following proportions.

**a.** 3 out of 4 is equivalent to _____ out of 12

**b.** 3 out of 4 is equivalent to _____ out of 32

**c.** 3 out of 4 is equivalent to _____ out of 100

**d.** Write the resulting proportion from part c using a fraction format.

**9. a.** Explain why the following ratios are equivalent.

    **i.** 27 out of 75          **ii.** 63 out of 175         **iii.** 36 out of 100

**b.** Write each ratio in fraction form.

**c.** Determine the "reduced" form of the equivalent fractions from part b.

**d.** With which of the equivalent ratios in part a do you feel most comfortable? Explain.

The number 100 is a very familiar quantity of comparison: There are 100 cents in a dollar and frequently 100 points on a test. Therefore, people feel most comfortable with a ratio such as 70 out of 100 or 36 out of 100.

> The phrase "out of 100" is commonly referred to by its Latin equivalent, *percent*. Per means "division" and cent means "100," so **percent** means "divide by 100."

Therefore, 70 out of 100 can be rephrased as 70 percent and written in the familiar notation 70%, which equals $70 \div 100 = \frac{70}{100} = 0.70$. Similarly, 36 out of 100 can be rephrased as 36 percent and written in the familiar notation $36\% = 36 \div 100 = \frac{36}{100} = 0.36$.

**10.** Complete the following table using Michael Jordan's field goal data from the beginning of the activity.

### Jordan's Relative Field Goal Performance

|  | VERBAL | FRACTION | DECIMAL | PERCENT |
|---|---|---|---|---|
| **GAME 1** | 9 out of 18 | $\frac{9}{18}$ | 0.50 | 50% |
| **GAME 2** |  |  |  |  |
| **GAME 3** |  |  |  |  |
| **GAME 4** |  |  |  |  |
| **GAME 5** |  |  |  |  |
| **GAME 6** |  |  |  |  |

## Solving Proportions

In an effort to increase the education level of their police officers, many municipalities are requiring new recruits to have at least a two-year college degree. A recent survey indicated that 1 out of 5 New York City (NYPD) police officers holds a four-year college degree. There were approximately 41,000 NYPD officers when the survey was conducted.

To calculate the number of four-year college degree holders, you can start with the proportion statement

$$1 \text{ out of } 5 \;=\; \underline{\;\;?\;\;} \text{ out of } 41{,}000$$

This proportion can be written in fraction form as

$$\frac{1}{5} = \frac{n}{41{,}000},$$

where $n$ is the unknown quantity of the proportion.

> One method of solving proportions uses the fact that the two mathematical statements
>
> $$\frac{a}{b} = \frac{c}{d} \quad \text{and} \quad a \cdot d = b \cdot c$$
>
> are equivalent.

Transforming the statement on the left (containing two fractions) into the statement on the right is commonly called **cross multiplication** because the numerator of the first fraction is multiplied by the denominator of the second and the numerator of the second fraction is multiplied by the denominator of the first.

You can use cross multiplication to solve proportions as demonstrated in Example 1:

**Example 1**   *Solve the proportion* $\dfrac{2}{5} = \dfrac{n}{6000}.$

SOLUTION

| | |
|---|---|
| Original proportion: | $\dfrac{2}{5} = \dfrac{n}{6000}$ |
| Cross multiply: | $2 \cdot 6000 = 5 \cdot n$ |
| Divide both sides by 5: | $\dfrac{2 \cdot 6000}{5} = \dfrac{\cancel{5} \cdot n}{\cancel{5}}$ |
| Simplify: | $2400 = n$ |

**11.** Use the cross-multiplication method to solve the proportion $\dfrac{1}{5} = \dfrac{n}{41{,}000}.$

**12.** Solve the following proportions.

a. 2 out of 3 = _____ out of 36       b. $\dfrac{2}{3} = \dfrac{n}{45}$

## Application

New York State has taken a leading position in raising the standards of its high school graduates. In the year 2003, every graduate needed to pass a series of rigorous subject-matter tests called Regents exams. Currently, your cousin lives in a New York State county in which only 6 out of 10 graduates receive Regents diplomas.

**13.** If 5400 students in your cousin's county earned a Regents diploma last year, estimate (without actually doing a calculation) the total number of high school graduates in that county last year.

This situation differs from the NYPD situation at the beginning of the activity because the total number is not known. The 5400 represents that part of the total number of high school graduates who earned a Regents diploma. Written as a proportion,

6 out of 10 = 5400 out of ___?___

**14. a.** Rewrite this proportion in fraction form. Let $n$ represent the unknown.

b. To determine the total number of students, use cross multiplication to calculate the unknown denominator in part a.

**15.** Solve these proportions.

a. 2 out of 3 = 80 out of _____.       b. $\dfrac{2}{3} = \dfrac{216}{n}$

## SUMMARY
### Activity 1.4

1. When comparisons using quotients are made between different quantities of the same kind, the comparison is called a **ratio**.

2. Ratios can be expressed verbally (4 out of 5), as a fraction $\frac{4}{5}$, as a division $(5\overline{)4})$, as a decimal (0.80), or as a percent (80%).

3. Two ratios are said to be equivalent if the ratios have equal numerical values. The mathematical statement that two ratios are equivalent is called a **proportion**.

4. A proportion expressed in fraction form, $\frac{a}{b} = \frac{c}{d}$, is equivalent to the statement $ad = bc$.

5. Problems that involve **proportional reasoning** usually include a known ratio $\frac{a}{b}$ and a given piece of information, either a "part" or a "total" value, resulting in the proportion:

$$\frac{a}{b} = \frac{part}{total}$$

The missing value can be determined by cross multiplying and solving the resulting equation.

## EXERCISES
### Activity 1.4

1. Here are your scores on three graded assignments. On which assignment did you perform best?

   **a.** 25 out of 30          **b.** 30 out of 40          **c.** 18 out of 25

2. At competitive colleges, the admissions office often compares the number of students accepted to the total number of applications received. This comparison is known as the *selectivity index*. The admissions office also compares the number of students who actually attend to the number of students who have been accepted for admission. This comparison is known as the *yield*. Complete the following table to determine the selectivity index and yield (in percent format) for colleges A, B, and C.

| | NUMBER OF APPLICANTS | NUMBER ACCEPTED | NUMBER ATTENDING | SELECTIVITY INDEX | YIELD (AS A %) |
|---|---|---|---|---|---|
| COLLEGE A | 5500 | 3500 | 1000 | | |
| COLLEGE B | 8500 | 4800 | 2100 | | |
| COLLEGE C | 4200 | 3200 | 900 | | |

Which college do you think is the most competitive? The least competitive? Explain.

3. Solve each proportion for the unknown quantity.

   a. $\dfrac{2}{3} = \dfrac{x}{48}$
   b. $\dfrac{5}{8} = \dfrac{120}{x}$
   c. $\dfrac{3}{20} = \dfrac{x}{3500}$

*In Exercises 4–12, write a proportion that represents the situation and then determine the unknown value in the proportion.*

4. A conservationist can estimate the total number of a certain type of fish in a lake by using a technique called "capture-mark-recapture." Suppose a conservationist marks and releases 100 rainbow trout into a lake. A week later she nets 50 trout in the lake and finds 3 marked fish. An estimate of the number of rainbow trout in the lake can be determined by assuming that the proportion of marked fish in the sample taken is the same as the proportion of marked fish in the total population of rainbow trout in the lake. Use this information to estimate the population of rainbow trout in the lake.

5. The school taxes on a house assessed at $210,000 are $2340. At the same tax rate, what are the taxes (to the nearest dollar) on a house assessed at $275,000?

6. According to the 2000 U.S. Census, 7 out of every 25 homes are heated by electricity. At this rate, predict how many homes in a community of 12,000 would be heated by electricity.

7. A hybrid car can travel 70 miles on one gallon of gas. Determine the amount of gas needed for a 500 mile trip.

8. A normal 10 cc specimen of human blood contains 1.2 g of hemoglobin. How much hemoglobin would 16 cc of the same blood contain?

9. The ratio of the weight of an object on Mars to the weight of an object on Earth is 0.4 to 1. How much would a 170 pound astronaut weigh on Mars?

10. The ancient Greeks thought that the most pleasing shape for a rectangle was one for which the ratio of length to width was 8 to 5. This ratio is called the Golden Ratio. If the length of a rectangular painting is 20 inches, determine the width of the painting in order for the length and width of the painting to have the Golden Ratio.

11. The designers of sport shoes assume that the force exerted on the soles of shoes in a jump shot is proportional to the weight of the person jumping. A 140-pound athlete exerts a force of 1960 pounds on his shoe soles when he returns to the court floor after a jump. Determine the force that a 270-pound professional basketball player exerts on the soles of his shoes when he returns to the court floor after shooting a jump shot.

12. Your high school softball team won 80% of the games it played this year. If your team won 20 games, how many games did it play?

**ACTIVITY 1.5**
Fuel Economy

**OBJECTIVES**

1. Apply rates directly to solve problems.

2. Use proportions to solve problems.

3. Use unit or dimensional analysis to solve problems.

You are excited about purchasing a reliable used car that will help with your commute to high school. Concerned about the cost of driving, you do some research on the Internet and come across a Web site that lists fuel efficiency, in miles per gallon (mpg), for five cars that you are considering. You record the mpg for city and highway driving in the following table.

1. **a.** For each of the cars listed in the following table, how many city miles can you travel per week on five gallons of gasoline? Explain the calculation you will do to obtain the answers. Record your answers in the third column of the table.

## Fuel for Thought

| MAKE/MODEL | CITY MPG | CITY MILES ON 5 GAL OF GAS | HIGHWAY MPG | GAL NEEDED TO DRIVE 304 MILES | FUEL TANK CAPACITY IN GAL |
|---|---|---|---|---|---|
| Chevrolet Cobalt | 32 | | 41 | | 13.2 |
| Ford Focus | 28 | | 36 | | 13.2 |
| Honda Civic | 33 | | 39 | | 13.2 |
| Hyundai Accent | 28 | | 36 | | 11.9 |
| Toyota Corolla | 34 | | 41 | | 11.9 |

**b.** The roundtrip drive to your high school is 29 city miles, which you do five days a week. Which of the cars would get you to school each week on five gallons of gas?

2. Suppose your roundtrip commute to a summer job would be 304 highway miles per week. How many gallons of gas would each of the cars require? Explain the calculation you do to obtain the answers. Record your answers to the nearest tenths in the fifth column of the above table.

## Rates and Unit Analysis

Miles per gallon (mpg) is an example of a rate. Mathematically, a **rate** is a comparison of two quantities that have different units of measurement. Numerically, you calculate with rates as you would with ratios. Paying attention to what happens to the units of measurement during the calculation is critical to determining the unit of the result.

> **DEFINITION**
>
> A **rate** is a comparison, expressed as a quotient, of two quantities that have different units of measurement.
>
> **Unit analysis** (sometimes called *dimensional analysis*) uses units of measurement as a guide in setting up a calculation or writing an equation involving one or more rates. When the calculation or equation is set up properly, the result is an answer with the appropriate units of measurement.

There are two common methods for solving problems involving rates. One method is to apply the known rate directly by multiplication or division. The second method is to set up and solve a proportion equation. In each method, you use the units of measurement as a guide in setting up the calculation or writing the appropriate equation. Example 1 demonstrates these two methods.

## Example 1

**Direct Method:**   Apply a known rate directly by multiplication or division to solve a problem.

In Problem 1, the known rate is miles per gallon. You can write miles per gallon in fraction form, $\dfrac{\text{number of miles}}{1 \text{ gal}}$. The fuel economy rating for the Chevrolet Cobalt is $\dfrac{32 \text{ miles}}{1 \text{ gal}}$. To determine how many city miles you can travel on five gallons of gasoline, you multiply the known rate by 5 gal as follows:

$$\frac{32 \text{ miles}}{1 \text{ gal}} \cdot 5 \text{ gal} = 160 \text{ miles}.$$

Notice that the unit of measurement, gallon, occurs in both the numerator and the denominator. You divide out common units of measurement in the same way that you divide out common numerical factors.

**Proportion Method:**   Set up and solve a proportion.

Form two fractions, $\dfrac{a}{b}$ and $\dfrac{c}{d}$, set them equal to one another and solve the resulting proportion.

Step 1. The first fraction, $\dfrac{a}{b}$, is the known rate. Its numerator represents one measurement unit and its denominator the other unit. In Problem 1, the known rate is $\dfrac{32 \text{ miles}}{1 \text{ gallon}}$.

Step 2. To determine the second fraction, $\dfrac{c}{d}$, the measurement unit of the numerator $c$ must have the same unit as the numerator of the known rate (miles). The denominator $d$ must have the same measurement unit as the denominator of the known rate (gallons).

You know that you have five gallons of gas. Therefore, five gallons is the denominator $d$. The unknown is the number of miles that you can drive on five gallons.

Represent the unknown in the numerator by a symbol such as $x$. The numerator $c$ is $x$ miles. Therefore, the fraction $\frac{c}{d}$ is

$$\frac{x \text{ miles}}{5 \text{ gallons}}.$$

Step 3. Set the two fractions $\frac{a}{b}$ and $\frac{c}{d}$ equal to each other to obtain a proportion, $\frac{a}{b} = \frac{c}{d}$. In Problem 1, the proportion is

$$\frac{32 \text{ miles}}{1 \text{ gallon}} = \frac{x \text{ miles}}{5 \text{ gallons}}.$$

Step 4. Solve $\frac{32}{1} = \frac{x}{5}$ to obtain $x = 160$ miles.

Therefore, in the Chevrolet Cobalt, you can drive 160 miles on five gallons of gas.

3. Solve the following problems by both methods, and compare the results, which should be the same.

   a. The gas tank of a Ford Focus holds 13.2 gallons. How many highway miles can you travel on a full tank of gas?

   b. The Toyota Corolla gas tank holds 11.9 gallons. Is it possible to travel as far on the highway in this car as in the Ford Focus?

In Problem 2, you were asked to determine how many gallons of gas were required to drive 304 highway miles. Using the direct method, you may have known to divide the total miles by the miles per gallon. For example, in the case of the Honda Civic, $\frac{304}{39} = 7.8$ gallons.

One way to be sure the problem is set up correctly is to use the units of measurement. In Problem 2, you are determining the number of gallons. Set up the calculation so that miles will divide out and the remaining measurement unit will be gallons.

$$304 \text{ miles} \cdot \frac{1 \text{ gallon}}{39 \text{ miles}}$$

$$\frac{304}{39} \text{ gallons} = 7.8 \text{ gallons}$$

This example shows that a rate may be expressed in two ways. For miles and gallons, the rate can be expressed as $\dfrac{\text{miles}}{\text{gallon}}$ or as $\dfrac{\text{gallon}}{\text{miles}}$. To solve a problem, you choose the form so that all measurement units can be divided out except the measurement unit of the answer.

Alternatively, you may have set up a proportion.

$$\frac{39 \text{ miles}}{1 \text{ gallon}} = \frac{304 \text{ miles}}{x \text{ gallons}}$$

$$39x = 304$$

$$x = \frac{304}{39}$$

$$x = 7.8 \text{ gallons}$$

4. After you purchase your car, you would like to take a trip to see a good friend in another state. The highway distance is approximately 560 miles. Solve the following problems by the direct method and by the proportion method, and compare your results.

   a. If you bought the Hyundai Accent, how many gallons of gas would you need to make the round-trip?

   b. How many tanks of gas would you need for the trip?

## PROCEDURE: Methods for Solving Problems Involving Rates

### Direct Method: Multiply and Divide by the Known Rate

1. Identify the unit of the result.
2. Set up the calculation so the appropriate units will divide out, leaving the unit of the result.
3. Multiply or divide the numbers as usual to obtain the numerical part of the result.
4. Divide out the common units to obtain the unit of the answer.

### Proportion Method: Set Up and Solve a Proportion

1. Identify the known rate, and write it in fractional form.
2. Identify the given information and the quantity to be determined.
3. Write a second fraction, placing the given information and the quantity $x$ in the same positions as their units in the known rate.
4. Equate the two fractions to obtain a proportion.
5. Solve the equation for $x$, affixing the correct unit to the numerical result.

## Using Unit Analysis to Solve a Problem

5. You are on a part of a 1500-mile trip where gas stations are far apart. Your car is averaging 40 miles per gallon and you are traveling at 60 miles per hour (mph). The fuel tank holds twelve gallons of gas, and you just filled the tank. How long is it before you have to fill the tank again?

   You can solve this problem in two parts, as follows:

   a. Determine how many miles you can travel on one tank of gas.

   b. Use the result of part a to determine how many hours you can drive before you have to fill the tank again.

Problem 5 is an example of applying consecutive rates to solve a problem. Part a was the first step and part b was the second step. Alternatively, you can also determine the answer in a *single calculation* by considering what the measurement unit of the answer should be. In this case, it is hours per tank. Therefore, you will need to set up the calculation so that you can divide out miles and gallons.

$$\frac{40 \text{ miles}}{1 \text{ gal}} \cdot \frac{12 \text{ gal}}{1 \text{ tank}} \cdot \frac{1 \text{ hour}}{60 \text{ miles}} = \frac{8 \text{ hours}}{1 \text{ tank}}$$

Notice that miles and gallons divide out to leave hours per tank as the measurement unit of the answer.

PROCEDURE: **Using Unit Analysis to Solve Problems**

To apply consecutive rates:

1. Identify the measurement unit of the result.
2. Set up the sequence of multiplications so that the appropriate units divide out, leaving the appropriate measurement unit of the result.
3. Multiply and divide the numbers as usual to obtain the numerical part of the result.
4. Check that the appropriate measurement units divide out, leaving the expected unit for the result.

6. You have been driving for several hours and notice that your car's 13.2-gallon fuel tank registers half empty. How many more miles can you travel if your car is averaging 65 miles per gallon?

## Unit Conversion

In many countries, distance is measured in kilometers (km) and gasoline in liters. A mile is equivalent to 1.609 kilometers, and a liter is equivalent to 0.264 gallons. Each of these equivalences can be treated as a rate and written in fraction form. Thus, the fact that a mile is equivalent to 1.609 kilometers is written as $\frac{1.609 \text{ km}}{1 \text{ mile}}$ or $\frac{1 \text{ mile}}{1.609 \text{ km}}$. Using the fraction form, you can convert one measurement unit to another by applying multiplication or division directly, or you can use a proportion.

7.  Your friend joins you on a trip through Canada, where gasoline is measured in liters and distance in kilometers.

   a.  Write the equivalence of liters and gallons in fraction form.

   b.  If you bought 20 liters of gas, how many gallons did you buy?

8.  To keep track of mileage and fuel needs in Canada, your friend suggests that you convert your car's miles per gallon into kilometers per liter. Your car's highway fuel efficiency is 45 miles per gallon. What is its fuel efficiency in kilometers per liter?

**SUMMARY**
**Activity 1.5**

1.  A **rate** is a comparison, expressed as a quotient, of two quantities that have different units of measurement.

2.  **Unit analysis** (sometimes called *dimensional analysis*) uses units of measurement as a guide in setting up a calculation or writing an equation involving one or more rates. When the calculation or equation is set up properly, the result is an answer with the appropriate units of measurement.

3.  Two common methods to solve problems involving rates:

   **Direct Method: Multiply or divide directly by rates to solve problems:**

   1.  Identify the measurement unit of the result.

   2.  Set up the calculation so that the appropriate measurement units will divide out, leaving the unit of the result.

   3.  Multiply or divide the numbers as usual to obtain the numerical part of the result.

   4.  Divide out the common measurement units to obtain the unit of the answer.

**Proportion Method: Set up and solve a proportion**

1. Identify the known rate, and write it in fractional form.

2. Identify the given information and the unknown quantity to be determined.

3. Write a second fraction, placing the given information and unknown quantity $x$ in the same position as the measurement units in the known rate.

4. Equate the two fractions to obtain a proportion.

5. Solve the equation for $x$, affixing the correct unit to the numerical result.

**4.** Applying several rates consecutively:

1. Identify the measurement unit of the result.

2. Set up the sequence of multiplications so the appropriate measurement units divide out, leaving the unit of the result.

3. Multiply and divide the numbers as usual to obtain the numerical part of the result.

4. Check that the appropriate measurement units divide out, leaving the expected unit of the result.

## EXERCISES
### Activity 1.5

Use the conversion tables in Appendix B of this textbook for conversion equivalencies.

**1.** The length of a football playing field is 100 yards between the opposing goal lines. What is the length of the football field in feet?

**2.** The distance between New York City, New York, and Los Angeles, California, is approximately 4485 kilometers. What is the distance between these two major cities in miles?

**3.** The aorta is the largest artery in the human body. In the average adult, the aorta attains a maximum diameter of about 1.18 inches where it adjoins the heart. What is the maximum diameter of the aorta in centimeters? In millimeters?

**4.** In the Himalaya Mountains along the border of Tibet and Nepal, Mount Everest reaches a record height of 29,035 feet. How high is Mt. Everest in miles? In kilometers? In meters?

**5.** The average weight of a mature human brain is approximately 1400 grams. What is the equivalent weight in kilograms? In pounds?

**6.** Approximately 4.5 liters of blood circulates in the body of the average human adult. How many quarts of blood does the average person have? How many pints?

**7.** How many seconds are in a day? In a week? In a year?

8. The following places are three of the wettest locations on Earth. For each site, determine the rainfall in centimeters per year. Record your results in the third column of the table.

### Looks Like Rain

| LOCATIONS | ANNUAL RAINFALL (IN INCHES) | ANNUAL RAINFALL (IN cm) |
|---|---|---|
| Mawsynram, Meghalaya, India | 467 | |
| Tutenendo, Colombia | 463.5 | |
| Mt. Waialeale, Kauai, Hawaii | 410 | |

9. Jewelry is commonly weighed in carats. Five carats are equivalent to one gram. How many grams of gold are contained in a 24-carat gold chain? How many ounces?

10. Tissues of living organisms consist primarily of organic compounds; that is, they contain carbon molecules known as proteins, carbohydrates, and fats. A healthy human body is approximately 18% carbon by weight. Determine how many pounds of carbon your own body contains. How many kilograms?

## Activities 1.1–1.5    What Have I Learned?

*Activities 1.1 through 1.5 gave you an opportunity to develop some problem-solving strategies. Apply the skills you used in this section to solve the following problems:*

1. Your last class for the day is over! As you grab a water bottle and settle down to read a chapter of text for tomorrow's class, you notice a group of students forming a circle outside and beginning to randomly kick an odd-looking ball from person to person. You notice that there are 12 students in the circle and that they are able to keep the object in the air as they kick it. Sometimes they kick it to the person next to them; other times they kick it to someone across the circle.

   a. Suppose each student kicks the Hacky-Sack (you've discovered the odd-looking ball has a name) exactly once to each of the others in the circle. How many total kicks would that take? Explain your method.

   b. One student in the circle invites you and another student to join them for a total of 14. How many kicks would it now take if each student kicks the Hacky-Sack exactly once to each of the others? How do you arrive at your answer?

   c. George Polya's book, *How to Solve It,* outlines a four-step process for solving problems.

      i. Understand the problem (determine what is involved).

      ii. Devise a plan (look for connections to obtain the idea of a solution).

      iii. Carry out the plan.

      iv. Look back at the completed solution (review and discuss it).

   Describe how your procedures in parts a and b correspond with Polya's suggestions.

**2.** You are assigned to read *War and Peace* for your literature class. The edition you have contains 1232 pages. You time yourself and estimate that you can read 12 pages in one hour. You have five days before your exam on this book. Will you be able to finish reading it before the exam?

**3.** On a 40-question practice test for this course, you answered 32 questions correctly. On the test itself, you correctly answered 16 out of 20 questions. Does this mean that you did better on the practice test than you did on the test itself? Explain.

**4.** In 2000, Florida's total population was 15,982,378 persons and 183 out of every 1000 residents were 65 years and older. Show how you would determine the actual number of Florida residents who were 65 years or older in 2000.

**5.** Submit two articles from a newspaper, magazine, or the Internet, in which ratios and proportions are used. Write a brief summary explaining how the ratios and proportions are used in each article.

**Activities 1.1–1.5** How Can I Practice?

**1.** Solve the following problem by applying the four steps of problem solving given in Activity 1.3. Use the strategy of solving an algebraic equation.

Your average reading speed is 160 words per minute. There are approximately 800 words on each page of the textbook you need to read. Approximately how long will it take you to read 50 pages of your textbook?

**2.** You need to buy grass seed for a new lawn. The lawn will cover a rectangular plot that is 60 feet by 90 feet. Each ounce of grass seed will cover 120 square feet.

**a.** How many ounces of grass seed will you need to buy?

**b.** If the grass seed you want only comes in one-pound bags, how many bags will you need to buy?

**3.** Translate each statement into a formula.

**a.** The total weekly earnings equal $12 per hour times the number of hours worked.

**b.** The total time traveled equals the distance traveled divided by the average speed.

**c.** The distance between two cities, measured in feet, is equal to the distance measured in miles times 5280 feet per mile.

**4.** Use your formulas in Exercise 3 to answer the following questions.

 **a.** If you make $12 per hour, what will your earnings be in a week when you work 35 hours?

 **b.** If you earned $336 last week (still assuming $12 per hour), how many hours did you work?

 **c.** If you travel 480 miles at an average speed of 40 miles per hour, for how many hours were you traveling?

 **d.** The distance between Dallas and Houston is 244 miles. How far is the distance in feet?

**5.** What will the temperature be in degrees Fahrenheit when it is 40° Celsius outside? Use the formula $F = (9C \div 5) + 32$.

**6.** Solve the following proportions.

 **a.** 3 out of 5 = _____ out of 20      **b.** $\frac{3}{5} = \frac{n}{765}$

 **c.** $\frac{3}{5} = \frac{27}{n}$      **d.** $\frac{3}{5} = \frac{1134}{n}$

*In Exercises 7–15, write a proportion that represents the situation and then determine the unknown value in the proportion.*

**7.** You correctly answered two-thirds of the questions on your history exam. There were 75 questions on the exam. How many questions did you answer correctly?

**8.** During a recent infestation by beetles, $\frac{2}{3}$ of the ash trees in a local park were destroyed. If 120 trees were destroyed, how many ash trees were originally in the park?

**9.** Your high school freshman class consists of 760 students. In recent years, only 4 out of 7 students actually graduated in four years. Approximately how many of your classmates are expected to graduate in four years?

**10.** Your car averages 380 miles on a 14-gallon tank of gas. You run out of gas on a deserted highway, but have $\frac{1}{2}$ gallon of lawn mower gas with you. Will you be able to reach the nearest gas station 15 miles away?

**11.** As part of your job as a quality-control inspector in a factory you can check 16 parts in 3 minutes. How long will it take you to check 80 parts?

12. Your car averages about 27 miles per gallon on highways. With gasoline priced at $2.599 per gallon, how much will you expect to spend on gasoline during your 500-mile trip?

13. You currently earn $11.50 per hour. Assuming that you work 40-hour weeks with no raises, what total gross salary will you earn in the next five years?

14. You are traveling at 75 miles per hour on a straight stretch of highway in Nevada. It is noon now. When will you arrive at the next town 120 miles away?

15. To estimate the size of the grizzly bear population in a national park, rangers tagged and released 12 grizzly bears into the park. A few months later, 2 out of 21 grizzly bears sighted were tagged. Assuming the proportion of tagged bears in the population, estimate the number of grizzly bears in the population of this national park.

**ACTIVITY 1.6**
Hot in Texas

**OBJECTIVES**

1. Identify input and output in situations involving two variable quantities.

2. Identify a functional relationship between two variables.

3. Identify the independent and dependent variables.

4. Use a table to numerically represent a functional relationship between two variables.

5. Represent a functional relationship between two variables graphically.

6. Identify trends in data pairs that are represented numerically and graphically, including increasing and decreasing.

A key step in the problem-solving process is to look for relationships and connections between the variable quantities in a given situation. Problems encountered in the world around us, including the environment, medicine, economics, and the Internet, are often very complicated and contain several variables. In this text, you will primarily deal with situations that contain two variables. In many of these situations, the variables will have a special relationship called a **function**.

## Function

It is July, and you have just moved to Midland-Odessa, Texas. The area is in the middle of a heat spell. The high temperature for each of the last 5 days has exceeded 100°F. You are curious about the temperatures you will experience while living in Texas. You discover that the National Weather Service has calculated the average monthly high temperatures in Midland-Odessa over the period from 1971 to 2000. This information is shown in the following table. Note that January is represented by 1, February is represented by 2, and so forth.

| MONTH OF THE YEAR | 1 | 2 | 3 | 4 | 5 | 6 | 7 | 8 | 9 | 10 | 11 | 12 |
|---|---|---|---|---|---|---|---|---|---|---|---|---|
| AVERAGE MONTHLY HIGH TEMPERATURE, °F | 56.8 | 63.0 | 70.9 | 78.8 | 86.8 | 92.7 | 94.3 | 92.8 | 86.1 | 77.4 | 65.9 | 58.4 |

This situation involves two variables, the month and the average monthly high temperature. Typically, one variable is designated as the **input** and the other is called the **output**. The input is the value given first, and the output is the value that corresponds to, or is determined by, the given input value. The input variable is often represented by the letter $x$. The output variable is frequently represented by the letter $y$.

1. In the temperature situation, identify the input variable and the output variable.

2. **a.** For an input of 7 (July), what is the average high temperature (output)?

   **b.** For an input of 1 (January), what is the average high temperature (output)?

   **c.** For each value of input (month), how many different outputs (average high temperature) are there?

The set of data in the table is an example of a mathematical function.

> **DEFINITION**
>
> A **function** is a correspondence between an input variable and an output variable that assigns a single, unique output value to each input value. Therefore, for a function, any given input value has exactly one corresponding output value. If $x$ represents the input variable and $y$ represents the output variable, then the function assigns a single, unique $y$-value to each $x$-value.

**3.** Explain how the data in the previous table fit the description of a function.

A functional relationship is stated as follows: "The output variable is a function of the input variable." Using $x$ for the input variable and $y$ for the output variable, then the functional relationship is stated "$y$ is a function of $x$." Because the input for the temperature function is the month and the output is the average high temperature for that month, you write that the average high temperature is a function of the month.

**Example 1** *Consider the following table listing the official high temperature (in °F) in the village of Lake Placid, New York, during the first week of January. Note that the date has been designated the input and the high temperature on that date the output. Is the high temperature a function of the date?*

**Almost Freezing**

| DATE (INPUT) | 1 | 2 | 3 | 4 | 5 | 6 | 7 |
|---|---|---|---|---|---|---|---|
| TEMPERATURE (OUTPUT) | 25 | 30 | 32 | 24 | 23 | 27 | 30 |

SOLUTION

From this table, you observe that the high temperature is a function of the date. For each date there is exactly one high temperature. The relationship in this Example can be visualized as follows:

| DATE (INPUT) | TEMPERATURE (OUTPUT) |
|---|---|
| 1 ⟶ | 25 |
| 2 ⟶ | 30 |
| 3 ⟶ | 32 |
| 4 ⟶ | 24 |
| 5 ⟶ | 23 |
| 6 ⟶ | 27 |
| 7 ⟶ | 30 |

If $d$ represents the input (date), and $T$ represents the output (temperature), then $T$ is a function of $d$.

Example 2  *Determine if the amount of postage for a letter is a function of the weight of the letter. Give a reason for your answer.*

SOLUTION

Yes, the situation does describe a function. The weight of the letter is the input, and the amount of postage is the output. Each letter has one weight. This weight determines the postage necessary for the letter. There is only one amount of postage for each letter. Therefore, for each value of input (weight of the letter) there is one output (postage). Note that if $w$ represents the input (weight of the letter), and $p$ represents the output (postage), then $p$ is a function of $w$.

4. Determine whether or not each situation describes a function. Give a reason for your answer.

   a. The amount of property tax you have to pay is a function of the assessed value of the house.

   b. The weight of a letter in ounces is a function of the postage paid for mailing the letter.

DEFINITION

For all functions, the input variable is called the **independent** variable, and the output variable is called the **dependent** variable. If $x$ represents the input variable, and $y$ represents the output variable, then $x$ is the independent variable and $y$ is the dependent variable.

5. The independent variable in Example 1 is the date. The dependent variable is the temperature. Identify the independent and dependent variables in Example 2.

## Representing Functions Numerically

The input/output pairing in the temperature function on page 44 is presented as a **table of matched pairs**. In such a situation, the function is defined **numerically**. Another way to define a function numerically is as a set of **ordered pairs**.

DEFINITION

An **ordered pair** of numbers consists of two numbers written in the form

$$(x, y),$$

where $x$ represents the independent variable and $y$ represents the dependent variable. The order in which they are listed is significant.

Example 3   *The ordered pair (3, 4) is distinct from the ordered pair (4, 3). In the ordered pair (3, 4), 3 is the x-value and 4 is the y-value. In the ordered pair (4, 3), 4 is the x-value and 3 is the y-value.*

> **DEFINITION**
>
> A function may be defined **numerically** as a set of ordered pairs $(x, y)$, where $x$ represents the input and $y$ represents the output. No two ordered pairs have the same $x$-value and different $y$-values.

**6.** Write three other ordered pairs for the Texas temperature function.

## Representing Functions Graphically

You may have seen an ordered pair before as the coordinates of a point in a **rectangular coordinate system**, typically using ordered pairs of the form $(x, y)$, where $x$ is the input (independent variable) and $y$ is the output (dependent variable). The first value, the horizontal coordinate, indicates the directed distance (right or left) from the vertical axis. The second value, the vertical coordinate, indicates the directed distance (up or down) from the horizontal axis.

*The variables may not always be represented by x and y, but the horizontal axis will always be the input axis, and the vertical axis will always be the output axis.*

**7.** Plot each ordered pair in the Texas temperature table on the following grid. Set your axes and scales by noting the smallest and largest values for both input and output. Label each axis by the variable name. *Remember, the scale for the horizontal axis does not have to be the same as the scale for the vertical axis. However, each scale (vertical and horizontal) must be divided into equal intervals.*

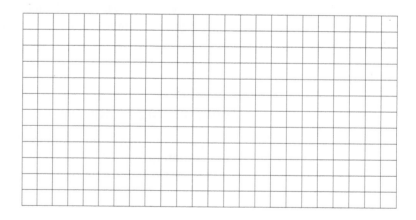

The preceding graph, which consists of a set of labeled axes and 12 points, presents the same information that is in the Texas temperature table on page 43, but in a different way. It shows the information as a graph and therefore defines the function **graphically**.

**8.** In Example 1, the high temperature in Lake Placid is a function of the date.

    **a.** Convert to ordered pairs all the values in the Almost Freezing table on page 45.

    **b.** Plot each ordered pair as a point on an appropriately scaled and labeled set of coordinate axes.

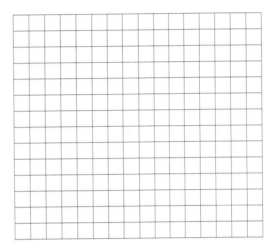

## More Graphing

Living on Earth's surface, you experience a relatively narrow range of temperatures. You may know what $-20°F$ (or $-28.9°C$) feels like on a bitterly cold winter day. Or you may have sweated through $100°F$ (or $37.8°C$) during summer heatwaves. If you were to travel below Earth's surface and above Earth's atmosphere, you would discover a wider range of temperatures. The following graph displays a relationship between the altitude and temperature. Note that the altitude is measured from Earth's surface. That is, Earth's surface is at altitude 0.

**TEMPERATURE VERSUS ALTITUDE**

Use this graph to answer Problem 9.

**9. a.** With what variable and units of measure is the horizontal axis labeled?

**b.** What is the practical significance of the positive values of this quantity?

**c.** What is the practical significance of the negative values of this quantity?

**d.** How many kilometers are represented between the tick marks on the horizontal axis?

**10. a.** With what variable and units of measure is the vertical axis labeled?

**b.** What is the practical significance of the positive values of this quantity?

**c.** What is the practical significance of the negative values of this quantity?

**d.** How many degrees Celsius are represented between the tick marks on the vertical axis?

Recall, the two perpendicular coordinate axes divide the plane into four **quadrants**. The quadrants are labeled counterclockwise, using Roman numerals, with quadrant I being the upper-right quadrant.

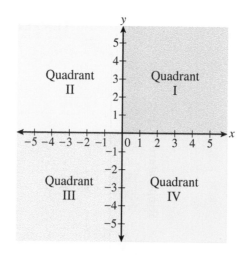

**11.** The following graph displays eight points selected from the temperature versus altitude graph on page 47.

**TEMPERATURE VERSUS ALTITUDE**

**a.** What is the practical meaning of the point with coordinates (150, 361)?

**b.** What is the practical meaning of the point with coordinates (100, −78)?

**c.** What is the practical meaning of the point with coordinates (−20, 430)?

**d.** In which quadrant are the points (120, 87), (150, 361), and (200, 581) located?

**e.** In which quadrant are the points (−10, 101) and (−20, 430) located?

**f.** In which quadrant are the points (20, −56) and (100, −78) located?

**g.** Are there any points located in quadrant III? What is the significance of your answer?

## Increasing and Decreasing Functions

There are many other advantages to having the function in graphical form. For example, you are often interested in determining how the output values change as the input values increase.

> **DEFINITION**
>
> A function is **increasing** if its graph goes up to the right, **decreasing** if its graph goes down to the right, and **constant** if its graph is horizontal. In each case, you are viewing the graph as a point moves along the curve from left to right, that is, as the input values increase.

Example 4

    **a.** The graph of this function is always increasing. The graph rises from left to right.

    **b.** The graph of this function is decreasing because its graph falls from left to right.

    **c.** The graph of this function is constant, because the graph goes neither up nor down. The $y$-value is always 3 no matter what the $x$-value is.

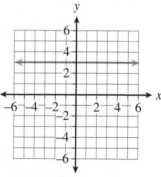

**12.** Is the following function increasing, decreasing, or constant over the domain displayed in the window?

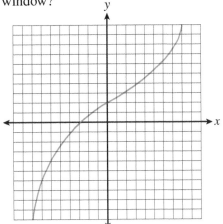

**1.** A **variable**, usually represented by a letter, is a quantity that may change in value from one particular instance to another.

**2.** In a situation involving two variables, one variable is designated the **input** and the other the **output**. The input is the value given first, and the output is the value that corresponds to or is determined by the given input value.

**3.** A **function** is a correspondence relating an input variable (*independent variable*) and an output variable (*dependent variable*) so that a single, unique output value is assigned to each input value. In such a case, you state that the output variable is a function of the input variable.

**4.** An **ordered pair** of numbers consists of two numbers written in the form

(input value, output value).

The order in which they are listed is significant.

**5.** Functions may be defined **numerically** using ordered pairs of numbers. The ordered pairs are always given in the form (input value, output value). These can be displayed as a table of values or points on a graph. For each input value, there is one and only one corresponding output value.

**6.** When a function is represented **graphically,** the $x$ and $y$ data pairs are represented as plotted points on a grid called a *rectangular coordinate system*. The $x$-variable is referenced on the horizontal axis. The $y$-variable is referenced on the vertical axis.

**7.** The two perpendicular coordinate axes divide the plane into four **quadrants**. The quadrants are labeled counterclockwise, using Roman numerals, with quadrant I being the upper-right quadrant.

II | I
---|---
III | IV

**8.** A function is **increasing** if its graph rises to the right, **decreasing** if its graph falls to the right, and constant if its graph is horizontal.

**1.** The weights and heights of six mathematics students are given in the following table:

### Weighty Issues

| WEIGHT (IN POUNDS) | HEIGHT (IN CENTIMETERS) |
|---|---|
| 165 | 172 |
| 123 | 157 |
| 212 | 183 |
| 175 | 178 |
| 165 | 163 |
| 147 | 167 |

**a.** In the statement, "Height is a function of weight," which variable is the input and which is the output?

**b.** Is height a function of weight for the six students? Explain using the definition of function.

**c.** In the statement, "Weight is a function of height," which variable is the input and which is the output?

**d.** Is weight a function of height for the six students? Explain using the definition of function.

**e.** For all students, is weight a function of height? Explain.

*For Exercises 2–7, determine whether or not each of the situations describes a function. Give a reason for your answer. For each functional relationship, determine the independent and dependent variables.*

**2. a.** The amount of federal income tax you pay is a function of your taxable income.

    **b.** The value of your car is a function of the total mileage on the car.

**3. a.** The letter grade in this course is a function of your numerical grade.

    **b.** The numerical grade in this course is a function of the letter grade.

**4. a.** The input is any number and the output is the square of the number.

    **b.** The square of a number is the input and the output is the number.

**5.** In the following table, elevation is the input and amount of snowfall is the output.

| ELEVATION (IN FEET) | SNOWFALL (IN INCHES) |
|---|---|
| 2000 | 4 |
| 3000 | 6 |
| 4000 | 9 |
| 5000 | 12 |

**6.** Number of hours using the Internet is the input variable, and the monthly cost for the Internet service is $19.95, regardless of the number of hours of usage.

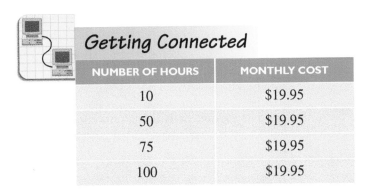

*Getting Connected*

| NUMBER OF HOURS | MONTHLY COST |
|---|---|
| 10 | $19.95 |
| 50 | $19.95 |
| 75 | $19.95 |
| 100 | $19.95 |

**7.** Each of the following tables defines a relationship between an input $x$ and an output $y$. Which of the relationships represent functions? Explain your answers.

**a.**

| $x$ | −8 | −3 | 0 | 6 | 9 | 15 | 24 | 38 | 100 |
|---|---|---|---|---|---|---|---|---|---|
| $y$ | 24 | 4 | 9 | 72 | −14 | −16 | 53 | 29 | 7 |

**b.**

| $x$ | −8 | −5 | 0 | 6 | 9 | 15 | 24 | 24 | 100 |
|---|---|---|---|---|---|---|---|---|---|
| $y$ | 24 | 4 | 9 | 72 | 14 | −16 | 53 | 29 | 7 |

**c.**

| $x$ | −8 | −3 | 0 | 6 | 9 | 15 | 24 | 38 | 100 |
|---|---|---|---|---|---|---|---|---|---|
| $y$ | 24 | 4 | 9 | 72 | 4 | −16 | 53 | 24 | 7 |

**8.** You work for the National Weather Service and are asked to study the average daily temperatures in Anchorage, Alaska. You calculate the mean of the average daily temperatures for each month. You decide to place the information on a graph in which the date is the input and the temperature is the output. You also decide that January 1950 will correspond to the month 0 as indicated by the dot on the input scale. Determine the quadrant in which you would plot the points that correspond to the following data.

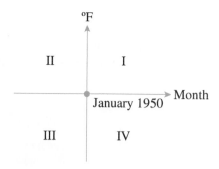

**a.** The average daily temperature for January 1936 was −15°F.

**b.** The average daily temperature for July 1963 was 63°F.

**c.** The average daily temperature for July 1910 was 71°F.

**d.** The average daily temperature for January 1982 was –21°F.

**9.** Measurements in wells and mines have shown that the temperatures within the earth generally increase with depth. The following table shows average temperatures for several depths below sea level.

## A Hot Topic

| DEPTH (km) BELOW SEA LEVEL | 0 | 25 | 50 | 75 | 100 | 150 | 200 |
|---|---|---|---|---|---|---|---|
| TEMPERATURE (°C) | 20 | 600 | 1000 | 1250 | 1400 | 1700 | 1800 |

**a.** Represent the data from the table graphically on the grid following part *d*. Place depth along the horizontal axis and temperature along the vertical axis.

**b.** How many units does each tick mark on the horizontal axis represent?

**c.** How many units does each tick mark on the vertical axis represent?

**d.** Explain your reasons for selecting the particular scales that you used.

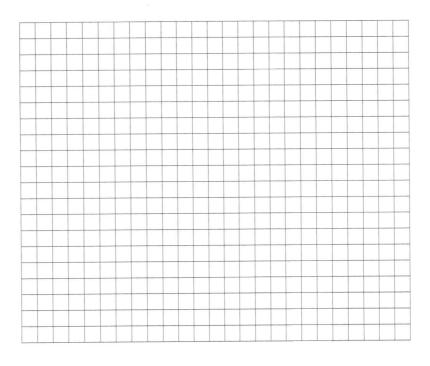

**e.** Which representation (table or graph) presents the information and trends in this data more clearly? Explain your choice.

**10.** The following table presents the average recommended weights for given heights for 25- to 29-year-old medium-framed women (wearing 1-inch heels and 3 pounds of clothing). Consider height to be the input variable and weight to be the output variable. As ordered pairs, height and weight take on the form (h, w). Designate horizontal (input) axis as the h-axis, and the vertical (output) axis as the w-axis. Since all values of the data are positive, the points will lie in quadrant I only.

| h, HEIGHT (in.) | 58 | 60 | 62 | 64 | 66 | 68 | 70 | 72 |
|---|---|---|---|---|---|---|---|---|
| w, WEIGHT (lb) | 115 | 119 | 125 | 131 | 137 | 143 | 149 | 155 |

Plot the ordered pairs in the height-weight table on the following grid. Note the consistent spacing between tick marks on each axis. The distance between tick marks on the horizontal axis represents 2 inches. On the vertical axis the distance between tick marks represents 5 pounds.

**Note:** The slash marks (//) near the origin indicate that the interval from 0 to 56 on the horizontal axis and the interval from 0 to 115 on the vertical axis are not shown. That is, only the part of the graph containing the plotted points is shown.

**ACTIVITY 1.7**

Fill 'er Up

**OBJECTIVES**

1. Write the equation to define a function.

2. Determine the domain and range of a function.

3. Identify the independent and the dependent variables of a function.

You probably need to fill your car with gas more often than you would like, so you drive around looking for the best price per gallon.

1. There are two variables that determine the cost of a fill-up. What are they? Be specific.

2. Suppose the local gas station is selling gas at a special sale price of $2.47$\frac{9}{10}$ per gallon. Now one of the variables in Problem 1 will become a constant. The value of a constant will not vary throughout the problem. The cost of a fill-up is now dependent on only one variable, the number of gallons of gas pumped.

   a. Complete the following table:

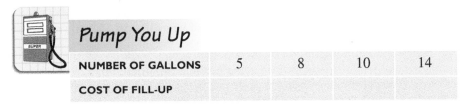

| Pump You Up | | | | |
|---|---|---|---|---|
| NUMBER OF GALLONS | 5 | 8 | 10 | 14 |
| COST OF FILL-UP | | | | |

   b. Is the cost of a fill-up a function of the number of gallons pumped? Explain.

   c. Identify the independent and dependent variables.

3. a. Write a statement that describes how the cost of a fill-up is determined.

   b. Let $g$ represent the number of gallons of gasoline pumped and $c$ represent the cost of the fill-up. Translate the verbal statement (a relationship between variables stated in words) in part a into a symbolic statement (an equation) that expresses $c$ in terms of $g$.

## Defining Functions by a Symbolic Rule (Equation)

The symbolic rule (equation) $c = 2.479g$ represents the third method of defining a function. Recall that the other two methods are numerically (tables and ordered pairs) and graphically.

4. a. Use the given equation to determine the cost of a fill-up that required 8 gallons of gas.

   b. Explain the steps that you used to determine the cost in part a.

Function notation is an efficient and convenient way of representing the dependent variable. The equation $c = 2.479g$ may be written using the function notation by replacing the dependent variable $c$ with $f(g)$ as follows:

$$f(g) = 2.479g, \text{ where } c = f(g).$$

The letter $f$ in the notation $f(g)$ represents the name of the function. The letter within the parenthesis always represents the independent variable. The notation $f(g)$ is simply another way of representing the dependent variable $c$. Remember,

$$c = f(g) = 2.479g$$

Now, the cost of 5 gallons of gas can be represented by $f(5)$. To evaluate $f(5)$, substitute 5 for $g$ in $f(g) = 2.479g$ as follows:

$$f(5) = 2.479(5) = 12.395$$

The results can be written as $f(5) = 12.395$ or as the ordered pair (5,12.395). Therefore, 5 gallons of gas will cost $12.40 (rounded to the nearest cent).

**5. a.** Write the cost of 8 gallons of gas using function notation and evaluate. Write the result as an ordered pair.

   **b.** Use the equation for the cost-of-fill-up function to evaluate $f(12)$, and write a sentence describing its meaning. Write the result as an ordered pair.

## Real Numbers

The numbers that you will be using as input and output values in this text will be real numbers. A real number is any rational or irrational number.

A rational number is any number that can be expressed as the quotient of two integers (negative and positive counting numbers as well as zero).

Example 1   *Rational numbers include the following:*

$$\frac{3}{4} \quad -\frac{7}{8} \quad 2\frac{1}{3} = \frac{7}{3} \quad 5 = \frac{5}{1} \quad 0 = \frac{0}{1} \quad -3\frac{1}{4} = -3.25 \quad \frac{2}{3} = 0.666\ldots = 0.\overline{6}$$

An irrational number is a real number that cannot be expressed as a quotient of two integers.

Example 2   *Irrational numbers include* $\sqrt{2}, -\sqrt{7}, \sqrt[3]{5}, \pi.$

All of the numbers in Examples 1 and 2 are real numbers. A real number can be represented as a point on the number line.

## Domain and Range

**6.** Can any real number be substituted for the variable *g* in the cost of fill-up function? Describe the values of *g* that make sense, and explain why they do.

> **DEFINITION**
>
> The collection of all possible values of the independent variable is called the **domain** of the function. The **practical domain** is the collection of replacement values of the independent variable that makes practical sense in the context of the problem.

**Example 3**   *The practical domain in Problem 6 is the real numbers 0 through 20, assuming that 20 gallons is the maximum capacity of your gas tank. The value of g would be 0 if your gas tank is totally full and 20 if your gas tank is totally empty.*

Following is the graph of the cost-of-fill-up function defined by $c = 2.479g$ over its practical domain.

The domain for the general function defined by $c = 2.479g$, with no connection to the context of the problem, is the set of all real numbers, since any real number can be substituted for $g$ in $2.479g$. Following is a graph of $c = 2.479g$ for any real number $g$.

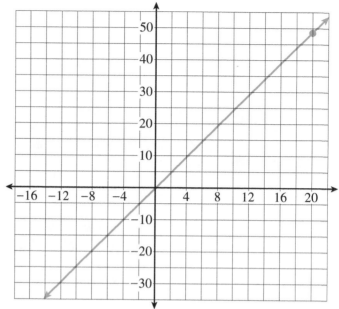

When a value from the domain is substituted for the independent variable and the corresponding output is evaluated, the result is a value of the dependent variable.

**DEFINITION**

The collection of all possible values of the dependent variable is the **range** of the function. The practical range corresponds to the practical domain.

**Example 4** *Consider the following table that gives the percentage of mothers in the workforce with children under the age of 6 from 1999 to 2004.*

| YEAR | PERCENTAGE |
|------|------------|
| 1999 | 64.4 |
| 2000 | 65.3 |
| 2001 | 64.4 |
| 2002 | 64.1 |
| 2003 | 62.9 |
| 2004 | 62.2 |

*Source:* U.S. Department of Labor.

Although the table contains only six pairs of numbers, it represents a function. The input or independent variable is the year, and the output or dependent variable is the percentage. The domain of the function is {1999, 2000, 2001, 2002, 2003, 2004} because these are all the input values. The range of the function is {62.2, 62.9, 64.1, 64.4, 65.3} because this is the set of all of the output values. Note that although 64.4 occurs twice in the table as an output value, it is listed only once in the range.

**7. a.** What is the practical range for the cost function defined by $f(g) = 2.479g$ if the practical domain is 0 to 20?

**b.** What is the range of this function if it has no connection to the context of the problem?

**8.** Use the symbolic form of the gas cost of fill-up function, $f(g) = 2.479g$, to evaluate $f(0)$, $f(5)$, $f(10)$, $f(15)$, and $f(20)$, and complete the following table. Note that the variable $g$ increases by 5 units. In such a case, you say that $g$ increases by an **increment** of 5 units.

| NUMBER OF GALLONS OF GAS NEEDED, $g$ | COST OF FILL-UP, $f(g)$ |
|---|---|
| 0 | |
| 5 | |
| 10 | |
| 15 | |
| 20 | |

A numerical form of the cost of fill-up function is a table or a collection of ordered pairs. When a function is defined in symbolic form, you can use technology to generate the table. The TI-83/84 Plus calculator is a function grapher. The $y$ variables $Y_1$, $Y_2$, and so on represent function output (dependent) variables. The input, or independent variable, is $x$. The steps to build tables with the TI-83/84 Plus can be found in Appendix A.

Appendix

**9.** Use your graphing calculator to generate a table of values for the function represented by $f(g) = 2.479g$ to check your values in the table in Problem 8. The screens on your calculator should appear as follows:

## Gross Pay Function

**10.** If you work for an hourly wage, your gross pay is a function of the number of hours that you work.

**a.** What is the independent variable? What is the dependent variable?

**b.** If you earn $8 per hour, complete the following table:

| NUMBER OF HOURS | 0 | 3 | 5 | 7 | 10 | 12 |
|---|---|---|---|---|---|---|
| GROSS PAY | | | | | | |

**c.** Plot the ordered pairs determined in part b on an appropriately scaled and labeled set of axes.

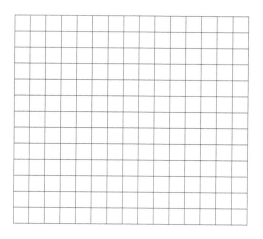

**d.** Let $n$ represent the number of hours worked and $f(n)$ represent the gross pay. Write an equation for $f(n)$ in terms of $n$.

**e.** Evaluate $f(10)$ and write a sentence explaining the meaning of $f(10)$.

**f.** What are the practical domain and the practical range of the function? Explain.

---

**SUMMARY**
**Activity 1.7**

1. **Independent variable** is another name for the input variable of a function.

2. **Dependent variable** is another name for the output variable of a function.

3. The collection of all possible replacement values for the independent variable is called the **domain of the function**. The **practical domain** is the collection of replacement values of the independent variable that makes practical sense in the context of the problem.

4. The collection of all values of the dependent variable of a function is called the **range of the function**. When a function describes a real situation or phenomenon, its range is often called the **practical range** of the function.

5. When a function is represented by an equation, the function may also be written in **function notation**. For example, given $y = 2x + 3$, you can replace $y$ with $f(x)$ and rewrite the equation as $f(x) = 2x + 3$.

In Exercises 1 and 2,
a. Identify the independent and dependent variables.
b. Let x represent the independent variable. Use function notation to represent the dependent variable.
c. Translate the written statement into an equation.

1. Sales tax is a function of the price of an item. The amount of sales tax is 0.08 times the price of the item. Use $h$ to represent the function.

2. The Fahrenheit measure of temperature is a function of the Celsius measure. The Fahrenheit measure is 32 more than 9/5 times the Celsius measure. Use $g$ to represent the function.

For each function in Exercises 3–5, evaluate $f(2)$, $f(-3.2)$, and $f(a)$.

3. $f(d) = 2d - 5$

4. $f(t) = -16t^2 + 7.8t + 12$

5. $f(x) = 4$

In Exercises 6–8, construct a table of values of four ordered pairs for the given function. Check your results using the table feature of your graphing calculator.

6. $g(x) = x^2$. Start the independent variable $x$ at 3 and use an increment of 2.

| x | g(x) |
|---|------|
|   |      |
|   |      |
|   |      |
|   |      |

**7.** $h(x) = \dfrac{1}{x}$. Start the x-values at 10 and use an increment of 10.

| x | h(x) |
|---|---|
|   |   |
|   |   |
|   |   |
|   |   |

**8.** $f(x) = 3.5x + 6$. Start the x-values at 0 and use an increment of 5.

| x | f(x) |
|---|---|
|   |   |
|   |   |
|   |   |
|   |   |

**9. a.** The distance you travel while hiking is a function of how fast you hike and how long you hike at this rate. You usually maintain a speed of three miles per hour while hiking. Write a statement that describes how the distance that you travel is determined.

**b.** Identify the independent and dependent variables of this function.

**c.** Write the statement in part a using function notation. Let $t$ represent the independent variable. Let $h$ represent the function, and $h(t)$ the dependent variable.

**d.** Use the equation from part c to determine the distance traveled in four hours.

**e.** Evaluate $h(7)$ and write a sentence describing its meaning. Write the result as an ordered pair.

**f.** Determine the domain and range of the general function.

**g.** Determine the practical domain and the practical range of the function.

**h.** Use your calculator to generate a table of values beginning at zero with an increment of 0.5.

| x | g(x) |
|---|------|
|   |      |
|   |      |
|   |      |
|   |      |
|   |      |
|   |      |
|   |      |

**10.** Determine the domain and range of each function.

**a.** $\{(-2, 4), (0, 3), (5, 8), (8, 11)\}$

**b.** $\{(-6, 5), (-2, 5), (0, 5), (3, 5)\}$

**11.** According to the AAA, it costs approximately $0.689 per mile to own and operate a car. The total cost is a function of the number of miles driven and can be represented by the function $C = 0.689m$. When you finally take your car to the junkyard, the odometer reads 157,200 miles.

**a.** Identify the input variable.

**b.** Identify the output variable.

**c.** Use $f$ to represent the function and rewrite $C = 0.689m$ using function notation.

**d.** Evaluate $f(10,000)$ and write a sentence describing its meaning. Write the result as an ordered pair.

**e.** Use the table feature of your calculator to create a table of values with a beginning input of 0. Use increments of 50,000 miles.

    **f.** What is the practical domain for this situation?

    **g.** What is the practical range for this situation?

**12.** To change a Celsius temperature to Fahrenheit, use the formula $F = 1.8C + 32$. You are concerned only with temperatures between freezing and boiling.

    **a.** What is the practical domain of the function?

    **b.** What is the practical range of the function?

**13.** Your high school service organization has volunteered to help with Spring Cleanup Day at a youth summer camp. You have been assigned the job of supplying paint for the exterior of the bunkhouses. You discover that 1 gallon of paint will cover 400 square feet of flat surface.

    **a.** If $n$ represents the number of gallons of paint you supply and $s$ represents the number of square feet you can cover with the paint, complete the following table:

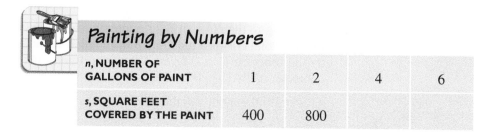

**Painting by Numbers**

| $n$, NUMBER OF GALLONS OF PAINT | 1 | 2 | 4 | 6 |
|---|---|---|---|---|
| $s$, SQUARE FEET COVERED BY THE PAINT | 400 | 800 | | |

    **b.** Let $n$ be the independent variable and $s$ be the dependent variable. Plot the ordered pairs determined in part a on an appropriately scaled and labeled set of axes.

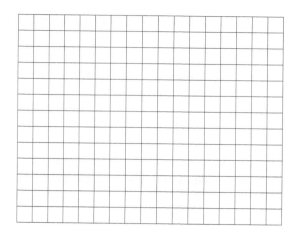

   **c.** Let $s$ be represented by $f(n)$, where $f$ is the name of the function. Determine $f(6)$.

   **d.** Write a sentence explaining the meaning of $f(4) = 1600$.

**14.** Give an example of a function that you may encounter in your daily life or that describes something about the world around you.

   **a.** Identify the independent and the dependent variables.

   **b.** Write the function in the form "output is a function of the input."

   **c.** Explain how the example fits the definition of a function.

**ACTIVITY 1.8**
Mathematical
Modeling

**OBJECTIVES**

1. Identify a mathematical model.
2. Solve problems using formulas as models.
3. Develop a function model to solve a problem.
4. Recognize patterns and trends between two variables using tables as models.

After an automobile accident, the investigating police officers often estimate the speed of the vehicle by measuring the length of the tire skid distance. The following table gives the average skid distances for an automobile with good tires on dry pavement.

### The Long and Short of It

| SKID DISTANCE (FEET) | SPEED (MPH) |
| --- | --- |
| 28 | 25 |
| 54 | 35 |
| 89 | 45 |
| 132 | 55 |
| 184 | 65 |
| 244 | 75 |
| 313 | 85 |
| 390 | 95 |

1. Does the table data define speed as a function of skid distance? Explain using the definition of function.

2. Identify the independent variable and the dependent variable.

3. Plot the data as ordered pairs on an appropriately scaled and labeled set of coordinate axes. Remember, the values of the independent variable appear along the horizontal axis, and the values of the dependent variable appear along the vertical axis.

After a particular accident, a skid distance was measured to be 200 feet. From the table, the investigating officer knows that the speed of the vehicle was between 65 and 75 miles per hour. She would, however, like to be able to be more precise in reporting the speed. One way of getting values that are not listed in the table is to use a graph or equation of a function that best fits the actual data.

Note that the points on the graph in Problem 3 do not appear to lie exactly on a specific curve. However, calculators use a special mathematical process to produce an equation that best fits actual data. From the data in the table, The Long and Short of It, the TI-83/84 Plus can be used to generate the following equation:

$$y = -0.00029x^2 + 0.31x + 18.6 \text{ (coefficients are rounded), (1)}$$

where $x$ represents the skid distance in feet and $y$ represents the speed in miles per hour. The process for generating such equations is covered in later activities.

Appendix

**4. a.** Enter the function equation above into your calculator. For help with the TI-83/84 Plus, see Appendix A. The screen should appear as follows:

**b.** The values in the table, The Long and Short of It, can help to set appropriate window values in your calculator to view the graph. Starting at a minimum skid distance of 0, a reasonable maximum value of the skid distance in this situation would be 450 feet. Beginning at a minimum speed of 0, a reasonable maximum speed value would be 100 mph. Using these settings, the window screen should appear as follows:

**c.** Display your graph using the window settings from part b. Your graph should resemble the following:

**5. a.** By pressing the trace button and the left and right arrow keys, you can display the $x$-$y$ values of points on the graph on the bottom of the display. Use the trace feature of your calculator to approximate the speed of the car when the length of the skid distance is 200 feet. You can obtain the exact value for any $x$-value between Xmin and Xmax by entering the $x$-value while in trace mode and pressing ENTER. Your screen should appear as follows:

**b.** Use your calculator to verify the result in part a by evaluating $-0.00029(200)^2 + 0.31(200) + 18.6$.

> The equation $y = -0.00029x^2 + 0.31x + 18.6$ is called a **mathematical model**. A mathematical model is a mathematical form, such as a formula, an equation, a graph, or a table, that fits or approximates the important features of a given situation. Such models can then be used to estimate, make predictions, and draw conclusions about the given situation.

The process of developing a mathematical model to represent a given situation involves several steps. First, you need to identify the problem and develop a well-defined question about what you want to know. For example, in the automobile accident situation, can you determine the speed of the car when the brakes are applied?

Next, you look for relationships and connections between the variables that are involved in the situation. You may also need to make assumptions about the situation before you begin to construct the mathematical model.

6. What are some of the variable quantities present in determining what you want to know in the automobile accident situation? What assumptions did you make?

Using your mathematical and problem solving skills, you can now translate the features and relationships you have identified into a mathematical model. The model can be used to answer the questions that you originally raised.

Finally, you need to verify that the mathematical model you have developed accurately represents the situation under investigation.

7. How well does the mathematical model (equation 1) determine the speed of the car for a given skid distance? Explain how you came to this conclusion.

Note that one way to verify the accuracy of your mathematical model is to collect data and compare the data to the results predicted by the model. In the speed and skid-distance situation, the use of data actually helped you determine the model. By observing patterns revealed by the data and graph, an appropriate model was developed.

The process just described to develop a mathematical model is called **mathematical modeling**. The development and use of mathematical models to help solve simple to extremely complicated problems is a very important use of mathematics.

## Modeling with Formulas

In Activity 1.3, you used formulas to model situations in geometry, business, and science. In almost every field of study, you are likely to encounter formulas that relate two or more variables represented by letters. Problems 8 and 9 feature formulas used in the health field.

**8.** Medical researchers have determined that for exercise to be beneficial, a person's desirable heart rate, $R$, in beats per minute, can be approximated by the formulas

$$R = 143 - 0.65a \text{ for women}$$
$$R = 165 - 0.75a \text{ for men,}$$

where $a$ represents the person's age.

  **a.** If the desirable heart rate for a woman is 130 beats per minute, how old is she?

  **b.** If the desirable heart rate for a man is 135 beats per minute, how old is he?

**9.** The basal energy rate is the daily amount of energy (measured in calories) needed by the body at rest to maintain body temperature and the basic life processes of respiration, cell metabolism, circulation, and glandular activity. As you may suspect, the basal energy rate differs for individuals, depending on their gender, age, height, and weight. The formula for the basal energy rate for men is

$$B = 655.096 + 9.563W + 1.85H - 4.676A,$$

where $B$ is the basal energy rate (in calories), $W$ is the weight (in kilograms), $H$ is the height (in centimeters), and $A$ is the age (in years).

  **a.** A male patient is 70 years old, weighs 55 kilograms, and is 172 centimeters tall. A total daily caloric intake of 1000 calories is prescribed for him. Determine if he is being properly fed.

  **b.** A man is 178 centimeters tall and weighs 84 kilograms. If his basal energy rate is 1500 calories, how old is the man?

## Tables as Models

In Activity 1.6, you encountered several tables of matched pairs of values for situations involving two variables. These tables serve as models that help represent the relationship between the quantities involved. Patterns are revealed and often lead to an equation that can model the relationship more completely.

For example, you feel colder on a windy cold day than the air temperature indicates. This is commonly referred to as windchill.

10. Suppose the wind is a constant 20 mph. The following table gives the wind chill temperature (how cold your skin feels) for various air temperatures.

| AIR TEMPERATURE °F | 40 | 30 | 20 | 10 | 0 | −10 | −20 |
|---|---|---|---|---|---|---|---|
| WINDCHILL TEMPERATURE (20-MPH WIND) | 30 | 17 | 4 | −9 | −22 | −35 | −48 |

    a. What relationship do you observe between the windchill temperature and the air temperature?

    b. Estimate the windchill temperature for an air temperature of −30°F.

    c. If the windchill speed is 30 mph, how would you expect the windchill temperatures in the table to change?

11. The following windchill chart has been published by the National Weather Service. Note that the formula used to generate the table values is based on scientific knowledge and experiments.

### Windchill Chart

**Temperature (°F)**

| Wind (mph) | 40 | 35 | 30 | 25 | 20 | 15 | 10 | 5 | 0 | −5 | −10 | −15 | −20 | −25 | −30 | −35 | −40 | −45 |
|---|---|---|---|---|---|---|---|---|---|---|---|---|---|---|---|---|---|---|
| 5 | 36 | 31 | 25 | 19 | 13 | 7 | 1 | −5 | −11 | −16 | −22 | −28 | −34 | −40 | −46 | −52 | −57 | −63 |
| 10 | 34 | 27 | 21 | 15 | 9 | 3 | −4 | −10 | −16 | −22 | −28 | −35 | −41 | −47 | −53 | −59 | −66 | −72 |
| 15 | 32 | 25 | 19 | 13 | 6 | 0 | −7 | −13 | −19 | −26 | −32 | −39 | −45 | −51 | −58 | −64 | −71 | −77 |
| 20 | 30 | 24 | 17 | 11 | 4 | −2 | −9 | −15 | −22 | −29 | −35 | −42 | −48 | −55 | −61 | −68 | −74 | −81 |
| 25 | 29 | 23 | 16 | 9 | 3 | −4 | −11 | −17 | −24 | −31 | −37 | −44 | −51 | −58 | −64 | −71 | −78 | −84 |
| 30 | 28 | 22 | 15 | 8 | 1 | −5 | −12 | −19 | −26 | −33 | −39 | −46 | −53 | −60 | −67 | −73 | −80 | −87 |
| 35 | 28 | 21 | 14 | 7 | 0 | −7 | −14 | −21 | −27 | −34 | −41 | −48 | −55 | −62 | −69 | −76 | −82 | −89 |
| 40 | 27 | 20 | 13 | 6 | −1 | −8 | −15 | −22 | −29 | −36 | −43 | −50 | −57 | −64 | −71 | −78 | −84 | −91 |
| 45 | 26 | 20 | 12 | 5 | −2 | −9 | −16 | −23 | −30 | −37 | −44 | −51 | −58 | −65 | −72 | −79 | −86 | −93 |
| 50 | 26 | 19 | 12 | 4 | −3 | −10 | −17 | −24 | −31 | −38 | −45 | −52 | −60 | −67 | −74 | −81 | −88 | −95 |
| 55 | 25 | 18 | 11 | 4 | −3 | −11 | −18 | −25 | −32 | −39 | −46 | −54 | −61 | −68 | −75 | −82 | −89 | −97 |
| 60 | 25 | 17 | 10 | 3 | −4 | −11 | −19 | −26 | −33 | −40 | −48 | −55 | −62 | −69 | −76 | −84 | −91 | −98 |

Frostbite Times ▨ 30 minutes ▨ 10 minutes ▨ 5 minutes

Windchill (°F) $= 35.74 + 0.6215T - 35.75(V^{0.16}) + 0.4275T(V^{0.16})$

Where, $T$ = Air Temperature (°F) $V$ = Wind Speed (mph)

a. In the windchill chart, locate the table values in Problem 10.

b. If the wind is blowing at 30 mph, use the windchill chart to complete the following table.

| AIR TEMPERATURE °F | 40 | 30 | 20 | 10 | 0 | −10 | −20 |
|---|---|---|---|---|---|---|---|
| WINDCHILL TEMPERATURE (30-MPH WIND) | | | | | | | |

c. If the wind speed is 40 mph, what is the windchill temperature if the air temperature is −20°F?

## Modeling with Functions

Many of the mathematical models you will use to solve problems in this course will be function models. As you learned in Activities 1.5 and 1.6, functions can be represented by tables, graphs, and equations. Problem 12 gives you a sample of how to develop a function model to solve a problem.

12. As part of a community service project at your high school, you are organizing a fund-raiser at the neighborhood roller rink. Money raised will benefit a summer camp for children with special needs. The admission charge is $4.50 per person, $2.00 of which is used to pay the rink's rental fee. The remainder is donated to the summer camp fund.

a. State a question that you want answered in this situation.

b. What two variables are involved in this problem?

c. Which variable can best be designated as the dependent variable? As the independent variable?

d. Complete the following table.

| INDEPENDENT VARIABLE | 1 | 2 | 3 | 4 | 5 | 6 | 7 | 8 |
|---|---|---|---|---|---|---|---|---|
| DEPENDENT VARIABLE | | | | | | | | |

e. State in words the relationship between the independent and dependent variables.

f. Let $x$ represent the number attending and $y$ represent the amount donated. Translate the written statement in part e as an equation.

**g.** If 91 tickets are sold, use the equation model developed in part f to determine the amount donated to the summer camp fund.

**h.** If the maximum capacity of the rink is 200 people, what is the maximum amount that can be donated?

You will learn more about using graphs as mathematical models in Activity 1.13.

## SUMMARY
### Activity 1.8

1. A **mathematical model** is a mathematical form, such as a formula, an equation, a graph, or a table, that fits or approximates the important features of a given situation.

2. **Mathematical modeling** is the process of developing a mathematical model for a given situation.

## EXERCISES
### Activity 1.8

1. The speed, $s$, of an ant (in centimeters per second) is related to the temperature, $t$ (in degrees Celsius), by the formula

$$s = 0.167t - 0.67.$$

**a.** If the temperature is 40°C, how fast is the ant moving?

**b.** If an ant is moving at 4 centimeters per second, what is the temperature?

2. The pressure, $p$, of water (in pounds per square foot) at a depth of $d$ feet below the surface is given by the formula

$$p = 15 + \frac{15}{33}d.$$

**a.** If a diver is 100 feet below the surface, what is the pressure of the water on the diver?

**b.** On November 14, 1993, Francisco Ferreras reached a record depth for breath-held diving. During the dive, he experienced a pressure of 201 pounds per square foot. What was his record depth?

**3.** The following formula is used by the National Football League (NFL) to calculate quarterback ratings:

$$R = \frac{250C + 12.5Y + 1000T - 1250I + 6.25A}{3A},$$

where $R$ = quarterback rating
$A$ = passes attempted
$C$ = passes completed
$Y$ = passing yardage
$T$ = touchdown passes
$I$ = number of interceptions

In the 2005–2006 regular season, Tom Brady, quarterback for the New England Patriots, and Brett Favre, for the Green Bay Packers, had the following player statistics:

| PLAYER | PASSES ATTEMPTED | PASSES COMPLETED | PASSING YARDAGE | NUMBER OF TOUCHDOWN PASSES | NUMBER OF INTERCEPTIONS |
|---|---|---|---|---|---|
| Tom Brady | 530 | 334 | 4110 | 26 | 14 |
| Brett Favre | 607 | 372 | 3881 | 20 | 29 |

**a.** Determine the quarterback rating for Tom Brady for the 2005–2006 NFL football season.

**b.** Determine the quarterback rating for Brett Favre.

**c.** Visit www.nfl.com and select stats to obtain the rating of your favorite quarterback.

**4. a.** You want to invest money in order to receive the best return. You have two options.

Option 1: Invest at 6% simple annual interest for 10 years.

Option 2: Invest at 5% interest compounded annually.

The following tables model the growth of $2000 over a 10-year period using the two options.

| | NUMBER OF YEARS | | | | | | | | | |
|---|---|---|---|---|---|---|---|---|---|---|
| | **1** | **2** | **3** | **4** | **5** | **6** | **7** | **8** | **9** | **10** |
| **6% SIMPLE ANNUAL INTEREST** | 2120 | 2240 | 2360 | 2480 | 2600 | 2720 | 2840 | 2960 | 3080 | 3200 |
| **5% COMPOUNDED ANNUALLY** | 2100 | 2205 | 2315.30 | 2431 | 2552.60 | 2680.20 | 2814.20 | 2954.90 | 3102.70 | 3257.80 |

Describe any trends or patterns that you observe in the data.

**b.** The amount of your investment in option 1 can be determined by the following formula

$$A = P + Prt,$$

where $A$ = amount of the investment
$P$ = principal or amount invested
$r$ = annual percentage rate (expressed as a decimal)
$t$ = number of years invested

Use the formula to determine the amount of your $2000 investment in option 1 after 20 years. What is the total amount of interest earned?

**c.** The amount of your investment in option 2 can be determined by

$$A = P(1 + r)^t,$$

where $A$ = amount of the investment
$P$ = principal
$r$ = annual percentage rate (expressed as a decimal)
$t$ = number of years invested

Use the formula to determine the amount of your $2000 investment in option 2 after 20 years.

**d.** Which option would you choose? Explain.

5. The following table gives the number of people infected by the flu over a given number of months.

| NUMBER OF MONTHS | 0 | 1 | 2 | 3 | 4 | 5 |
|---|---|---|---|---|---|---|
| NUMBER OF PEOPLE INFECTED | 1 | 5 | 13 | 33 | 78 | 180 |

Describe any trends or patterns that you observe.

6. The value of almost everything you own (assets), such as a car, computer, or house, depreciates (goes down) over time. When an asset's value decreases by a fixed amount each year, the depreciation is called straight-line depreciation.

Suppose your truck has an initial value of $12,400 and depreciates $820 per year.

a. State a question that you might want answered in this situation.

b. What two variables are involved in this problem?

c. Which variable can best be designated as the dependent variable? As the independent variable?

d. Complete the following table.

| INDEPENDENT VARIABLE | 1 | 2 | 3 | 4 | 5 |
|---|---|---|---|---|---|
| DEPENDENT VARIABLE | | | | | |

e. State in words the relationship between the independent and dependent variables.

f. Use appropriate letters to represent the variables involved and translate the written statement in part e as an equation.

g. If you plan to keep the truck for 7 years, determine the value of the truck at the end of this period. Explain the process you used.

h. What assumption was made regarding the rate of depreciation of the truck? Does this seem reasonable?

**ACTIVITY 1.9**
Fund-Raiser
Revisited

**OBJECTIVES**

1. Solve an equation numerically.

2. Solve an equation graphically.

3. Distinguish between a situation represented by a graph of distinct points versus a continuous graph.

In Problem 12 of Activity 1.8, you developed the following equation to model the fund-raiser situation:

$$y = 2.50x,$$

where $x$ represents the number of admission tickets sold, and $y$ represents the amount of money donated to the summer camp fund.

Since the variable $y$ is written by itself on one side, you say the equation is "solved for $y$."

## Evaluating an Algebraic Expression

In the following example, you are asked to determine a value for the dependent variable $y$ for a given value of the independent variable $x$.

> Example 1  *Use the equation $y = 2.5x$ to determine the amount of money raised if 84 tickets are sold. Stated another way, determine $y$ for a value of $x = 84$.*
>
> SOLUTION:
>
> Step 1: Substitute 84 for $x$ in the equation $y = 2.5x$:
>
> $$y = 2.50\,(84)$$
>
> Step 2: Perform the arithmetic operations on the right-hand side to obtain the $y$-value:
>
> $$y = \$210$$
>
> Note that the expression $2.50x$ has been **evaluated** for $x = 84$ to obtain the corresponding $y$-value.

Appendix

A graphing calculator is an excellent tool for generating $x$-$y$ tables. Instructions for generating tables using a TI-83/84 Plus are given in Appendix A.

1. Use the equation $y = 2.50x$ to complete the table. Verify using the table feature of a graphing calculator.

| $x$, NUMBER OF TICKETS SOLD | $y$, AMOUNT RAISED (\$) |
|---|---|
| 26 | |
| 94 | |
| 278 | |

## Solving Equations Numerically and Graphically

Suppose the goal is to raise a total of at least \$200 for the summer camp fund. You can determine how many tickets to sell to raise \$200 by replacing $y$ with 200 in $y = 2.50x$ to produce the **equation**

$$200 = 2.50x.$$

The problem now is to solve the equation for $x$. There are three different methods for solving such equations: numerical, graphical, and algebraic. The numerical and graphical methods are often quite useful, but frequently overlooked. Problems 2 and 3 will illustrate the numerical and graphical solution techniques.

**2. a.** Use a table of values to estimate how many tickets must be sold to raise $200. Begin by estimating a value for $x$ so that the expression $2.50x$ is close to 200. For example, $x = 100$ tickets produces a value of 250. In this case, increase or decrease your guesses for $x$ until you obtain 200.

| $x$, NUMBER OF TICKETS SOLD | $y$, AMOUNT RAISED ($) |
|---|---|
|  |  |
|  |  |
|  |  |
|  |  |
|  |  |

This approach, consisting of a guess, check, and repeat, is a **numerical method** for solving the equation $200 = 2.50x$ for $x$.

**b.** List at least one disadvantage of solving an equation numerically.

**3.** Recall that the practical domain for $x$ (number of tickets sold) of the summer camp situation is 0, 1, 2, 3, . . ., 200. Some of the $x$-$y$ pairs are shown in the following graph.

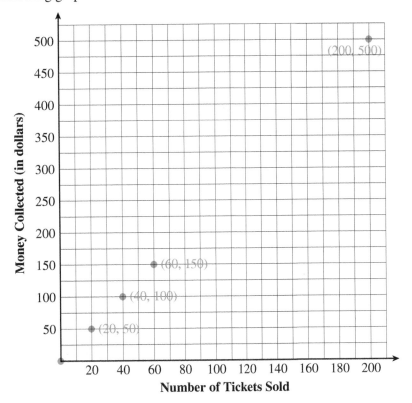

    **a.** The point (60, 150) lies on the graph. Interpret the meaning of the coordinates 60 and 150 in the fund-raiser situation.

    **b.** Connect the points on the graph in Problem 3 to form a line. Use this line to estimate how many tickets must be sold to raise at least $200. Remember, you need to determine $x$ when $y = 200$.

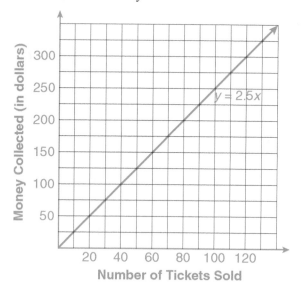

    **c.** Explain the process you used in part b.

> The approach in part b is the **graphical method** for solving the equation $200 = 2.50x$ for $x$.

    **d.** List at least one disadvantage to using a graphing approach to solving an equation.

In Problem 3b, the points of the scatterplot were connected to form a smooth continuous line. This was done as a graphing aid to help solve the given equation graphically. The practical domain of the fund-raiser function is 0, 1, 2, …, 200. Therefore, the graph of the fund-raiser function consists of just distinct points.

  **4.** Consider the general equation $y = 2.50x$ where $x$ is not restricted to whole numbers as it is for number of tickets sold.

    **a.** What is the replacement set for the input variable $x$?

**b.** Complete the following table for selected input values.

| x | y = 2.50x |
|------|-----------|
| -100 | |
| -75 | |
| -50 | |
| -25 | |
| 0 | |
| 25 | |
| 50 | |
| 75 | |
| 100 | |

**c.** The points from the table in part b are plotted on the following grid and a straight line is drawn through them. Compare the graph with the graph of $y = 2.50x$ in Problem 3b where the input $x$ represents the number of tickets sold.

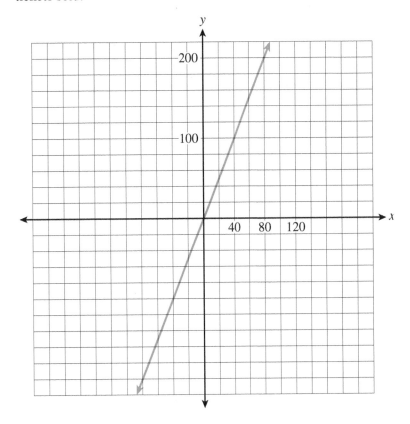

**5.** The recommended weight of an adult male can be approximated by the formula

$$w = 5.5h - 220,$$

where $w$ = recommended weight

$h$ = height in inches.

**a.** What is a possible practical domain for the weight function defined by the given formula?

**b.** Complete the following table. If you are using a graphing calculator, remember to replace the independent variable $h$ with $x$ and the dependent variable $w$ with $y$.

| $h$, HEIGHT IN INCHES | 60 | 64 | 68 | 72 | 76 | 80 |
|---|---|---|---|---|---|---|
| $w$, WEIGHT IN POUNDS | | | | | | |

**c.** Plot the points determined in part b.

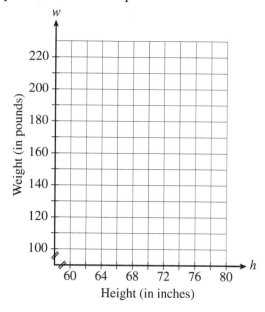

**d.** Connect the points in the graph to form a continuous line segment from (60, 110) to (80, 220). Are all the points on this line segment on the graph of the weight function? Explain.

**e.** Write an equation that can be used to determine the height of a male whose recommended weight is 165 pounds.

**f.** Solve the equation in part e using a numerical approach.

**g.** Solve the equation in part e using a graphical approach.

1. To solve an equation using a **numerical approach**, use a guess, check, and repeat process.

2. To solve an equation using a **graphical approach**, read the appropriate coordinates on the graph of the equation relating $x$ and $y$.

3. A **solution** of an equation containing one variable is a replacement value for the variable that produces equal values on both sides of the equation.

4. A graph is said to be **continuous**, if you can place your pencil on any point on the graph and then trace the entire graph without lifting the pencil off the paper. The graph has no breaks or holes.

1. Your local gas station is having a super sale and is selling regular unleaded gasoline for three hours at $1.239 per gallon.

   **a.** Let $x$ be the independent variable representing the number of gallons purchased. Let $C$ be the dependent variable representing the total cost of the fuel. Write an equation relating $x$ and $C$.

   **b.** What is the practical domain for $x$?

   **c.** Use the equation from part a to complete the following table.

| x, NUMBER OF GALLONS PURCHASED | 5 | 10 | 15 | 20 |
|---|---|---|---|---|
| c, TOTAL COST OF THE PURCHASE | | | | |

**d.** You have only $10 with you. Use the equation from part a to write an equation that can be used to determine how many gallons you can purchase.

**e.** Solve your equation from part d using a numerical approach.

**f.** The graph of the equation determined in part a is given below. Use the graph to estimate the number of gallons you can purchase with $10.

**Number of Gallons Purchased**

2. You are president of the high school band booster club. You have arranged for the school's jazz band to perform at a local coffee shop for three hours. In exchange for the performance, the booster club will receive three-quarters of the shop's gross receipts during that three-hour period.

**a.** Let $x$ be the independent variable representing the gross receipts of the coffee shop during the performance. Let $y$ be the dependent variable representing the share of the gross receipts that the coffee shop will donate to the band boosters. Write an equation relating $x$ and $y$.

**b.** Use the equation from part a to complete the following table.

| x, TOTAL GROSS RECEIPTS ($) | 250 | 500 | 750 | 1000 |
|---|---|---|---|---|
| y, BOOSTERS' SHARE ($) | | | | |

**c.** If the coffee shop presents you with a check for $650, what were the gross receipts during the performance? Estimate your answer using a numerical approach.

**d.** The graph of the equation determined in part a is given below. Use a graphical approach to estimate the gross receipts from part c.

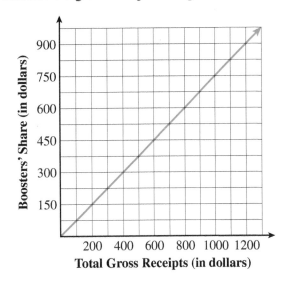

**3.** A tennis ball is dropped from the top of the Empire State Building in New York City. The following table gives the ball's distance from ground level at a given time after it is dropped.

| TIME (SEC) | 1 | 2 | 3 | 4 | 5 | 6 | 7 |
|---|---|---|---|---|---|---|---|
| DISTANCE (FT) | 1398 | 1350 | 1270 | 1158 | 1014 | 838 | 630 |

The Empire State Building is 1414 feet tall. Use the information in the table to approximate the time when the ball will have fallen half the height of the building.

**4. a.** The depth (inches) of water that accumulates in the spring soil from melted snow can be determined by dividing the cumulative winter snowfall (inches) by 12. Translate this statement into an equation, using $I$ for the accumulated inches of water and $n$ for the inches of fallen snow.

**b.** Determine the amount of water that accumulates in the soil if 25 inches of snow falls.

**c.** Write an equation that can be used to determine the total amount of winter snow that accumulates 6 inches of water in the soil.

**d.** Solve the equation in part c using a numerical approach.

**e.** Solve the equation in part c using a graphing approach.

**ACTIVITY 1.10**
Leasing a Copier

**OBJECTIVES**

1. Develop a mathematical model in the form of an equation.

2. Solve an equation using an algebraic approach.

As part of a special summer program at your high school, you are an intern in a law office. You are asked by the office manager to gather some information about leasing a copy machine for the office. The sales representative at Western Supply Company recommends a 50-copy/minute copier to satisfy the office's copying needs. The copier leases for $455 per month, plus 1.5 cents a copy. Maintenance fees are covered in the monthly charge. The lawyers would own the copier after 39 months.

**1. a.** The total monthly cost depends upon the number of copies made. Identify the independent and dependent variables.

**b.** Write a statement in words to determine the total monthly cost in terms of the number of copies made during the month.

**c.** Complete the following table.

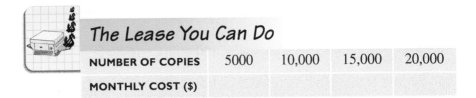

**The Lease You Can Do**

| NUMBER OF COPIES | 5000 | 10,000 | 15,000 | 20,000 |
|---|---|---|---|---|
| MONTHLY COST ($) | | | | |

**d.** Translate the statement in part b into an equation. Let $n$ represent the number of copies made during the month and $c$ represent the total monthly cost.

**2. a.** Use the result obtained in Problem 1d to determine the monthly cost if 12,000 copies are made.

**b.** Is 12,000 a replacement value for the independent or for the dependent variable?

In Problem 2, you determined the cost by evaluating the expression $0.015n + 455$ for $n = 12,000$.

**3.** Suppose the monthly budget for leasing the copier is $800.

**a.** Is 800 a value for $n$ or a value for $c$?

**b.** If the monthly budget is $800, write an equation that can be used to determine the number of copies in the month.

**4.** Use the result in Problem 1d to write an equation that can be used to determine the number, $n$, of copies that can be made with a monthly budget of $c = 800$.

Notice in Problem 4 that $n$ is not isolated by itself on one side of the equation. To isolate $n$, you need to undo two operations: the addition of 455 and the multiplication by 0.015. You do this by reversing the sequence of operations, replacing each operation by its inverse.

Example 1    *The following example illustrates a systematic algebraic procedure by undoing two operations to solve an equation.*

Solve for $x$:   $120 = 3x + 90$

$$120 = 3x + 90$$
$$\underline{-90 \qquad\quad -90}$$
$$30 = 3x$$
$$\frac{30}{3} = \frac{3x}{3}$$
$$10 = x$$

Step 1:  To undo the addition by 90, subtract 90 from each side of the equation.

Step 2:  To undo the multiplication of 3, divide each side of the equation by 3.

The variable $x$ has been isolated on the right side with coefficient 1; the solution is 10.

Check:    $120 \overset{?}{=} 3(10) + 90$

$120 \overset{?}{=} 30 + 90$

$120 = 120$

Note that the algebraic procedure emphasizes that an equation can be thought of as a scale whose arms are in balance. The equals sign can be thought of as the balancing point.

As you perform the appropriate inverse operation to solve the equation $120 = 3x + 90$ for $x$, you must maintain the balance as you perform each step in the process. If you subtract 90 from one side, then you must subtract 90 from the other side. Similarly, if you divide one side by 3, then you must divide the other side by 3.

**5. a.** Solve the equation in Problem 4 using the algebraic procedure outlined in Example 1.

**b.** Verify your answer in part a using either a numerical or graphical approach.

6. For each of the following, substitute the given value of $y$ and use an algebraic approach to solve the resulting equation for $x$.

a. If $y = 3x - 5$ and $y = 10$, determine $x$.

b. If $y = 30 - 2x$ and $y = 24$, determine $x$.

c. If $y = \frac{3}{4}x - 21$ and $y = -9$, determine $x$.

d. If $-2x + 15 = y$ and $y = -3$, determine $x$.

## SUMMARY
### Activity 1.10

1. The goal of **solving an equation** of the form $ax + b = c$, where $a \neq 0$, for the variable $x$ is to isolate the variable $x$ (with coefficient 1) on one side of the equation.

2. Use **inverse operations** to isolate the variable. Apply the inverse operations in the following order:

**Step 1:** Undo the addition of $b$ by subtracting $b$ from each side of the equation; undo the subtraction of $b$ by adding $b$ to each side of the equation.

**Step 2:** Undo the multiplication of the variable $x$ by the nonzero coefficient $a$ by dividing each side of the equation by $a$.

## EXERCISES
### Activity 1.10

1. A long-distance telephone plan costs $4.95 a month, plus 10 cents per minute, or part thereof, for any long-distance call made during the month.

a. Write a statement to determine the total monthly cost for your long-distance calls for the month.

b. Translate the statement in part a into an equation, using $c$ to represent the total monthly cost and $n$ to represent the total number of long-distance minutes for the month.

c. Determine the monthly cost if 250 minutes of long-distance calls are made.

**d.** If you budget $50 per month for long-distance calls, how many minutes can you call in the month?

2. You are considering taking some courses at your local community college on a part-time basis for the upcoming school year. For a student who carries fewer than twelve credits (the full-time minimum), the tuition is $155 for each credit hour taken. All students, part-time or full-time, must pay a $20 parking fee for the semester. This fixed fee is added directly to your tuition and is included in your total bill.

   **a.** Complete the following table, where $t$ represents the total bill and $n$ represents the number of credit hours taken.

| NUMBER OF CREDIT HOURS, $n$ | 1 | 2 | 3 | 4 | 5 | 6 |
|---|---|---|---|---|---|---|
| TOTAL BILL, $t$($) | | | | | | |

   **b.** Write an equation to determine the total bill, $t$, for a student carrying fewer than twelve credit hours. Use $n$ to represent the number of hours taken for the semester.

   **c.** Determine the total bill if you take nine credit hours.

   **d.** Suppose you have $1000 to spend on the total bill. How many credit hours can you carry for the semester?

3. Your senior year class is organizing an entertainment night to benefit charities in the community. You are a member of the budget committee for the class project. The committee suggests a $10 per person admission donation for food, nonalcoholic beverages, and entertainment. The committee determines that the fixed costs for the event (food, drinks, posters, tickets, etc.) will total $2100. The college is donating the use of the gymnasium for the evening.

   **a.** The total revenue (gross income before expenses are deducted) depends on the number, $n$, of students who attend. Write an expression in terms of $n$ that represents the total revenue if $n$ students attend.

   **b.** Profit is the net income after expenses are deducted. Write an equation expressing the profit, $p$, in terms of the number, $n$, of students who attend.

**c.** If the gymnasium holds a maximum of 700 people, what is the maximum amount of money that can be donated to charity?

**d.** Suppose that the members of the committee want to be able to donate at least $1500 to community charities. How many students must attend in order to have a profit of $1500?

**4.** When an asset depreciates by a fixed amount per year, the depreciation is called straight-line depreciation (see Problem 6 on page 77). Suppose a car has an initial value of $15,000 and depreciates $950 per year.

**a.** Let $v$ represent the value of the car after $t$ years. Write an equation that expresses $v$ in terms of $t$.

**b.** What is the value of the car after four years?

**c.** How long will it take for the value of the car to decrease to $10,000?

**5.** The cost, $c$, in dollars, of mailing a priority overnight package weighing one pound or more is given by the formula $c = 2.085x + 15.08$, where $x$ represents the weight of the package in pounds.

**a.** Determine the cost of mailing a package that weighs 10 pounds.

**b.** Determine the weight of a package that costs $56.78 to mail.

6. Archaeologists and forensic scientists use the length of human bones to estimate the height of individuals. A person's height, $h$, in centimeters, can be determined from the length of the femur, $f$ (the bone from the knee to the hip socket), in centimeters, using the following formulas:

   Man:       $h = 69.089 + 2.238f$

   Woman:    $h = 61.412 + 2.317f$

   a. A partial skeleton of a man is found. The femur measures 50 centimeters. How tall was the man?

   b. What is the length of the femur for a woman who is 150 centimeters tall?

7. Let $p$ represent the perimeter of an isosceles triangle that has two equal sides of length $a$, and a third side of length $b$. The formula for the perimeter is $p = 2a + b$. Determine the length of the equal side of an isosceles triangle having perimeter of $\frac{3}{4}$ yard and third side measuring $\frac{1}{3}$ yard.

8. The recommended weight of an adult male is given by the formula $w = \frac{11}{2}h - 220$, where $w$ represents his recommended weight in pounds and $h$ represents his height in inches. Determine the height of a man whose recommended weight is 165 pounds.

9. Housing prices in your neighborhood have been increasing steadily since you bought your home in 1995. The relationship between the market value of your home and the length of time you have been living there can be expressed algebraically by the rule

$$V = 130,000 + 3500x,$$

where $x$ is the length of time (in years) in your home and $V$ is the market value (in dollars).

**a.** Complete the following table:

| YEAR | x | MARKET VALUE |
|------|---|--------------|
| 1995 |   |              |
| 2000 |   |              |
| 2003 |   |              |

**b.** Determine the value of your home in 2005.

**c.** In which year will the value of your home reach $186,000?

**10.** Use an algebraic approach to solve each of the following equations for $x$.

**a.** $10 = 2x + 12$

**b.** $-27 = -5x - 7$

**c.** $3x - 26 = -14$

**d.** $24 - 2x = 38$

**e.** $5x - 15 = 15$

**f.** $-4x + 8 = 8$

**g.** $12 + \frac{1}{5}x = 9$

**h.** $\frac{2}{3}x - 12 = 0$

**i.** $0.25x - 14.5 = 10$

**j.** $5 = 2.5x - 20$

**ACTIVITY 1.11**
Comparing
Energy Costs

**OBJECTIVES**

1. Develop mathematical models to solve problems.

2. Write and solve equations of the form $ax + b = cx + d$.

3. Use the distributive property to solve equations involving grouping symbols.

4. Solve formulas for a specified variable.

An architect is hired to design a home. She obtains the following information regarding the installation and operating costs of two types of heating systems: solar and electric.

### Some Like It Hot

| TYPE OF HEATING SYSTEM | INSTALLATION COST | OPERATING COST PER YEAR |
|---|---|---|
| Solar | $25,600 | $200 |
| Electric | $5500 | $1600 |

**1. a.** Determine the total cost of the solar heating system after five years of use.

**b.** Write a statement for the total cost of the solar heating system in terms of the number of years of use.

**c.** Let $x$ represent the number of years of use and $c$ represent the total cost of the solar heating system. Translate the statement in part b into an equation.

**d.** Use the equation from part c to complete the following table:

| NUMBER OF YEARS IN USE, $x$ | 5 | 10 | 15 | 20 |
|---|---|---|---|---|
| TOTAL COST, $c$ | | | | |

**2. a.** Determine the total cost of the electric heating system after five years of use.

**b.** Write a statement for the total cost of the electric heating system in terms of the number of years of use.

**c.** Let $x$ represent the number of years of use and $c$ represent the total cost of the electric heating system. Translate the statement in part b into an equation.

**d.** Use the equation from part c to complete the following table:

| NUMBER OF YEARS IN USE, $x$ | 5 | 10 | 15 | 20 |
|---|---|---|---|---|
| TOTAL COST, $c$ | | | | |

The installation cost of solar heating is much more than that of the electric system, but the operating cost per year of the solar system is much lower. Therefore, it is reasonable to think that the total cost for the electric system will eventually "catch up" and surpass the total cost of the solar system.

3. Compare the table values for total heating costs in Problems 1d and 2d. Estimate in what year the total cost for electric heating will "catch up" and surpass the total cost for solar heating. Explain.

4. The year in which the total costs of the two heating systems are equal can be determined algebraically. Write an equation you can solve to determine when the total heating costs are the same by setting the expressions in the symbolic rules in Problems 1c and 2c equal to each other.

The following example demonstrates a systematic algebraic procedure that you can use to solve equations similar to the equation in Problem 4. Remember that your goal is to isolate the variable on one side of the equation with coefficient 1 by applying the appropriate inverse operations.

Example 1   *Solve for x:* $2x + 14 = 8x + 2$

SOLUTION

First, add and/or subtract terms appropriately so that all terms involving the variable are on one side of the equals sign and all other terms are on the other side.

$$2x + 14 = 8x + 2 \qquad \text{Subtract } 8x \text{ from both sides and combine like terms.}$$
$$\underline{-8x \qquad\quad -8x}$$
$$-6x + 14 = 2$$
$$\underline{\qquad -14 = -14} \qquad \text{Subtract 14 from each side and combine like terms.}$$
$$-6x \qquad\;\; = -12$$
$$\frac{-6x}{-6} = \frac{-12}{-6} \qquad \text{Divide each side by } -6, \text{ the coefficient of } x.$$
$$x = 2$$

Check: $2(2) + 14 = 8(2) + 2$
$$4 + 14 = 16 + 2$$
$$18 = 18$$

**5.** In Example 1, the variable terms are combined on the left side of the equation. Solve the equation $2x + 14 = 8x + 2$ by combining the variable terms on the right side.

**6. a.** Solve the equation in Problem 4 for $x$.

   **b.** Interpret what your answer in part a represents in the context of the heating system situation.

## Purchasing a Car

You are interested in purchasing a new car and have narrowed the choice to a Honda Accord LX (4 cylinder) and a Passat GLS (4 cylinder). Being concerned about the value of the car depreciating over time, you search the Internet and obtain the following information:

### Driven Down

| MODEL OF CAR (2005) | MARKET SUGGESTED RETAIL PRICE (MSRP) ($) | ANNUAL DEPRECIATION ($) |
|---|---|---|
| Accord LX | 20,925 | 1730 |
| Passat GLS | 24,995 | 2420 |

*Data: Kelley Blue Book*

**7. a.** Complete the following table:

| YEARS THE CAR IS OWNED | VALUE OF ACCORD LX ($) | VALUE OF PASSAT GLS ($) |
|---|---|---|
| 1 | | |
| 2 | | |
| 3 | | |

**b.** Will the value of the Passat GLS ever be lower than the value of the Accord LX? Explain.

**c.** Let $v$ represent the value of the car after $x$ years of ownership. Write a symbolic rule to determine $v$ in terms of $x$ for the Accord LX.

**d.** Write a symbolic rule to determine $v$ in terms of $x$ for the Passat GLS.

**e.** Write an equation to determine when the value of the Accord LX will equal the value of the Passat GLS.

**f.** Solve the equation in part e.

## NBA Basketball Court

You and your friend are avid professional basketball fans and discover that your mathematics instructor shares your enthusiasm for basketball. During a mathematics class, your instructor tells you that the perimeter of an NBA basketball court is 288 feet and the length is 44 feet more than its width. He challenges you to use your algebra skills to determine the dimensions of the court. To solve the problem, you and your friend use the following plan.

**8. a.** Let $w$ represent the width of the court. Write an expression for the length in terms of the width, $w$.

**b.** Using the formula for perimeter of a rectangle, $P = 2l + 2w$, and the information given to obtain an equation containing just the variable $w$.

**c.** Solve the equation you obtained in part b by first applying the distributive property and then combining like terms in the expression involving $w$.

**d.** What are the dimensions of an NBA basketball court?

## Solving Formulas for a Specified Variable

9. Windchill temperature, $w$, produced by a 30-mile-per-hour wind at various Fahrenheit degrees can be modeled by the formula

$$w = 1.6t - 49.$$

a. Use the formula $w = 1.6t - 49$ to determine the windchill temperature if the air temperature is 7°F.

b. On a cold day in Texas, the wind is blowing at 30 miles per hour. If the windchill temperature is reported to be $-18°F$, then what is the air temperature on that day? Use the formula $w = 1.6t - 49$.

The formula $w = 1.6t - 49$ is said to be solved for $w$ in terms of $t$ because the variable $w$ is isolated by itself on one side of the equation. To determine the windchill temperature, $w$, for air temperature $t = 7°F$ (Problem 9a), you simply substitute 7 for $t$ in $1.6t - 49$ and do the arithmetic:

$$w = 1.6(7) - 49 = -37.8°F$$

In Problem 9b, you needed to determine the air temperature, $t$, for a given windchill temperature. In this case, you substitute $-18$ for $w$ in $w = 1.6t - 49$, and then solve the resulting equation for $t$.

If you had to determine the corresponding $t$-value for several different $w$-values, you would have to solve several equations for $t$. It is much more convenient and efficient to solve the original formula $w = 1.6t - 49$ for $t$ and then use the new equation to determine values of $t$.

**Example 2**   *Solving the formula $w = 1.6t - 49$ for $t$ is similar to solving the equation $-18 = 1.6t - 49$ for $t$.*

$$
\begin{array}{ll}
-18 = 1.6t - 49 & \qquad w = 1.6t - 49 \\
\underline{+49 \qquad\quad +49} & \qquad \underline{+49 \qquad\quad +49} \qquad \text{Add 49 to each side.} \\
31 = 1.6t & \qquad w + 49 = 1.6t \\
\\
\dfrac{31}{1.6} = \dfrac{1.6t}{1.6} & \qquad \dfrac{w + 49}{1.6} = \dfrac{1.6t}{1.6} \qquad \text{Divide each side by 1.6.} \\
\\
19.4 \approx t & \qquad \dfrac{w + 49}{1.6} = t
\end{array}
$$

The new formula is $t = \dfrac{w + 49}{1.6}$ or $t = \dfrac{w}{1.6} + \dfrac{49}{1.6}$, which is equivalent to $t = 0.625w + 30.625$.

To solve the equation $w = 1.6t - 49$ for $t$ means to isolate the variable $t$ (with coefficient 1) on one side of the equation, with all other terms on the opposite side.

**10.** Redo Problem 9b using the new formula derived in Example 2 that expresses *t* in terms of *w*.

**11. a.** If the wind speed is 15 miles per hour, the windchill can be approximated by the formula $w = 1.4t - 32$, where *t* is the air temperature in degrees Fahrenheit. Solve the formula for *t*.

**b.** Use the new formula from part a to determine the air temperature, *t*, if the windchill temperature is $-10°F$.

**12.** Solve each of the following formulas for the specified variable.

**a.** $A = lw$ for *w*

**b.** $p = c + m$ for *m*

**c.** $P = 2l + 2w$ for *l*

**d.** $R = 165 - 0.75a$ for *a*

**e.** $V = \pi r^2 h$ for *h*

**f.** $P = 2l + 2w$ for *w*

**g.** $V(P + a) = k$ for *P*

## Additional Practice

**13.** Solve each of the following equations for *x*. Remember to check your result in the original equation.

**a.** $2x + 9 = 5x - 12$

**b.** $21 - x = -3 - 5x$

**c.** $2(x - 3) = -8$        **d.** $2(x - 4) + 6 = 4x - 7$

## SUMMARY
### Activity 1.11

1. General strategy for solving equations for a variable, such as $x$.

- Remove parentheses, if necessary, by applying the distributive property.

- Combine like terms that appear on the same side of the equation.

- Write the equation so that the product of the coefficient and the variable is on one side and all other numbers and variables are on the other side. This is generally accomplished by adding and/or subtracting terms so that all terms involving the variable you are solving for are on one side of the equation and all terms involving numbers and other variables appear on the other side.

- Solve for the variable by dividing each side of the equation by the nonzero coefficient of the variable.

- Check the result in the original equation to be sure that the value of the variable produces a true statement.

2. To solve a **formula** for a variable, isolate that variable (with coefficient 1) on one side of the equation with all other terms on the "opposite" side.

## EXERCISES
### Activity 1.11

1. You need to rent a truck so you contact two local rental companies and acquire the following information for the one-day cost of renting a truck:

       Company 1: $39.95 per day, plus $0.19 per mile

       Company 2: $19.95 per day, plus $0.49 per mile

Let $x$ represent the number of miles driven in one day and $C$ represent that total daily rental cost ($).

**a.** Write an equation that represents the total daily rental cost from company 1 in terms of the number of miles driven.

**b.** Write an equation that represents the total daily rental cost from company 2 in terms of the number of miles driven.

**c.** Write an equation to determine for what mileage the one-day rental cost would be the same.

**d.** Solve the equation you obtained in part c.

**e.** For which mileages would company 2 have the lower price?

**2.** You are considering installing a security system in your new house. You gather the following information about similar security systems from two local home security dealers:

Dealer 1: $3560 to install and $15 per month monitoring fee

Dealer 2: $2850 to install and $28 per month for monitoring

You see that the initial cost of the security system from dealer 1 is much higher than that of the system from dealer 2, but that the monitoring fee is lower. You want to determine which is the better system for your needs.

Let $x$ represent the number of months that you have the security system, and $C$ represent the cumulative cost ($).

**a.** Write an equation that represents the total cost of the system from dealer 1 in terms of the number of months you have the system.

**b.** Write an equation that represents the total cost of the system from dealer 2 in terms of the number of months you have the system.

**c.** Write an equation to determine the number of months for which the total cost of the systems will be equal.

**d.** Solve the equation in part c.

**e.** If you plan to live in the house and use the system for ten years, which system would be less expensive?

3. You are able to get three summer jobs to help save for college expenses. In your job as a cashier, you work twenty hours per week and earn $6.50 per hour. Your second and third jobs are both at a local hospital. There you earn $8.50 per hour as a payroll clerk and $6.00 per hour as an aide. You always work ten hours less per week as an aide than you do as the payroll clerk. Your total weekly salary depends on the number of hours that you work at each job.

   a. Determine the independent and dependent variables for this situation.

   b. Explain how you calculate the total amount earned each week.

   c. If $x$ represents the number of hours that you work as a payroll clerk, represent the number of hours that you work as an aide in terms of $x$.

   d. Write an equation that describes the total amount you earn each week. Use $x$ to represent the input variable and $y$ to represent the output variable. Simplify the expression as much as possible.

   e. If you work twelve hours as a payroll clerk, how much will you make in one week?

   f. What is a practical domain for $x$? Would eight hours at your payroll job be a realistic replacement value? What about fifty hours?

   g. When you don't work as an aide, what is your total weekly salary?

   h. If you plan to earn a total of $505 in one week from all jobs, how many hours would you have to work at each job? Is the total number of hours worked realistic? Explain.

**i.** Solve the equation in part d for $x$ in terms of $y$. When would it be useful to have the equation in this form?

**4.** A florist sells roses for $1.50 each and carnations for $0.85 each. Suppose you purchase a bouquet of one dozen flowers consisting of roses and carnations.

   **a.** Let $x$ represent the number of roses purchased. Write an expression in terms of $x$ that represents the number of carnations purchased.

   **b.** Write an expression that represents the cost of purchasing $x$ roses.

   **c.** Write an expression that represents the cost of purchasing the carnations.

   **d.** What does the sum of the expressions in parts b and c represent?

   **e.** Suppose you are willing to spend $14.75. Write an equation that can be used to determine the number of roses that can be included in a bouquet of one dozen flowers consisting of roses and carnations.

   **f.** Solve the equation in part e to determine the number of roses and the number of carnations in the bouquet.

**5.** The viewing window of a certain calculator is in the shape of a rectangle.

   **a.** Let $w$ represent the width of the viewing window in centimeters. If the window is 5 centimeters longer than it is wide, write an expression in terms of $w$ for the length of the viewing window.

   **b.** Write a symbolic rule that represents the perimeter, $P$, of the viewing window in terms of $w$.

**c.** If the perimeter of the viewing window is 26 centimeters, determine the dimensions of the window.

*Solve the equations in Exercises 6–17.*

**6.** $5x - 4 = 3x - 6$

**7.** $3x - 14 = 6x + 4$

**8.** $0.5x + 9 = 4.5x + 17$

**9.** $4x - 10 = -2x + 8$

**10.** $0.3x - 5.5 = 0.2x + 2.6$

**11.** $4 - 0.025x = 0.1 - 0.05x$

**12.** $5t + 3 = 2(t + 6)$

**13.** $3(w + 2) = w - 14$

**14.** $21 + 3(x - 4) = 4(x + 5)$

**15.** $2(x + 3) = 5(2x + 1) + 4x$

**16.** $500 = 0.75x - (750 + 0.25x)$        **17.** $1.5x + 3(22 - x) = 70$

**18.** The National Weather Service reports the daily temperature in degrees Fahrenheit. The scientific community, as well as Canada and most of Europe, reports temperature in degrees Celsius. The Celsius, C, and Fahrenheit, F, temperature readings are related by the formula

$$F = 1.8C + 32$$

**a.** Determine the Fahrenheit reading corresponding to the temperature at which water boils, $100°C$.

**b.** Solve the formula $F = 1.8C + 32$ for $C$.

**c.** Use the new formula from part b to answer part a.

**19.** The number of women enrolled in college has steadily increased. The following table gives the enrollment, in millions, of women in a given year.

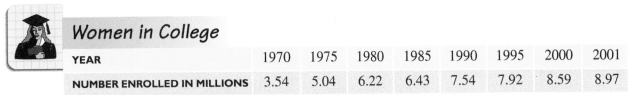

| **Women in College** | | | | | | | | |
|---|---|---|---|---|---|---|---|---|
| **YEAR** | 1970 | 1975 | 1980 | 1985 | 1990 | 1995 | 2000 | 2001 |
| **NUMBER ENROLLED IN MILLIONS** | 3.54 | 5.04 | 6.22 | 6.43 | 7.54 | 7.92 | 8.59 | 8.97 |

*Source:* U.S. Department of Education, National Center for Education Statistics

Let $t$ represent the number of years since 1970. The number $N$ (in millions) of women enrolled in college can be modeled by the formula

$$N = 0.158t + 4.092.$$

**a.** Estimate in what year women's college enrollment will reach 10 million.

    **b.** Solve the equation $N = 0.158t + 4.092$ for $t$.

    **c.** Use the new formula in part b to estimate the year in which women's enrollment will reach 11 million.

Solve each of the following formulas for the specified variable.

**20.** $E = IR$ for $I$              **21.** $C = 2\pi r$ for $r$

**22.** $P = 2a + b$ for $b$       **23.** $P = R - C$ for $R$

**24.** $P = 2l + 2w$ for $w$      **25.** $R = 143 - 0.65a$ for $a$

**26.** $A = P + Prt$ for $r$       **27.** $y = mx + b$ for $m$

**28.** $m = g - vt^2$ for $g$      **29.** $m = g - vt^2$ for $v$

**PROJECT ACTIVITY 1.12**
Summer Job
Opportunities

You will be attending college this fall, so it is important for you to find a summer job that pays well. Luckily, the classified section of your newspaper lists numerous summer job opportunities in sales, road construction, and food service. The advertisements for all these positions welcome applications from high school students. All positions involve the same 10-week period during the summer.

## Sales

A new electronics store opened recently. There are several sales associate positions that pay an hourly rate of $7.25 plus a 5% commission based on your total weekly sales. You would be guaranteed at least 30 hours of work per week, but not more than 40 hours.

## Construction

Your state's highway department hires college students every summer to help with road construction projects. The hourly rate is $13.50 with the possibility of up to 10 hours per week in overtime, for which you would be paid time and a half. Of course, the work is totally dependent on good weather, and so the number of hours that you would work per week could vary.

## Restaurants

Local restaurants experience an increase in business during the summer. There are several positions for wait staff. The hourly rate is $3.60, and the weekly tip total ranges from $300 to $850. You are told that you can expect a weekly average of approximately $520 in tips. You would be scheduled to work five dinner shifts of 6.5 hours each for a total of 32.5 hours per week. However, on slow nights you might be sent home early, perhaps after working only 5 hours. Thus, your total weekly hours might be fewer than 32.5.

All of the jobs would provide an interesting summer experience. Your personal preferences might favor one position over another. Keep in mind that you have a lot of college expenses.

1. At the electronics store, sales associates average $8000 in sales each week.

   a. Based on the expected weekly average of $8000 in sales, calculate your gross weekly paycheck (before any taxes or other deductions) if you worked a full 40-hour week in sales.

   b. Use the average weekly sales figure of $8000 and write a symbolic rule for your weekly earnings, $s$, where $x$ represents the total number of hours you would work.

    **c.** What would be your gross paycheck for the week if you worked 30 hours and still managed to sell $8000 in merchandise?

    **d.** You are told that you would typically work 35 hours per week if your total electronic sales do average $8000. Calculate your typical gross paycheck for a week.

    **e.** You calculate that to pay college expenses for the upcoming academic year, you need to gross at least $675 a week. How many hours would you have to work in sales each week? Assume that you would sell $8000 in merchandise.

2. In the construction job, you would average a 40-hour workweek.

    **a.** Calculate your gross paycheck for a typical 40-hour workweek.

    **b.** Write a symbolic rule for your weekly salary, $s$, for a week with no overtime. Let $x$ represent the total number of hours worked.

    **c.** If the weather is ideal for a week, you can expect to work 10 hours in overtime (over and above the regular 40-hour workweek). Determine your total gross pay for a week with 10 hours of overtime.

    **d.** The symbolic rule in part b can be used to determine the weekly salary, $s$, when $x$, the total number of hours worked, is less than or equal to 40 (no overtime). Write a symbolic rule to determine your weekly salary, $s$, if $x$ is greater than 40 hours.

**e.** Suppose it turns out to be a gorgeous summer and your supervisor says that you can work as many hours as you want. If you are able to gross $800 a week, you will be able to afford to buy a computer. How many hours would you have to work each week to achieve your goal?

**3.** The restaurant job involves working a maximum of five dinner shifts of 6.5 hours each.

    **a.** Calculate what your gross paycheck would be for an exceptionally busy week of five 6.5-hour dinner shifts and $850 in tips.

    **b.** Calculate what your gross paycheck would be for an exceptionally slow week of five 5-hour dinner shifts and only $300 in tips.

    **c.** Calculate what your gross paycheck would be for a typical week of five 6.5-hour dinner shifts and $520 in tips.

    **d.** Use $520 as your typical weekly total for tips, and write a symbolic rule for your gross weekly salary, $s$, where $x$ represents the number of hours.

    **e.** Calculate what your gross paycheck would be for a 27-hour week and $520 in tips.

    **f.** During the holiday week of July 4, you would be asked to work an extra dinner shift. You are told to expect $280 in tips for that night alone. Assuming a typical work-week for the rest of the week, would working that extra dinner shift enable you to gross at least $950?

**4.** You would like to make an informed decision in choosing one of the three positions. Based on all the information you have about the three jobs, fill in the following table.

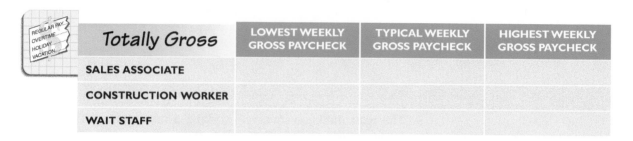

| Totally Gross | LOWEST WEEKLY GROSS PAYCHECK | TYPICAL WEEKLY GROSS PAYCHECK | HIGHEST WEEKLY GROSS PAYCHECK |
| --- | --- | --- | --- |
| SALES ASSOCIATE | | | |
| CONSTRUCTION WORKER | | | |
| WAIT STAFF | | | |

**5.** Money may be the biggest factor in making your decision. But it is summer, and it would be nice to enjoy what you are doing. Discuss the advantages and disadvantages of each position. What would be your personal choice? Why?

**6.** You decide that you would prefer an indoor job. Use the algebraic rules you developed for the sales job in Problem 1b and for the restaurant position in Problem 3d to calculate how many hours you would have to work in each job to receive the same weekly salary.

**ACTIVITY 1.13**
Graphs Tell
Stories

**OBJECTIVES**

1. Describe in words what a graph tells you about a given situation.

2. Sketch a graph that best represents the situation described in words.

3. Identify increasing, decreasing, and constant parts of a graph.

4. Identify minimum and maximum points on a graph.

5. Identify a functional relationship graphically using the vertical line test.

The expression "A picture is worth a thousand words" is a cliché, but it is true. Mathematical models are often easier to understand when presented in visual form. To understand such pictures, you need to practice going back and forth between graphs and word descriptions.

Every graph shows how the independent and dependent variables change in relation to one another. As you read a graph from left to right, the $x$-variable is increasing in value. The graph indicates the change in the $y$-values (increasing, decreasing, or constant) as the $x$-values increase.

Graphs are always constructed so that as you read the graph from left to right, the $x$-variable increases in value. The graph shows the change (increasing, decreasing, or constant) in the $y$-values as the $x$-values increase.

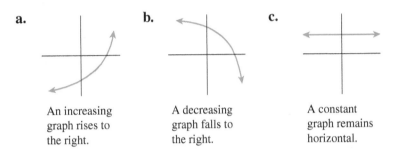

a.
An increasing graph rises to the right.

b.
A decreasing graph falls to the right.

c.
A constant graph remains horizontal.

If a graph increases and then decreases, the point where the graph changes from rising to falling is called a **maximum point**. The $y$-value of this point is called a **local maximum value**. If a graph decreases and then increases, the point where the graph changes from falling to rising is called a **minimum point**. The $y$-value of this point is called a **local minimum value**.

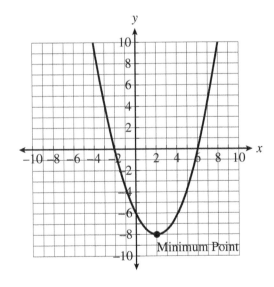

Example 1 *The following graph describes your walk from the parking lot to the library.*

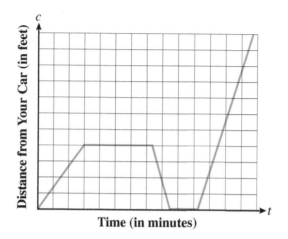

As you read this graph from left to right, it shows how your distance from your car changes as time passes. One possible scenario this graph describes is:

You leave your car and walk at a steady pace toward the library. You meet some friends and stop to chat for a while. You realize that you forgot something and quickly return to your car. After rummaging around for a while, you hurry off to the library.

How did anyone come up with this from the graph? Look at the graph in sections.

**a.** The first increasing line segment indicates you are moving away from your car because the time and the distance are increasing.

**b.** The first horizontal section indicates that your distance from the car is constant, so you are standing still.

**c.** The decreasing line segment indicates your distance from the car is decreasing. When it reaches the horizontal axis, it tells you that you are back at your car.

**d.** The second horizontal segment indicates you stay at your car for a time.

**e.** The final increasing segment is steeper and longer than the first, so you are moving away from the car faster and farther than in the first segment.

## Graphs to Stories

The graphs in Problems 1–4 present visual images of several situations. Each graph shows how the *y*-values change in relation to the *x*-values. In each situation, identify the independent variable and the dependent variable. Then, interpret the situation; that is, describe, in words, what the graph is telling you about the situation. Indicate whether the graph rises, falls, or is constant and whether the graph reaches either a minimum (smallest) or maximum (largest) *y*-value.

**1.** A person's core body temperature (°F) in relation to time of day

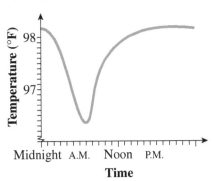

**a.** Independent: _____   Dependent: _____

**b.** Interpretation:

**2.** Performance of a simple task in relation to interest level

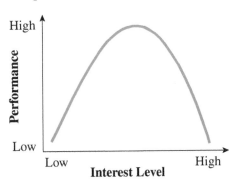

**a.** Independent: _____   Dependent: _____

**b.** Interpretation:

**3.** Net profit of a particular business in relation to time given quarterly

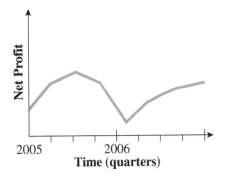

    **a.** Independent: _____      Dependent: _____

    **b.** Interpretation:

**4.** Annual gross income in relation to number of years

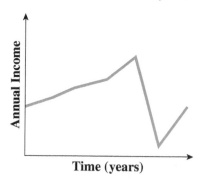

    **a.** Independent: _____      Dependent: _____

    **b.** Interpretation:

## Stories to Graphs

In Problems 5 and 6, sketch a graph that best represents the situation described. Note that in many cases, the actual values are unknown, so you will need to estimate what seems reasonable to you. Remember to label your axes and identify the independent/dependent variables.

**5.** You drive to visit your parents, who live 100 miles away. Your average speed is 50 miles per hour. On arrival, you stay for five hours and then return home, again at an average speed of 50 miles per hour. Graph your distance from home, from the time you leave until you return home.

**6.** You just started a new job that pays 6 dollars per hour, with a raise of 2 dollars per hour every six months. After one and a half years, you receive a promotion that gives you a wage increase of 5 dollars per hour, but your next raise won't come for another year. Sketch a graph of your wage over your first *two and a half* years.

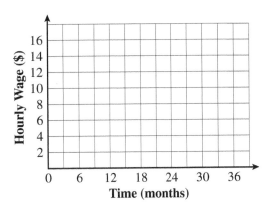

## Representing Functions Graphically

Although each of the graphs in Problems 1–6 has a different shape and different properties, they all reflect a functional relationship between the independent and dependent variables. In the following problem, you will explore this special relationship or correspondence more closely.

**7. a.** Use the graph in Problem 1 to complete the following table. Estimate the temperature for each value of time.

| TIME OF DAY | 1 A.M. | 5 A.M. | 7 A.M. | 10 A.M. | 12 NOON | 1 P.M. |
|---|---|---|---|---|---|---|
| BODY TEMPERATURE (°F) | | | | | | |

**b.** How many corresponding temperatures are assigned to any one particular time?

For any specific time of day, there is one and only one corresponding temperature. Therefore, the body temperature is a function of the time of day.

**8.** The following graph shows the distance from home over a 9-hour period as described in Problem 5.

**a.** Use the graph to complete the following table.

| TIME (hours) | 1 | 3 | 4 | 8 | 9 |
|---|---|---|---|---|---|
| DISTANCE FROM HOME (miles) | | | | | |

**b.** Is the distance from home a function of the time on the trip? Explain.

**9.** The following graph shows the height of a roller coaster as it moves away from its starting point and goes through its first loop.

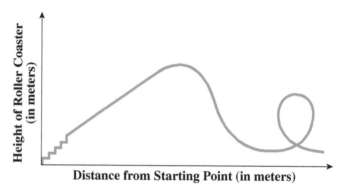

Is the height of the roller coaster a function of the distance of the coaster from the starting point?

## Vertical Line Test

You can determine directly from a graph whether or not there is a functional relationship between the two variables.

**10. a.** Refer to the graph in Problem 1 on page 113, and select any specific time of day along the horizontal (*x*) axis. Then, move straight up or down (vertically) from that value of time to locate the corresponding point on the graph. How many points do you locate for any given time?

**b.** If you locate only one point in part a, explain why this would mean that body temperature is a function of the time of day.

**c.** If you had located more than one point on the graph in part a, explain why this would mean that body temperature is not a function of time.

The procedure in Problem 10 is referred to as the **vertical line test**.

> **DEFINITION**
>
> In the **vertical line test**, a graph represents a function if any vertical line drawn through the graph intersects the graph no more than once.

**11.** Use the vertical line test on the graphs in Problems 2 through 4 to verify that each graph represents a function.

**12.** Use the vertical line test to determine which of the following graphs represent functions. Explain.

**a.**

**b.**

**c.**

**d.**

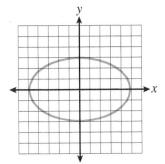

**SUMMARY**
**Activity 1.13**

1. In the **vertical line test**, a graph represents a function if any vertical line drawn through the graph intersects the graph no more than once.

2. If a graph increases and then decreases, the point where the graph changes from rising to falling is called a **maximum point**. The $y$-value of this point is called a **local maximum value**. If a graph decreases and then increases, the point where the graph changes from falling to rising is called a **minimum point**. The $y$-value of this point is called a **local minimum value**.

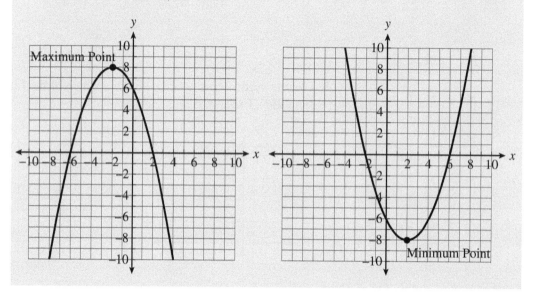

**EXERCISES**
**Activity 1.13**

1. You are a technician at the local power plant, and you have been asked to prepare a report that compares the output and efficiency of the six generators in your sector. Each generator has a graph that shows output of the generator as a function of time over the previous week, Monday through Sunday. You take all the paperwork home for the night (your supervisor wants this report on his desk at 7:00 A.M.), and to your dismay your cat scatters your pile of papers out of the neat order in which you left them. Unfortunately, the graphs for generators A through F were not labeled (you will know better next time!). You recall some information and find evidence elsewhere for the following facts.

   • Generators A and D were the only ones that maintained a fairly steady output.

   • Generator B was shut down for a little more than two days during midweek.

   • Generator C experienced a slow decrease in output during the entire week.

   • On Tuesday morning, there was a problem with generator E that was corrected in a few hours.

   • Generator D was the most productive over the entire week.

   Match each graph with its corresponding generator. Explain in complete sentences how you arrive at your answers.

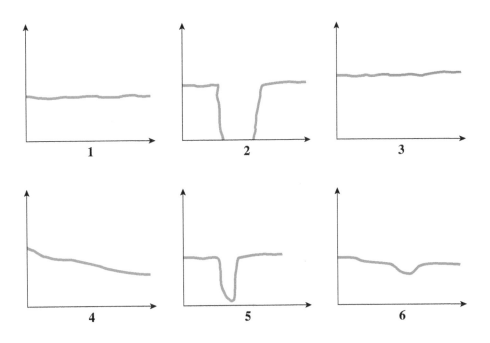

In Exercises 2 and 3, identify the independent variable and the dependent variable. Then interpret the situation being represented. Indicate whether the graph rises, falls, or is constant and whether the graph reaches either a minimum (smallest) or maximum (largest) output value.

**2.** Time required to complete a task in relation to number of times the task is attempted

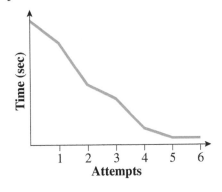

**a.** Independent: _____     Dependent: _____

**b.** Interpretation:

**3.** Number of units sold in relation to selling price

**a.** Independent: _____ Dependent: _____

**b.** Interpretation:

**4.** You leave home on Friday afternoon for your weekend getaway. Heavy traffic slows you down for the first half of your trip, but you make good time by the end. Express your distance from home as a function of time.

**5.** Your small business started slowly, losing money in its first 2 years, then breaking even in year three. By the fourth year, you made as much as you lost in the first year and then doubled your profits each of the next 2 years. Graph your profit as the output and time as the input.

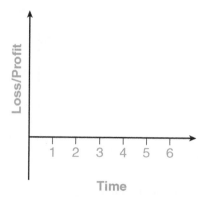

**6.** Use the vertical line test to determine which of the following graphs represents a function. Explain your answer.

a.

b.

c.

**ACTIVITY 1.14**

Heating
Schedule

**OBJECTIVES**

1. Obtain a new graph from an original graph using a vertical shift.

2. Obtain a new graph from an original graph using a horizontal shift.

3. Identify vertical and horizontal shifts.

4. Write a new formula for a function for which its graph has been shifted vertically or horizontally.

The cost of fuel oil is rising and is affecting the school district's budget. In order to save money, the building maintenance supervisor of the high school has decided to keep the building warm only during school hours.

1. Sketch a graph that best represents the following building heating schedule which begins at midnight.

   At midnight, the building temperature is 55°F. This temperature remains constant until 4 A.M., at which time the temperature of the building steadily increases. By 7 A.M., the temperature is 68°F. The temperature is maintained at a constant 68°F until 7 P.M., when the temperature begins a steady decrease. By 10 P.M., the temperature is back to 55°F.

Now, suppose the building maintenance supervisor is instructed by the Board of Education to increase the temperature of the building by a constant 3°F.

2. **a.** On the graph in Problem 1, sketch a graph that represents the new building heat schedule over a 24-hour period, starting at midnight.

   **b.** Describe how the graph in part a can be obtained from the original graph of the building heating schedule in Problem 1.

The graph of the new heating schedule in Problem 2 represents a **vertical shift** of the original graph. The graph has been shifted vertically upward by 3 units.

3. The heating schedule for a warehouse is represented by the following graph.

a.  As a cost saving measure, the building superintendent decides to drop the temperature of the warehouse by 2°F. Using the given graph, sketch a graph that represents the new heat schedule.

b.  Describe how the graph of the new heating schedule can be obtained from the original graph.

## Horizontal Shift

4.  The following graph represents the heating schedule in an office building.

The building superintendent needs to change the heating schedule by moving everything two hours earlier.

a.  On the given graph, sketch a graph that represents the new heating schedule. Describe the new schedule in words.

b.  Describe how the graph of the new heating schedule can be obtained from the original graph.

The graph of the new heating schedule in Problem 4 represents a **horizontal shift** of the original graph. The original graph has been shifted two units horizontally to the left.

5.  a.  The heating schedule for the warehouse in Problem 3 is delayed by 2 hours. Sketch a graph that represents the new heating schedule.

**b.** Describe how the graphs of the new and original heating schedule are related.

## Function Formulas for a Graph Resulting from Vertical or Horizontal Shift

**6. a.** Use a graphing calculator to graph the squaring function, defined by $y = x^2$, in a standard window. The screen should appear as follows:

Note: The squaring function is an example of a quadratic function. Quadratic functions are studied in detail in Chapter 4.

**b.** Graph $y_2 = x^2 + 2$ on the same coordinate axis as $y = x^2$ in part a.

**c.** Describe how the graph for $y_2 = x^2 + 2$ can be obtained from the graph of $y = x^2$.

**d.** Now, let $y_3 = x^2 - 3$. Use a graphing calculator to graph the function defined by this equation. Describe how the graph can be obtained from the graph of $y = x^2$.

**e.** The graph of $y = x^2 + c$ represents a vertical shift of the graph of $y = x^2$. How do you determine if the graph is shifted vertically upward or vertically downward?

**7. a.** Use a graphing calculator to sketch a graph of $y_2 = (x + 2)^2$ on the same coordinate axis as $y = x^2$. The screen should appear as follows:

**b.** Does the graph of $y_2 = (x + 2)^2$ represent a shift of the graph $y = x^2$? If yes, describe the type of shift.

**c.** Use a graphing calculator to sketch a graph of $y_3 = (x - 4)^2$ on the same coordinate axis as $y = x^2$. Describe how the graph of $y_3 = (x - 4)^2$ can be obtained from the graph of $y = x^2$.

**d.** The graph of $y = (x + c)^2$ represents a horizontal shift of the graph of $y = x^2$. How do you determine if the shift is to the right or left?

In Problem 6b, adding 2 to the output (the square of a number) results in a vertical shift of the graph of the squaring function. Using function notation, if $y = f(x) = x^2$, then

$$y = x^2 + 2 = f(x) + 2 \text{ is the upward vertical shift of } y = f(x) = x^2.$$

Since $y = f(x) + 2$ involves a change to the output value, $f(x)$, vertical shifts result from "outside" changes to the function.

In Problem 7b, adding 2 to the input value $x$ **before** the squaring is done results in a horizontal shift of the graph of the squaring function. Using function notation, if $y = f(x) = x^2$, then

$$y = (x + 2)^2 = f(x + 2) \text{ is a horizontal shift to the left of } y = f(x) = x^2.$$

Since $y = f(x + 2)$ involves a change to the input value, $x$, horizontal shifts result from "inside" changes to the function.

The results from Problems 6 and 7 can be generalized as follows:

In general,

1. If a function is defined by $y = f(x)$, and $c$ is a constant, then the graph of $y = f(x) + c$ is the graph of $y = f(x)$ shifted vertically $|c|$ units. If $c > 0$, then the shift is upward. If $c < 0$, then the shift is downward.

2. If a function is defined by $y = f(x)$, and $c$ is a constant, then the graph of $y = f(x + c)$ is the graph of $y = f(x)$ shifted horizontally $|c|$ units. If $c > 0$, then the shift is to the left. If $c < 0$, the shift is to the right.

A vertical or horizontal shift of the graph of a function is called a **translation**. A translation does not change the shape of the graph. It translates (moves) the graph into a new position in the plane.

8. The graph of the absolute value function, defined by $y = |x|$, is

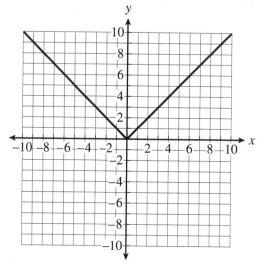

Determine the graph of each of the following translations of the absolute value function. Describe the shift in words. Verify your results using a graphing calculator.

Note: Absolute value functions are discussed in more detail in Chapter 2.

a. $y = |x| + 5$                            b. $y = |x + 5|$

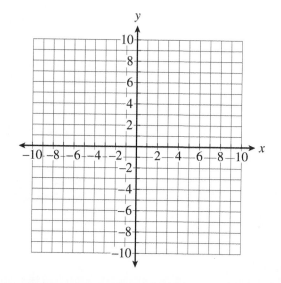

**c.**  $y = |x| - 2$     **d.**  $y = |x - 2|$

 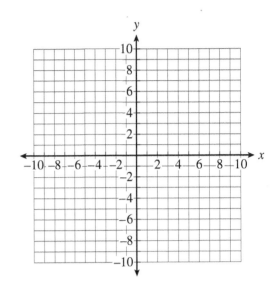

9. The graph of the squaring function, defined by $y = x^2$, is translated (shifted) in parts a–d. Write the equation of the resulting graph.

   **a.** vertical shift of the graph 3 units upward

   **b.** vertical shift of the graph 5 units downward

   **c.** horizontal shift of the graph 2 units to the left

   **d.** horizontal shift of the graph 4 units to the right

**10.** The graph of $y = (x - 3)^2 + 5$ involves a vertical and horizontal shift of the graph of $y = x^2$. Use the patterns discussed in this activity to sketch the graph. Verify using a graphing calculator.

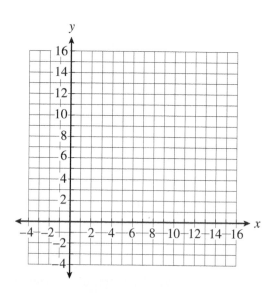

## SUMMARY
**Activity 1.14**

1. In a **vertical shift** of a graph, a positive constant is added to (upward shift) or subtracted from (downward shift) each output value. As a result, the graph is moved vertically upward or vertically downward.

2. In a **horizontal shift** of a graph, a positive constant is first added to (shift left) or subtracted from (shift right) each input value. As a result, the graph is moved horizontally to the left or horizontally to the right.

3. In general, if a function is defined by $y = f(x)$, and $c$ is a constant, then the graph of

   **i.** $y = f(x) + c$ is the graph of $y = f(x)$ shifted vertically $|c|$ units. If $c > 0$, then the shift is upward. If $c < 0$, then the shift is downward.

   **ii.** $y = f(x + c)$ is the graph of $y = f(x)$ shifted horizontally $|c|$ units. If $c > 0$, then the shift is to the left. If $c < 0$, the shift is to the right.

4. A vertical or horizontal shift of the graph of a function is called a **translation**. A translation does not change the shape of the graph. It translates (moves) the graph into a new position in the coordinate plane.

**1.** The graph of the absolute value function is given in Problem 8.

Match each of the graphs in parts a–d with the corresponding shift of the graph of the absolute value function from i–iv.

   **i.** vertical shift of the graph 3 units upward

   **ii.** vertical shift of the graph 3 units downward

  **iii.** horizontal shift of the graph 3 units to the right

  **iv.** horizontal shift of the graph 3 units to the left

**a.**

**b.**

**c.**

**d.**

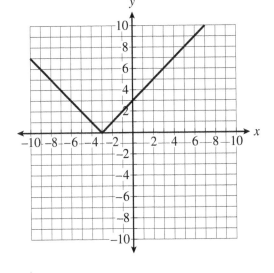

**2.** In parts a–d, sketch a new graph by performing the specified shift on the given graph.

    **a.** Vertical shift of the graph
       3 units downward.

    **b.** Horizontal shift of the graph
       2 units to the right.

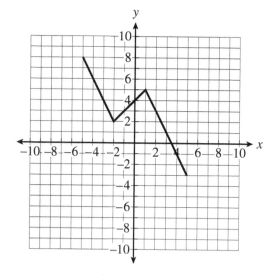

    **c.** Vertical shift of the graph
       4 units upward.

    **d.** Horizontal shift of the graph
       3 units to the left.

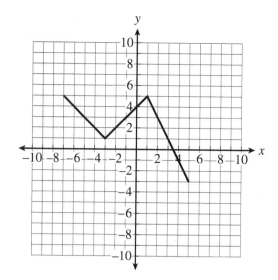

**3.** The graphs below are horizontal translations of the basic squaring function, $f(x) = x^2$. Write the equation for each function. Check your answer by graphing on your calculator.

**a.**                                    **b.**

                    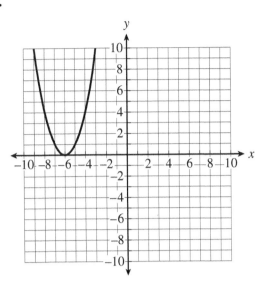

**4.** Given the graph of $y = f(x)$, translate as indicated by the given equation to graph a new function in parts a–c.

**a.** $y = f(x) - 3$          **b.** $y = f(x + 2)$          **c.** $y = f(x) + 2$

          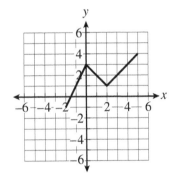

**5.** Describe in words how the graph of the basic absolute value function will be translated in each case. Check by graphing on your calculator.

   **a.** $y = |x - 5|$

   **b.** $y = |x| - 7$

   **c.** $y = 2 + |x + 4|$

**6.** Write the equation for each described function. Check by graphing on your calculator.

   **a.** The squaring function shifted down 8 units.

   **b.** The absolute value function shifted to the left 4 units.

   **c.** The linear function $y = 3x$ shifted to the right 5 units.

   **d.** The squaring function shifted up 3 units and to the left 6 units.

7. Each of the following graphs represents the translation of the indicated basic function. Write the equation for each graph. Check by graphing on your calculator.

   **a.** Translation of $y = x^2$

   **b.** Translation of $y = |x|$

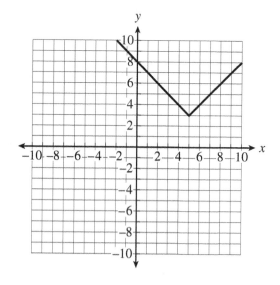

8. A computer technician charges a flat fee of $50 for an on-site service call and $75 per hour thereafter. The following graph represents the total cost $c$ as a function of the number of hours.

   **a.** What is the equation for this function?

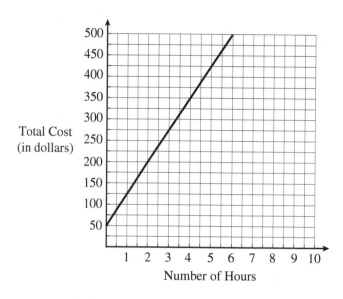

Number of Hours

   **b.** Suppose the flat fee for an on-site service increases by 20 dollars. How does the increase affect the cost?

**c.** Sketch a graph of the new cost function.

**d.** Describe how the new graph can be obtained from the original graph.

**e.** Write an equation for the new cost function in part c.

**9.** The speed limits over a four mile stretch of country road is represented by the following graph.

If all the speed limits are to be reduced by 5 MPH, sketch the new graph and describe how it is obtained from the original graph.

**10.** A new car depreciates in value over time. Assuming a straight-line depreciation, the car will decrease in value the same amount every year. If a car is purchased in 2005 for $32,000, and decreases in value $2000 every year, the graph shows the car's value, where $x$ represents the years since purchase.

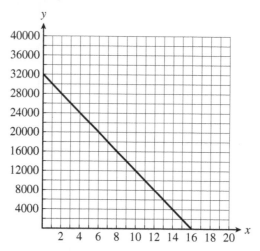

**a.** What is the equation for this function?

**b.** If you want the independent variable $x$ to be the actual year, instead of the number of years since 2005, how would the graph be shifted?

**c.** Write the equation for this translated function, where $x$ represents the actual year.

**d.** What will be the new $y$-intercept for this translated graph, and does it have any practical significance?

**Activities 1.6–1.14**   What Have I Learned?

1. What is the mathematical definition of a function? Give a real-life example, and explain how this example satisfies the definition of a function.

2. Describe how you can tell from a graph when a function is increasing and when it is decreasing.

3. Identify four different ways that a function can be defined. Give an example of each.

4. Use your newspaper to find at least 4 examples of functions and report your findings back to the class. For each example, you should do the following:

   a. Explain how the example satisfies the definition of a function.

   b. Describe how the function is defined (see Problem 3).

   c. Identify the independent and dependent variables.

   d. Determine the domain of the function.

5. The notation $g(t)$ represents the weight (in grams) of a melting ice cube $t$ minutes after being removed from the freezer. Interpret the meaning of $g(10) = 4$.

6. The graph of $y = |x + 2| - 3$ involves a horizontal and vertical shift of the graph of the function defined by $y = |x|$.

   a. Sketch a graph of $y = |x + 2| - 3$ by first doing a horizontal shift of the graph of $y = |x|$, followed by a vertical shift of the graph resulting from the horizontal shift.

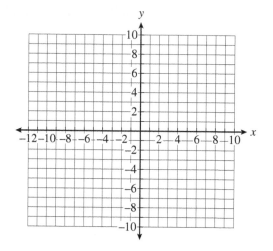

   b. Now, sketch a graph of $y = |x + 2| - 3$ by first doing the vertical shift of the graph of $y = |x|$, followed by the horizontal shift.

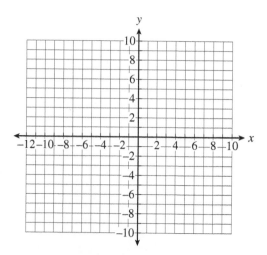

   c. Compare the graphs in parts a and b.

# Activities 1.6–1.14    How Can I Practice?

1. You bought a company in 2004 and have tracked the company's profits and losses from its beginning in 1998 to the present. You decide to graph the information where the number of years since 2004 is the $x$-variable and profit or loss for the year is the $y$-variable. Note that the year 2004 corresponds to 0 on the $x$-axis. Determine the quadrant or axis on which you would plot the points that correspond to the following data. If your answer is on an axis, indicate between which quadrants the point is located.

   a. The loss in 2000 was $1500.

   b. The profit in 2005 was $6000.

   c. The loss in 2006 was $1000.

   d. In 2002, there was no profit or loss.

   e. The profit in 1999 was $500.

   f. The loss in 2004 was $800.

2. Fish need oxygen to live, just as you do. The amount of dissolved oxygen (D.O.) in water is measured in parts per million (ppm). Trout need a minimum of 6 ppm to live.

   The data in the table shows the relationship between the temperature of the water and the amount of dissolved oxygen present.

   | TEMP (°C) | 11 | 16 | 21 | 26 | 31 |
   |---|---|---|---|---|---|
   | D.O. (in ppm) | 10.2 | 8.6 | 7.7 | 7.0 | 6.4 |

   a. Represent the data in the table graphically. Place temperature along the horizontal axis and dissolved oxygen along the vertical axis.

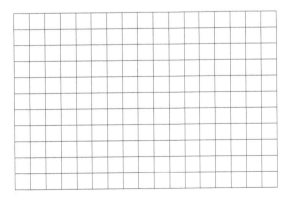

**b.** What general trend do you notice in the data?

**c.** In which of the 5-degree temperature intervals given in the table does the dissolved oxygen content change the most?

**d.** Which representation (table or graph) presents the information and trends more clearly?

**3.** When you were born, your uncle invested $1000 for you in a local bank. Your bank has compounded the interest continuously at a rate of 6%. The following graph shows how your investment grows.

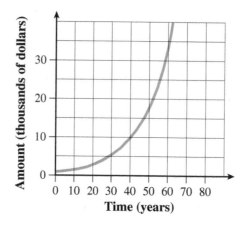

**a.** Which variable is the independent variable?

**b.** How much money did you have when you were 10 years old?

**c.** Estimate in what year your original investment will have doubled.

**d.** If your college bill is estimated to be $2600 in the first year of college, will you have enough to pay the bill with these funds? (Assume that you attend when you are eighteen.) Explain.

**4.** You decide to lose weight and will cut down on your calories to lose 2 pounds a week. Suppose that your present weight is 180 pounds. Sketch a graph covering twenty weeks showing your projected weight loss. Describe your graph. If you stick to your plan, how much will you weigh in three months (13 weeks)?

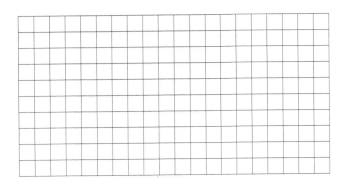

**5.** A taxicab driver charges a flat rate of $2.50 plus $1.50 per mile. The fare $F$ (in dollars) is a function of the distance driven, $x$ (in miles). The driver wants to display a table for her customers to show approximate fares for different locations within the city.

   **a.** Write an equation for $F$ in terms of $x$.

   **b.** Use the equation to complete the following table.

| x | 0.25 | 0.5 | 0.75 | 1.0 | 1.5 | 2.0 | 3.0 | 5.0 | 10.0 |
|---|------|-----|------|-----|-----|-----|-----|-----|------|
| F |      |     |      |     |     |     |     |     |      |

**6.** Interpret each situation represented by the following graphs. That is, describe, in words, what the graph is saying about the relationship between the variables. Indicate what occurs when either a minimum or maximum value is reached.

   **a.** Hours of daylight per day in relation to time of year.

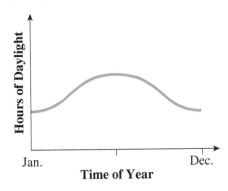

**b.** Population of fish in a pond in relation to the number of years since stocking.

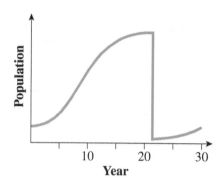

**c.** Distance from home (in miles) in relation to driving time (in hours).

**d.** Amount of money saved per month in relation to amount of money earned.

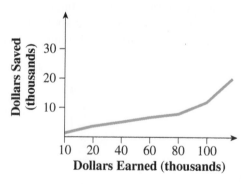

**7.** In the following situations, determine the independent and dependent variables, and then sketch a graph that best describes the situation. Remember to label the axes with the names of the variables.

**a.** Sketch a graph that approximates average temperatures where you live as a function of the number of months since January.

Independent variable:_____

Dependent variable: _____

**b.** If you don't study, you would expect to do poorly on the next test. If you study several hours, you should do quite well, but if you study for too many more hours, your test score will probably not improve. Sketch a graph of your test score as a function of study time.

Independent variable: _____    Dependent variable: _____

In Exercises 8–15, solve each equation for *x*.

**8.** $2(x + 4) = 12$

**9.** $3x + 2(x - 6) = x + 4$

**10.** $\frac{1}{3}(2x + 3) = 3(x + 1)$

**11.** $(2x - 5) - (4 - 3x) = 11$

**12.** $\frac{1}{2}x + \frac{1}{3}x + 5 = x$

**13.** $1.50x + 0.85(12 - x) = 14.75$

**14.** $-7 = -3(x - 7) + 2x + 1$

**15.** $2[6x - 7(x - 1)] = 5x - 21$

**16.** The cost of printing a brochure to advertise your lawn-care business is a flat fee of $10 plus $0.08 per copy. Let $C$ represent the total cost of printing and $x$ represent the number of copies you order.

**a.** Write a symbolic rule that expresses the relationship between $C$ and $x$.

**b.** Organize the data into a table of values. Begin with 1000 copies, increase by increments of 1000, and end with 5000 copies.

| NUMBER OF COPIES, $x$ | TOTAL COST ($), $C$ |
|---|---|
|  |  |
|  |  |
|  |  |
|  |  |
|  |  |

**c.** Graph the data obtained in part b. Use a straightedge to connect the points and extend the graph. Scale the axes appropriately so that you can plot the ordered pair corresponding to 10,000 copies.

**d.** What is the total cost of printing 8000 copies?

**e.** You have $500 to spend on advertising. How many copies can you have printed for that amount?

**17.** Solve each of the following equations for the given variable:

    **a.** $d = rt$ for $r$                      **b.** $P = a + b + c$ for $b$

**c.** $A = P + Prt$ for $r$     **d.** $y = 4x - 5$ for $x$

**e.** $w = \dfrac{4}{7}h + 3$ for $h$

**18.** A volatile stock began the last week of the year worth $x$ dollars per share. The following table shows the changes during that week. If you own 30 shares, write an equation that represents the total value, $V$, of your stock at the end of the week.

| DAY | 1 | 2 | 3 | 4 | 5 |
|---|---|---|---|---|---|
| CHANGE IN VALUE/SHARE | Doubled | Lost 10 | Tripled | Gained 12 | Lost half its value |

**19.** You planned a trip with your best friend. You had only four days for your trip and planned to travel $x$ hours each day.

The first day, you stopped for sightseeing and lost two hours of travel time. The second day, you gained one hour because you did not stop for lunch. On the third day, you traveled well into the night and doubled your planned travel time. On the fourth day, you traveled only a fourth of the time you planned because your friend was sick. You averaged 45 miles per hour for the first two days and 48 miles per hour for the last two days.

**a.** How many hours, in terms of $x$, did you travel the first two days?

**b.** How many hours, in terms of $x$, did you travel the last two days?

**c.** Express the total distance, $D$, traveled over the four days as an equation in terms of $x$. Simplify the equation. Recall that distance = average rate · time.

**d.** Write an equation that expresses the total distance, $y$, you would have traveled had you traveled exactly $x$ hours each day at the average speeds indicated above. Simplify the equation.

**e.** If you anticipated traveling for seven hours each day, how many miles did you actually go on your trip?

**f.** How many miles would you have gone had you traveled exactly seven hours each day?

**20.** You read about a full-time summer position in sales at the Cameron-Dylan Furniture Store. The job pays $260 per week plus 20% commission on sales over $1000.

**a.** Explain how you would calculate the total amount earned each week.

**b.** Let $x$ represent the dollar amount of sales for the week. Write a symbolic rule that expresses your earnings, $E$, for the week in terms of $x$.

**c.** Write an equation to determine how much furniture you must sell to have a gross salary of $500 for the week.

**d.** Solve the equation in part c.

**e.** Is the total amount of sales reasonable? Explain

**21.** As a prospective employee in a furniture store, you are offered a choice of salary. The following table shows your options.

| OPTION 1 | $100 per week | Plus 30% of all sales |
|---|---|---|
| OPTION 2 | $150 per week | Plus 15% of all sales |

**a.** Write an equation to represent the total salary, $S$, for option 1 if the total sales are $x$ dollars per week.

**b.** Write an equation to represent the total salary, $S$, for option 2 if the total sales are $x$ dollars per week.

**c.** Write an equation that you could use to determine how much you would have to sell in a week to earn the same salary under both plans.

**d.** Solve the equation in part c. Interpret your result.

**e.** What is the common salary for the amount of sales found in part d?

**f.** Graph the two equations from parts a and b on the following grid. Locate the point of the common salary and use the graph to determine which option provides the larger salary for furniture sales more than $333 per week.

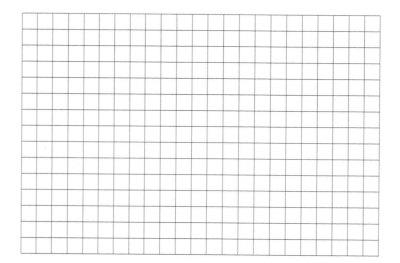

**22.** A triathlon includes swimming, long-distance running, and cycling.

**a.** Let $x$ represent the number of miles the competitors swim. If the long-distance run is 10 miles longer than the distance swum, write an expression that represents the distance the competitors run in the event.

**b.** The distance the athletes cycle is 55 miles longer than they run. Use the result in part a to write an expression in terms of $x$ that represents the cycling distance of the race.

**c.** Write an expression that represents the total distance of all three phases of the triathlon. Simplify the expression.

**d.** If the total distance of the triathlon is 120 miles, write and solve an equation to determine $x$. Interpret the result.

**e.** What are the lengths of the running and cycling portions of the race?

**23.** The following graph is a sketch of the step function. Note that an open circle indicates that the point is not included in the graph.

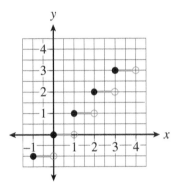

In parts a–d, sketch a new graph of the step function by performing the specified translation.

**a.** Vertical shift of the graph 1 unit upward.

**b.** Vertical shift of the graph 1 unit downward.

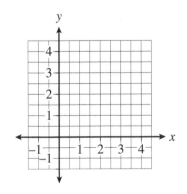

**c.** Horizontal shift of the graph 1 unit to the right.

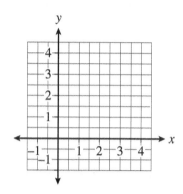

**d.** Horizontal shift of the graph 1 unit to the left.

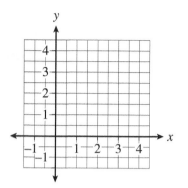

**24.** The graph of the function defined by $y = f(x)$ is

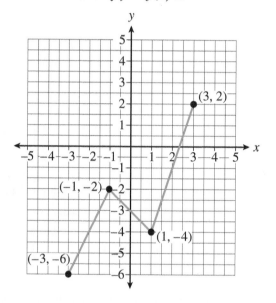

Sketch a graph of each function defined by the given equation. Describe the type of shift that was performed on the original graph.

**a.** $y = f(x) + 3$

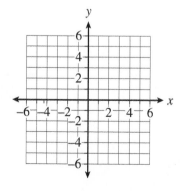

**b.** $y = f(x + 3)$

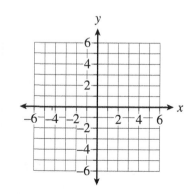

# Summary

*The bracketed numbers following each concept indicate the activity in which the concept is discussed.*

| CONCEPT / SKILL | DESCRIPTION | EXAMPLE |
|---|---|---|
| **Problem solving** [1.2], [1.3] | Problem-solving strategies include:<br>• discussing the problem<br>• organizing information<br>• drawing a picture<br>• recognizing patterns<br>• doing a simpler problem | You drive for 2 hours at an average speed of 47 mph. How far do you travel?<br>$d = rt$<br>$d = \dfrac{47\text{mi}}{\text{hr}} \cdot 2 \text{ hr} = 94 \text{ mi}$ |
| **Variable** [1.3] | A quantity or quality that may change in value from one particular instance to another, usually represented by a letter. When a variable describes an actual quantity, its values must include the unit of measurement of that quantity. | The number of miles you drive in a week is a variable. Its value may (and usually does) change from one week to the next. $x$ and $y$ are commonly used to represent variables. |
| **Formulas** [1.3] | A formula shows the arithmetic relationship between two or more quantities; each quantity is represented by a letter or symbol. | $F = ma$ for $m = 120$ and $a = 25$<br>$F = 120 \cdot 25 = 3000$ |
| **Applying a known ratio to a given piece of information** [1.4] | Total × known ratio = unknown part<br>Part ÷ known ratio = unknown total | Forty percent of the 350 children play an instrument; 40% is the known ratio; 350 is the total.<br>$350 \times 0.40 = 140$   A total of 140 children play an instrument. Twenty-four children, constituting 30% of the marching band, play the saxophone; 30% is the known ratio, 24 is the part.<br>$24 \div 0.30 = 80$   A total of 80 children are in the marching band. |
| **Solving a proportion** [1.4] | $\dfrac{a}{b} = \dfrac{c}{d}, b \neq 0, d \neq 0$<br>Equivalently, $a \cdot d = b \cdot c$ | $\dfrac{7}{30} = \dfrac{x}{4140}$<br>$30 \cdot x = 7 \cdot 4140$<br>$x = \dfrac{7 \cdot 4140}{30} = 966$ |
| **Using unit (or dimensional) analysis to solve conversion problems** [1.5] | 1. Identify the unit of the result.<br>2. Set up the sequence of multiplications so the appropriate units cancel, leaving the unit of the result.<br>3. Multiply and divide the numbers as usual to obtain the numerical part of the result.<br>4. Check that the appropriate units cancel, leaving the expected unit of the result. | To convert your height of 70 inches to centimeters:<br>$70 \text{ in.} \cdot \dfrac{2.54 \text{ cm}}{1 \text{ inch}} = 177.8 \text{ cm}$ |

| | | |
|---|---|---|
| **Input variable** [1.6] | The input variable, often represented by $x$, is the value given first in a relationship. | In the relationship between the perimeter and the side of a square, $P = 4s$, $s$ is the input variable. |
| **Output variable** [1.6] | The output, often represented by $y$, is the value that corresponds to or is determined by the given input value ($x$). | In the relationship between the perimeter and the side of a square, $P = 4s$, $P$ is the output variable. |
| **Function** [1.6] | A function is a correspondence between an input ($x$) variable and an output ($y$) variable that assigns a single, unique output value ($y$) to each input value ($x$). | See Example 1 in Activity 1.6. |
| **Ordered pair** [1.6] | An ordered pair of numbers consists of two numbers written in the form $(x, y)$, where $x$ is the input and $y$ is the output. The order in which they are listed is significant. | (2, 3) is an ordered pair. In this pair, 2 is the input and 3 is the output. |
| **Verbally defined function** [1.6] | A function is defined verbally when it is defined using words. | The high temperature in Houston, Texas, is a function of the day of the year, because for each day there is one high temperature. |
| **Graphically defined function** [1.6] | A function is defined graphically when the $x$-variable is represented on the horizontal axis and the $y$-variable on the vertical axis. | |
| **Numerically defined function** [1.6] | A function is defined numerically using ordered pairs, or presented as a table of matched pairs. | See Example 1 in Activity 1.6. |
| **Horizontal axis** [1.6] | In graphing an $x$-$y$ relationship, the variable $x$ is referenced on the horizontal axis (often called the $x$-axis). | |
| **Vertical axis** [1.6] | In graphing an $x$-$y$ relationship, the variable $y$ is referenced on the vertical axis (often called the $y$-axis). | |
| **Rectangular coordinate system** [1.6] | Allows every point in the plane to be identified by an ordered pair of numbers, determined by the distance of the point from two perpendicular number lines (called coordinate axes) that intersect at their respective 0 values, the origin. | |

| | | |
|---|---|---|
| **Scaling** [1.6] | Setting the same distance between each pair of adjacent tick marks on an axis. | Scale is 1 |
| **Quadrants** [1.6] | Two perpendicular coordinate axes divide the plane into four quadrants, labeled counterclockwise with quadrant I being the upper-right quadrant. | |
| **Point in the plane** [1.6] | Points that are identified by an ordered pair of numbers $(x, y)$ in which $x$ represents the horizontal distance from the origin and $y$ represents the vertical distance from the origin. | $(2, 30)$ are the coordinates of a point in the first quadrant located 2 units to the right and 30 units above the origin. |
| **Independent variable** [1.7] | Independent variable is another name for the $x$-variable (the input) of a function. | See Example 4 of Activity 1.7. |
| **Dependent variable** [1.7] | Dependent variable is another name for the $y$-variable (the ouput) of a function. | See Example 4 of Activity 1.7. |
| **Domain of a function** [1.7] | The domain of the function is the collection of all replacement values for the independent variable. | See Example 4 in Activity 1.7. |
| **Practical domain of a function** [1.7] | The practical domain is the collection of replacement values of the independent variable that makes practical sense in the context of the situation. | See Example 3 in Activity 1.7. |
| **Range of a function** [1.7] | The range of a function is the collection of all dependent variable values of a function. | See Example 3 in Activity 1.7. |
| **Practical range of a function** [1.7] | The practical range is the collection of all dependent variable values that make practical sense in the context of the situation. | See Example 3 in Activity 1.7. |
| **Mathematical model** [1.8] | A mathematical model is a mathematical structure such as a formula, a graph, or a table, that fits or approximates the important features of a given situation. | See Problems 8 and 10 in Activity 1.8. |
| **Solution of an equation** [1.9] | The solution of an equation is a replacement value for the variable that makes both sides of the equation equal in value. | 3 is a solution of the equation $4x - 5 = 7$. |

| | | |
|---|---|---|
| **Solve an equation using a numerical approach** [1.9] | To solve an equation using a numerical approach use a guess, check and repeat process. This process can be automated using the table feature of a graphing calculator. | $4x - 7 = 5$ <br><br> try $x = 2$, $4(2) - 7 = 1$ (too low) <br><br> try $x = 4$, $4(4) - 7 = 9$ (too high) <br><br> try $x = 3$, $4(3) - 7 = 5$ (This is it!) |
| **Solve an equation graphically** [1.9] | To solve an equation graphically, first graph the equation. Then locate the point that has the desired value as its $y$-coordinate. The value of the $x$-coordinate of that point is the solution of the equation. | Solve $-2x + 3 = 5$ <br><br>  <br><br> The output value is 5 when the input value is $-1$. Therefore, $-1$ is the solution. |
| **Evaluate an algebraic expression** [1.9] | To evaluate an algebraic expression replace the variable(s) by its (their) assigned value(s) and perform the indicated arithmetic operation(s). | Evaluate $3x^2 - 2x + 4$ when $x = 2$. <br><br> $3(2)^2 - 2(2) + 4$ <br> $3 \cdot 4 - 4 + 4$ <br> $12 - 4 + 4$ <br> $12$ |
| **Isolate a variable in an equation** [1.9], [1.10] | Write the equation so that the variable you are solving for is on one side and all other numbers and variables are on the other side. | The variable $y$ is isolated in the equation $y = 3x + 25$. |
| **How to solve an equation for a given variable** [1.9], [1.10] | Add and/or subtract appropriate terms so that all terms involving the variable you are solving for are on one side of the equation and all terms involving numbers and other variables appear on the other side. Then, combine like terms, and finally divide and/or multiply by the coefficient of the variable. | $4x + 7 + 5x = 7 + 2x - 13$ <br> $9x + 7 = 2x - 6$ <br> $7x = -13$ <br> $x = -13/7$ |
| **Solve an equation algebraically for a specified variable** [1.9], [1.10] | An algebraic approach to solving an equation is complete when the variable of interest is alone on one side of the equation with coefficient 1, and the other side is simplified. | $4x + 7 + 5x = 7 + 2x - 13$ <br> $9x + 7 = 2x - 6$ <br> $7x = -13$ <br> $x = -13/7$ |

| | | |
|---|---|---|
| **Solve a formula for a given variable** [1.11] | To solve a formula, collect the term containing the variable of interest on one side of the equation, with all other terms on the other side. Then, divide both sides of the equation by the coefficient of the variable. | $2(a + b) = 8 - 5a$ for $a$ <br> $2a + 2b = 8 - 5a$ <br> $2a + 5a = 8 - 2b$ <br> $7a = 8 - 2b$ <br> $a = \dfrac{8 - 2b}{7}$ |
| **Distributive property** [1.11] | $\underbrace{a \cdot (b + c)}_{\text{factored form}} = \underbrace{a \cdot b + a \cdot c}_{\text{expanded form}}$ | $4(x + 6) = 4 \cdot x + 4 \cdot 6$ <br> $\qquad\qquad = 4x + 24$ |
| **General strategy for solving equations algebraically** [1.11] | General strategy for solving an equation algebraically: <br> 1. Simplify the expressions on each side of the equation. <br> 2. Collect the variable term on one side of the equation. <br> 3. Solve for the variable by dividing each side of the equation by the coefficient of the variable. <br> 4. Check your result in the original equation. | $3(2x - 5) + 2x = 9$ <br> $6x - 15 + 2x = 9$ <br> $8x - 15 = 9$ <br> $8x = 24$ <br> $x = 3$ <br> Check: <br> $3(2 \cdot 3 - 5) + 2 \cdot 3 =$ <br> $3(6 - 5) + 6 =$ <br> $3 \cdot 1 + 6 =$ <br> $9$ |
| **Vertical line test** [1.13] | In the **vertical line test**, a graph represents a function if any vertical line drawn through the graph intersects the graph no more than once. | 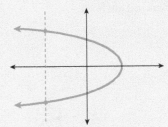 <br> This graph is not a function. |
| **Increasing function** [1.13] | The graph of an increasing function rises to the right. | 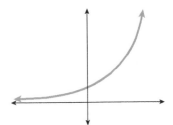 |
| **Decreasing function** [1.13] | The graph of a decreasing function falls to the right. |  |

| **Constant function** [1.13] | The graph of a constant function is a horizontal line. | 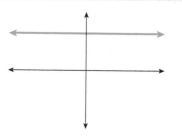 |
|---|---|---|
| **Vertical shift** [1.14] | A positive constant is added to (upward shift) or subtracted from (downward shift) each output value. As a result, the graph is moved vertically upward or vertically downward. |  Vertical shift of the graph of $y = x^2$ 2 units upward. |
| **Horizontal shift** [1.14] | A positive constant is first added to (shift left) or subtracted from (shift right) each input value. As a result, the graph is moved horizontally to the left or horizontally to the right. | 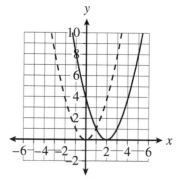 Horizontal shift of the graph of $y = x^2$ 2 units to the right. |

1. Determine whether each of the following is a function.

   **a.** The loudness of the stereo system is a function of the position of the volume dial.

   **b.** $\{(2, 9), (3, 10), (2, -9)\}$

   **c.**

2. For an average yard, the fertilizer costs $20. You charge $8 per hour to do yard work. If $x$ represents the number of hours worked on the yard, and $y$ represents the total cost, including fertilizer, complete the following table:

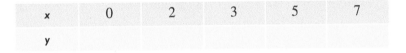

| x | 0 | 2 | 3 | 5 | 7 |
|---|---|---|---|---|---|
| y | | | | | |

   **a.** Is the total cost a function of the hours worked? Explain.

   **b.** What is the independent variable?

   **c.** Which is the dependent variable?

   **d.** Which value(s) of the domain would not be realistic for this situation? Explain.

3. As a real estate salesperson, you earn a small salary, plus a percentage of the selling price of each house you sell. If your salary is $100 a week, plus 3.5% of the selling price of each house sold, what must your total annual home sales be for you to gross $30,000 in one year? Assume that you work 50 weeks per year.

**4.** Use the formula $I = Prt$ to evaluate $I$, given the following information.

   **a.** $P = \$2000, r = 5\%, t = 1$

   **b.** $P = \$3000, r = 6\%, t = 2$

**5.** Use the formula $P = 2(w + l)$, to evaluate $P$ for the following information.

   **a.** $w = 2.8$ and $l = 3.4$

   **b.** $w = 7\frac{1}{3}$ and $l = 8\frac{1}{4}$

**6.** Solve the given equations, and check your results.

   **a.** $4(x + 5) - x = 80$         **b.** $-5(x - 3) + 2x = 6$

   **c.** $38 = 57 - (x + 32)$      **d.** $-13 + 4(3x + 5) = 7$

   **e.** $5x + 3(2x - 8) = 2(x + 6)$    **f.** $-4x - 2(5x - 7) + 2 = -3(3x + 5) - 4$

   **g.** $-32 + 6(3x + 4) = -(-5x + 38) + 3x$

**7.** You visit some relatives in Syracuse, New York. You want to drive to Buffalo to see Niagara Falls. The cost of renting a car for a day is $25, plus 15 cents per mile.

   **a.** Identify the independent variable.

   **b.** Identify the dependent variable.

   **c.** Use $x$ to represent the independent variable and $y$ to represent the dependent variable. Write an equation rule that models the daily rental cost in terms of the number of miles driven.

   **d.** Complete the following table.

**e.** Plot the points from the table in part d. Then draw the line through all five points.

| x | 100 | 200 | 300 | 400 | 500 |
|---|-----|-----|-----|-----|-----|
| y |     |     |     |     |     |

(Make sure you label your axes and use appropriate scaling.)

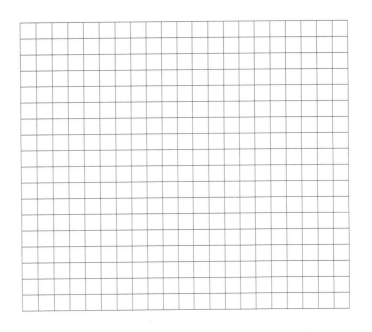

**f.** The distance from Syracuse to Buffalo is 153 miles. Estimate from the graph in part e how much it will cost to travel from Buffalo to Syracuse and back.

**g.** Use the mathematical model in part c to determine the exact cost of this trip.

**h.** You have budgeted $115 for car rental for your day trip. Use your graph to estimate the greatest number of miles you can travel in the day and not exceed your allotted budget? Estimate from your graph.

**i.** Use the mathematical model in part c to determine the exact number of miles you can travel in the day and not exceed $115.

**j.** What are realistic replacement values for the independent variable if you rent the car for only one day?

8. The proceeds from your high school talent show to benefit a local charity totaled $950. Since the seats were all taken, you know that 500 people attended. The cost per ticket was $1.50 for students and $2.50 for adults. Unfortunately, you misplaced the ticket stubs that would indicate how many students and how many adults attended. You need this information for accounting purposes and future planning.

   a. Let $n$ represent the number of students who attended. Write an expression in terms of $n$ to represent the number of adults who attended.

   b. Write an expression in terms of $n$ that will represent the proceeds from the student tickets.

   c. Write an expression in terms of $n$ that will represent the proceeds from the adult tickets.

   d. Write an equation that indicates that the total proceeds from the student and adult tickets totaled $950.

   e. How many student tickets and how many adult tickets were sold?

9. You have an opportunity to be the manager of a day camp for the summer. You know that your fixed costs for operating the camp are $600 per week, even if there are no campers. Each camper who attends costs the management $10 per week. The camp charges each camper $40 per week.

   Let $x$ represent the number of campers.

   a. Write an equation in terms of $x$ that represents the total cost, $C$, of running the camp per week.

   b. Write an equation in terms of $x$ that represents the total income (revenue), $R$, from the campers per week.

   c. Write an equation in terms of $x$ that represents the total profit, $P$, from the campers per week.

   d. How many campers must attend for the camp to break even with revenue and costs?

**e.** The camp would like to make a profit of $600. How many campers must enroll to make that profit?

**f.** How much money would the camp lose if only 10 campers attend?

**g.** Use your graphing calculator to graph the revenue and cost equations. Compare the break-even point from the graph (point of intersection) with your answer in part d.

10. Solve each of the following equations for the specified variable.

**a.** $I = Prt$, for $P$

**b.** $f = v + at$, for $t$

**c.** $2x - 3y = 7$, for $y$

11. You contact the local print shop to produce a commemorative booklet for your high school theater group. It is the group's twenty-fifth anniversary, and in the booklet you want a short history plus a description of all the theater productions for the past 25 years in the booklet. It costs $750 to typeset the booklet and 25 cents for each copy produced.

**a.** Write a mathematical model that gives the total cost, $C$, in terms of the number, $x$, of booklets produced.

**b.** Use the equation from part a to determine the total cost of producing 500 booklets.

**c.** How many booklets can be produced for $1000?

**d.** Suppose the booklets are sold for 75 cents each. Write an equation for the total revenue, $R$, from the sale of $x$ booklets.

**e.** How many booklets must be sold to break even? That is, for what value of $x$ is the total cost of production equal to the total amount of revenue?

**f.** How many booklets must be sold to make a $500 profit?

**12.** You are designing a cylindrical container as new packaging for a popular brand of coffee. The current package is a cylinder with a diameter of 4 inches and a height of 5.5 inches. The volume of a cylinder is given by the formula

$$V = \pi r^2 h,$$

where $V$ is the volume (in cubic inches), $r$ is the radius (in inches), and $h$ is the height (in inches).

How much coffee does the current container hold? Round your answer to the nearest tenth of a cubic inch.

**13.** You have been asked to alter the dimensions of the container in Problem 12 so that the new package will contain less coffee. To save money, the company plans to sell the new package for the same price as before.

You will do. this in one of two ways:

    **i.** By increasing the diameter and decreasing the height by $\frac{1}{2}$ inch each, (resulting in a slightly wider and shorter can), or,

    **ii.** By decreasing the diameter and increasing the height by $\frac{1}{2}$ inch each (resulting in a slightly narrower and taller can).

  **a.** Determine which new design, if either, will result in a package that holds less coffee than the current one.

  **b.** By what percent will you have decreased the volume?

**14.** In parts a–d, sketch a graph of the new function resulting from the specified translation of the given graph.

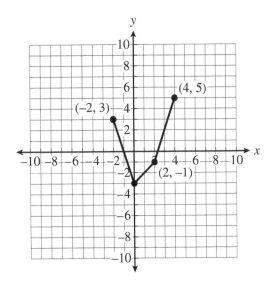

**a.** Vertical shift of the graph 3 units downward.

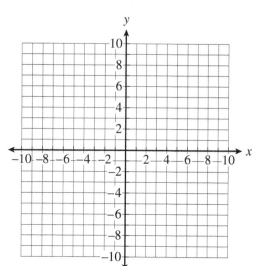

**b.** Vertical shift of the graph 5 units upward.

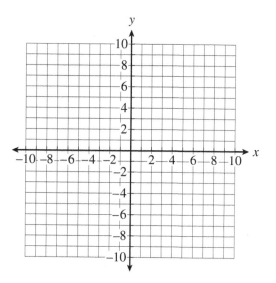

**c.** Horizontal shift of the graph 2 units to the left.

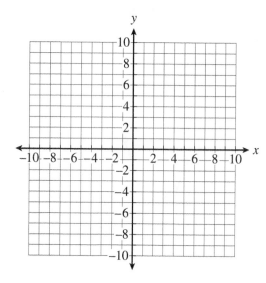

**d.** Horizontal shift of the graph 4 units to the right.

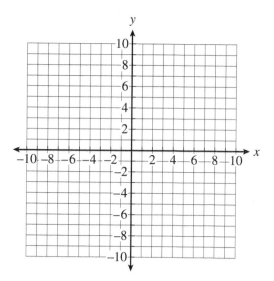

**15.** The graph of the function defined by $y = g(x)$ is

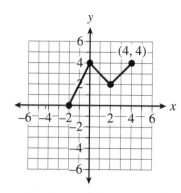

Sketch a graph of each of the following functions defined by the given equation. Describe the type of shift that you performed on the original graph.

**a.** $y = g(x) - 2$

A vertical shift of the graph of $y = g(x)$ 2 units downward.

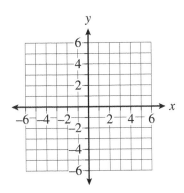

**b.** $y = g(x - 2)$

A horizontal shift of the graph of $y = g(x)$ 2 units to the right.

# CHAPTER 2

# Linear Function Models and Problem Solving

**ACTIVITY 2.1**
How Fast Did
You Lose?

**OBJECTIVE**

1. Determine the average rate of change.

You are a member of a health and fitness club. The club's registered dietitian and your personal trainer helped you develop a special eight-week diet and exercise program. The data in the following table represents your weight, $w$, as a function of time, $t$, over an eight-week period.

### Time Weights for No One

| TIME (weeks) | 0 | 1 | 2 | 3 | 4 | 5 | 6 | 7 | 8 |
|---|---|---|---|---|---|---|---|---|---|
| WEIGHT (lb) | 140 | 136 | 133 | 131 | 130 | 127 | 127 | 130 | 126 |

1. **a.** Plot the data points using ordered pairs of the form $(t, w)$. For example, $(3, 131)$ is a data point that represents your weight at the end of the third week.

The resulting graph of points in Problem 1 is called a **scatterplot**.

**b.** What is the practical domain of this function?

**c.** What is the practical range of this function?

**2. a.** What was your weight at the beginning of the program?

**b.** What was your weight at the end of the first week?

**3.** To see how the health program is working for you, you analyze your weekly weight changes during the eight-week period.

**a.** During which week(s) does your weight increase?

**b.** During which week(s) does your weight decrease?

**c.** During which week(s) does your weight remain unchanged?

## Average Rate of Change

**4.** Your weight decreases during each of the first five weeks of the program.

**a.** Determine the actual change in your weight over the first five weeks of the program by subtracting your initial weight from your weight at the end of the first five weeks.

**b.** What is the sign (positive or negative) of your answer? What is the significance of this sign?

**c.** Determine the change in the $t$-value over the first five weeks; that is, from $t = 0$ to $t = 5$.

**d.** Write the ratio of the change in weight from part a to the change in time in part c. Interpret the meaning of this ratio.

The change in weight describes how much weight you have gained or lost, but it does not tell how quickly you shed those pounds. That is, a loss of 3 pounds in one week is more impressive than a loss of 3 pounds over a month's time. Dividing the change in weight by the change in time gives an average rate at which you have lost weight over this period of time. Its units are weight units per time unit—in this case, pounds per week.

The ratio in Problem 4d,

$$\frac{-13 \text{ pounds}}{5 \text{ weeks}} = -2.6 \text{ pounds per week,}$$

is called the **average rate of change** of weight with respect to time over the first five weeks of the program. It can be interpreted as an average loss of 2.6 pounds each week for the first five weeks of the program.

## Delta Notation

The change in the values of a variable is so important that special symbolic notation has been developed to denote it.

The uppercase Greek letter delta $\Delta$ is used with a variable's name to represent a change in the value of the variable from a starting point to an ending point.

For example in Problem 4, the notation $\Delta w$ represents the change in value of the dependent variable, weight $w$. It is calculated by subtracting the initial value of $w$, denoted by $w_1$, from the final value of $w$, denoted by $w_2$. Symbolically, this change is represented by

$$\Delta w = w_2 - w_1.$$

In the case of Problem 4a, the change in weight over the first five weeks can be calculated as:

$$\Delta w = w_2 - w_1 = 127 - 140 = -13 \text{ lb.}$$

In the same way, the change in value of the independent variable, time ($t$), is written as $\Delta t$ and is calculated by subtracting the initial value of $t$, denoted by $t_1$, from the final value of $t$, denoted by $t_2$. Symbolically, this change is represented by

$$\Delta t = t_2 - t_1.$$

In Problem 4c, the change in the number of weeks can be written using $\Delta$ notation as follows:

$$\Delta t = t_2 - t_1 = 5 - 0 = 5 \text{ weeks}$$

The average rate of change of weight over the first five weeks of the program can now be symbolically written as follows:

$$\frac{\Delta w}{\Delta t} = \frac{-13}{5} = -2.6 \text{ lb per week}$$

Note that the symbol $\Delta$ for delta is the Greek version of $d$, for difference, the result of a subtraction that produces the change in value.

5. Using $\Delta$ notation, determine the average rate of change of weight over the last four weeks of the program.

> **DEFINITION**
>
> The ratio $\frac{\Delta w}{\Delta t}$ is called the **average rate of change** of weight, $w$, with respect to weeks, $t$. In general, the average rate of change is
>
> $$\frac{\Delta w}{\Delta t} = \frac{w_2 - w_1}{t_2 - t_1},$$
>
> where $(t_1, w_1)$ is the initial point and $(t_2, w_2)$ is the final point.

## Graphical Interpretation of the Average Rate of Change

**6. a.** On the graph in Problem 1, connect the points (0, 140) and (5, 127) with a line segment. Does the line segment rise, fall, or remain horizontal as you follow it from left to right?

   **b.** Recall that the average rate of change over the first five weeks was $-2.6$ pounds per week. What does the average rate of change tell you about the line segment drawn in part a?

**7. a.** Determine the average rate of change of your weight over the time period from $t = 5$ to $t = 7$ weeks. Include the appropriate sign and units.

   **b.** Interpret the rate in part a with respect to your diet.

   **c.** On the graph in Problem 1, connect the points (5, 127) and (7, 130) with a line segment. Does the line segment rise, fall, or remain horizontal as you follow it from left to right?

   **d.** How is the average rate of change of weight over the given two-week period related to the line segment you draw in part c?

**8. a.** At what rate is your weight changing during the sixth week of your diet; that is, from $t = 5$ to $t = 6$?

**b.** Interpret the rate in part a with respect to your diet.

**c.** Connect the points (5, 127) and (6, 127) on the graph with a line segment. Does the line segment rise, fall, or remain horizontal as you follow it from left to right?

**d.** How is the average rate of change in part a related to the line segment drawn in part c?

**9. a.** What is the average rate of change of your weight over the period from $t = 4$ to $t = 7$ weeks?

**b.** Explain how the rate in part a reflects the progress of your diet over those three weeks.

**1.** Let $y_1$ represent the corresponding value for the $x_1$ and $y_2$ represent the corresponding value for the $x_2$. As the variable $x$ changes in value from $x_1$ to $x_2$,

   **a.** the change in $x$ is represented by $\Delta x = x_2 - x_1$

   **b.** the change in $y$ is represented by $\Delta y = y_2 - y_1$

**2.** The quotient $\dfrac{\Delta y}{\Delta x} = \dfrac{y_2 - y_1}{x_2 - x_1}$ is called the **average rate of change** of $y$ with respect to $x$ over the $x$-interval from $x_1$ to $x_2$. The units of measurement of the quantity $\dfrac{\Delta y}{\Delta x}$ are *y-units* per *x-unit*.

**3.** The line segment connecting the points $(x_1, y_1)$ and $(x_2, y_2)$

   **a.** increases from left to right if $\dfrac{\Delta y}{\Delta x} > 0$

   **b.** decreases from left to right if $\dfrac{\Delta y}{\Delta x} < 0$

   **c.** remains constant if $\dfrac{\Delta y}{\Delta x} = 0$

## EXERCISES
### Activity 2.1

1. For the years between 1900 and 2000, the following table presents the median ages (output) of U.S. men at the time when they first married.

| INPUT, year | 1900 | 1910 | 1920 | 1930 | 1940 | 1950 | 1960 | 1970 | 1980 | 1990 | 2000 |
|---|---|---|---|---|---|---|---|---|---|---|---|
| OUTPUT, age | 25.9 | 25.1 | 24.6 | 24.3 | 24.3 | 22.8 | 22.8 | 23.2 | 24.7 | 26.1 | 26.8 |

a. During which decade(s) did the median age at first marriage increase for men?

b. During which decade(s) did the median age at first marriage decrease?

c. During which decade(s) did the median age at first marriage remain unchanged?

d. During which decade(s) was the change in median age at first marriage the greatest?

2. Graph the data from Exercise 1, and connect consecutive points with line segments. Then answer the following questions using the graph.

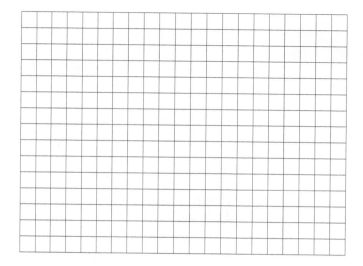

a. During which decade(s) is your graph increasing?

**b.** During which decade(s) is the graph decreasing?

**c.** During which decade(s) is your graph horizontal?

**d.** During which decade(s) is the graph the steepest?

**e.** Compare the answers of the corresponding parts (a–d) of Exercises 1 and 2. What is the relationship between the sign of the output change for a given input interval and the direction (rising, falling, horizontal) of the graph in that interval?

Use the data in Exercise 1 to answer Exercises 3–6.

**3. a.** Determine the average rate of change in median age per year from 1950 to 1990.

**b.** Describe what the average rate of change in part a represents in this situation.

**c.** Determine the average rate of change in median age per year from 1930 to 1960.

**4.** During what decade period did the average age increase the most?

**5. a.** What does it mean in this situation if the average rate of change is negative?

**b.** Determine at least one ten-year period when the average rate of change is negative.

**c.** What trend would you observe in the graph if the average rate of change were negative? That is, would the graph increase, decrease, or remain constant?

**6. a.** Is the average rate of change zero over any ten-year period? If so, when?

**b.** What does an average rate of change of zero mean in this situation?

    **c.** What trend would you observe in the graph during this period? That is, would the graph go up, go down, or be horizontal?

*The following table gives information about new hotel construction in the U.S. from 1997 to 2001:*

| YEAR, $t$ | 1997 | 1998 | 1999 | 2000 | 2001 |
|---|---|---|---|---|---|
| HOTELS CONSTRUCTED, $h$ | 1476 | 1519 | 1402 | 1246 | 1047 |

Use the table of data to answer Exercises 7 and 8.

    **7.** Plot the data points using ordered pairs of the form $(t, h)$.

    **8. a.** Determine the average rate of change of new hotel construction from 1997 to 1998.

       **b.** Determine the average rate of change from 1998 to 1999.

       **c.** Compare the average rate of change from 1997 to 1998 with the rate of change from 1998 to 1999.

       **d.** When the average rate of change is negative, what trend will you observe in the graph? What does that mean in this situation?

**9.** Between 1960 and 2003, the size and shape of automobiles in the United States have changed almost annually. The fuel consumed by these vehicles has also changed. The following table describes the average fuel consumed per year per passenger car in gallons of gasoline.

| YEAR, $t$ | 1960 | 1970 | 1980 | 1990 | 1995 | 2000 | 2002 | 2003 |
|---|---|---|---|---|---|---|---|---|
| GALLONS CONSUMED PER PASSENGER CAR (average) | 668 | 760 | 576 | 520 | 530 | 547 | 555 | 550 |

**a.** Determine the average rate of change, in gallons of fuel used per passenger car, from 1960 to 1970.

**b.** Determine the average rate of change, in gallons of gas per year, from 1960 to 1990.

**c.** Determine the average rate of change, in gallons of gas per year, from 1995 to 2003.

**d.** Determine the average rate of change, in gallons of gas per year, between 1960 and 2003.

**e.** What does the result in part d mean in this situation?

**10.** The National Weather Service recorded the following temperatures one February day in Chicago:

| TIME OF DAY | 10 A.M. | 12 NOON | 2 P.M. | 4 P.M. | 6 P.M. | 8 P.M. | 10 P.M. |
|---|---|---|---|---|---|---|---|
| TEMPERATURE (°F) | 30 | 35 | 36 | 36 | 34 | 30 | 28 |

**a.** Determine the average rate of change (including units and sign) of temperature with respect to time over the entire twelve-hour period given in the table.

**b.** Over which period(s) of time is the average rate of change zero? What, if anything, can you conclude about the actual temperature fluctuation within this period?

**c.** What is the average rate of change of temperature with respect to time over the evening hours from 6 P.M. to 10 P.M.? Interpret this value (including units and sign) in a complete sentence.

**d.** Write a brief paragraph describing the temperature and its fluctuations during the twelve-hour period in the table.

**ACTIVITY 2.2**
The Snowy Tree
Cricket

**OBJECTIVES**

1. Identify linear functions by a constant average rate of change.

2. Interpret slope as an average rate of change.

3. Determine the slope of the line drawn through two points.

4. Identify increasing and decreasing linear functions using slope.

5. Determine the slope and the equation of a horizontal and vertical line.

One of the more familiar late-evening sounds during the summer is the rhythmic chirping of a male cricket. Of particular interest is the snowy tree cricket, sometimes called the temperature cricket. It is very sensitive to temperature, speeding up or slowing down its chirping as the temperature rises or falls. The following data shows how the number of chirps per minute of the snowy tree cricket is related to temperature.

## Timely Noise

| T, TEMPERATURE (°F) | N, NUMBER OF CHIRPS/MINUTE |
|---|---|
| 55 | 60 |
| 60 | 80 |
| 65 | 100 |
| 70 | 120 |
| 75 | 140 |
| 80 | 160 |

1. Crickets are usually silent when the temperature falls below 55°F. What is a possible practical domain for the snowy tree cricket function?

2. **a.** Determine the average rate of change of the number of chirps per minute with respect to temperature as the temperature increases from 55°F to 60°F.

   **b.** What are the units of measure of this rate of change?

3. **a.** How does the average rate of change determined in Problem 2 compare with the average rate of change as the temperature increases from 65°F to 80°F?

   **b.** Determine the average rate of change of number of chirps per minute with respect to temperature for the temperature intervals given in the following table. The results from Problems 1 and 2 are already recorded. Add several more of your own choice. List all your results in the table.

| TEMPERATURE INCREASES | AVERAGE RATE OF CHANGE (number of chirps/minute with respect to temperature) |
|---|---|
| From 55° to 65°F | 4 |
| From 60° to 80°F | 4 |
| From 55° to 75°F | |
| From 60° to 80°F | |
| | |
| | |

c. What can you conclude about the average rate of increase in the number of chirps per minute for any particular increase in temperature?

4. For any 7° increase in temperature, what is the expected increase in chirps per minute?

5. Plot the data pairs (temperature, chirps per minute) from the table preceding Problem 1. What type of graph is suggested by the pattern of points?

*Note:* Use a double slash (//) to indicate that the horizontal axis has been compressed between 0 and 50, and the vertical axis between 0 and 60.

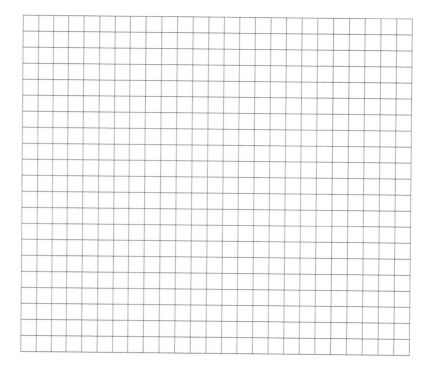

## Linear Functions

If the average rate of change in $x$ with respect to $y$ remains constant (stays the same) for *any* two points in a data set, the points will lie on a straight line. That is, $y$ is a **linear** function of $x$. Conversely, if all the points of a data set lie on a straight line when graphed, the average rate of change of $y$ with respect to $x$ will be constant for any two data points.

   **6.** From the graph in Problem 5, would you conclude that the number of chirps per minute is a linear function of the temperature? Explain.

As you will see in the following activities, many situations in the world around us can be modeled by linear functions.

## Slope of a Line

You have seen that the average rate of change between any two points on a line is always the same constant value. This value has a geometric interpretation as well— it describes the "steepness" of the line and is called the **slope** of the line.

   **7. a.** What is the slope of the line in the snowy tree cricket situation?

   **b.** Because the slope of this line is positive, what can you conclude about the direction of the line as the independent variable (temperature) increases in value?

   **c.** What is the practical meaning of slope in this situation?

The slope of a line is often denoted by the letter $m$. It can be determined by selecting *any* two points on the line and calculating the average rate of change between them. That is, if $(x_1, y_1)$ and $(x_2, y_2)$ represent two points on a line, then the slope of the line is calculated by the following formula:

$$m = slope = \frac{\Delta y}{\Delta x} = \frac{y_2 - y_1}{x_2 - x_1}, \text{ and where } x_1 \neq x_2$$

**Example 1** *Determine the slope of the line containing the points (1, −2) and (3, 8).*

SOLUTION

Let $x_1 = 1$, $y_1 = -2$, $x_2 = 3$, and $y_2 = 8$; so

$$m = \frac{y_2 - y_1}{x_2 - x_1} = \frac{8 - (-2)}{3 - 1} = \frac{10}{2} = \frac{5}{1} = 5.$$

**8.** Determine the slope of the line in the snowy tree cricket situation using delta notation. Select any two points from the table preceding Problem 1 for $(x_1, y_1)$ and $(x_2, y_2)$.

On a graph, slope is the ratio of two distances. The $\Delta y$ represents a vertical distance (rise) from one point to another point on the same line. The $\Delta x$ represents a horizontal distance (run) between the same points. For example, in the snowy tree cricket situation, the slope of the line between the points (55, 60) and (56, 64) as well as between (56, 64) and (57, 68) is $\frac{4}{1}$, as shown on the following graph.

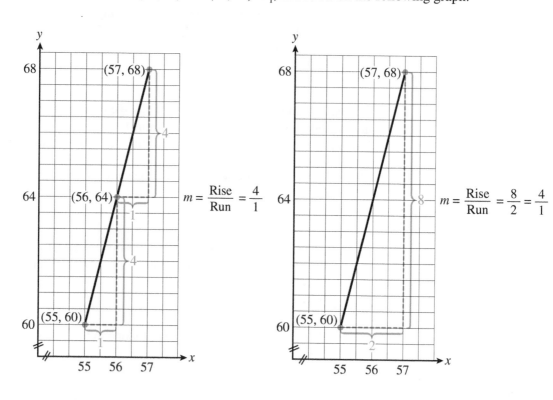

**DEFINITION**

From its geometric meaning, slope may be determined from a graph by the formula:

$$m = \text{slope} = \frac{\text{rise}}{\text{run}} = \frac{\text{distance up } (+) \text{ or down } (-)}{\text{distance right } (+) \text{ or left } (-)}$$

The slope can be used to locate additional points on a graph, as demonstrated in Problem 9.

**9. a.** Consider the line containing the point $(-6, 4)$ and having slope $\frac{3}{4}$. Plot the point and then determine two additional points on the line. Draw a line through these points.

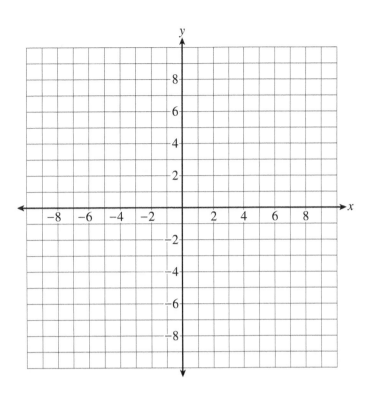

**b.** Which line increases most rapidly: a line with slope 3 or a line having slope $\frac{3}{4}$? Explain.

The graph of a line having positive slope rises from left to right. Such a line represents an **increasing function**.

## Decreasing Linear Function

While on a trip, you notice that the video screen on the airplane, in addition to showing movies and news, records your altitude (in kilometers) above the ground. As the plane starts its descent (at time $x = 0$), you record the following data:

### Cleared for a Landing

| TIME, $x$ (min) | ALTITUDE, $y$ (km) |
|---|---|
| 0 | 12 |
| 2 | 10 |
| 4 | 8 |
| 6 | 6 |
| 8 | 4 |
| 10 | 2 |

**10. a.** What is the average rate of change in the altitude of the plane from two to six minutes into the descent? Pay careful attention to the sign of this rate of change.

**b.** What are the units of measurement of this average rate of change?

**c.** Determine the average rate of change over several other input intervals.

**d.** What is the significance of the signs of these average rates of change?

**e.** Based on your calculation in parts a and c, do you think that the data lie on a single straight line? Explain.

**f.** What is the practical meaning of slope in this situation?

**g.** By how much does the altitude of the plane change for each three-minute change in time during the descent?

**11. a.** Plot the data points from the table preceding Problem 10, and verify that the points lie on a line. What is the slope of the line?

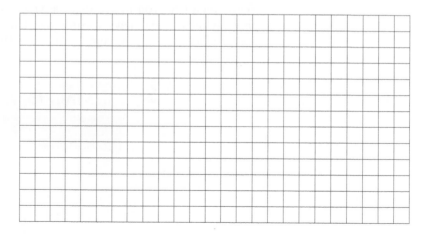

**b.** Explain to a classmate the method you used to determine the slope in part a.

**12. a.** The slope of the line for the descent function in this activity is negative. What does this tell you about how the altitude changes as the time increases in value?

**b.** Is the descent function an increasing or decreasing function?

## Zero Slope

**13. a.** Your town has just authorized funding to build a new ramp for skateboarding. When the ramp is complete, you and your friends will be able to pay a monthly fee of $12.50 to use the ramp for as many hours as you wish. Complete the table of values below where $x$ is the number of hours per month that each person who pays the fee uses the ramp and $y$ is the total cost per month for each person.

| x, TIME (in hours) | 5 | 10 | 15 | 20 |
|---|---|---|---|---|
| y, COST (in $) | | | | |

**b.** Use the data points from the table to sketch the graph.

**c.** Describe the graph in words.

**d.** Choose two ordered pairs from part a and determine the slope, $m$, of the line. What is the practical meaning of the slope in this situation?

**e.** The equation of the horizontal line in part b is $y = 12.50$. Does this make sense? Explain.

> **DEFINITION**
>
> A graph in which the output $y$ is a constant or, equivalently, $f(x)$ is a constant, is a **horizontal line**. The equation of a horizontal line is $y = c$ (or $f(x) = c$), where $c$ is some fixed real number. The slope of any horizontal line is zero.

14. Determine three ordered pairs that satisfy each of the following equations. Then sketch the graph of each constant function on the same coordinate axes.

    **a.** $y = -2$            **b.** $f(x) = 1$

    **c.** $g(x) = \frac{5}{2}$

## Undefined Slope

15. You apply for a part-time job at the skateboarding rink to help cover your weekly expenses. The following table gives your weekly salary, $x$, and corresponding weekly expenses, $y$, for a typical month.

| $x$, WEEKLY SALARY IN DOLLARS | 70 | 70 | 70 | 70 |
|---|---|---|---|---|
| $y$, WEEKLY EXPENSES IN DOLLARS | 45 | 35 | 50 | 60 |

    **a.** Sketch a graph of the given data points.

**b.** Describe the graph in words.

**c.** Choose two ordered pairs from the table and determine the slope, *m*.

**d.** Is *y* a function of *x*? Explain using the definition of a function.

**e.** Do the ordered pairs in the table satisfy the equation $x = 70$? Explain why or why not.

**f.** Can you graph the equation $x = 70$ using your graphing calculator? Explain.

> **DEFINITION**
>
> A graph in which *x* is a constant is a **vertical line**. The equation of a vertical line is $x = a$, where *a* is some fixed real number. The slope of a vertical line is **undefined**.

**16.** Determine three ordered pairs that satisfy each of the following equations, and then sketch each graph.

   **a.** $x = -2$

   **b.** $x = 4$

   **c.** $x = \dfrac{5}{2}$

1. A **linear function** is one whose average rate of change of $y$ with respect to $x$ from any one data point to any other data point is always the same (constant) value.

2. The **graph** of a linear function is a line whose slope is the constant rate of change of the function.

3. The **slope of a line segment** joining two points $(x_1, y_1)$ and $(x_2, y_2)$ is denoted by $m$ and can be calculated using the formula $m = \dfrac{\Delta y}{\Delta x} = \dfrac{y_2 - y_1}{x_2 - x_1}$. Geometrically, $\Delta y$ represents a vertical distance (rise), and $\Delta x$ represents a horizontal distance (run).

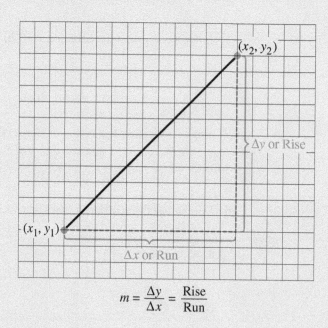

$(x_2, y_2)$

$\Delta y$ or Rise

$(x_1, y_1)$

$\Delta x$ or Run

$$m = \frac{\Delta y}{\Delta x} = \frac{\text{Rise}}{\text{Run}}$$

Therefore, $m = \dfrac{\Delta y}{\Delta x} = \dfrac{\text{rise}}{\text{run}}$.

4. The graph of every linear function with **positive slope** is an increasing line, rising to the right. The function is then said to be an **increasing function**.

5. The graph of every linear function with **negative slope** is an decreasing line, falling to the right. The function is called a **decreasing function**.

6. The graph of $y = c$ or $f(x) = c$ is a **horizontal line**. In this case, $f$ is called a constant function. Every point on this line has a $y$-coordinate equal to $c$. A horizontal line has slope of zero.

7. The graph of $x = a$ is a **vertical line**. Every point on this line has an $x$-coordinate equal to $a$. The slope of a vertical line is undefined.

1. In a science lab, you collect the following sets of data. Which of the four data sets are linear functions? If linear, determine the slope.

a.

| TIME (sec) | 0 | 10 | 20 | 30 | 40 |
|---|---|---|---|---|---|
| TEMPERATURE (°C) | 12 | 17 | 22 | 27 | 32 |

b.

| TIME (sec) | 0 | 10 | 20 | 30 | 40 |
|---|---|---|---|---|---|
| TEMPERATURE (°C) | 41 | 23 | 5 | −10 | −20 |

c.

| TIME (sec) | 3 | 5 | 8 | 10 | 15 |
|---|---|---|---|---|---|
| TEMPERATURE (°C) | 12 | 16 | 24 | 28 | 36 |

d.

| TIME (sec) | 3 | 9 | 12 | 18 | 21 |
|---|---|---|---|---|---|
| TEMPERATURE (°C) | 25 | 23 | 22 | 20 | 19 |

2. a. You are a member of a health and fitness club. A special diet and exercise program has been developed for you by the club's registered dietitian and your personal trainer. You weigh 181 pounds and would like to lose 2 pounds every week. Complete the following table of values for your desired weight each week:

| N, NUMBER OF WEEKS | 0 | 1 | 2 | 3 | 4 |
|---|---|---|---|---|---|
| W, DESIRED WEIGHT (lb) | | | | | |

**b.** Plot the data points.

**c.** Explain why your desired weight is a linear function of time. What is the slope of the line containing the five data points?

**d.** What is the practical meaning of slope in this situation?

**e.** How long will it take to reach your ideal weight of 168 pounds?

3. Your aerobics instructor informs you that to receive full physical benefit from exercising, your heart rate must be maintained at a certain level for at least twelve minutes. The proper exercise heart rate for a healthy person, called the target heart rate, is determined by the person's age. The relationship between these two quantities is illustrated by the data in the following table.

| A, AGE (years) | 20 | 30 | 40 | 50 | 60 |
|---|---|---|---|---|---|
| R, TARGET HEART RATE (beats per minute) | 140 | 133 | 126 | 119 | 112 |

**a.** Does the data in the table indicate that the target heart rate is a linear function of age? Explain.

**b.** What is the slope of the line for this data? What are the units?

c. What is the practical domain for age, $A$?

d. Plot the data points on coordinate axes where both axes start with zero. Connect the points with a line.

4. Determine the slope of each of the following lines:

i.

ii.

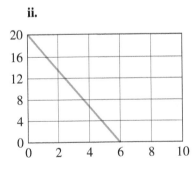

**5.** Each question refers to the graph that accompanies it. The graphed line in each grid

   **a.** How fast is the car traveling? Explain how you obtained your result.

   **b.** How can you determine visually from the following graph which car is going faster? Verify your answer to the first question by calculating the speed of each car.

   **c.** Describe in words the movement of the car that is represented by the following graph:

**6. a.** Determine the slope of each of the following lines:

  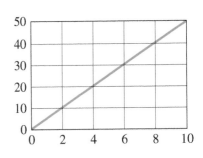

 

**b.** At first glance, the three graphs in part a may appear to represent the same line. Do they?

**7.** For each of the following, determine three additional points on the line. Then sketch a graph of the line.

**a.** A line contains the point $(-5, 10)$ and has slope $\frac{2}{3}$.

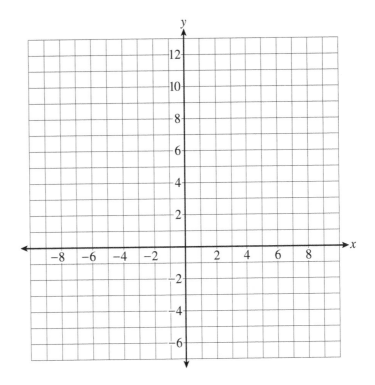

**b.** A line contains the point $(3, -4)$ and has slope 5.

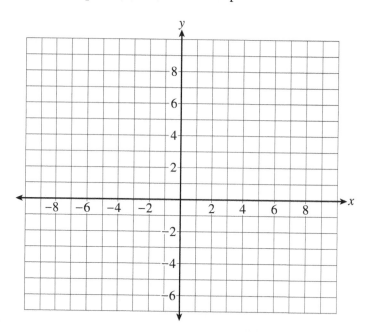

8. The concept of slope arises in many practical applications. When designing and building roads, engineers and surveyors need to be concerned about the grade of the road. The grade, usually expressed as a percent, is one way to describe the steepness of the finished surface of the road. For example, a 5% grade means that the road has a slope (rise over run) of $0.05 = \dfrac{5}{100}$.

5 ft

100 ft

**a.** If a road has a 5% upward grade over a 1000-foot run, how much higher will you be at the end of that run than at the beginning?

**b.** What is the grade of a road that rises 26 feet over a distance of 500 feet?

9. The American National Standards Institute (ANSI) requires that the slope for a wheelchair ramp does not exceed $\frac{1}{12}$.

    **a.** Does a ramp that is 160 in. long and 10 in. high meet the requirements of ANSI? Explain.

    **b.** A ramp for a wheelchair must be 20 inches high. Determine the minimum length of the ramp so that it meets the ANSI requirement.

    **c.** Are there any wheelchair ramps in your school? If so, determine a way to measure the slope. What is the slope?

10. **a.** Sketch the graph of the horizontal line through the point $(-2, 3)$.

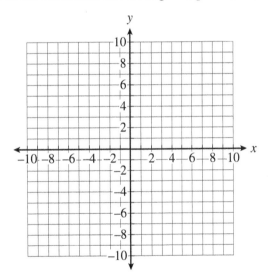

    **b.** Write the equation of a horizontal line through the point $(-2, 3)$.

    **c.** What is the slope of the line?

    **d.** Does the graph represent a function? Explain.

**11. a.** Sketch the graph of the vertical line through $(-2, 3)$.

**b.** Does the graph represent a function? Explain.

**c.** Write the equation of a vertical line through the point $(-2, 3)$.

**d.** What is the slope of the line?

**12.** Explain the difference between a line with a zero slope and a line with an undefined slope.

**13.** You are retained as a consultant for a major computer company. You receive $2000 per month as a fee no matter how many hours you work.

**a.** Using $x$ to represent the number of hours you work each month, write an equation to represent the total amount received from the company each month.

**b.** Complete the following table of values.

| HOURS WORKED PER MONTH | 15 | 25 | 35 |
|---|---|---|---|
| FEE PER MONTH (in $) | | | |

**c.** Use your graphing calculator to sketch the graph of this function.

**d.** What is the slope of the line? What is the practical meaning of the slope in this situation?

**e.** Describe the graph of the function.

## ACTIVITY 2.3
*Depreciation*

### OBJECTIVES

1. Identify whether a situation can be modeled by a linear function.

2. Determine *x*- and *y*-intercepts of a graph.

3. Identify the practical meaning of *x*- and *y*-intercepts.

4. Develop the slope-intercept model of an equation of a line.

5. Use the slope-intercept formula to determine *x*- and *y*-intercepts.

6. Determine the zeros of a linear function.

You have decided to buy a new Honda Accord LX, but you are concerned about the value of the car depreciating over time. You search the Internet and obtain the following information at www.intellichoice.com:

2008 Accord LX

- Suggested retail price          $20,025
- Depreciation per year          $1,385 (assume constant)

**1. a.** Complete the following table in which *V* represents the value of the car after *n* years of ownership.

### Accordingly

| *n*, YEARS | *V*, VALUE IN DOLLARS |
|------------|------------------------|
| 0          |                        |
| 1          |                        |
| 2          |                        |
| 3          |                        |
| 5          |                        |
| 8          |                        |

**b.** Is the value of the car a function of the number of years of ownership? Explain.

**c.** What is the independent variable? What is the dependent variable?

**2. a.** Select two ordered pairs of the form (*n*, *V*) from the table in Problem 1 and determine the average rate of change.

**b.** What are the units of measure of the average rate of change?

**c.** What is the practical meaning of the sign of the average rate of change?

**d.** Select two different ordered pairs and compute the average rate of change.

**e.** Select two ordered pairs not used in parts a or d, and compute the average rate of change.

**f.** Using the results in parts a, d, and e, what can you infer about the average rate of change over any interval of time?

**3. a.** Is the value, $V$, of the car a linear function of the number of years, $n$, of ownership? Explain using the definition of linear function.

**b.** Is this function increasing, decreasing, or constant?

## Graph of a Linear Function

**4.** Consider the ordered pairs of the form $(n, V)$, and plot each ordered pair in Problem 1 on an appropriately scaled and labeled set of axes. Connect the points to see if there is a pattern.

The graph of a linear function is a nonvertical line. Remember that the constant average rate of change is called the **slope** of the line and is denoted by the letter $m$.

**5. a.** What is the slope of the line graphed in Problem 4?

**b.** What is the relationship between the slope of the line and the average rate of change?

**c.** What is the practical meaning of slope in this situation?

## Vertical Intercept (y-intercept)

> **DEFINITION**
>
> In general, the **vertical intercept** is the point where the graph crosses, or intercepts, the vertical axis. If the dependent variable is represented by $y$, the vertical intercept is called the **y-intercept**. The corresponding $x$-value of the $y$-intercept is always zero.

**6. a.** Using the table of data in Problem 1 or the graph in Problem 4, determine the $V$-intercept. Note that the dependent variable in the car depreciation situation is represented by $V$, the value of the car. Therefore, the vertical intercept is called the $v$-intercept.

**b.** What is the practical meaning of the $v$-intercept in this situation? Include units.

## Slope-Intercept Form of a Linear Equation

**7. a.** Review how you determined the value, $V$, of the car in Problem 1 for a given number of years, $n$, of ownership. Write an equation for $V$ in terms of $n$ that models this situation.

**b.** Use your graphing calculator to sketch a graph of this equation. Use the window Xmin $= -2$, Xmax $= 16$, Ymin $= -500$, and Ymax $= 25,000$.

**c.** How does this graph compare to your graph in Problem 4?

**8.** Recall that the slope of your line is $m = -1385$ and the $V$-intercept is $(0, 20,025)$. How is this information contained in the equation of the line you determined in Problem 7a?

> **DEFINITION**
>
> The coordinates of all points $(x, y)$ on the line with slope $m$ and $y$-intercept $(0, b)$ satisfy the equation
>
> $$y = mx + b \quad \text{or} \quad y = b + mx.$$
>
> This is called the **slope-intercept form** of the equation of a line.

Note that the coefficient of $x$, which is $m$, is the *slope* of the line. The constant term, $b$, is the *y-coordinate of the y-intercept*. If $f(x)$ replaces $y$, the equation $y = mx + b$ can be written as

$$f(x) = mx + b.$$

**Example 1**    *The slope-intercept form of the equation of the line with slope 3 and vertical intercept $(0, -6)$ is $y = 3x - 6$. Using function notation and replacing $y$ with $f(x)$, the equation becomes $f(x) = 3x - 6$.*

**9.** Identify the slope and $y$-intercept of the line whose equation is given. Write the $y$-intercept as an ordered pair.

   **a.** $y = -2x + 5$

   **b.** $s = \frac{3}{4}t + 2$

   **c.** $q = 2 - r$

   **d.** $y = \frac{5}{6} + \frac{x}{3}$

## Horizontal Intercepts (*x*-intercepts)

**DEFINITION**

In general, a **horizontal intercept** of a graph is a point where the graph meets or crosses the horizontal axis. If the independent variable is represented by $x$, the horizontal intercept is called the **x-intercept**. The $y$-value of the $x$-intercept is always zero.

**Example 2**    *Consider the equation $y = 2x - 10$.*

**a.** The $y$-intercept occurs where the line crosses the vertical axis, i.e., where $x = 0$. Letting $x = 0$, $y = 2(0) - 10$ or $y = -10$. The $y$-intercept is $(0, -10)$.

**b.** The $x$-intercept occurs where the line crosses the horizontal axis, that is, where $y = 0$.

Letting $y = 0$,

$$0 = 2x - 10$$
$$\underline{+10 \qquad\quad +10} \qquad \text{Add 10 to each side.}$$
$$10 = 2x$$
$$\frac{10}{2} = \frac{2x}{2} \qquad \text{Divide each side by 2.}$$
$$5 = x$$

Therefore, the $x$-intercept is $(5, 0)$.

**c.** You can now sketch a graph of $y = 2x - 10$ by plotting the x- and y-intercepts and connecting the points.

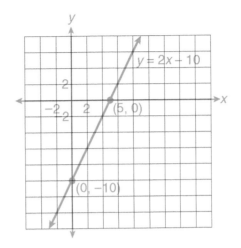

**10. a.** Determine the n-intercept of the graph of the car value equation $V = -1385n + 20{,}025$.

**b.** What is the practical significance of the n-intercept? Include units.

## Converting Celsius to Fahrenheit

**11.** The temperature on a warm summer day may be 27°. Your refrigerator is set at 5°. You set your oven to 180° to cook a turkey. If these temperatures seem strange, it is because they are measured on the Celsius scale. If the TV weather forecaster says it is going to be 65°F tomorrow, you know what that temperature will feel like and can dress accordingly. How should you dress if the reporter says it will be 10°C? Most of us need to convert Celsius to Fahrenheit so we can better understand the temperature. The equation that relates Celsius measure to Fahrenheit measure is:

$$F = 1.8C + 32,$$

where $C$ is the Celsius measure and $F$ is the Fahrenheit measure.

**a.** Use the equation to complete the following table:

| C | −10 | 0 | 5 | 10 | 27 | 100 |
|---|-----|---|---|----|----|-----|
| F |     |   |   |    |    |     |

**b.** Sketch a graph of the equation $F = 1.8C + 32$ by plotting the ordered pairs in part a.

**c.** Determine the average rate of change of $F$ as $C$ increases from 0 to 100.

**d.** What is the slope of the line? How does the slope compare to the average rate of change in part c?

**e.** Is the function increasing, decreasing, or constant?

**f.** Determine the intercepts of the graph using the equation of the line. Verify your results using the graph of the line.

**g.** What is the practical significance of each intercept in this situation?

## Zeros of a Function

The $x$-values of the $x$-intercepts of a function's graph are called the **zeros** of the function. To determine the zeros of a function defined by $f(x) = 2x - 6$, proceed as if you were trying to determine the $x$-intercepts of the graph. Simply set $f(x) = 0$ and solve for $x$.

**12.** Determine the zeros of the function defined by $f(x) = 2x - 6$.

---

**SUMMARY**
Activity 2.3

**1.** A function for which the average rate of change between any pair of points remains constant is called a **linear function**.

**2.** The graph of a linear function is a nonvertical line. The constant average rate of change is called the **slope** and is denoted by the letter $m$ (from the French verb *mon-ter*, "to climb" or "rise").

3. The **slope** of a line segment joining two points $(x_1, y_1)$ and $(x_2, y_2)$ is denoted by $m$ and is defined by $m = \dfrac{y_2 - y_1}{x_2 - x_1}$, where $x_1 \neq x_2$.

4. The **y-intercept** $(0, b)$ of a graph is the point where the graph crosses the y-axis. The **x-intercept** $(a, 0)$ of a graph is the point, where the graph crosses the x-axis.

5. The x-value of the x-intercept of the graph of a function is called a **zero** of the function.

6. The slope-intercept form of the equation of a line is $y = mx + b$.

7. To determine the $b$-value of the y-intercept $(0, b)$ from $y = mx + b$, set $x = 0$ and solve for $y$.

8. To determine the $a$-value of the x-intercept $(a, 0)$ from $y = mx + b$, set $y = 0$ and solve for $x$.

9. If the **slope** of a linear function is **positive**, the graph of the function increases (rises to the right).

10. If the **slope** of a linear function is **negative**, the graph of the function decreases (falls to the right).

## EXERCISES
### Activity 2.3

1. Determine whether the following functions are linear. If they are, determine the constant average rate of change, called the slope of the line.

   a.

   | x | y |
   |---|---|
   | 0 | −1 |
   | 1 | 9 |
   | 2 | 19 |

   b.

   | x | 2 | 4 | 6 |
   |---|---|---|---|
   | y | 11 | 8 | −1 |

   c. $\{(-2, 18), (2, 9), (6, 0)\}$

2. Determine whether the following tables contain data that represent a linear function. Assume that the first row of the table is the x-variable and the second row is the y-variable. Explain your reasoning.

   a. You owe your grandmother $1000. She paid for your first semester at community college. The conditions of the loan are that you must pay her back the whole amount in one payment using a simple interest rate of 6% per year. She doesn't care in which year you pay her. The table contains data values to represent how much money you will owe your grandmother one, two, three, or four years later.

   | YEAR | 1 | 2 | 3 | 4 |
   |---|---|---|---|---|
   | AMOUNT OWED (in $) | 1060 | 1120 | 1180 | 1240 |

**b.** You decide to invest $1000 of your 401(k) funds into an account that pays 5.5% interest compounded continuously. The table contains data that represent the amount an initial investment of $1000 is worth at the end of each year.

| YEAR | 1 | 2 | 3 | 4 | 5 |
|---|---|---|---|---|---|
| TOTAL INVESTMENT (in $) | 1057 | 1116 | 1179 | 1246 | 1317 |

**3.** You belong to a health-and-fitness center. You and your friends are enrolled in the center's weight-loss program. The charts contain data that represent the weight over a four-week period for you and your two friends. Determine which charts contain data that is linear and explain why.

**a.**

| WEEK | 1 | 2 | 3 | 4 |
|---|---|---|---|---|
| WEIGHT (in lb) | 150 | 147 | 144 | 141 |

**b.**

| WEEK | 1 | 2 | 3 | 4 |
|---|---|---|---|---|
| WEIGHT (in lb) | 183 | 178 | 174 | 171 |

**c.**

| WEEK | 1 | 2 | 3 | 4 |
|---|---|---|---|---|
| WEIGHT (in lb) | 160 | 160 | 160 | 160 |

**4.** Consider the equation $y = -2x + 5$.

**a.** Construct a table of five ordered pairs that satisfy the equation.

| x | | | | | |
|---|---|---|---|---|---|
| y | | | | | |

**b.** What is the slope of the line represented by the equation?

**c.** What is the y-intercept?

**d.** What is the x-intercept?

**e.** Sketch a graph of the line using each of the following methods:

Method 1:  Plot the five ordered pairs.

Method 2:  Plot one point and use the slope to obtain additional points on the line.

Method 3:  Plot the intercepts.

**5. a.** Determine the slope of the line that goes through the points $(2, -7)$ and $(0, 5)$.

**b.** Determine the $y$-intercept of this line.

**c.** What is the equation of the line through these points? Write the equation in function notation.

**d.** What is the $x$-intercept?

**6.** A car is traveling on a highway. The distance (in miles) from its destination and the time (in hours) is given by the equation $d = 420 - 65t$.

**a.** What is the $d$-intercept of the line?

**b.** What is the practical meaning of the $d$-intercept?

**c.** What is the slope of the line represented by the equation?

**d.** What is the practical meaning of the slope determined in part c?

**e.** What is the *t*-intercept?

**f.** What is the practical domain of this function?

**g.** Graph the equation, both by hand and with your graphing calculator, to verify your answers.

7. The following table gives a jet's height above the ground (in feet) as a function of time (in seconds) as the jet makes its landing approach to the runway:

| t (in seconds) | h (in feet) |
|---|---|
| 0 | 3500 |
| 5 | 3000 |
| 10 | 2500 |
| 15 | 2000 |
| 20 | 1500 |
| 25 | 1000 |

**a.** Is this function linear? Explain.

**b.** Calculate the slope using the formula $m = \dfrac{\Delta h}{\Delta t}$.

**c.** What is the significance of the sign of the slope in part b?

**d.** Determine where the graph crosses the *h*-axis.

**e.** Write the equation in slope-intercept form.

**f.** Determine the *t*-intercept. What is its significance in this situation?

**8.** Determine the zeros of the function whose equation is given.

   **a.** $y = 4x + 2$ 　　　　　　　　　　**b.** $y = \dfrac{x}{2} - 3$

**9. a.** Use your graphing calculator to graph the linear functions defined by the following equations: $y = 2x - 3, y = 2x, y = 2x + 2, y = 2x + 5$. Discuss the similarities and the differences of the graphs.

   **b.** Use your graphing calculator to graph the linear functions defined by the following equations: $y = x - 2, y = 2x - 2, y = -x - 2, y = -2$. Discuss the similarities and the differences in the graphs.

   **c.** Use your graphing calculator to graph the linear functions defined by the following equations: $y = 3x, y = -2x, y = \frac{1}{2}x, y = -5x$. Discuss the similarities and differences in the graphs.

**ACTIVITY 2.4**

Family of
Functions

**OBJECTIVES**

1. Identify the effect of changes in the equation of a line on its graph.

2. Identify the effect of changes in the graph of a line on its equation.

3. Identify the change in the graph and equation of a basic function as a translation, reflection, or vertical stretch or shrink.

A primary objective of this textbook is to help you develop a familiarity with the graphs, equations, and properties of a variety of functions, including linear, quadratic, exponential, and logarithmic. You will group these functions into families and identify the similarities within a family and the differences between families.

The family of functions being investigated in this chapter is linear functions. As you have discovered in previous activities, there are strong relationships between the equation of a line and its corresponding graph. Recognizing such relationships will help you identify patterns in the equations and graphs of other families of functions.

## Vertical and Horizontal Shifts Revisited

**1.** Determine the slope and intercepts of the line having equation $y = 2x$.

**2. a.** Using a graphing calculator, sketch a graph in the standard window of each of the following. What do you observe?

$$y_1 = 2x, \ y_2 = 2x + 2, \ y_3 = 2x + 6$$

**b.** Now, sketch a graph of each of the following. What do you observe?

$$y_1 = 2x, \ y_2 = 2x - 3, \ y_3 = 2x - 5$$

**c.** The equations in parts a and b are of the form $y = 2x + c$, where $c$ is a constant. What is the effect of $c$ on the graph of $y = 2x$?

**d.** The graph of $y = 2x + 6$ is a vertical shift of the graph of $y = 2x$ upward by 6 units. As a result, which intercept of the graph is changed by exactly 6 units?

**e.** Does adding a constant $c$ to the output value have any effect on the slope of the line?

**3. a.** Use a graphing calculator to sketch a graph of $y_1 = 2x$, $y_2 = 2(x + 1)$, $y_3 = 2(x + 4)$, and $y_4 = 2(x + 5.5)$. What do you observe?

**b.** The equations in part a are of the form $y = 2(x + c)$, where $c > 0$. What is the effect of $c$ on the graph of $y = 2x$?

**c.** Describe how the graph of $y = 2(x - 3)$ can be obtained from the graph of $y = 2x$. Verify using a graphing calculator.

**d.** The graph of $y = 2(x + 4)$ is a horizontal shift of the graph $y = 2x$ horizontally to the left 4 units. As a result, which intercept of the graph of $y = 2x$ changed by 4 units?

**e.** Does adding a constant $c$ to the input $x$ have any effect on the slope of the line $y = 2x$?

Now, look carefully at the graphs of $y_1 = 2x$, $y_2 = 2x + 6$, $y_3 = 2(x + 3)$ from Problems 2 and 3. Note that a horizontal shift 3 units to the left of the graph of $y = 2x$, results in the same graph as a vertical shift upward 6 units. Is this true for all functions? Problem 4 uses the squaring function to demonstrate that this is not generally true.

**4. a.** Using a graphing calculator, sketch a graph of each of the following in the standard window.

$$y_1 = x^2, y_2 = x^2 + 6, y_3 = (x + 3)^2$$

**b.** For the squaring function, does a horizontal shift 3 units to the left of the graph result in the same graph as a vertical shift 6 units upward?

## Reflections

**5. a.** Consider the linear function defined by $y = x$. Using a graphing calculator, graph the equation $y = -x$ in the same standard window as $y = x$. What do you observe?

> The graph of $y = -x$ is a **reflection** of the graph of $y = x$ across the x-axis.

**b.** When a graph is reflected across the x-axis, the x-value of each point remains the same. What happens to the corresponding y-values?

> In general, if the graph of $y = f(x)$ is reflected across the x-axis, then the equation of the resulting graph is $y = -f(x)$. The graphs of $y = f(x)$ and $y = -f(x)$ are mirror images across the x-axis. The y-values of the graph of $y = f(x)$ changes in sign. The x-values remain the same.

**6.** Reflect each of the following graphs across the x-axis. If a formula is given for the graph, write the equation of the reflected graph. Where possible, verify using a graphing calculator.

**a.** $y = 2x$

**b.** $y = x^2$

**c.**

**d.**

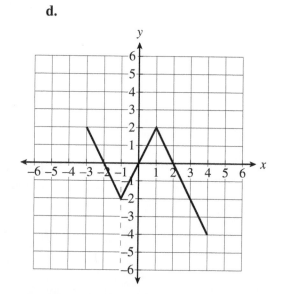

**7. a.** Determine the slope and intercepts of the graph of $y = f(x) = 3x + 6$.

**b.** Graph the function defined by $y = 3x + 6$. Verify using a graphing calculator.

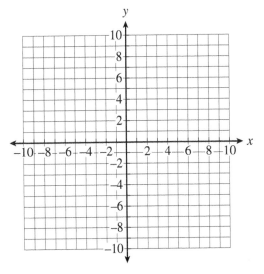

**c.** On the graph in part b, reflect the graph of $y = 3x + 6$ across the $x$-axis.

**d.** Write the equation of the reflected graph in part c.

**e.** Use a graphing calculator to verify the graph in part d.

**f.** Determine the slope and intercepts of the reflected graph.

**g.** Compare the slopes and intercepts of the graph of $y = 3x + 6$ and its reflection across the $x$-axis.

**8.** Consider the graph of the function defined by $y = f(x) = 3x + 6$ in Problem 7.

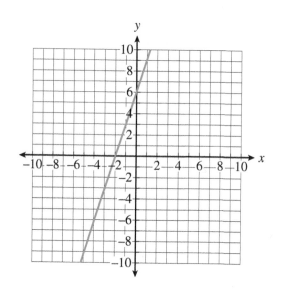

**a.** Determine an equation for $y_2 = f(-x)$. That is, replace $x$ with $-x$ in the equation for $f$.

**b.** Determine the slope and intercepts of the graph of $y_2 = f(-x)$.

**c.** Sketch a graph of $y = f(-x)$ on the same coordinate axis as $y = f(x)$.

**d.** How can the graph of $y = f(-x)$ be obtained from the graph of $y = f(x)$?

The graph of $y_2 = f(-x) = -3x + 6$ is a reflection of the graph of $y = f(x) = 3x + 6$ across the $y$-axis.

**e.** When a graph is reflected across the $y$-axis, the $y$-values of each point remain the same. What happens to the corresponding $x$-values?

**f.** Compare the slopes and intercepts of the graph of $f(x) = 3x + 6$ and its reflection across the $y$-axis $f(-x) = -3x + 6$.

**9.** Reflect each of the following across the $y$-axis. If a formula is given for the graph, write the equation of the reflected graph. Where possible, verify using a graphing calculator.

**a.** $y = 2x - 8$

**b.** $y = x^2$

**c.**

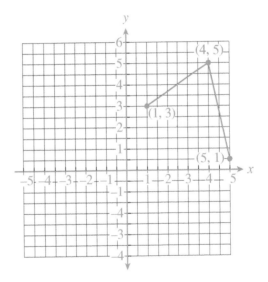

## Vertical Stretch and Shrink of a Graph

You have just purchased a stereo system that includes an amplifier. The purpose of the amplifier is to take the signal from a component part (such as the compact disc player), and boost the signal in order to power a set of speakers.

The following graph shows a situation where a sound has been amplified 5 times.

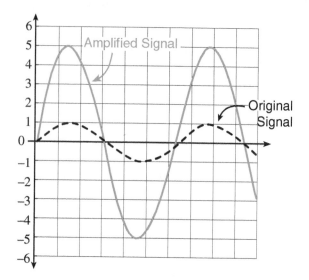

The transformation of the graph of the original signal into the graph of the amplified signal is called a **vertical stretch**. Note that the height of the graph of the amplified signal is 5 times as high as the original signal. The number 5 is called the **stretch factor**. Therefore, if $y = g(x)$ is the equation of the original signal, the equation of the amplified graph is $y = 5\,g(x)$.

In general, if the graph of $y = f(x)$ is vertically stretched by a factor of $a$, then the equation of the stretched graph is $y = a\,f(x)$. The number $a$ is called the stretch factor. The $y$-value of each point in the graph of $y = f(x)$ is multiplied by a factor of $a$. The $x$-values remain fixed.

How does a vertical stretch of the graph of a line affect the properties of the graph?

**10. a.** Using a graphing calculator, sketch a graph of each of the following in a standard window. What do you observe?

$$y_1 = x, \; y_2 = 2x, \; y_3 = 5x$$

**b.** How does the vertical stretch of the graph of $y = x$ affect its graph?

**11. a.** Determine the slope and intercepts of the graph of $y = g(x) = 2x + 3$

**b.** Graph the function defined by $y = 2x + 3$. Verify using a graphing calculator.

**c.** Write an equation that represents a vertical stretch of the graph of $y = 2x + 3$ by a factor of 3.

**d.** Graph the line having equation in part c on the same coordinate axis as the graph of $y = 2x + 3$. Verify using a graphing calculator.

**e.** Determine the slope and intercepts of the vertically stretched graph.

**f.** Compare the slopes and intercepts with the graph of the original function.

**12. a.** Using a graphing calculator, sketch a graph of each of the following in a standard window.

$$y_1 = x, y_2 = 0.5x$$

**b.** Is the graph of $y = 0.5x$ a vertical stretch of the graph of $y = x$? Explain.

In general, if $a$ is a positive constant, then the graph of $y = a f(x)$ is the graph of $y = f(x)$
  **i.** vertically shrunk by a factor of $a$, if $0 < a < 1$.
  **ii.** vertically stretched by a factor of $a$, if $a > 1$.

Vertical and horizontal shifts (also called translations), reflections, and vertical stretches and shrinks are all examples of **transformations**. These are ways in which the graph of a given function can be changed or transformed.

13. If the graph of a line is vertically stretched or shrunk, explain why the x-intercept of the line is not affected? See Problem 11f.

14. The graph of $y = -2x + 1$ can be interpreted as a combination of transformations of the graph of $y = x$. Sketch a graph of $y = -2x + 1$ by performing the following changes in the graph of $y = x$: First, a vertical stretch; second, a reflection; last, a vertical shift. Each transformation should be performed in the natural order of operations. Verify using a graphing calculator.

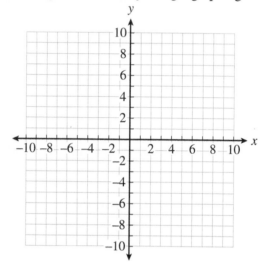

The transformations discussed in this activity can be applied to the graph of any function, as you will see in subsequent activities, as well as some of the exercises that follow.

15. Consider the basic absolute value function, $f(x) = |x|$, which is then changed by four transformations described in parts a–d. To determine the final equation for this function, you will consider one transformation at a time.

   a. Graph the basic absolute value function that has been shifted 3 units to the left.

   Write the equation for the absolute value function that has been shifted 3 units to the left.

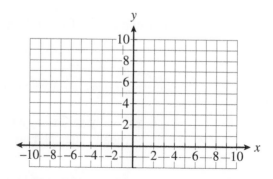

**b.** Graph the function in part a, which is then stretched vertically by a factor of 2.

Write the equation for the function in part a, which is then stretched vertically by a factor of 2.

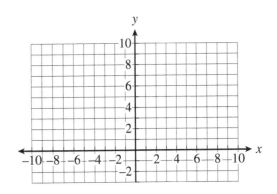

**c.** Graph the function in part b, which is then reflected across the *x*-axis.

Write the equation for the function in part b, which is then reflected across the *x*-axis.

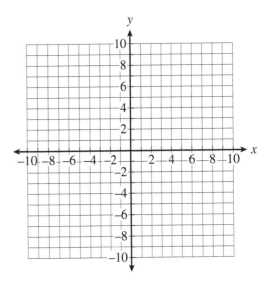

**d.** Finally, graph the function in part c, which is then shifted upward 5 units. Write the equation for this final graph.

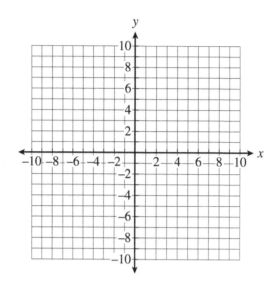

**e.** Check your final function by graphing the equation on your calculator.

<hr>

**SUMMARY**
**Activity 2.4**

1. In a **vertical shift** of a graph, a positive constant is added to (upward shift) or subtracted from (downward shift) each output value. As a result, the graph is moved vertically upward or vertically downward.

2. In a **horizontal shift** of a graph, a positive constant is first added to (shift left) or subtracted from (shift right) each input value. As a result, the graph is moved horizontally to the left or horizontally to the right.

3. In general, if a function is defined by $y = f(x)$, and $c$ is a constant, then the graph of

   **i.** $y = f(x) + c$ is the graph of $y = f(x)$ shifted vertically $|c|$ units. If $c > 0$, then the shift is upward. If $c < 0$, then the shift is downward.

   **ii.** $y = f(x + c)$ is the graph of $y = f(x)$ shifted horizontally $|c|$ units. If $c > 0$, then the shift is to the left. If $c < 0$, the shift is to the right.

4. The graph of $y = -x$ is a **reflection** of the graph of $y = x$ across the $x$-axis.

5. If the graph of $y = f(x)$ is reflected across the $x$-axis, then the equation of the resulting graph is $y = -f(x)$. The graphs of $y = f(x)$ and $y = -f(x)$ are mirror images across the $x$-axis. The $y$-value of each point in the original graph changes sign. The $x$-value of each point remains the same.

6. If the graph of $y = f(x)$ is reflected across the $y$-axis, then the equation of the resulting graph is $y = f(-x)$. The graphs of $y = f(x)$ and $y = f(-x)$ are mirror images across the $y$-axis. The $x$-value of each point in the original graph changes sign. The $y$-value of each point remains the same.

7. If the graph of $y = f(x)$ is vertically stretched by a factor of $a > 0$, then the equation of the stretched graph is $y = af(x)$. The number $a$ is called the **stretch factor**. The $y$-value of each point in the graph of $y = f(x)$ is multiplied by a factor of $a$. The $x$-values remain fixed.

**8.** In general, if a function is defined by $y = f(x)$, and $a$ is a positive constant, then the graph of

   **i.** $y = af(x)$ is the graph of $y = f(x)$ vertically shrunk by a factor of $a$, if $0 < |a| < 1$.

   **ii.** $y = af(x)$ is the graph of $y = f(x)$ vertically stretched by a factor of $a$, if $a > 1$.

**9.** Vertical and horizontal shifts (also called translations), reflections, and vertical stretches and shrinks are all examples of **transformations**.

## EXERCISES
### Activity 2.4

**1.** Describe in words how the basic linear function, $f(x) = x$, is transformed by each equation.

   **a.** $y = 3x$

   **b.** $y = x - 4$

   **c.** $y = -x$

   **d.** $y = \dfrac{1}{2}x + 3$

**2.** Write the equation for the basic squaring function, $f(x) = x^2$, that has been transformed by

   **a.** reflecting across the $x$-axis.

   **b.** shifting down 6 units.

   **c.** stretching vertically by a factor of 4.

   **d.** shifting right 3 units and shrinking vertically by a factor of $\frac{1}{3}$.

Check each equation by graphing on your calculator.

**3.** For each function graphed below, sketch the graph of the new function after it is transformed as described.

    **a.** Shift left 3 and reflect across *x*-axis.

                                                       **b.** Stretch vertically by a factor of 2, then shift down 3 units.

 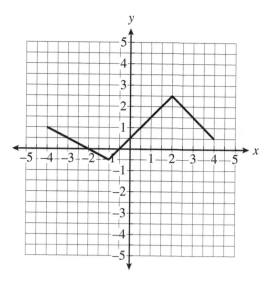

**4.** For each linear function graphed below, describe how $f(x) = x$ is transformed, write the equation for the line, and then check by graphing on your calculator.

    **a.**                                                                 **b.**

**c.**

**d.**

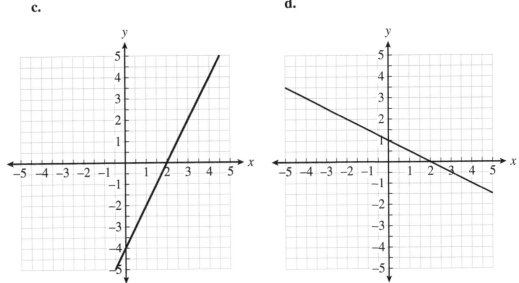

**5.** If the point $(3, -5)$ is on the graph of $y = f(x)$ and the graph is transformed with a vertical stretch by a factor of 5, then reflected across the $x$-axis, what must be the coordinates of one point on the new graph?

**6.** If the point $(-2, 8)$ is on the graph of $y = f(x)$ and the graph is transformed with a vertical shrink by a factor of $\frac{1}{2}$ then shifted down 5 units, what must be the coordinates of one point on the new graph?

**7.** If the point $(-5, 2)$ is on the graph of $y = f(x)$ and the graph is transformed with a horizontal shift of 3 units to the right, then a reflection across the $x$-axis, what must be the coordinates of one point on the new graph?

**ACTIVITY 2.5**

Predicting
Population

**OBJECTIVES**

1. Write an equation for a linear function given its slope and y-intercept.

2. Write linear functions in slope-intercept form $y = mx + b$.

3. Determine the relative error in a measurement or prediction using a linear model.

4. Interpret the slope and y-intercept of linear functions in contextual situations.

5. Use the slope-intercept form of linear equations to solve problems.

According to the U.S. Bureau of the Census, the population of the United States was approximately 132 million in 1940 and 151 million in 1950.

For this activity, assume that the rate of change of population with respect to time is a constant value over the decade from 1940 to 1950. This means you are assuming that the relationship between the independent variable time and the dependent variable population is linear.

**1. a.** Write the given data as ordered pairs of the form $(t, P(t))$, where $t$ is the number of years since 1940 and $P(t)$ is the corresponding population, in millions.

**b.** Plot the two data points, and draw a straight line through them. Label the horizontal axis from 0 to 25 and the vertical axis from 130 to 180.

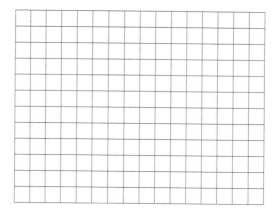

**2. a.** What is the average rate of change of population from $t = 0$ (1940) to $t = 10$ (1950)?

**b.** What is the slope of the line connecting the two points in part a? What is the practical meaning of the slope in this situation?

**3.** What is the $P$-intercept of this line? What is the practical meaning of this intercept in this situation?

**4. a.** Use the slope and $P$-intercept from Problems 2 and 3 to write an equation for the line.

**b.** Assume that the average rate of change you determined in Problem 2 stays the same through 1960. Use the equation in part a to predict the U.S. population in 1960. Also estimate the population in 1960 from the graph.

The **error** in a prediction is the difference between the observed value (actual value that was measured) and the predicted value. The **relative error** of a prediction is the ratio of the error to the observed value. That is,

$$\text{relative error} = \frac{\text{observed value} - \text{predicted value}}{\text{observed value}} = \frac{\text{error}}{\text{observed value}}.$$

**5. a.** The relative error is usually reported as a percent. The actual U.S. population in 1960 was approximately 179 million. What is the *relative error* (expressed as a percent) in your prediction?

**b.** What do you think was the cause of your prediction error?

**6.** You want to develop a population model based on more recent data. The U.S. population was approximately 249 million in 1990 and 281 million in 2000.

**a.** Plot these data points using ordered pairs of the form $(t, P(t))$, where $t$ is the number of years since 1990 (now, $t = 0$ corresponds to 1990). Draw a line through the points.

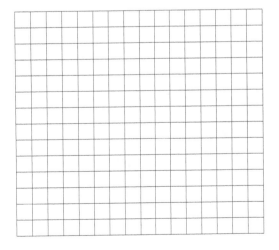

   **b.** Determine the slope of the line in part a. What is the practical meaning of the slope in this situation? How does this slope compare with the slope in Problem 2?

   **c.** In which decade, 1940–1950 or 1990–2000, did the U.S. population increase more rapidly? Explain your answer in terms of slope.

   **d.** Determine the $P$-intercept of the line in part a.

   **e.** Write the equation of the line in part a.

**7. a.** Use the equation $P(t) = 3.2t + 249$, also called a linear model, developed in Problem 6 to predict the population in 2010. What assumptions do you make about the average rate of change of the population in this prediction?

   **b.** According to the linear model in $P(t) = 3.2t + 249$, in what year will the population be 350 million?

---

## SUMMARY
### Activity 2.5

**1.** The **error** in a prediction is the difference between the observed value and the predicted value. The **relative error** in prediction is the ratio of the error to the observed value. That is,

$$\text{relative error} = \frac{\text{observed value} - \text{predicted value}}{\text{observed value}} = \frac{\text{error}}{\text{observed value}}.$$

Relative error is usually reported as a percent.

**EXERCISES**
**Activity 2.5**

**1. a.** Use the equation $P(t) = 3.2t + 249$ developed in Problem 6 to predict the U.S. population in the year 2005. What assumptions are you making about the rate of change of the population in this prediction? Recall that $t$ is the number of years since 1990.

**b.** The actual U.S. population in 2005 was approximately 296 million. What is the relative error in your prediction?

**c.** What do you think was the cause of the prediction error?

**2. a.** According to the U.S. Bureau of the Census, the population of California in 2000 was approximately 34.10 million and was increasing at a rate of approximately 630,000 people per year. Let $P(t)$ represent the California population (in millions) and $t$ represent the number of years since 2000. Complete the following table.

| t | P(t) (in millions) |
|---|---|
| 0 | |
| 1 | |
| 2 | |

**b.** What information in part a indicates that the California population growth is linear with respect to time? What are the slope and vertical intercept of the graph of the population data?

**c.** Write a linear function rule for $P(t)$ in terms of $t$.

**d.** Use the linear function in part c to estimate the population of California in 2004.

**e.** Population data from the State of California Department of Finance is used by California state agencies in developing their programs and policies. The Department of Finance estimated that the population of California in 2004 was approximately 36.59 million. Determine the relative error (as a percent) between your prediction in part d and the estimate actually used by the state of California.

**f.** Use the linear model from part c to predict the population of California in 2010.

**3. a.** The population of Atlanta, Georgia, was 2.96 million in 1990 and 4.11 million in 2000. This information is summarized in the accompanying table, where $t$ is the number of years since 1990 and $P(t)$ represents the population (in millions) at a given time $t$.

| $t$ | $P(t)$ |
|---|---|
| 0 | 2.96 |
| 10 | 4.11 |

Assume that the average rate of change of the population over this ten-year period is constant. Determine this average rate.

**b.** Plot the two data points, and draw a line through them. Label the horizontal axis from 0 to 25 and the vertical axis from 0 to 8.

**c.** Determine the slope and $P$-intercept of the line in part b.

**d.** Write an equation to model Atlanta's population, $P(t)$ (in millions), in terms of $t$.

**e.** Use this linear model to predict Atlanta's population in 2020.

**4. a.** The population of Portland, Oregon, was 2.39 in 1990 and 2.36 million in 2000. If $t$ represents the number of years since 1990, and $P(t)$ represents the population (in millions) at a given time, $t$, summarize the given information in the accompanying table.

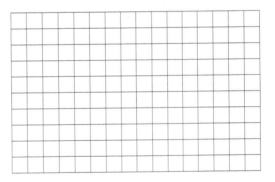

| $t$ | $P(t)$ |
|---|---|
|  |  |
|  |  |

**b.** Plot the two data points on appropriately scaled and labeled coordinate axes. Draw a line connecting the points.

**c.** What is the slope of the line? What is the practical meaning of the slope in this situation?

**d.** What is the $P$-intercept of the line? What is the practical meaning of the intercept in this situation?

**e.** Write an equation to model Portland's population, $P(t)$, in terms of $t$.

**f.** Use this linear model to predict the population of Portland in 2020.

**5.** In each part, determine the equation of the line for the given information:

**a.** Two points on a line are (0, 4) and (7, 18). Use the points to first determine the slope and $y$-intercept. Then write the equation of the line.

**b.** The graph has $y$-intercept (0, 6) and contains the point (2, 1).

**6. a.** In 1990, the rate of change of the world population was approximately 0.09125 billion per year (or approximately 1 million people every four days). The world population was estimated to be 5.3 billion in 1990. Write an equation to model the population, $P$ (in billions), in terms of $t$, where $t$ is the number of years since 1990 ($t = 0$ corresponds to 1990).

**b.** Use the linear model to predict the world population in 2020.

**c.** According to the model, when will the population of the world be double the 1990 population?

**ACTIVITY 2.6**
Housing Prices

**OBJECTIVES**

1. Determine the equation for a linear function that includes two given points.

2. Interpret the slope and $y$-intercept of a linear function in contextual situations.

3. Use the point-slope form $y - k = m(x - h)$ of linear equations to solve problems.

You have been aware of a steady increase in housing prices in your neighborhood since 2000. The house across the street sold for $125,000 in 2003, and then sold again in 2007 for $150,000. This data can be written in a table, where $n$ represents the number of years since 2000 and $P$ represents the sale price of a typical house in your neighborhood.

| NUMBER OF YEARS SINCE 2000, $n$ | HOUSING PRICE (thousands of $), $P$ |
|---|---|
| 3 | 125 |
| 7 | 150 |

1. Plot the two points on the grid below, and sketch the line containing them. Extend the line so that it intersects the $P$-axis. Scale the $n$-axis to include the period of years from 2000 to 2010 (from $n = 0$ to $n = 10$). Scale the $P$-axis by increments of 25, starting at 0 and continuing through 250.

2. **a.** Use the points in the table to determine the slope of the line. What are its units of measurement?

**b.** What is the practical meaning of the slope in this situation?

If you assume that the average rate of increase of housing prices remains constant, then the price, $P$, of the house is a linear function of the number, $n$, of years since 2000. Therefore, the relationship between $P$ and $n$ can be modeled by an equation written in the slope-intercept form, $P = mn + b$.

3. **a.** What is the value of the slope $m$ (see Problem 2)?

**b.** Write the equation $P = mn + b$, replacing $m$ with its value.

**c.** Use the ordered pair (3, 125) from the table and rewrite the equation in part b by replacing $P$ and $n$ with the appropriate values in the ordered pair.

**d.** Solve the equation in part c for $b$, the $P$-intercept of the graph of the line.

**e.** Interpret the value of the $P$-intercept $b$ in the housing price function.

**f.** Finally, rewrite the equation $P = mn + b$, replacing $b$ and $m$ with their respective values.

In Problem 3, you determined a linear equation in the slope-intercept form, using two ordered pairs that satisfy the equation. You determined the slope $m$ in part 3a and the vertical intercept $b$ in part 3d. There is a general method for writing a linear equation from two ordered pairs, based on the method of Problem 3.

Let $(h, k)$ be a known point on a line and let $(x, y)$ be any other point on the line. The slope $m$ of the line is determined by the two ordered pairs, $(h, k)$ and $(x, y)$.

$$m = \frac{\Delta y}{\Delta x} = \frac{y - k}{x - h}, \text{ so}$$
$$y - k = m(x - h)$$

The last equation, $y - k = m(x - h)$, gives a linear equation in **point-slope form**.

**Example 1**   *Write an equation of the linear function whose graph is a line containing the points $(-1, 3)$ and $(2, 9)$.*

SOLUTION

**Step 1.** Determine the slope of the line.

$$m = \frac{9 - 3}{2 - (-1)} = \frac{6}{3} = 2$$

**Step 2.** Choose any point on the line and substitute for $h$ and $k$. Using the point-slope form $y - k = m(x - h)$ with $m = 2$ and $(h, k) = (-1, 3)$, you have

$$y - 3 = 2(x-(-1))$$
$$y - 3 = 2(x + 1)$$

**Step 3.** Solve the equation in step 2 for $y$.

$$y = 3 + 2x + 2, \text{ or } y = 2x + 5$$

Since the independent and dependent variables for the housing price function are $n$ and $P$ respectively, the point-slope form for the line is $p - k = m(n - h)$.

**4. a.** Use the ordered pair (3, 125) for $(h, k)$ and $m = 6.25$ to write the point-slope form of the housing price function.

**b.** Simplify the right side of the point-slope form of the equation, solve for $P$, and compare the result to the slope-intercept form in Problem 3f.

**c.** Repeat parts a and b using the ordered pair $(7, 150)$ for $(h, k)$.

Problem 4 demonstrates that you obtain the same equation of the line regardless of which point you use for $(h, k)$.

**5.** The basal energy requirement is the daily number of calories that a person needs to maintain basic life processes. For a 20-year-old male who weighs 75 kilograms and is 190.5 centimeters tall, the basal energy requirement is 1952 calories. If his weight increases to 95 kilograms, he will require 2226 calories.

The given information is summarized in the following table.

| 20-YEAR-OLD MALE, 190.5 CENTIMETERS TALL | | |
| --- | --- | --- |
| w, WEIGHT (kg) | 75 | 95 |
| B, BASAL ENERGY REQUIREMENT (cals) | 1952 | 2226 |

**a.** Assume that the basal energy requirement, $B$, is a linear function of weight, $w$ for a 20 year old male who is 190.5 cm tall. Determine the slope of the line containing the two points indicated in the above table.

**b.** What is the practical meaning of the slope in the context of this situation?

**c.** Using the point-slope form, determine an equation that expresses $B$ in terms of $w$ for a 20-year-old, 190.5 cm tall male.

**d.** Does the $B$-intercept have any practical meaning in this situation? Determine the practical domain of the basal energy function.

**SUMMARY**
**Activity 2.6**

1. To determine the equation of a line when two points on the line are known:

**Step 1.** Determine the **slope** of the line: $m = \dfrac{\Delta y}{\Delta x}$.

**Step 2.** If the $x$-value of one of the points is zero, then $b$ is the $y$-value of this point ($y$-intercept) and you can write the equation in **slope-intercept form**, $y = mx + b$.

**Step 3.** If neither point has an $x$-value of zero, then choose one of the points as $(h, k)$ and write the equation in **point-slope form**, $y - k = m(x - h)$. Then, solve for $y$.

**EXERCISES**
**Activity 2.6**

1. Federal income tax paid by an individual single taxpayer is a function of taxable income. The following table represents the 2005 federal tax for various taxable incomes.

| $i$, TAXABLE INCOME ($) | 15,000 | 16,500 | 18,000 | 19,500 | 21,000 | 22,500 | 24,000 |
|---|---|---|---|---|---|---|---|
| $t$, 2005 FEDERAL TAX ($) | 1,889 | 2,114 | 2,339 | 2,564 | 2,789 | 3,014 | 3,239 |

   **a.** Plot the data points, with taxable income $i$ as input and 2005 tax $t$ as output. Scale the input axis from $0 to $24,000 and the output axis from $0 to $4000. Explain why the relationship is linear.

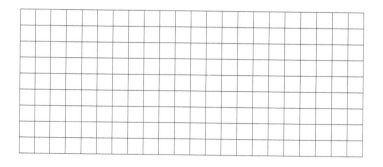

   **b.** Determine the slope of the line. What is the practical meaning of the slope?

   **c.** Use the point-slope form to write an equation to model this situation. Use the variable $i$ to represent the taxable income and the variable $t$ to represent the federal tax owed.

**d.** What is the *t*-intercept? Does it make sense?

**e.** Use the equation from part c to determine the federal tax owed by a college student having a taxable income of $8600.

**f.** Use the equation from part c to determine the taxable income of a single person who paid $1686 in federal taxes for 2005.

*In Exercises 2–8, determine the equation of the line that has the given slope and passes through the given point. Then sketch a graph of the line.*

**2.** $m = 3$, through the point $(2, 6)$      **3.** $m = -1$, through the point $(5, 0)$

**4.** $m = 7$, through the point $(-3, -5)$   **5.** $m = 0.5$, through the point $(8, 0.5)$

**6.** $m = 0$, through the point $(5, 2)$ **7.** $m = -4.2$, through the point $(-4, 6.8)$

**8.** Undefined slope, through the point $(2, -3)$

*In Exercises 9–14, determine the equation of the line that passes through the given points. Use the table feature of a graphing calculator to confirm that the coordinates of both points satisfy your equation.*

**9.** $(2, 6)$ and $(4, 16)$ **10.** $(-5, 10)$ and $(5, -10)$

**11.** $(3, 18)$ and $(8, 33)$ **12.** $(0, 6)$ and $(-10, 0)$

**13.** $(10, 2)$ and $(-3, 2)$

**14.** $(3.5, 8.2)$ and $(3.5, 7.3)$

**15.** You have just been offered your first job. The following table gives the salary schedule for the first few years of employment. Bonuses are not included. Let $s$ represent your salary after $x$ years of employment.

| YEARS OF EMPLOYMENT, $x$ | SALARY, $s$ ($) |
|:---:|:---:|
| 0 | 32,500 |
| 1 | 34,125 |
| 2 | 35,750 |
| 3 | 37,375 |

**a.** Is the salary a linear function of the years of employment? Explain.

**b.** What is the practical domain for the input variable $x$?

**c.** Scale and label the axes appropriately and plot the points from the table on the following grid.

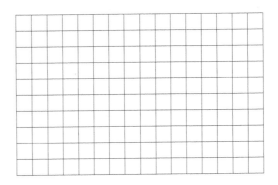

    **d.** Determine the slope of the line containing the points.

    **e.** What is the practical meaning of the slope in this situation?

    **f.** Write an equation to determine the salary, $s$, after $x$ years of employment.

    **g.** What is the $s$-intercept? What is the practical meaning of the intercept in this situation?

    **h.** Assume that the rate of increase in your salary remains the same. Use the equation model to determine your salary after eight years of employment.

**16.** The following table gives the distance, $d$, in miles of a boat from a marina as a linear function of time, $t$, in hours.

| $t$ (IN HOURS) | $d$ (IN MILES) |
|---|---|
| 2 | 75 |
| 4 | 145 |

    **a.** Determine the slope of the line. What is the practical meaning of slope in this situation?

    **b.** Write the equation of the line in slope-intercept form.

**17.** According to the Hudson Institute, from 1980 to 2000, the number of U.S. lawyers increased in thousands from 506 to 1026.

    **a.** The number of U.S. lawyers is a function of the number of years since 1980 (use 0 to represent the year 1980, 1 to represent 1981, and so forth). Write the two ordered pairs describing this situation.

    **b.** Assume that this function is linear, and write the slope-intercept equation of the line that represents this data.

**c.** What is the practical meaning of the slope in this equation? (Remember, your slope is in thousands.)

**d.** How many lawyers were there in the United States in 1995?

**18.** Straight-line depreciation helps spread the cost of new equipment over a number of years. The value of your company's copy machine after 1 year will be $14,700 and after 4 years will be $4800.

**a.** Write a linear function that will determine the value of the copy machine for any specified year.

**b.** The salvage value is the value of the equipment when it gets replaced. What will be the salvage value of the copier if you plan to replace it after 5 years?

**ACTIVITY 2.7**
Body Fat
Percentage

**OBJECTIVES**

1. Construct scatterplots from sets of data pairs.

2. Recognize when patterns of points in a scatterplot have a linear form.

3. Recognize when the pattern in the scatterplot shows that the two variables are positively related or negatively related.

4. Identify individual data points, called outliers, that fall outside the general pattern of the other data.

5. Estimate and draw a line of best fit through a set of points in a scatterplot.

6. Determine residuals between the actual value and the predicted value for each point in the data set.

7. Use a graphing calculator to determine a line of best fit by the least-squares method.

8. Measure the strength of the correlation (association) by a correlation coefficient.

9. Recognize that a strong correlation does not necessarily imply a linear or a cause-and-effect relationship.

Your body fat percentage is simply the percentage of fat your body contains. If you weigh 150 pounds and have a 10% body fat, your body consists of 15 pounds of fat and 135 pounds of lean body mass (bone, muscle, organs, tissue, blood, etc.).

A certain amount of fat is essential to bodily functions. Fat regulates body temperature, cushions and insulates organs and tissues, and is the main form of the body's energy storage. The American Council on Exercise has established the following categories for females and males based upon body fat percentage.

| CLASSIFICATION | FEMALE (% FAT) | MALE (% FAT) |
| --- | --- | --- |
| Essential Fat | 10–12 % | 2–4 % |
| Athletes | 14–20 % | 6–13 % |
| Fitness | 21–24 % | 14–17 % |
| Acceptable | 25–31 % | 18–25 % |
| Obese | 32% plus | 25% plus |

Hydrostatic measurement (body composition analysis through immersion of a person's body in water) is considered the most accurate method of determining body fat percentage. However, in most clinical or applied situations, underwater weighing is not practical.

A group of researchers is searching for alternative methods to measure body fat percentage. They first investigate if there is an association between body fat percentage and a person's weight. The body fat percentage of 19 male subjects is accurately determined, using hydrostatic weighing method. Then, each subject is weighed, using a traditional scale. The results are recorded in the following table:

| w, Weight (pounds) | 175 | 181 | 200 | 159 | 195 | 192 | 205 | 173 | 187 | 188 | 240 | 175 | 168 | 246 | 160 | 215 | 155 | 146 | 219 |
| --- | --- | --- | --- | --- | --- | --- | --- | --- | --- | --- | --- | --- | --- | --- | --- | --- | --- | --- | --- |
| y, Body Fat % | 16 | 21 | 25 | 6 | 22 | 30 | 32 | 21 | 25 | 19 | 15 | 22 | 9 | 38 | 14 | 27 | 12 | 10 | 30 |

1. Plot the data points as ordered pairs of the form $(w, y)$ on an appropriately scaled and labeled coordinate axis.

In this situation, you are interested in determining if body fat percentage is related to body weight. The graph in Problem 1, called a **scatterplot**, is an ideal tool to identify patterns in the relationship between two variables.

2. **a.** Does there appear to be a linear relationship between weight $w$ and body fat percentage $y$?

   **b.** As body weight increases, what is the general trend in the values of the body fat percentage?

   **c.** Identify any data points that fall outside the general trend or pattern of the other data points. Such data points are called **outliers**. Explain.

3. **a.** Use a straightedge to draw a single line through the points (175, 16) and (200, 25). This line can be used to represent the linear trend in the data.

   **b.** Determine the slope of the line in part a.

   **c.** Determine the equation of the line.

**d.** Use the linear model in part c to predict the body fat percentage of a male weighing 192 pounds. How does the predicted value compare to the actual value of 30%?

## Residuals

In almost every situation in which predictions are made from data, it is important to investigate the residuals. **Residuals** are the difference between the actual value and the predicted value for each point in your data. Symbolically stated, you have

$$E = y - \hat{y},$$

where $E$ represents the residual, $y$ is the actual value of the dependent variable, and $\hat{y}$, read "y-hat", is the predicted value for a given $x$.

Residuals represent the error between the actual value and the value predicted by the model.

**4. a.** Determine the residual in Problem 3d.

**b.** If a residual is positive, what does that tell you about the predicted value?

**5. a.** Determine the residual for a body weight of 168 pounds.

**b.** If the residual is negative, what does that tell you about the prediction?

**c.** What if the residual error is zero? What must be true about the predicted value of body fat percentage?

**6.** The residuals can be used to determine how well a particular line fits the data.

**a.** Determine all the residuals for the body fat versus weight data, using the linear model from Problem 3. Use your graphing calculator to create a table to easily display the values. On the TI-83/84 Plus, enter the body fat percentage data by first pressing STAT and choosing Edit. Then, enter the weight data ($w$-values) in $L_1$ and the body fat % data in $L_2$. Your equation can be entered in $L_3$, and then using $L_4 = L_2 - L_3$, the residuals will appear in $L_4$. (See Appendix A for TI-83/84 Plus procedures)

Appendix

Record the predicted body fat % values and corresponding residuals in the following table.

| Weight (pounds) $w$ | Body Fat % $y$ | Predicted Body Fat % $\hat{y}$ | Residual $E = y - \hat{y}$ | $E^2$ |
|---|---|---|---|---|
| 175 | 16 | | | |
| 181 | 21 | | | |
| 200 | 25 | | | |
| 159 | 6 | | | |
| 195 | 22 | | | |
| 192 | 30 | | | |
| 205 | 32 | | | |
| 173 | 21 | | | |
| 187 | 25 | | | |
| 188 | 19 | | | |
| 240 | 15 | | | |
| 175 | 22 | | | |
| 168 | 9 | | | |
| 246 | 38 | | | |
| 160 | 14 | | | |
| 215 | 27 | | | |
| 155 | 12 | | | |
| 146 | 10 | | | |
| 219 | 30 | | | |

**b.** If the line is a good estimate of the linear pattern, there should be approximately half the points above the line and half below. Is that the case with your line?

**c.** The sum of all the residuals should be close to zero, if the line is a reasonably good fit. What is the sum of the residuals in this case? (Use sum($L_4$) on TI-83/84 Plus)

## Regression Line

There is an established method for determining the line of best fit. The method depends on calculus to find the line which will have the smallest possible sum of all the squares of the residuals. The line which is determined by this method is called the **least squares regression line**.

**7. a.** Determine the squares of the residuals in Problem 6. You can use the TI-83/84 Plus again by entering the list $L_5 = L_4{}^2$. Record your results in the last column of the table in Problem 6. Then use sum($L_5$) to determine the sums of the squares of the residuals.

**b.** The regression line can be determined with your calculator by pressing STAT , choosing CALC and option 4: LinReg($ax + b$), rounding the coefficients to four decimal places. Your screen should appear as follows:

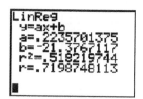

**c.** When you use the calculator to find the regression line, the residuals have already been calculated and stored for you. They are in a list, which can be found under LIST (2nd STAT ) then scroll down under the NAMES menu until you see RESID. Determine the sum of the residuals and the sum of the squares of the residuals for the regression line model. Then compare with the results in Problem 6.

Note that the sum of the squares of the residuals for any other linear model will be greater than what you found for the regression line. Hence the name, least squares regression line.

**8. a.** Produce the scatterplot for the body fat versus weight data, along with the graph of the regression line and the original line from Problem 3. (See Appendix A for TI-83/84 Plus procedures.) Your screen should appear as follows:

**b.** Describe how the two lines compare. What do you think might be the cause of any significant differences?

**c.** Use the regression line model to predict the body fat percentage for a male that weighs 225 pounds.

**d.** Interpret the practical meaning of the slope of the regression line in this context.

## Linear Correlation

When a linear pattern is evident in a scatterplot, there is said to be a linear correlation between the two variables. (When the word correlation appears by itself, it usually means **linear** correlation.) Your calculator window in Problem 7b should have included a value for $r$, called the **correlation coefficient**. (If it didn't, see Appendix A to enter DiagnosticOn.)

Appendix

$$r = 0.7198748113 \text{ or } r = 0.72$$

Note that the correlation coefficient is generally rounded to the nearest hundredth.

The value of the correlation coefficient indicates how strong a linear relationship exists between the two variables under consideration. The value of $r$ ranges between $-1$ and $1$. When the value of $r$ is closer to zero, you would conclude that there is little or no linear correlation. The closer $r$ is to either $1$ or $-1$ the stronger the linear correlation between the two variables.

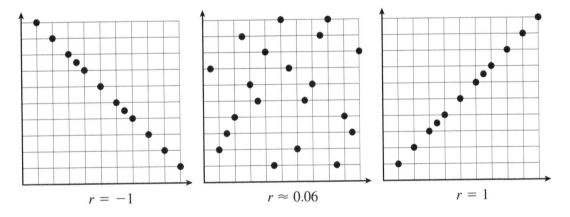

$r = -1$        $r \approx 0.06$        $r = 1$

If $r = 1$, then all the data points lie exactly on a straight line with positive slope. In this case there is a perfect positive correlation. If $r = -1$, then all the decreasing data points lie exactly on a straight line with negative slope. In this case there is a perfect negative correlation. The strength of the correlation is generally best described by both the correlation coefficient and a visual interpretation of the scatterplot. The following scatterplots with their respective correlation coefficients should help make this clear.

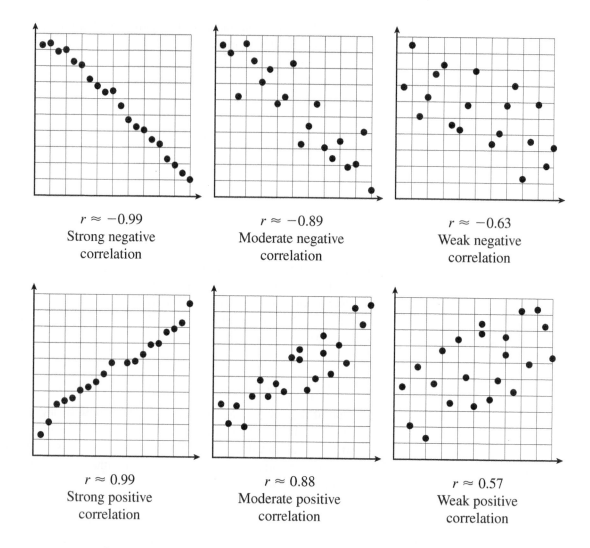

$r \approx -0.99$
Strong negative
correlation

$r \approx -0.89$
Moderate negative
correlation

$r \approx -0.63$
Weak negative
correlation

$r \approx 0.99$
Strong positive
correlation

$r \approx 0.88$
Moderate positive
correlation

$r \approx 0.57$
Weak positive
correlation

**9.** For each of the following, match the correlation coefficient $r$ with the corresponding scatterplot of data points.

**a.** $r = 0.84$        **b.** $r = 0.53$        **c.** $r = -0.45$

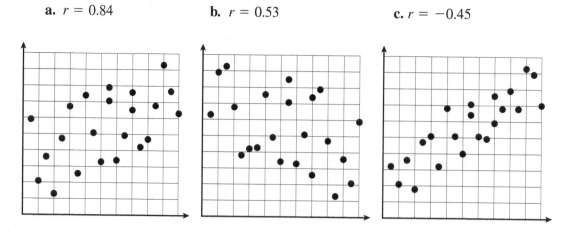

Be careful. The correlation coefficient can be dramatically affected by outlying values as demonstrated in Problem 10.

**10.** Recall from Problem 2c, the outlier for the body fat vs. weight data was the point (240,15). The correlation coefficient was $r = 0.72$.

    **a.** Recalculate the regression line and correlation coefficient when the outlier is removed from the data. What significant differences do you observe?

    **b.** Use your new regression line to predict the body fat percentage of a 225 pound male, and compare with your result from problem 8c, when you used the old regression line model.

A correlation coefficient value of $r = 0.85$ suggests a moderately strong linear association between two variables. However, as demonstrated in Problem 11, a line may not be the best model or representation of the data.

**11. a.** Produce a scatterplot for the following table of values. How would you describe the association between $x$ and $y$?

| x | 0.5 | 0.5 | 1 | 1 | 1.5 | 2 | 2.5 | 3 | 3.5 | 4 | 4.5 | 5 | 5 | 5.5 | 5.5 | 6 | 6.5 | 7 | 7 | 7.5 | 8 | 8 |
|---|-----|-----|---|---|-----|---|-----|---|-----|---|-----|---|---|-----|-----|---|-----|---|---|-----|---|---|
| y | 3.2 | 2.9 | 2.5 | 2.1 | 2.6 | 1.8 | 2.6 | 2.2 | 3.2 | 2.9 | 3.1 | 3.6 | 4 | 4.1 | 3.1 | 3.9 | 4.9 | 4.6 | 5.3 | 6.3 | 7.4 | 6.2 |

    **b.** Determine the regression line equation and correlation coefficient. Does the coefficient confirm what you said in part a?

    **c.** Graph the regression line with the scatterplot. Do you think a different graph might better describe the pattern seen in the scatterplot?

## Regression Line Revisited

**12.** The research group is trying to determine a better predictor of body fat percentage. In addition to the weight of each of the 19 male subjects, the waist size of each subject was measured and recorded.

| w, waist (inches) | 32 | 36 | 38 | 33 | 39 | 40 | 41 | 35 | 38 | 33 | 40 | 36 | 32 | 44 | 33 | 41 | 34 | 34 | 44 |
|---|---|---|---|---|---|---|---|---|---|---|---|---|---|---|---|---|---|---|---|
| y, Body Fat % | 16 | 21 | 25 | 6 | 22 | 30 | 32 | 21 | 25 | 19 | 15 | 22 | 9 | 38 | 14 | 27 | 12 | 10 | 30 |

**a.** Plot the data points as ordered pairs of the form $(w, y)$ on an appropriately scaled and labeled coordinate axis.

**b.** Describe any patterns you observe in the scatterplot.

**c.** Use the linear regression feature of a graphing calculator to determine the equation of the regression line in this situation. What does the slope of this line tell you?

**d.** Determine the value of the correlation coefficient in this situation. What does it tell you about the relationship between waist size and body fat percentage?

**e.** Is waist size or body weight a more reliable predictor of body fat percentage? Explain.

## Cause-and-Effect Relationships

A strong correlation between two variables does not necessarily mean that a cause-and-effect relationship exists between the two variables. For example, there is a strong positive correlation between height and weight. However, an increase in height does not necessarily cause an increase in weight. There are many other variables that could cause the increase in weight such as gender, age, or body type. Such variables are often called **lurking variables**, hidden in the background and not explicitly measured.

13. **a.** Suppose your home is heated with natural gas. There is a strong positive correlation between the amount of natural gas usage and the outside temperature. Is there a cause-and-effect relationship between these two variables? Explain.

   **b.** In a 2002 publication, *The Natural History of the Rich*, the author claimed a positive correlation between people with two cars and a longer life span. Is there a cause—and—effect relationship between the number of cars you own and length of life? Explain.

---

**SUMMARY**
**Activity 2.7**

1. A **scatterplot** is a graph of individual data points, useful in determining visually how two variables may be related.

2. An **outlier** is a data point that lies far outside the general pattern of points in a scatterplot.

3. A line which lies within the middle of a linear pattern of data points in a scatterplot is sometimes called a **line of best fit**.

4. A **correlation coefficient**, $r$, measures how strongly two related variables follows a linear pattern. The value of $r$ ranges between $-1$ and $1$. When the value of $r$ is closer to zero, you would conclude that there is little or no linear correlation. The closer $r$ is to either 1 or $-1$, the stronger the linear correlation between the two variables. If $r < 0$, a negative correlation, then the linear pattern follows a negative slope. If $r > 0$, a positive correlation, then the linear pattern follows a positive slope.

5. A **residual** is the vertical distance between a data point and a best-fit line. In other words, it is the error between an actual data value and a value predicted by the linear model, $E = y - \hat{y}$, where $E$ represents the residual, $y$ is the actual value of the dependent variable, and $\hat{y}$, read "y-hat", is the predicted value for a given $x$.

6. A **regression line** is considered to be the best fit line for paired data. It is determined by the least squares method, meaning the sum of the squares of the residuals is as small as possible for the regression line, when compared to any other line.

1. For each of the following, determine if there is a positive or negative correlation between the independent variable $x$ and the dependent variable $y$.

   **a.** $x$ = age of a child, $y$ = height of a child

   **b.** $x$ = age of a car, $y$ = resale value of the car

2. During the spring and summer, a concession stand at a community Little League baseball field sells soft drinks and other refreshments. To prepare for the season, the concession owner refers to the previous year's files, in which he had recorded the daily soft drink sales (in gallons) and the average daily temperature (in Fahrenheit degrees). The data is shown in the table.

| t, TEMPERATURE (°F) | g, SOFT DRINK SALES (gal) |
|---|---|
| 52 | 35 |
| 55 | 42 |
| 61 | 50 |
| 66 | 53 |
| 72 | 66 |
| 75 | 68 |
| 77 | 72 |
| 84 | 80 |
| 90 | 84 |
| 94 | 91 |
| 97 | 95 |

   **a.** Plot the data points as ordered pairs of the form $(t, g)$.

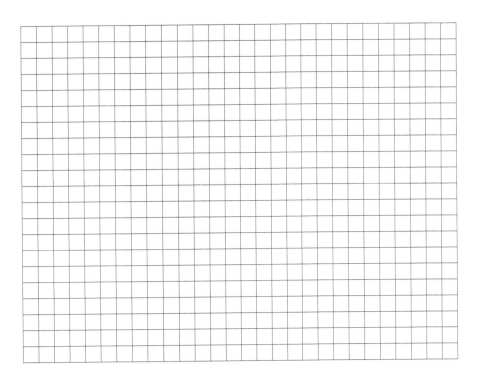

**b.** Does there appear to be a linear trend between the temperature, $t$ and the soft drink sales, $g$? Is there an exact linear fit?

**c.** Use a straightedge to draw a line of best fit through the points (84, 80) and (74, 65).

**d.** Use the coordinates of two points in part c to determine the slope of your line.

**e.** What is the equation of this line?

**f.** Complete the following table.

| t, TEMPERATURE | ACTUAL SALES | g, PREDICTED SALES | RESIDUALS |
|---|---|---|---|
| 52 | 35 | | |
| 55 | 42 | | |
| 61 | 50 | | |
| 66 | 53 | | |
| 72 | 66 | | |
| 75 | 68 | | |
| 77 | 72 | | |
| 84 | 80 | | |
| 90 | 84 | | |
| 94 | 91 | | |
| 97 | 95 | | |

**3. a.** Use your graphing calculator's statistics menu to determine the equation for the regression line in the situation in Exercise 2.

**b.** Determine the residuals for the regression line in part a. Proceed as you did in Exercise 2f.

| t, TEMPERATURE | ACTUAL SALES | G(t), PREDICTED SALES | RESIDUALS |
|---|---|---|---|
| 52 | 35 | | |
| 55 | 42 | | |
| 61 | 50 | | |
| 66 | 53 | | |
| 72 | 66 | | |
| 75 | 68 | | |
| 77 | 72 | | |
| 84 | 80 | | |
| 90 | 84 | | |
| 94 | 91 | | |
| 97 | 95 | | |

**c.** Compare the residual errors of your line of best fit in Problem 2f with the error of the least-squares regression line in part b.

**d.** Determine the correlation coefficient.

**4.** In 1966, the U.S. Surgeon General's health warnings began appearing on cigarette packages. The following data seems to demonstrate that public awareness of the health hazards of smoking has had some effect on consumption of cigarettes.

| | YEAR | | | | | | | |
|---|---|---|---|---|---|---|---|---|
| | 1997 | 1998 | 1999 | 2000 | 2001 | 2002 | 2003 | 2004 |
| % of total population 18 and older who smoke | 24.7 | 24.1 | 23.5 | 23.2 | 22.7 | 22.4 | 21.6 | 20.9 |

*Source:* U.S. National Center for Health Statistics.

**a.** Plot the given data as ordered pairs of the form $(t, P)$, where $t$ is the number of years since 1997 and $P$ is the percent of the total population (18 and older) who smoke. Appropriately scale and label the coordinate axes.

**b.** Determine the equation of the regression line that best represents the data.

**c.** Use the equation to predict the percent of the total population 18 and older that will smoke in 2010.

**5.** The number of Internet users in the United States has increased steadily over the past several years, as indicated in the following table.

| YEAR | NUMBER OF INTERNET USERS IN U.S. (in millions) |
|------|-----------------------------------------------|
| 2000 | 121 |
| 2001 | 127 |
| 2002 | 140 |
| 2003 | 146 |
| 2004 | 156 |
| 2005 | 163 |

**a.** Plot the data points on an appropriately scaled and labeled coordinate axis. Let $x$ represent the number of years since 2000.

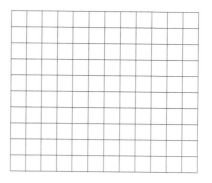

**b.** Use your graphing calculator's statistics menu (STAT) to determine the equation of the regression line.

**c.** What is the slope of the line in part b? What is the practical meaning of the slope?

**d.** Use the linear model from part b to predict when the number of Internet users in the U.S. will reach 200 million. How confident are you in this prediction?

**LAB
ACTIVITY 2.8**
Plot before
Calculating

**OBJECTIVE**

1. Understand the need to
first make a scatterplot of
the data before calculating
a correlation coefficient
and regression line.

In 1973, statistician Frank Anscombe published the article "Graphs in Statistical Analysis" in the *American Statistician*, vol. 27, pages 17–21. The article contained the following four sets of 11 pairs of data.

Data Set 1

| x | 10 | 8 | 13 | 9 | 11 | 14 | 6 | 4 | 12 | 7 | 5 |
|---|---|---|---|---|---|---|---|---|---|---|---|
| $y_1$ | 8.04 | 6.95 | 7.58 | 8.81 | 8.33 | 9.96 | 7.24 | 4.26 | 10.84 | 4.82 | 5.68 |

Data Set 2

| x | 10 | 8 | 13 | 9 | 11 | 14 | 6 | 4 | 12 | 7 | 5 |
|---|---|---|---|---|---|---|---|---|---|---|---|
| $y_2$ | 9.14 | 8.14 | 8.74 | 8.77 | 9.26 | 8.10 | 6.13 | 3.10 | 9.13 | 7.26 | 4.74 |

Data Set 3

| x | 10 | 8 | 13 | 9 | 11 | 14 | 6 | 4 | 12 | 7 | 5 |
|---|---|---|---|---|---|---|---|---|---|---|---|
| $y_3$ | 7.46 | 6.72 | 12.74 | 7.11 | 7.81 | 8.84 | 6.08 | 5.39 | 8.15 | 6.42 | 5.73 |

Data Set 4

| x | 8 | 8 | 8 | 8 | 8 | 8 | 8 | 8 | 8 | 8 | 19 |
|---|---|---|---|---|---|---|---|---|---|---|---|
| $y_4$ | 6.58 | 5.76 | 7.71 | 8.84 | 8.47 | 7.04 | 5.25 | 5.56 | 7.91 | 6.89 | 12.50 |

1. **a.** Without making scatterplots, determine the correlation coefficient $r$ and the regression line for each data set. Record your answers in the following table.

| | $r$, LINEAR CORRELATION COEFFICIENT | LINEAR REGRESSION EQUATION |
|---|---|---|
| Data Set 1 | | |
| Data Set 2 | | |
| Data Set 3 | | |
| Data Set 4 | | |

**b.** Compare the equations and correlation coefficients for the four sets of data.

**c.** What type of correlation between the variable $x$ and $y$ is indicated by the correlation coefficient?

**2. a.** Make a scatterplot for each of the four data sets.

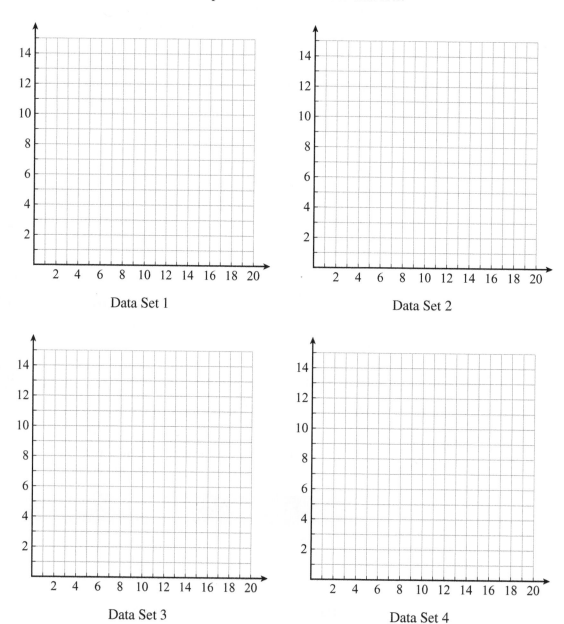

Data Set 1

Data Set 2

Data Set 3

Data Set 4

**b.** Draw the regression line on each of the scatterplots.

**3. a.** A correlation coefficient value of $r = 0.816$ indicates a strong positive association between the two variables $x$ and $y$. However, does that mean a line is the best fit for the data?

In which of the four cases would you use the regression line having equation $y = 0.5x + 3$ to make predictions for $y$? Explain.

**4. a.** The Data Set 3 has an outlier. Remove the outlier from the data set and recalculate the equation of the regression line.

**b.** What is the value of the correlation coefficient? What does this indicate?

**5.** What was Mr. Anscombe trying to demonstrate using his four data sets?

**ACTIVITY 2.9**

College Tuition

The following graphic contains the average tuition and required fees for all 4-year colleges from 1987 through 2003.

**OBJECTIVES**

1. Determine the equation of a regression line using a graphing calculator.

2. Use the regression equation to interpolate and extrapolate.

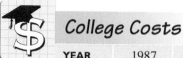

| YEAR | 1987 | 1992 | 1996 | 1999 | 2001 | 2003 |
|------|------|------|------|------|------|------|
| COST | $5964 | $8238 | $10,330 | $11,888 | $12,922 | $14,504 |

1. **a.** Let $t$, the number of years since 1987, represent the independent variable and $c$, the average cost, the dependent variable. Determine an appropriate scale, and plot the data points from the accompanying table. Therefore, $t = 0$ corresponds to the year 1987, $t = 5$ to 1992, $t = 9$ to 1996, and so on.

**b.** Describe any patterns in the scatterplot.

2. **a.** Enter the tuition data into your calculator by pressing ⌐STAT⌐ and choosing EDIT.

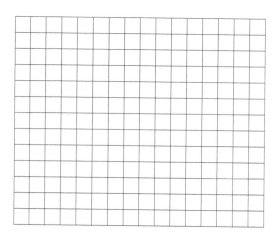

**b.** Enter the year data in L1 and the tuition data in L2.

c. Determine the regression line by pressing STAT, choosing CALC and option 4: LinReg(*ax* + *b*).

d. Write the result, rounding the coefficients to three decimal places.

e. Determine the correlation coefficient.

4. Now use the regression equation you determined in Problem 2 to model the tuition data. Use the table feature on your graphing calculator to determine the model's predicted output in the following table.

| INPUT, *t* | ACTUAL OUTPUT, *c* | MODEL'S PREDICTED OUTPUT |
|---|---|---|
| 0 | 5964 | |
| 5 | 8238 | |
| 9 | 10,330 | |
| 12 | 11,888 | |
| 14 | 12,922 | |
| 16 | 14,504 | |

**DEFINITION**

Using a regression model to predict an output within the boundaries of the input values of the given data is called **interpolation**. Using a regression model to predict an output outside the boundaries of the input values of the given data is called **extrapolation**. In general, interpolation is more reliable than extrapolation.

5. a. Use the regression equation to predict the average tuition and fees at private 4-year colleges in 1993 (*t* = 6). Is this an example of interpolation or extrapolation?

b. Use the regression equation to predict the average tuition and fees at private 4-year colleges in 2005. Is this an example of interpolation or extrapolation?

**c.** Use the regression line to estimate the year in which average tuition and fees will be at least $20,000.

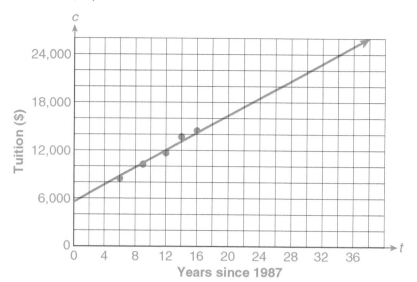

**6.** Over the past quarter century, the number of bachelor's degrees conferred by degree-granting institutions has steadily increased. The following table contains data on the number of bachelor's degrees (in thousands) earned by women in a given year. The input $t$ represents the number of years since 1977.

| | YEAR | | | | | | |
| --- | --- | --- | --- | --- | --- | --- | --- |
| | 1977 | 1981 | 1985 | 1990 | 1995 | 2000 | 2004 |
| $t$, NUMBER OF YEARS SINCE 1977 | 0 | 4 | 8 | 13 | 18 | 23 | 27 |
| $f(t)$, NUMBER OF DEGREES IN THOUSANDS | 423 | 465 | 492 | 558 | 634 | 708 | 775 |

**a.** Sketch a scatterplot of the given data.

**b.** Enter the data into your graphing calculator, and determine a linear regression model to represent the data. Write the result here.

**c.** What is the slope of the line? What is the practical meaning of the slope in this situation?

**d.** Use the regression model to predict the number of bachelor's degrees that will be granted in the year 2010.

## SUMMARY
### Activity 2.9

1. The linear regression equation is the linear equation that "best fits" a set of data.

2. The regression line is a mathematical model for the data.

3. **Interpolation** is the process of using a regression equation to predict a value of $y$ for an $x$-value that lies within the boundaries of the given data.

4. **Extrapolation** is the process of using a regression equation to predict a value of $y$ for an $x$-value that lies outside the boundaries of the given data.

## EXERCISES
### Activity 2.9

**1. a.** Plot the following data:

| x | 0 | 3 | 6 | 9 | 12 | 15 | 18 |
|---|---|---|---|---|----|----|----|
| y | −0.8 | 6.3 | 13.1 | 19.6 | 27.0 | 33.5 | 40.8 |

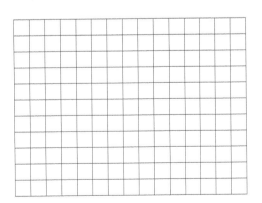

**b.** With a straightedge, draw a line that you think looks like the line of best fit. Does this data appear to be linear?

**c.** Use your graphing calculator to determine the equation of the regression line. Write the result below.

**d.** Use your equation from part c to predict the value of $y$ when $x = 10$.

  **e.** Use your equation from part c to predict the value of $y$ when $x = 25$.

  **f.** Which prediction, in part d or e, would be more accurate? Explain.

2. Public debt increased at a relatively constant rate from 1986 to 1996. The following table gives the average debt per capita (in thousands of dollars) for selected years, where $t = 0$ corresponds to the year 1986:

| t (in years since 1986) | 0 | 2 | 4 | 6 | 8 | 10 |
|---|---|---|---|---|---|---|
| d (in thousands of dollars) | 8.77 | 10.53 | 13.00 | 15.85 | 18.02 | 19.81 |

*Source:* Bureau of Public Debt, U.S. Department of the Treasury

  **a.** Plot the data.

  **b.** Use your graphing calculator to determine the equation of the regression line. Write the result here.

  **c.** What is the slope of the line? What is the practical meaning of slope in this situation?

  **d.** Use your regression line to determine the average debt of an individual in 1990 $(t = 4)$. Compare your result with the actual value of $13,000 in 1990.

  **e.** Use the regression equation to predict the average debt of an individual in 2002.

  **f.** What is the process called that you used to make the prediction in part e?

## Collecting and Analyzing Data

**3.** One measure of how well the American economy is doing is the number of new houses built in a given year. Your economics teacher has asked the class to investigate trends in new home construction in recent years and to predict the number of new homes that will be constructed in 2010.

Use the U.S. Bureau of the Census* as a resource to obtain the latest data available on new home construction from 2000 to 2007. Work with a group and be prepared to give an oral presentation of your findings to the class. The presentation should include visual displays showing any tables, scatterplots, regression equations and graphs used in the problem solving process.

Each member of the group should submit a report of the group's findings. The report should contain the following information:

**a.** The source(s) of the data.

**b.** A description of the dependent and independent variables.

**c.** A table and scatterplot of the data.

**d.** Identification of any patterns in the scatterplot.

**e.** A linear regression equation and correlation coefficient for the data.

**f.** A table of residuals between the actual data values and values predicted by the linear model and a description of whether it is reasonable to use a linear equation to model the data.

**g.** A prediction of the number of new homes to be constructed in 2010 and a description of the level of confidence in this prediction.

**h.** State a conclusion of the data analysis process.

---

* The U.S. Bureau of the Census gathers large amounts of data about the United States and its population. This information is published in the Statistical Abstract of the United States. The publication is available on the Internet as well as in print form at most libraries. This is an excellent source of data on a variety of topics.

**LAB ACTIVITY**
**2.10**
Body Parts

**OBJECTIVES**

1. Collect and organize data in a table.
2. Plot data in a scatterplot.
3. Recognize linear patterns in paired data.

Variables arise in many common measurements. Your height is one measurement that has probably been recorded frequently from the day you were born. In this project, you are asked to pair up and make the following body measurements: height ($h$); arm span ($a$), the distance between the tips of your two middle fingers with arms outstretched; wrist circumference ($w$); foot length ($f$); and neck circumference ($n$). For consistency, measure the lengths in inches.

**1.** Gather the data for your entire class, and record it in the following table:

## Inch by Inch

| STUDENT | HEIGHT (h) | ARM SPAN (a) | WRIST (w) | FOOT (f) | NECK (n) | |
|---------|------------|--------------|-----------|----------|----------|--|
|  |  |  |  |  |  |  |
|  |  |  |  |  |  |  |
|  |  |  |  |  |  |  |
|  |  |  |  |  |  |  |
|  |  |  |  |  |  |  |
|  |  |  |  |  |  |  |
|  |  |  |  |  |  |  |
|  |  |  |  |  |  |  |
|  |  |  |  |  |  |  |
|  |  |  |  |  |  |  |
|  |  |  |  |  |  |  |
|  |  |  |  |  |  |  |
|  |  |  |  |  |  |  |

**2.** What are some relationships you can identify, based on a visual inspection of the data? For example, how do the heights relate to the arm spans?

3. Construct a scatterplot for heights versus arm span on the grid below, carefully labeling the axes and marking the scales. Does the scatterplot confirm what you may have guessed in Problem 2?

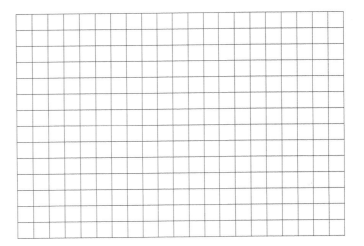

4. Use your calculator to create scatterplots for the following pairs of data, and state whether or not there appears to be a linear relationship. Comment on how the scatterplots either confirm or go against the observations you made in Problem 2.

| VARIABLES | LINEAR RELATIONSHIP? |
|---|---|
| Height versus Foot Length | |
| Arm Span versus Wrist | |
| Foot Length versus Neck Circumference | |

5. Determine a linear regression equation to represent the relationship between the two variables in Problems 3 and 4 that show the strongest linear pattern.

## Predicting Height from Bone Length

An anthropologist studies human physical traits, place of origin, social structure, and culture. Anthropologists are often searching for the remains of people who lived many years ago. A forensic scientist studies the evidence from a crime scene in order to help solve a crime. Both of these groups of scientists use various characteristics and measurements of the human skeletal remains to help determine physical traits such as height, as well as racial and gender differences.

In the average person, there is a strong relationship between height and the length of two major arm bones (the humerous and the radius), as well as the length of the two major leg bones (the femur and the tibia).

Anthropologists and forensic scientists can closely estimate a person's height from the length of just one of these major bones.

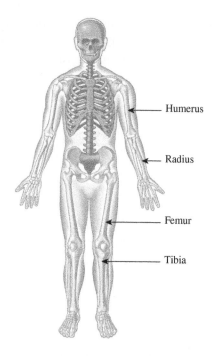

6. Each member of the class should measure his or her leg from the center of the kneecap to the bone on the outside of the hip. This is the length of the femur. Record the results in the appropriate place in the last column of the table in Problem 1.

   a. If you want to predict height from the length of the femur, which variable should represent the independent variable? Explain.

   b. Make a scatterplot of the data on a carefully scaled and labeled coordinate axes.

   c. Describe any patterns you observe in the scatterplot.

   d. Determine the correlation coefficient. Describe any correlation between the two variables.

   e. Determine the equation of the regression line for the data.

   f. Use the equation of the regression line in part e to predict the height of a person whose femur measures 17 inches.

g. Anthropologists have developed the following formula to predict the height of a male based on the length of his femur:

$$h = 1.888L + 32.010$$

where $h$ represents the height in inches and $L$ represents the length of the femur in inches. Use the formula to determine the height of the person whose femur measures 17 inches.

h. Compare your results from parts f and g. What might explain the difference between the height you obtained using the regression formula in part f and the height using the formula in part g?

i. Determine the regression line equation for femur length vs. height using just the male data from Problem 1. How does this new regression line equation compare with the formula $h = 1.888L + 32.010$ used by anthropologists?

7. a. Determine the linear regression equation (femur length vs. height) for the female data in Problem 1.

b. Compare your results to the formula used by anthropologists:

$$h = 1.945x + 28.679$$

where $h$ represents height in inches and $x$ represents femur length in inches.

8. The work of Dr. Mildred Trotter (1899–1991), in skeletal biology, led to the development of formulas used to estimate a person's height based on bone length. Her research also led to discoveries about the growth, racial and gender differences, and aging of the human skeleton. Write a brief report on the life and accomplishments of this remarkable scientist.

**ACTIVITY 2.11**

Long Distance
by Phone

**OBJECTIVES**

1. Graph a piecewise linear function.
2. Write a piecewise linear function to represent a given situation.
3. Determine if a piecewise function is continuous.
4. Graph a function defined by $y = |x - c|$.

A certain long-distance telephone carrier offers the following rates for calls outside the state in which you live: $0.15 per minute for the first 10 minutes, $0.08 per minute for each minute thereafter. Also, whereas most companies round up to the next minute for any fraction of a minute, this company charges for the exact duration of your call.

1. Complete the following table using time, $t$, in minutes, and cost, $c$, in dollars.

| $t$ (IN MINUTES) | 1 | 2 | 5 | 10 | 15 | 20 | 30 |
|---|---|---|---|---|---|---|---|
| $c$ (IN DOLLARS) | | | | | | | |

2. **a.** Write an equation that gives the cost, $c$, of a call in terms of time, $t$, if the call lasts 10 minutes or less.

   **b.** Write an equation that gives the cost, $c$, of a call, if the call lasts longer than 10 minutes. Remember, the input, $t$, is the total time of the call.

3. The cost is determined in two different ways, depending on the length of the call. In other words, the cost function is defined in pieces. At what input value does the definition change from the first to the second piece?

The resulting cost function is called a **piecewise function**.

This cost function is written in the following way.

$$c = f(t) = \begin{cases} 0.15t & \text{if } t \le 10 \\ 1.50 + 0.08(t - 10) & \text{if } t > 10. \end{cases}$$

The expression $0.15t$ is used to determine the total cost if the length of the call is less than or equal to 10 minutes (see Problem 2a). The expression $1.50 + 0.08(t - 10)$ is used to determine the total cost if the length of the call is more than 10 minutes (see Problem 2b).

4. **a.** What is the cost of a 6-minute call?

   **b.** Determine $f(23)$, and interpret the result in the context of the situation.

5. Sketch the graph of the cost function over the domain 0 to 30 minutes. Be sure to use an appropriate scale for the horizontal and vertical axes.

6. You can use your graphing calculator to graph the cost function. To accomplish this, you must enclose each piece of the function in parentheses with its domain also in parentheses. The inequality symbols are in the Test (a 2nd function) menu. The pieces are connected by plus signs as follows.

$$Y_1 = (0.15x)(x \le 10) + (1.5 + 0.08(x - 10))(x > 10).$$

Using the indicated window, your graph should appear as follows.

7. Another company gives the following promotion for your long-distance service.

   $0.99 for the first 20 minutes and $0.07 for each minute thereafter.

   a. Complete the following table using total time, $t$, in minutes and cost, $c$, in dollars.

| t (IN MINUTES) | 1 | 5 | 10 | 20 | 25 | 30 |
|---|---|---|---|---|---|---|
| c (IN DOLLARS) | | | | | | |

   b. Write an equation that gives the cost, $c$, of a call that lasts 20 minutes or less.

   c. Write an equation that gives the cost, $c$, if the call lasts longer than 20 minutes. Remember, $t$ is the total time of the call.

   d. Write a piecewise function for the cost of the long-distance service.

**e.** Sketch a graph of the cost function over the domain 0 to 30 minutes. Verify using your graphing calculator.

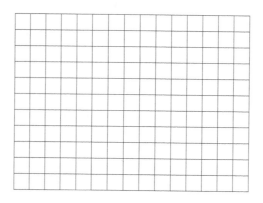

**f.** Is the cost function continuous for $t \geq 0$?

**g.** Determine the cost of a call that lasts 33 minutes.

## Cost of Natural Gas

Your natural gas bill is computed based on units of 1000 cubic feet. There are two parts to the bill: the gas charges and the delivery charges. The most expensive part is the delivery charges. For residential customers, the gas delivery charge for natural gas is billed in the following manner.

$40.74 for 0 to 3000 cubic feet,

$0.98 per thousand cubic feet for 3000 cubic feet to 50,000 cubic feet,

$0.15 per thousand cubic feet for each thousand cubic feet in excess of 50,000.

You can write a function that represents the total charge of natural gas delivery to your home. The output value will be calculated differently depending on whether you use 3000 cubic feet or less, more than 3000 cubic feet and less than or equal to 50,000 cubic feet, or more than 50,000 cubic feet. This piecewise function is determined in Problems 8–12.

**8. a.** Complete the following table, using $x$ to represent the total number of cubic feet used and $C$ to represent the total monthly charge for natural gas delivery.

*It's a Gas*

| x, **NUMBER OF 1000 CUBIC FEET** | 0 | 1 | 2 | 5 | 10 | 50 | 100 | 200 |
|---|---|---|---|---|---|---|---|---|
| c, **TOTAL MONTHLY COST** | | | | | | | | |

**b.** Write an equation to represent the delivery charge if you use 3000 cubic feet or less.

**c.** Write an equation to represent the delivery charge if the number of thousand cubic feet used is greater than 3 and less than or equal to 50. Remember, $x$ represents the total number of thousand cubic feet used.

**d.** Write an equation to represent the delivery charge if the number of thousand cubic feet used is more than 50.

**9.** Use the results from Problem 8 to write a piecewise delivery charge function $C$ representing the total cost of using $x$ thousand cubic feet over the following three intervals: $0 \le x \le 3$, $3 < x \le 50$, and $x > 50$

**10.** Use your graphing calculator to graph the piecewise function in Problem 9. To indicate $(3 < x \le 50)$, you must use two separate inequalities, $x > 3$ and $x \le 50$. Use the dot mode on the graphing calculator. Your graph should appear as follows.

**11. a.** What is the delivery charge if you use 157 thousand cubic feet of gas during the month?

**b.** If it costs $1.721 for each thousand cubic feet of gas used (gas supply charge), then what is the cost of the 157 thousand cubic feet used?

**c.** What was your total natural gas bill?

## Absolute Value Function

**12.** Consider the piecewise function defined by

$$f(x) = \begin{cases} -x & \text{if } x < 0 \\ x & \text{if } x \ge 0. \end{cases}$$

**a.** What is the domain of the function $f$?

**b.** Complete the following table.

| x | −4 | −3 | −2 | −4 | 0 | 1 | 2 | 3 | 4 |
|---|---|---|---|---|---|---|---|---|---|
| f(x) | | | | | | | | | |

**c.** Sketch a graph of the function f. Use your graphing calculator to verify the graph.

**d.** Describe the shape of the graph of function f.

**e.** What is the range of the function?

The function f defined in Problem 12 may look familiar. This function is the piecewise definition of the absolute value function defined by $f(x) = |x|$.

**13. a.** Use your graphing calculator to obtain the graph of $y = |x|$. The absolute value function is located in the Math menu under the Num submenu.

   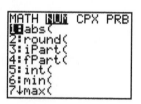

**b.** How does the graph compare to the graph in Problem 12?

**14. a.** Use your graphing calculator to sketch a graph of $y = |x - 2|$.

**b.** Describe how the graph of $y = |x - 2|$ can be obtained from the graph of $y = |x|$.

**c.** Describe how the graph of $y = |x| + 2$ can be obtained from the graph of $y = |x|$.

**d.** Describe how the graph of $y = -|x|$ can be obtained from the graph of $y = |x|$.

## SUMMARY
**Activity 2.11**

1. A **piecewise** function is a function that is defined differently for certain "pieces" of its domain.

2. The absolute value function is a special piecewise function defined by

$$|x| = \begin{cases} x & \text{if } x \geq 0 \\ -x & \text{if } x < 0 \end{cases}.$$

3. The absolute value of the linear function, $g(x) = |x - c|$, always has a V-shaped graph with a vertex at $(c, 0)$.

## EXERCISES
**Activity 2.11**

1. To travel outside the city limits, a certain taxicab company charges $1.20 for the first mile or less of travel. After the first mile, the charge is an additional $0.90 per mile.

   Complete the following table.

| x, NUMBER OF MILES OUTSIDE CITY LIMITS | 0 | 0.5 | 1 | 2 | 5 | 10 |
|---|---|---|---|---|---|---|
| c, TOTAL COST (IN $) | | | | | | |

   **a.** Write an equation for the total cost, $C$, of the first mile or less of travel.

   **b.** Write an equation that gives the total cost, $C$, if you travel more than 1 mile, all outside city limits.

   **c.** Write a piecewise function for the total cost, $C$.

**d.** Sketch a graph of the cost function over the domain 0 to 10 miles. Verify using your graphing calculator.

**e.** Determine the cost of a 12-mile taxi ride, all outside the city limits.

**2. a.** Sketch the graph of the piecewise function.

$$H(x) = \begin{cases} -2x + 3 & \text{if} \quad x < -2 \\ 4 & \text{if} \quad -2 \le x < 1. \\ x - 1 & \text{if} \quad x \ge 1 \end{cases}$$

**b.** Use your graphing calculator and compare the result with your sketch.

**c.** Is this piecewise function continuous? Explain.

**3.** You are an author about to publish your first novel, *Hockey in the 90s*. The book will sell for $25. You will be paid royalties of 10% on the first 15,000 copies sold, 12% on the next 6000 copies, and 16% on any additional copies.

   **a.** Write a piecewise function, $f$, that specifies the total royalties if $x$ copies are sold.

   **b.** Graph the function on your graphing calculator.

   **c.** Use your function from part a to determine if the royalty is $46,500 when 18,000 books are sold. Is the royalty $71,500 when 25,000 copies are sold? If you do not obtain these answers when substituting into the function, then discover where you went wrong.

   **d.** With the royalties from your book, you would like to pay for your advanced degree in journalism. It will cost $65,000. How many books must sell to cover the cost of the degree?

**4.** You receive a bill each month for your credit-card use. The bill indicates the minimum amount that is due by a certain date. The minimum amount due depends upon your unpaid balance. One credit-card company uses the following criteria to determine your bill.

   • The entire amount is due if the balance is less than $10.

   • A minimum of $10 is due if the balance is $10 or more but less than $500.

   • A minimum of $30 is due if the balance is $500 or more but less than $1000.

   • A minimum of $50 is due if the balance is $1000 or more but less than $1500.

   • A minimum of $70 is due if the balance is $1500 or more.

   **a.** Let $x$ represent the dollar amount of the unpaid balance. Complete the following table.

### Where Credit Is Due

| UNPAID BALANCE, (IN $) | 0 | 5 | 10 | 100 | 300 | 500 | 700 | 1200 | 1700 |
|---|---|---|---|---|---|---|---|---|---|
| MINIMUM AMOUNT DUE, M (IN $) | | | | | | | | | |

**b.** Write a piecewise function for the minimum payment due.

**c.** Sketch a graph of the minimum payment function. Verify using your graphing calculator.

**d.** Is the minimum payment function continuous?

**5. a.** Complete the following table where $f(x) = |x - 3|$ and $g(x) = |x + 3|$.

| x | −5 | −4 | −3 | −2 | −1 | 0 | 1 | 2 | 3 | 4 | 5 |
|---|----|----|----|----|----|---|---|---|---|---|---|
| f(x) | 8 | 7 | 6 | 5 | 4 | 3 | 2 | 1 | 0 | 1 | 2 |
| g(x) | 2 | 1 | 0 | 1 | 2 | 3 | 4 | 5 | 6 | 7 | 8 |

**b.** Sketch a graph of each of the functions $f$ and $g$. Verify using your graphing calculator.

**c.** Describe how the graphs of $f$ and $g$ can be obtained from the graph of $y = |x|$.

**d.** Write $f(x) = |x - 3|$ as a piecewise function.

**e.** What is the domain of $f(x)$? What is the domain of $g(x)$?

**f.** What is the range of $f(x)$? What is the range of $g(x)$?

**6. a.** Without using a table of values or a graphing calculator, sketch the graph of $f(x) = |x - 5|$.

**b.** Describe the location and shape of the graph of $g(x) = |x + 5|$.

**c.** Sketch the graph of $h(x) = |x| + 5$ without a graphing calculator or a table of values.

**d.** Describe the similarities and differences in the two graphs in parts b and c. Include shape, location, and intercepts.

## Activities 2.1–2.11   What Have I Learned?

1. What must be true about the average rate of change between any two points on the graph of an increasing function?

2. You are told that the average rate of change of a particular function is always negative. What can you conclude about the graph of that function and why?

3. Describe a step-by-step procedure for determining the average rate of change between any two points on the graph of a function. Use the points represented by (85, 350) and (89, 400) in your explanation.

4. A line is given by the equation $y = -4x + 10$.

   **a.** Determine its $x$- and $y$-intercepts algebraically from the equation.

   **b.** Use your graphing calculator to confirm these intercepts.

5. **a.** Does the slope of the line having the equation $4x + 2y = 3$ have a value of 4? Why or why not?

**b.** Solve the equation in part a for $y$ so that it is in the form $y = mx + b$.

**c.** What is its slope?

**6.** Explain the difference between a line with zero slope and a line with an undefined slope.

**7.** Describe how you recognize that a function is linear when it is given

    **a.** graphically.

    **b.** as an equation involving $x$ and $y$.

    **c.** numerically in a table.

**8.** Do vertical lines represent functions? Explain.

**Activities 2.1–2.11** How Can I Practice?

1. As part of your special diet and exercise program, you record your weight at the beginning of the program and each week thereafter. The following data gives your weight, $w$, over a five-month period:

| MONTHS (t) | 0 | 1 | 2 | 3 | 4 | 5 |
|---|---|---|---|---|---|---|
| WEIGHT, w (lb) | 196 | 183 | 180 | 177 | 174 | 171 |

a. Sketch a graph of the data on appropriately scaled and labeled axes.

b. Determine the average rate of change of your weight during the first three months. Be sure to include the units of measurement of this rate.

c. Determine the average rate of change during the five-month period.

d. On the graph in part a, connect the points (0, 196) and (3, 177) with a line segment. Does the line segment increase, decrease, or remain horizontal as you follow the line left to right?

e. What is the practical meaning of the average rate of change in this situation?

f. What can you say about the average rate of change of weight during any of the time intervals in this situation?

**2.** A function is linear because the rate of change of *y* with respect to *x* from point to point is constant. Use this idea to determine the missing *x* and *y* values in each table, assuming that each table represents a linear function.

**a.**

| x | y |
|---|---|
| 1 | 4 |
| 2 | 5 |
| 3 | |

**b.**

| x | y |
|---|---|
| 1 | 4 |
| 3 | 8 |
| 5 | |

**c.**

| x | y |
|---|---|
| 0 | 4 |
| 5 | 9 |
| 10 | |

**d.**

| x | y |
|---|---|
| −1 | 3 |
| 0 | 8 |
| | 13 |
| 2 | |

**e.**

| x | y |
|---|---|
| −3 | 11 |
| 0 | 8 |
| 3 | |
| | 2 |

**f.**

| x | y |
|---|---|
| −2 | −5 |
| 0 | −8 |
| | −11 |
| 4 | |

**g.** Explain how you used the idea of constant rate of change to determine the values in the tables.

**3.** The pitch of a roof is an example of slope in a practical setting. The roof slope is usually expressed as a ratio of rise over run. For example, in the building shown, the pitch is 6 to 24 or in fraction form as $\frac{1}{4}$.

**a.** If a roof has a pitch of 5 to 16, how high will the roof rise over a 24-foot run?

**b.** If a roof's slope is 0.25, how high will the roof rise over a 16-foot run?

**c.** What is the slope of a roof that rises 12 feet over a run of 30 feet?

4. Determine whether any of the following tables contain data that represent a linear function. In each case, give a reason for your answer.

**a.** You make an investment of $100 at 5% interest compounded semiannually. The following table represents the amount of money you will have at the end of each year.

| TIME (years) | AMOUNT ($) |
|---|---|
| 1 | 105.06 |
| 2 | 110.38 |
| 3 | 115.97 |
| 4 | 121.84 |

**b.** A cable TV company charges a $45 installation fee and $28 per month for basic cable service. The table values represent the total usage cost since installation.

| NUMBER OF MONTHS | 6 | 12 | 18 | 24 | 36 |
|---|---|---|---|---|---|
| TOTAL COST ($) | 213 | 381 | 549 | 717 | 1053 |

**c.** For a fee of $20 a month, you have unlimited video rental. Values in the table represent the relationship between the number of videos you rented each month and the monthly fee.

| NUMBER OF RENTALS | 10 | 15 | 12 | 9 | 2 |
|---|---|---|---|---|---|
| COST ($) | 20 | 20 | 20 | 20 | 20 |

**5.** After stopping your car at a stop sign, you accelerate at a constant rate for a period of time. The speed of your car is a function of the time since you left the stop sign. The following table shows your speedometer reading each second for the next seven seconds:

| t, TIME (sec) | s, SPEED (mph) |
| --- | --- |
| 0 | 0 |
| 1 | 11 |
| 2 | 22 |
| 3 | 33 |
| 4 | 44 |
| 5 | 55 |
| 6 | 55 |
| 7 | 55 |

**a.** Graph the data using ordered pairs of the form $(t, s)$.

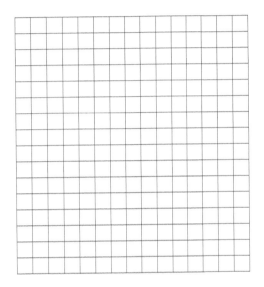

**b.** For what values of $t$ is the graph increasing?

**c.** What is the slope of the line segment during the period of acceleration?

**d.** What is the practical meaning of the slope in this situation?

**e.** For what values of $t$ is the speed a constant? What is the slope of the line connecting the points of constant speed?

**6. a.** The three lines shown in the following graphs appear to be different. Calculate the slope of each line.

**b.** Do the three graphs represent the same linear model? Explain.

**7. a.** Determine the slope of the line $y = -3x - 2$.

**b.** Determine the slope of the line $2x - 4y = 10$.

**c.** Determine the slope of the line from the following graph:

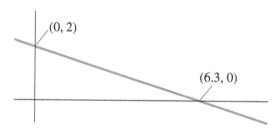

**8.** Determine the $x$- and $y$-intercepts for the graph of each of the following:

    **a.** $y = 2x - 6$                              **b.** $y = -\dfrac{3}{2}x + 10$

    **c.** $y = 10$

    **d.** $x = 5$

**9.** Determine the equation of each line.

    **a.** The line passes through the points $(2, 0)$ and $(0, -5)$.

    **b.** The slope is 7, and the line passes through the point $\left(0, \dfrac{1}{2}\right)$.

    **c.** The slope is 0, and the line passes through the point $(2, -4)$.

**10.** Sketch a graph of each of the following. Use your graphing calculator to verify your graphs.

    **a.** $y = 3x - 6$

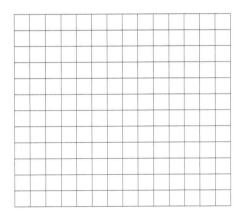

**b.** $y = -2x + 10$

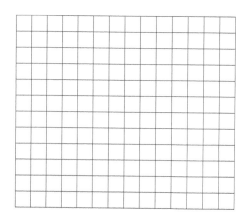

**11.** Write each equation in slope-intercept form to discover what the graphs have in common. Use your graphing calculator to verify your graphs.

    **a.** $3x - y = 0$          **b.** $y = 3x - 4$          **c.** $y - 3x = 6$

    **d.** Describe how the graphs in parts $b$ and $c$ can be obtained from the graph of $y = 3x$ in part $a$.

In Problems 12–15, determine the slope and the $x$- and $y$-intercepts of each line.

**12.** $y = 2x + 1$                                 **13.** $y = 4 - x$

**14. a.** $y = -2$                              **b.** $x = 2$

**15.** $-\dfrac{3}{2}x - 5 = y$

**16.** Find the equation of the line that passes through the points $(0, 4)$ and $(-5, 0)$.

**17.** Identify the independent and dependent variables, and write a linear equation model for each of the following situations. Then give the practical meaning of the slope and vertical intercept in each situation.

**a.** You make a down payment of $50 and pay $10 per month for your new computer.

**b.** You pay $16,000 for a new car whose value decreases by $1500 each year.

**18.** Suppose you enter Interstate 90 in Montana and drive at a constant speed of 75 miles per hour.

**a.** Write a linear model that represents the total distance, $d(t)$ traveled on the highway as a function of time, $t$, in hours.

**b.** Sketch a graph of the function. What are the slope and $d$-intercept of the line? What is the practical meaning of the slope?

**c.** How long would you need to drive at 75 miles per hour to travel a total of 400 miles?

**d.** You start out at 10:00 A.M. and drive for three hours at a constant speed of 75 miles per hour. You are hungry and stop for lunch. One hour later you resume your travel, driving steadily at 60 miles per hour until 6 P.M., when you reach your destination. How far will you have traveled? Sketch a graph that shows the distance traveled as a function of time.

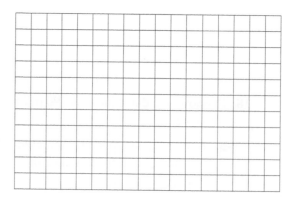

**19.** Determine the equation of the line passing through each pair of points.

   **a.** (0, 6) and (4, 14)

   **b.** $(-9, -7)$ and $(-7, -3)$

**20.** Determine the equation of the line shown on the following graph:

**21.** On an average winter day in Chicago, the Auto Club receives 125 calls from people who need help starting their cars. The number of calls varies, however, depending on the temperature. Here is some data giving the number of calls as a function of the temperature (in degrees Celsius).

| TEMPERATURE (°C) | NUMBER OF AUTO CLUB SERVICE CALLS |
|---|---|
| −12 | 250 |
| −6 | 190 |
| 0 | 140 |
| 4 | 125 |
| 9 | 100 |

   **a.** Sketch the given data on an appropriately scaled and labeled coordinate axes.

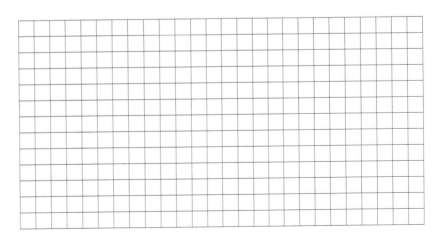

**b.** Use your graphing calculator to determine the equation of the regression line for the data in the preceding table.

**c.** Use your regression equation from part b, $y = -7.11x + 153.9$, to determine how many service calls the Auto Club can expect if the temperature drops to $-20°C$.

**22. a.** Graph the following piecewise function.

$$f(x) = \begin{cases} 2x - 1 & \text{if } x \le 1 \\ 3 & \text{if } 1 < x \le 4 \\ -4x & \text{if } x > 4 \end{cases}$$

**b.** Is this piecewise function continuous? Explain.

*The bracketed numbers following each concept indicate the activity in which the concept is discussed.*

| CONCEPT / SKILL | DESCRIPTION | EXAMPLE |
|---|---|---|
| **Delta notation for change** [2.1] | Let $y_1$ and $y_2$ represent the values corresponding to $x_1$ and $x_2$, respectively. As the variable $x$ changes in value from $x_1$ to $x_2$, the change is represented by $\Delta x = x_2 - x_1$ and the change in $y$ is represented by $\Delta y = y_2 - y_1$. | Given the $x$-$y$-pairs (4, 14) and (10, 32), $\Delta x = 10 - 4 = 6$ and $\Delta y = 32 - 14 = 18$. |
| **Average rate of change over an interval** [2.1] | The quotient $$\frac{\Delta y}{\Delta x} = \frac{y_2 - y_1}{x_2 - x_1}$$ is called the average rate of change of $y$ with respect to $x$ over the $x$-interval from $x_1$ to $x_2$. | <table><tr><td>x</td><td>-3</td><td>4</td><td>7</td><td>10</td></tr><tr><td>y</td><td>0</td><td>14</td><td>27</td><td>32</td></tr></table> The average rate of change over the interval from $x = 4$ to $x = 10$ is $$\frac{\Delta y}{\Delta x} = \frac{32 - 14}{10 - 4} = \frac{18}{6} = 3.$$ |
| **Linear function** [2.2] | A linear function is one whose average rate of change of $y$ with respect to $x$ from any one data point to any other data point is always the same (constant) value. | <table><tr><td>x</td><td>1</td><td>2</td><td>3</td><td>4</td></tr><tr><td>y</td><td>10</td><td>15</td><td>20</td><td>25</td></tr></table> The average rate of change between any two of these points is 5. |
| **Graph of a linear function** [2.2] | The graph of every linear function is a line. |  |
| **Slope of a line** [2.2] | The slope of the line that contains the two points $(x_1, y_1)$ and $(x_2, y_2)$ is denoted by $m$; $m = \dfrac{\Delta y}{\Delta x} = \dfrac{y_2 - y_1}{x_2 - x_1}$. | The slope of the line containing the two points (2, 7) and (5, 11) is $$\frac{11 - 7}{5 - 2} = \frac{4}{3}.$$ |
| **Positive slope** [2.2] | The graph of every linear function with positive slope is a line rising to the right. A linear function is increasing if its slope is positive. |  |

| | | |
|---|---|---|
| **Negative slope** [2.2] | The graph of every linear function with negative slope is a line falling to the right.<br>A linear function is decreasing if its slope is negative. | |
| **Zero slope** [2.2] | The graph of every linear function with zero slope is a horizontal line. Every point on a horizontal line has the same $y$-value. | |
| **Equation of a horizontal line** [2.2] | The slope, $m$, of a horizontal line is 0, and the $y$-value of each of its points is the same constant value, $c$. Its equation is $y = c$. | An equation of the horizontal line through the point $(-2, 3)$ is $y = 3$. |
| **Undefined slope** [2.2] | A line whose slope is not defined (because its denominator is zero) is a vertical line.<br>A vertical line is the only line that does not represent a function.<br>Every point on a vertical line has the same input value. | |
| **Equation of a vertical line** [2.2] | The graph of $x = a$ is a vertical line. | The graph of $x = 2$ is a vertical line 2 units to the right of the $y$-axis. |
| **$x$-intercept of a graph** [2.3] | The $x$-intercept is the point at which the graph crosses the $x$-axis. Its ordered-pair notation is $(a, 0)$; that is, the $y$-value is equal to zero. | A line with $x$-intercept $(-3, 0)$ crosses the $x$-axis 3 units to the left of the origin. |
| **$y$-intercept of a graph** [2.3] | The $y$-intercept is the point at which the graph crosses the $y$-axis. Its ordered-pair notation is $(0, b)$; that is, the $x$-value is equal to zero. | A line with $y$-intercept $(0, 5)$ crosses the $y$-axis 5 units above the origin. |
| **Slope-intercept form of the equation of a line** [2.3] | Represent the independent variable by $x$, the dependent variable by $y$. Denote the slope of the line by $m$, the $y$-intercept by $(0, b)$. Then the coordinate pair, $(x, y)$, of *every* point on the line satisfies the equation $y = mx + b$. | The line with equation $y = 3x + 4$ has a slope of 3 and $y$-intercept $(0, 4)$. The point $(2, 10)$ is on the line because its coordinates satisfy the equation:<br>$10 = 3(2) + 4$ |

| Rewriting the equation of a line in slope-intercept form [2.3] | A nonvertical line whose equation is not in slope-intercept form can be rewritten in slope-intercept form by solving the equation for $y$. | The equation of the line $5x - 2y = 6$ can be rewritten by solving for $y$: |
|---|---|---|

The equation of the line $5x - 2y = 6$ can be rewritten by solving for $y$:

$-2y = 6 - 5x$    Subtract $5x$.

$\dfrac{-2y}{-2} = \dfrac{6}{-2} - \dfrac{5x}{-2}$    Divide by $-2$.

$y = -3 + \dfrac{5}{2}x$ or $y = \dfrac{5}{2}x - 3$

**Identifying the slope and y-intercept** [2.3]

The slope can now be identified as the coefficient of the $x$-term. The $y$-intercept can be identified as the constant term.

The slope is $\dfrac{5}{2}$.

The $y$-intercept is $(0, -3)$.

---

**Reflection across the x-axis** [2.4]

If the graph of $y = f(x)$ is reflected across the $x$-axis, then the equation of the resulting graph is $y = -1f(x)$. The graphs of $y = f(x)$ and $y = -1f(x)$ are mirror images across the $x$-axis. The $y$-values of each point in the original graph changes sign. The $x$-values remain the same.

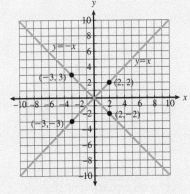

The graphs of $y = -1x$ is a reflection of $y = x$ across the $x$-axis.

---

**Vertical stretch and shrink** [2.4]

If the graph of $y = f(x)$ is vertically stretched (shrunk) by a factor of $a$, then the equation of the steretched (shrunk) graph is $y = af(x)$. The number $a$ is called the stretch (shrink) factor. The $y$-value of each point in the graph of $y = f(x)$ is multiplied by a factor of $a$. The $x$-values remain the same.

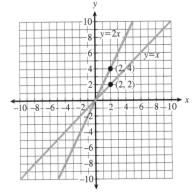

The graph of $y = 2x$ is a vertical stretch of the graph of $y = x$. The stretch factor is 2. The $y$-value of each point of the graph of $y = x$ is doubled to obtain the graph of $y = 2x$.

| **Graph of $y = c \cdot f(x)$, where $c$ is a positive constant** [2.4] | If $c$ is a positive constant, then the graph of $y = c \cdot f(x)$ is the graph of $y = f(x)$ <br> **i.** vertically shrunk by a factor of $c$, if $0 < c < 1$. <br> **ii.** vertically stretched by a factor of $c$, if $c > 1$. |  <br><br> The graph of $y = 2x$ is a vertical stretch of the graph of $y = x$. The graph of $y = 0.5x$ is a vertical shrink of the graph of $y = x$. |
|---|---|---|
| **Transformation** [2.4] | Vertical and horizontal shifts (also called translations), reflections across the $x$-axis, and vertical stretches and shrinks are all examples of transformations. | The graph of $y = -2x + 1$ can be interpreted as a combination of transformations, including vertical shift, stretch, and reflection. |
| **Using the slope and $y$-intercept to write an equation of the line** [2.5] | Given a line whose slope is $m$ and $y$-intercept is $(0, b)$, an equation of the line is $$y = mx + b.$$ | An equation of the line with slope $\frac{2}{3}$ and $y$-intercept $(0, -6)$ is $$y = \frac{2}{3}x - 6.$$ |
| **Determining an equation of a line given the coordinates of two points on the line** [2.5], [2.6] | Given $(x_1, y_1)$ and $(x_2, y_2)$, calculate the slope, $m = \dfrac{\Delta y}{\Delta x} = \dfrac{y_2 - y_1}{x_2 - x_1}$. Substitute the coordinates of either given point for $(h, k)$ and the value of the slope $m$ into the equation $y - k = m(x - h)$. Then, solve for $y$. | See Example 1 in Activity 2.6. |
| **Determining the $x$-intercept of a line given its equation** [2.5], [2.6] | Because the $x$-intercept is the point whose $y$-coordinate is 0, set $y = 0$ in the equation and solve for $x$. | Given the line with equation $y = 2x - 6$, set $y = 0$ to obtain equation $0 = 2x - 6$ $6 = 2x$ $3 = x$ The $x$-intercept is $(3, 0)$. |
| **Linear regression equation** [2.7], [2.8], [2.9] | The linear regression equation is the linear equation that best fits a set of data. | See Problem 2 in Activity 2.9. |

| | | |
|---|---|---|
| **Interpolation** [2.9] | Interpolation is the process of using a regression equation to predict a value of output for an input value that lies within the range of the original data. | See Problem 2 in Activity 2.9. |
| **Extrapolation** [2.9] | Extrapolation is the process of using a regression equation to predict a value of output for an input value that lies outside the range of the original data. | See Problem 2 in Activity 2.9. |
| **Piecewise function** [2.11] | A piecewise function is a function that is defined differently for certain "pieces" of its domain. | $f(x) = \begin{cases} x & \text{if } x \leq 2 \\ -x + 1 & \text{if } x > 2 \end{cases}$ |
| **Absolute value function** [2.11] | The absolute value function is the function defined by $$\lvert x \rvert = \begin{cases} x & \text{if } x \geq 0 \\ -x & \text{if } x < 0 \end{cases}$$ | $\lvert x \rvert = \begin{cases} x & \text{if } x \geq 0 \\ -x & \text{if } x < 0 \end{cases}$ |

# Gateway Review

1. For a certain yard, the fertilizer costs $20. You charge $8 per hour to do yard work. If $x$ represents the number of hours worked on the yard and $f(x)$ represents the total cost, including fertilizer, complete the following table.

| $x$ | 0 | 2 | 3 | 5 | 7 |
|------|----|----|----|----|----|
| $f(x)$ | 20 | 36 | 44 | 60 | 76 |

a. Is the total cost a function of the hours worked? Explain.

b. Which variable represents the input?

c. Which is the dependent variable?

d. Which value(s) of the domain would not be realistic for this situation? Explain.

e. What is the average rate of change from 0 to 3?

f. What is the average rate of change from 5 to 7?

g. What can you say about the rate of change between any two of the points?

h. What kind of relationship exists between the two variables?

i. Write this relationship in the form $f(x) = mx + b$.

j. What is the practical meaning of the slope in this situation?

k. What is the $y$-intercept? What is the practical meaning of this point?

l. Determine $f(4)$.

m. For what value(s) of $x$ does $f(x) = 92$? Interpret your answer in the context of the situation.

**2.** Which of the following sets of data represent a linear function?

**a.**

| x | 0 | 2 | 4 | 6 | 8 |
|---|---|---|---|---|---|
| f(x) | 14 | 22 | 30 | 38 | 46 |

**b.**

| x | 5 | 10 | 15 | 20 | 25 |
|---|---|---|---|---|---|
| y | 4 | 2 | 0 | −2 | −4 |

**c.**

| x | 1 | 3 | 4 | 6 | 7 |
|---|---|---|---|---|---|
| g(x) | 10 | 20 | 30 | 40 | 50 |

**d.**

| t | 0 | 10 | 20 | 30 | 40 |
|---|---|---|---|---|---|
| d | 143 | 250 | 357 | 464 | 571 |

**3. a.** Determine the slope of the line through the points $(5, -3)$ and $(-4, 9)$.

**b.** From the equation $3x - 7y = 21$, determine the slope.

**c.** Determine the slope of the line from its graph.

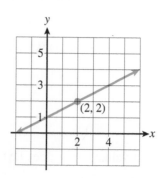

(2, 2)

292

**4.** Write the equation of the line described in each of the following.

    **a.** A slope of 0 and passing through the point $(2, 4)$

    **b.** A slope of 2 and a vertical intercept of $(0, 5)$

    **c.** A slope of $-3$ and passing through the point $(6, -14)$

    **d.** A slope of 2 and passing through the point $(7, -2)$

    **e.** A line with no slope passing through the point $(2, -3)$

    **f.** A slope of $-5$ and a horizontal intercept of $(4, 0)$

    **g.** A line passing through the points $(-3, -4)$ and $(2, 16)$

**5.** Given the following graph of the linear function, determine the equation of the line.

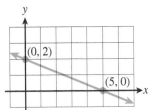

**6. a.** The building where your computer graphics store is located is 10 years old and has a value of $200,000. When the building was 1 year old, its value was $290,000. Assuming that the building's depreciation is linear, express the value of the building as a function, $f$, of its age, $x$, in years.

    **b.** What is the slope of the line? What is the practical meaning of the slope in this situation?

**c.** What is the *y*-intercept? What is the practical meaning of the *y*-intercept in this situation?

**d.** What is the *x*-intercept? What is the practical meaning of the *x*-intercept in this situation?

**7.** Determine the *y*-intercept of the following functions. Solve for *y* if necessary.

   **a.** $y = 2x - 3$

   **b.** $y = -3$

   **c.** $x - y = 3$

   **d.** What relationship do the graphs of these functions have to one another?

   **e.** Use your graphing calculator to graph the functions in parts a–c on the same coordinate axes. Compare your results with part d.

**8.** Determine the slopes and *y*-intercepts of each of the following functions. Solve for *y* if necessary.

   **a.** $y = -2x + 1$

   **b.** $2x + y = -1$

   **c.** $-4x - 2y = 6$

   **d.** What relationship do the graphs of these functions have to one another?

   **e.** Use your graphing calculator to graph the functions in parts a–c on the same coordinate axes. Compare your results with part d.

9. Determine the slopes and $y$-intercepts of each of the following functions. Solve for $y$ if necessary.

   a. $y = -3x + 2$

   b. $3x + y = 2$

   c. $6x + 2y = 4$

   d. What relationship do the graphs of these functions have to one another?

   e. For two lines to be parallel to each other, what has to be the same?

   f. For two lines to lie on top of each other (coincide), what has to be the same?

   g. Use your graphing calculator to graph the functions in parts a–c on the same coordinate axes. Compare your results with part d.

10. a. Graph the function defined by $y = -2x + 150$. Determine the intercepts. Make sure to include some negative values of $x$.

   b. Using your graphing calculator, verify the graph you have drawn in part a.

   c. Using the graph, determine the domain and range of the function.

   d. Assume that a 150-pound person starts a diet and loses 2 pounds per week for 15 weeks. Write the equation modeling this situation.

**e.** Compare the equation you found in part d with the one given in part a.

**f.** What is the practical meaning of the *x*- and *y*-intercepts you found in part a?

**g.** What is the practical domain and range of this function for the situation given in part d?

**11. a.** You pay a flat fee of $25 per month for your trash to be picked up, and it doesn't matter how many bags of trash you have. Use *x* to represent the number of bags of trash, and write a function, *f*, in symbolic form to represent the total cost of your trash for the month.

**b.** Sketch the graph of this function.

**c.** What is the slope of the line?

**12.** Sketch the graph of the following piecewise function.

$$f(x) = \begin{cases} 4x & \text{if } x < -2 \\ -x + 3 & \text{if } -2 \le x < 1 \\ 5 & \text{if } x \ge 1 \end{cases}$$

**13.** Is the function in Exercise 12 continuous?

**14.** You work as a special events salesperson for a golf course owned by your city. Your salary is based on the following. You receive a flat salary of $1500 per month for sales of $10,000 or less; for the next $30,000 of sales, you receive your salary plus 2% of the sales over $10,000 and up to $40,000; and for any sales exceeding $40,000, you receive your salary and commission of 4% of sales over $40,000.

    **a.** Write a piecewise function, $f$, that specifies the total monthly salary when $x$ represents the amount of sales for the month.

    **b.** Graph the function on your graphing calculator.

    **c.** What is your salary if your sales are $25,000?

    **d.** You need to make $3150 to cover your expenses this month. What will your sales have to be for your salary to be that amount?

**15.** During the years 1994–1998, the number of finishers in the top 30 marathons worldwide increased. The following table gives the total number of finishers (to the nearest hundred) each year, where $t$ represents the number of years after 1994.

| YEARS AFTER 1994, $t$ | 0 | 1 | 2 | 3 | 4 |
|---|---|---|---|---|---|
| NUMBER OF FINISHERS, $n$ | 7800 | 9100 | 10,000 | 10,900 | 12,100 |

    **a.** Enter the data from your table into your calculator. Determine the linear regression equation model, and write the result.

    **b.** What is the slope of the regression line? What is the practical meaning of the slope in this situation?

**c.** What is the *y*-intercept? What is the practical meaning of the *y*-intercept in this situation?

**d.** Use your graphing calculator to graph the regression line in the same screen as the scatterplot. How well do you think the line fits the data?

**e.** Use your regression model to predict the number of finishers worldwide in 2000.

**f.** Did you use interpolation or extrapolation to determine your result in part e? Explain.

**g.** Do you think that the prediction for the year 2024 will be as accurate as that in 2000? Explain.

**16. a.** Sketch the graph of $f(x) = |x + 2|$

**b.** Determine the interval over which the function is increasing. Over which interval is the function decreasing?

**c.** Determine the domain of the function.

**d.** Determine the range of the function.

**e.** Graph $g(x) = -|x + 2|$. How does the graph compare with the graph in part a?

**f.** Let $h(x) = |x| + 2$. Explain what makes the functions $f(x)$ and $h(x)$ similar. How are the functions different?

# Systems of Linear Equations and Inequalities

**ACTIVITY 3.1**
Business Checking
Account

**OBJECTIVES**

1. Solve a system of two linear equations numerically.

2. Solve a system of two linear equations graphically.

3. Solve a system of two linear equations using the substitution method.

4. Recognize the connections between the three methods of solution.

5. Interpret the solution to a system of two linear equations in terms of the problem's content.

In setting up your part-time business, you have two choices for a checking account at the local bank.

| | MONTHLY FEE | TRANSACTION FEE |
|---|---|---|
| **REGULAR** | $11.00 | $0.17 for each transaction |
| **BASIC** | $8.50 | $0.22 for each transaction in excess of 20 |

1. If you anticipate making about 50 transactions each month, which checking account will be more economical?

2. Let $x$ represent the number of transactions. Write an equation that expresses the total monthly cost, $C$, of the regular account in terms of $x$.

3. The equation model for the basic account is not expressed as easily, because the transaction fee does not apply to the first 20 transactions. Assuming that you will write at least 20 checks per month, determine a model for this situation.

4. **a.** Complete the following table for each account, showing the monthly cost for 20, 50, 100, 150, 200, 250, and 300 transactions. Estimate the number of transactions for which the cost of the two accounts comes the closest. If you have a graphing calculator, use the table feature to complete the table.

| NUMBER OF TRANSACTIONS | 20 | 50 | 100 | 150 | 200 | 250 | 300 |
|---|---|---|---|---|---|---|---|
| COST OF REGULAR ($) | 14.40 | 19.50 | | | | | |
| COST OF BASIC ($) | 8.50 | 15.10 | | | | | |

**b.** Use the table feature of the graphing calculator to determine the $x$-value that produces two identical $y$-values. What is that value?

**5. a.** Graph the cost equation for each account on the same coordinate axes. Plot the data points for $x \geq 20$ and then use a straightedge to draw a line connecting each set of points. Be sure to properly scale and label the axes.

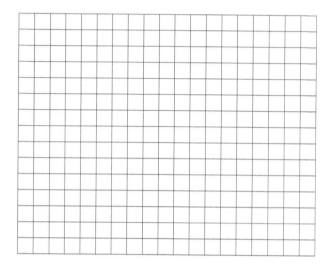

**b.** Estimate the coordinates of the point where the lines intersect. What is the significance of this point?

**c.** Verify your results from part b using your graphing calculator. Use the trace or intersect feature of the graphing calculator. See Appendix A for the procedure for the TI-83/84 Plus. Your final screens should appear as follows.

## System of Two Linear Equations

Two linear equations that relate the same two variables are called a **system of linear equations**. The two cost equations from Problems 2 and 3 form a system of two linear equations,

$$C = 0.17x + 11$$
$$C = 0.22x + 4.10,$$

where $x \geq 20$.

The **solution** of a system is the set of all ordered pairs that satisfy both equations. If the system has exactly one solution, the system is called **consistent**. The solution to the cost system is (138, 34.46). This solution represents the specific number of transactions ($x = 138$) that produce identical costs in both accounts ($34.46).

In Problem 4, you solved the cost system **numerically** by completing a table and noting the value of the input that resulted in the same output. In Problem 5, you solved the cost system **graphically** by determining the coordinates of the point of intersection.

You can also determine an exact solution by solving the system of equations **algebraically**. In Problem 6, you will explore one method—the **substitution method**—for solving systems of equations algebraically.

## Substitution Method for Solving a System of Two Linear Equations

Consider the following system of two linear equations:

$$y = 3x - 10$$
$$y = 5x + 14$$

To solve this system, you need to determine for what value of $x$ are the corresponding $y$-values the same. The goal of the substitution method is to write a single equation involving just one variable.

**6. a.** Use the two linear equations in the preceding system to write a single equation involving just one variable.

**b.** Solve the equation in part a for the variable.

**c.** Use the result in part b to determine the corresponding value for the other variable in the system.

**d.** Write the solution to this system as an ordered pair.

**e.** Verify this solution numerically as well as graphically using the intersection feature of your graphing calculator.

**7.** The algebraic process used in Problem 6 is called the **substitution method** for solving a system of two linear equations. Write a summary of this procedure.

**8. a.** Using the substitution method, solve the following system of checking account cost functions.

$$C = 0.17x + 11$$
$$C = 0.22x + 4.10$$

**b.** Compare your result with the answers obtained using a numerical approach (Problem 4) and a graphing approach (Problem 5).

**c.** Summarize your results by describing under what circumstances the basic account is preferable to the regular account.

**9.** The part-time business is growing to a full-time operation. You need to purchase a car for deliveries.

**a.** An American car costs $13,600 and depreciates $500 a year. Write an equation to determine the resale value, $V$, of the car after $x$ years of use.

**b.** A Japanese car costs $16,000 and depreciates $800 a year. Write an equation to determine the resale value, $V$, of this car after $x$ years of use.

**c.** Write a system of two linear equations that can be used to determine in how many years both cars will have the same resale value.

**d.** Solve this system numerically by completing the following table.

| NUMBER OF YEARS | VALUE OF AMERICAN CAR ($) | VALUE OF JAPANESE CAR ($) |
|---|---|---|
| 1 | | |
| 5 | | |
| 8 | | |
| 10 | | |
| 12 | | |

**e.** Solve the system graphically.

**f.** Solve the system algebraically using the substitution method.

**g.** Compare the results in parts d, e, and f.

Does every system of equations have exactly one solution? Attempt to solve the system in Problem 10 algebraically. Explain your result using a graphical interpretation.

**10.** $y = 2x + 2$
$\quad y = 2x - 1$

The linear system in Problem 10 is said to be **inconsistent**. There is no solution because the lines never intersect. Graphically, the slopes of the lines are equal, but the $x$-intercepts are different. Therefore, the graphs are **parallel lines**. Solving such a system algebraically results in a false equation such as $30 = 0$.

## SUMMARY
### Activity 3.1

1. Two equations that relate the same variables are called a **system of equations**. The solution of a system of equations is the set of all ordered pairs that satisfy both equations.

2. If $x$ is the independent variable and $y$ the dependent variable, then a system of two linear equations is often written in the form
$$y = ax + b$$
$$y = cx + d.$$

3. There are three standard methods for solving a system of equations:

   1. **Numerical method:** Make a table of values for both equations. Identify or estimate the $x$-value that produces the same $y$-value for both equations.

   2. **Graphical method:** Graph both equations on the same grid. If the two lines intersect, the coordinates of the point of intersection represent the solution of the system.

   3. **Substitution method:** Replace (or *substitute*) the variable $y$ in one equation with its algebraic expression in $x$ from the other equation. Solve for $x$. Substitute this $x$-value into either function rule to determine the corresponding $y$-value.

4. A linear system is **consistent** if there is at least one solution, the point of intersection of the graphs.

5. A linear system is **inconsistent** if there is no solution; the lines are parallel.

1. Two companies sell software products. In 2006, company A had total sales of $17.2 million. Its marketing department projects that sales will increase $1.5 million per year for the next several years. Company B had total sales of $9.6 million of software products in 2006 and projects that its sales will increase an average of $2.3 million each year.

Let $n$ represent the number of years since 2006.

   a. Write an equation that represents the total sales (in millions of dollars), $s$, of company A since 2006.

   b. Write an equation that represents the total sales (in millions of dollars), $s$, of company B since 2006.

   c. The two equations in parts a and b form a system. Solve this system to determine the year in which the total sales of both companies will be the same.

2. You are considering installing a security system in your new house. You gather the following information from two local home security dealers for similar security systems.

Dealer 1 charges $3565 to install and $15 per month for a monitoring fee and dealer 2 charges $2850 to install and $28 per month for a monitoring fee.

Although the initial fee of dealer 1 is much higher than that of dealer 2, the monitoring fee is lower.

Let $n$ represent the number of months you have the security system.

   a. Write an equation that represents the total cost, $c$, of the system with dealer 1.

   b. Write an equation that represents the total cost, $c$, of the system with dealer 2.

   c. Solve the system of equations that results from parts a and b to determine in how many months the total cost of the systems will be equal.

    **d.** Describe a circumstance under which the first security system would be preferable to the second system. Assume the two systems are identical except for the installation costs and fees.

*Use substitution to determine algebraically the exact solution to each system of equations in Exercises 3–7. Use the table feature or graphing capability of your calculator to verify these solutions.*

**3.** $p = q - 2$

    $p = -1.5q + 3$

**4.** $n = -2m + 9$

    $n = 3m - 11$

**5.** $y = 1.5x - 8$

    $y = -0.25x + 2.5$

**6.** $z = 3w - 1$

    $z = -3w - 1$

**7.** $y = -3x + 2$

   $y = -3x + 3$

**8.** You like to drive to a special store to buy your favorite gourmet jelly beans for a low price of $1.30 a pound. However, your best friend points out that you are spending about $3 on gas every time you drive to that store and that you might as well buy your jelly beans at your local supermarket for $2.10 a pound. You decide to show him that you are getting enough of those jelly beans to make it worth the trip.

   **a.** Let $x$ represent the number of pounds of jelly beans you purchase. Write an equation to determine the total cost, $C$, if you purchase the jelly beans at the specialty store. Remember to include the cost of the gas.

   **b.** Write an equation to determine the cost, $C$, if you purchase the jelly beans at the local supermarket.

   **c.** The two equations in parts a and b form a system of two linear equations. Solve this system using an algebraic approach.

**d.** Verify your solution using a numerical (table) and graphing approach.

**e.** How many pounds of jelly beans must you buy to make it worth the trip to the specialty store?

**9.** You want to hire someone to prune your trees and shrubs. One service you call charges a $15 consultation fee plus $8 an hour for the actual work. A neighborhood gardener says she does not include a consulting fee, but she charges $10 an hour for her work.

**a.** Write an equation that describes the pruning service's charge, $C$, as a function of $h$, the number of hours worked.

**b.** Write an equation that describes the local gardener's charge, $C$, as a function of $h$, the number of hours worked.

**c.** Whom would you hire for a 3-hour job?

**d.** When, if at all, would it be more economical to hire the other service? Set up and solve a system of equations to answer this question.

**e.** Use your graphing calculator to verify your results.

**10.** You and your friend are going rollerblading at a local park. There is a 5-mile path along the lake that begins at the concession stand. You rollerblade at a rate of 10 miles per hour, and your friend rollerblades at 8 miles per hour. You start rollerblading at the concession stand. Your friend starts farther down the path, 0.5 mile from the concession stand.

    **a.** Write an equation that models your distance from the concession stand as a function of time. What are the units of the input variable? output variable? (Recall that distance = rate · time.)

    **b.** Write an equation that models your friend's distance from the concession stand as a function of time.

    **c.** How long will it take you to catch up to your friend? In that time, how far will you have rollerbladed?

    **d.** Use your graphing calculator to verify your results.

## Collecting and Analyzing Data

**11.** The women's world record time in the 400-meter run is decreasing at a faster rate than the men's record times. A similar occurrence is happening in many events, including the men's and women's Olympic 500-meter speed skating and world record times in the 1500-meter run.

Choose one of these competitions and use linear functions to model the data for the women's event and for the men's event. Use the models to estimate when the women's record time will equal the men's record time.

Work in a group and be prepared to give a presentation to the class. The presentation should include visual displays showing the tables, scatterplots, and equations used in the problem solving process. Be sure to identify the source of your data.

**PROJECT
ACTIVITY 3.2**
Modeling a
Business

**OBJECTIVES**

1. Solve a system of two linear equations by any method.

2. Determine the break-even point of a linear system algebraically and graphically.

3. Interpret break-even points in contextual situations.

You are employed by a company that manufactures solar collector panels. To remain competitive, the company must consider many variables and make many decisions. Two major concerns are those variables and decisions that affect operating expenses (or costs) of making the product and those that affect the gross income (or revenue) from selling the product.

Costs such as rent, insurance, and utilities for the operation of the company are called *fixed costs*. These costs generally remain constant over a short period of time and must be paid whether or not any items are manufactured. Other costs, such as materials and labor, are called *variable costs*. These expenses depend directly on the number of items produced.

1. The records of the company show that fixed costs over the past year have averaged $8000 per month. In addition, each panel manufactured costs the company $95 in materials and $55 in labor. Write an equation for the total cost, $C(n)$, of producing $n$ solar collector panels in one month.

2. A marketing survey indicates that the company can sell all the panels it produces if the panels are priced at $350 each. The revenue (gross income) is the amount of money collected from the sale of the product. Write an equation for the revenue, $R(n)$, from selling $n$ solar collector panels in one month.

3. **a.** Complete the following table:

| $n$, NUMBER OF SOLAR PANELS | 0 | 10 | 20 | 30 | 40 | 50 | 60 |
|---|---|---|---|---|---|---|---|
| $C(n)$, TOTAL COST ($) | | | | | | | |
| $R(n)$, TOTAL REVENUE ($) | | | | | | | |

   **b.** Sketch a graph of the cost and revenue functions using the same set of coordinate axes.

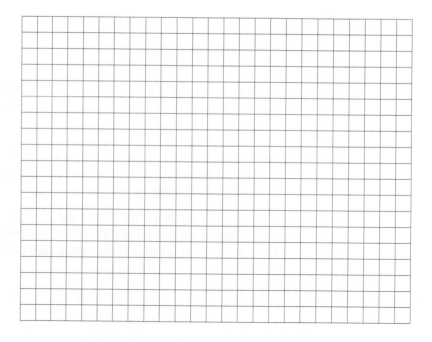

4. The point at which the cost and revenue functions are equal is called the *break-even point*.

   a. Estimate the break-even point on the graph.

   b. What system of equations must be solved to determine the break-even point for your company?

   c. Solve the system algebraically to determine the exact break-even point.

   d. Does your graph confirm the algebraic solution in part b?

5. Revenue exceeds costs when the graph of the revenue function is above the graph of the cost function. For what values of $n$ is $R(n)$ greater than $C(n)$? What do these values represent in this situation?

6. *Profit* is defined as revenue minus cost.

   a. Determine the profit when 25 panels are sold. What does the sign of your answer signify?

   b. Determine the profit when 60 panels are sold.

   c. Write an equation for the profit, $P(n)$, made by selling $n$ solar panels in one month.

**d.** Use your result in part c to compute the profit for selling 25 and 60 panels. How do your results compare with the answers in parts a and b?

**7. a.** Sketch a graph of the profit function $P(n) = 200n - 8000$.

**b.** Determine the intercepts of the graph. What is the meaning of each intercept in this situation?

**c.** What is the slope of the line? What is the practical meaning of slope in this situation?

**EXERCISES**
**Activity 3.2**

1. A company will break even when its revenue, $R$, exactly equals its cost, $C$. $C$ and $R$ depend on $x$, the number of bundles sold.

   You are the manager of a small company producing interlocking paving pieces, called pavers, for driveways. You sell the pavers in bundles that cost $200; each bundle contains 144 pavers. The total cost in dollars, $C(x)$, of producing $x$ bundles of pavers is modeled by $C(x) = 160x + 1000$.

   **a.** Write an equation for the revenue function in dollars, $R$, from the sale of the pavers.

   **b.** Determine the slope and the $C$-intercept of the cost function. Explain the practical meaning of each in this situation.

   **c.** Determine the slope and the $R$-intercept of the revenue function. Explain the practical meaning of each in this situation.

   **d.** Graph the two functions from parts b and c on the same set of axes. Estimate the break-even point from the graph. Express your answer as an ordered pair, giving units. Check your estimate of the break-even point by graphing the two functions on your graphing calculator.

   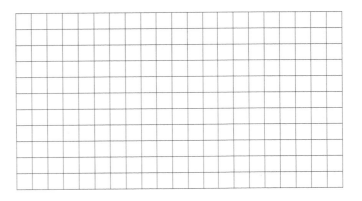

**e.** Determine the exact break-even point algebraically. If your algebraic solution does not approximate your answer from the graph in part d, explain why.

**f.** How many bundles of pavers does the company have to sell for it to break even?

**g.** What is the total cost to the company when you break even? Verify that the cost and revenue values are equal at the break-even point.

**h.** For what values of $x$ will your revenue exceed your cost?

**i.** As manager, what factors do you have to consider when deciding how many pavers to make?

**j.** If you knew you could sell only 30 bundles of pavers, would you make them? Consider how much it would cost you and how much you would make. What if you could sell only 20?

**ACTIVITY 3.3**
Healthy Lifestyle

**OBJECTIVES**

1. Solve a 2 × 2 linear system algebraically using the substitution method and the addition method.
2. Solve equations containing parentheses.

You are trying to maintain a healthy lifestyle. You eat a well-balanced diet and follow a regular schedule of exercise. One of your favorite exercise activities is a combination of walking and jogging in your nearby park.

On one particular day, it takes you 1.3 hours to walk and jog a total of 5.5 miles in the park. You are curious about the amount of time you spent walking and the amount of time you spent jogging during the workout.

Let $x$ represent the time you walked and $y$ represent the time you jogged.

**1.** Write an equation, using $x$ and $y$, for the total time of your walk/jog workout in the park.

**2. a.** If you walk at 3 miles per hour, write an expression that represents the distance you walked.

   **b.** If you jog at 5 miles per hour, write an expression that represents the distance you jogged.

   **c.** Write an equation for the total distance you walked/jogged in the park.

The situation just described can be represented by the following system.

$$x + y = 1.3$$
$$3x + 5y = 5.5.$$

Note that each equation in this system is in standard form $Ax + By = C$, where $A$, $B$ and $C$ are constants, $A$ and $B$ both not zero. One approach to solving this system is to solve each equation for one variable in terms of the other and then use the substitution method.

**3. a.** Solve each of the equations in the system above for $y$.

   **b.** Solve the system in part a using the substitution method.

   **c.** Check your answer graphically using your graphing calculator. You may want to use the window Xmin = −2.5, Xmax = 2.5, Ymin = −2.5, and Ymax = 2.5.

## Addition Method

Sometimes it is more convenient to leave each equation in the linear system in standard form $(Ax + By = C)$ rather than solving for one variable in terms of the other. Look again at the original system.

$$x + y = 1.3 \quad (1)$$
$$3x + 5y = 5.5 \quad (2)$$

If you apply the addition principle of algebra by adding the two equations (left side to left side and right side to right side), you may be able to obtain a single equation containing only one variable.

$$
\begin{array}{ll}
x + y = 1.3 & (1) \\
\underline{3x + 5y = 5.5} & (2) \\
4x + 6y = 6.8 &
\end{array}
$$

In this case, adding the equations does not eliminate a variable. But if you multiply both sides of equation 1 by $-5$, the coefficients of $y$ will be opposite, and the variable $y$ can be eliminated.

$$
\begin{array}{l}
-5(x + y) = -5(1.3) \rightarrow \quad -5x - 5y = -6.5 \\
\phantom{-5(x + y) = -5(1.3) \rightarrow} \quad \underline{3x + 5y = 5.5} \\
\phantom{-5(x + y) = -5(1.3) \rightarrow} \quad -2x + 0 \; = -1
\end{array}
$$
Add the corresponding sides of the equation.

$3x + 5y = 5.5$

Solving the resulting equation, $-2x = -1$, for $x$, you have

$$-2x = -1$$
$$x = \tfrac{1}{2} = 0.5.$$

Substituting for $x$ in $x + y = 1.3$, you have

$$0.5 + y = 1.3$$
$$\text{or } y = 0.8.$$

This method of solving systems algebraically is called the **addition method**.

To solve a $2 \times 2$ linear system by the addition method,

1. line up the like terms in each equation vertically;
2. if necessary, multiply one or both equations by constants so that the coefficients of one of the variables are opposite;
3. add the corresponding sides of the two equations.

4. Solve the following system again using the addition method. Multiply the appropriate equation by the appropriate factor to eliminate $x$ and solve for $y$ first.

$$x + y = 1.3$$
$$3x + 5y = 5.5$$

Not all systems will have convenient coefficients, and you may need to multiply one or both equations by a factor that will produce coefficients of the same variable that are additive inverses, or opposites.

**5.** Consider solving the following system with the addition method.

$$-2x + 5y = -16$$
$$3x + 2y = 5.$$

   **a.** Identify which variable you wish to eliminate. Multiply the appropriate equation by the appropriate factor so that the coefficients of your chosen variable are opposite. Show the two equations after you multiply by the factor. (Remember to multiply both sides of the equation by the factor.)

   **b.** Add the two equations to eliminate the chosen variable.

   **c.** Solve the resulting linear equation.

   **d.** Determine the complete solution. Remember to check by substituting into both of the original equations.

## Substitution Method Revisited

The substitution method of solving a $2 \times 2$ system of linear equations is generally used when each equation in the system is solved for one variable in terms of the other. However, it can be convenient to use the substitution method when only one of the equations is solved for a variable.

Note: as you solve a system such as the walk/jog system using the substitution method (see Example 1), you will encounter an equation involving parentheses. It would be an equation like

$$2(3x - 7) + 9 = -x + 2.$$

To solve this equation, you first simplify the expression on the left-hand side.

$$2(3x - 7) + 9 = -x + 2$$
$$6x - 14 + 9 = -x + 2$$
$$6x - 5 = -x + 2.$$

Use the addition principle to move all $x$-terms to one side,

$$6x - 5 = -x + 2$$
$$\underline{+x \qquad\quad +x}$$
$$7x - 5 = \qquad 2$$

Using the addition principle again to isolate the $x$-term, you have

$$\begin{array}{rcl} 7x - 5 &=& 2 \\ +5 && +5 \\ \hline 7x &=& 7 \end{array}$$

or $x = 1$.

---

**Example 1** *In the walk/jog system,*

$$x + y = 1.3 \quad \textbf{(1)}$$
$$3x + 5y = 5.5 \quad \textbf{(2)}$$

*you could solve equation 1 for y and then substitute for y in equation 2 as follows.*

**Step 1.** Solve $x + y = 1.3$ for $y$.

$$y = 1.3 - x.$$

**Step 2.** Substitute $1.3 - x$ for $y$ in equation 2.

$$3x + 5(1.3 - x) = 5.5$$

**Step 3.** Solve the resulting equation for $x$.

$$3x + 5(1.3 - x) = 5.5 \qquad \text{Remove the parentheses by applying the distributive property.}$$

$$3x + 6.5 - 5x = 5.5 \qquad \text{Collect like terms on the same side.}$$

$$-2x + 6.5 = 5.5$$

$$\underline{\quad -6.5 \quad -6.5 \quad} \qquad \text{Add the opposite of 6.5 to both sides.}$$

$$-2x = -1 \qquad \text{Divide each side by } -2.$$

$$\frac{-2x}{-2} = \frac{-1}{-2}$$

$$x = 0.5$$

**Step 4.** From equation 1, $y = 0.8$ as before.

---

**6. a.** Solve the following linear system using the substitution method in which you solve only one of the equations for a variable.

$$x - y = 5$$
$$4x + 5y = -7.$$

**b.** Check your answer in part a by solving the system using the addition method.

## SUMMARY
**Activity 3.3**

1. There are two methods for solving a 2 × 2 system of linear equations algebraically:

   **a.** the substitution method and

   **b.** the addition method.

2. To solve linear systems by substitution,

   **Step 1.** solve one or both equations for a variable;

   **Step 2.** substitute the expression that represents the variable in one equation for that variable in the other equation;

   **Step 3.** solve the resulting equation for the remaining variable;

   **Step 4.** substitute the value from step 3 into one of the original equations, and solve for the other variable.

3. To solve linear systems by addition with equations written in the form $Ax + By = C$

   **Step 1.** multiply one equation or both equations by the number(s) that will make the coefficients of one of the variables opposites;

   **Step 2.** add the two equations to eliminate one variable and solve the resulting equation;

   **Step 3.** substitute the value from step 2 into one of the original equations, and solve for the other variable.

## EXERCISES
**Activity 3.3**

1. Solve each of the following equations.

   **a.** $5(x + 3) + 4 = 6x - 1 - 5x$

   **b.** $-3(1 - 2x) - 3(x - 4) = -5 - 4x$

   **c.** $2(x + 3) - 4x = 5x + 2$

**2.** Solve the following systems algebraically using the substitution method.

**a.** $y = 3x + 1$

$y = 6x - 0.5$

**b.** $y = 3x + 7$

$2x - 5y = 4$

**c.** $2x + 3y = 5$

$-2x + y = -9$

**d.** $4x + y = 10$

$2x + 3y = -5$

**3.** Solve the following systems algebraically using the addition method.

**a.** $y = 2x + 3$

$y = -x + 6$

**b.** $2x + y = 1$

$-x + y = -5$

**4.** Solve the system both graphically and algebraically.

$3x + y = -18$

$5x - 2y = -8$

**5.** A catering service placed an order for eight centerpieces and five glasses, and the bill was $106. For the wedding reception, they were short one centerpiece and six glasses and had to reorder. This order came to $24. Let $x$ represent the cost of one centerpiece, and let $y$ represent the cost of one glass.

   **a.** Write a system of equations that represents both orders.

   **b.** Solve the system using the substitution method. Interpret your solution.

   **c.** Check your result in part b using the addition method.

   **d.** Use your graphing calculator to solve the system.

**ACTIVITY 3.4**

How Long Can
You Live?

**OBJECTIVES**

1. Solve linear inequalities in one variable numerically and graphically.

2. Use properties of inequalities to solve linear inequalities in one variable algebraically.

3. Solve compound inequalities in one variable algebraically and graphically.

4. Use interval notation to represent a set of real numbers by an inequality.

Life expectancy in the United States is steadily increasing, and the number of Americans aged 100 or older will exceed 850,000 by the middle of this century. Medical advancements have been a primary reason for Americans living longer. Another factor has been the increased awareness of maintaining a healthy lifestyle.

The life expectancies at birth for men and women born after 1975 in the United States can be modeled by the following functions.

$$W(x) = 0.106x + 77.01$$
$$M(x) = 0.200x + 68.94,$$

where $W(x)$ represents the life expectancy for women, $M(x)$ represents the life expectancy for men, and $x$ represents the number of years since 1975 that the person was born. That is, $x = 0$ corresponds to the year 1975, $x = 5$ corresponds to 1980, and so forth.

**1. a.** Complete the following table.

| *Counting the Years* | YEAR | | | | | |
|---|---|---|---|---|---|---|
| | 1975 | 1980 | 1985 | 1990 | 1995 | 2000 |
| *x*, YEARS SINCE 1975 | 0 | 5 | 10 | 15 | 20 | 25 |
| W(x) | | | | | | |
| M(x) | | | | | | |

**b.** For people born between 1975 and 2000, do men or women have the greater life expectancy?

**c.** Is the life expectancy of men or women increasing more rapidly? Explain using slope.

You would like to determine in what birth years the life expectancy of men is greater than that of women. The phrase "greater than" indicates a mathematical relationship called an **inequality**. Symbolically, the relationship can be represented by

$$\underbrace{M(x)}_{\substack{\text{Life expectancy} \\ \text{for men}}} \quad \underbrace{>}_{\text{is greater than}} \quad \underbrace{W(x)}_{\substack{\text{life expectancy} \\ \text{for women.}}}$$

Other commonly used phrases that indicate inequalities are given in the following example.

Example 1

| STATEMENT, WHERE $x$ REPRESENTS A REAL NUMBER | TRANSLATION TO AN INEQUALITY |
|---|---|
| $x$ is greater than 10 | $x > 10$  or  $10 < x$ |
| $x$ is less than 10 | $x < 10$  or  $10 > x$ |
| $x$ is at least 10 | $x \geq 10$ (also read, "$x$ is greater than or equal to 10") |
| $x$ is at most 10 | $x \leq 10$ (also read, "$x$ is less than or equal to 10") |

2. Substitute the appropriate expressions for $M(x)$ and $W(x)$ in $M(x) > W(x)$ to obtain an inequality involving $x$ that can be used to determine the birth years for which the life expectancy of men is greater than that of women.

## Solving Inequalities in One Variable Numerically and Graphically

**DEFINITION**

**Solving an inequality in one variable** is the process of determining the values of the variable that make the inequality a true statement. These values are called the **solutions** of the inequality.

3. Solve the inequality in Problem 2 numerically. That is, continue to construct a table of values (see Problem 1) until you determine the values of the years $x$ (inputs) for which $0.200x + 68.94 > 0.106x + 77.01$. Use the table feature of your graphing calculator.

Therefore, if the trends given by the equations for $M(x)$ and $W(x)$ continue, the approximate solution to the inequality $M(x) > W(x)$ is $x > 86$. That is, according to the models, after the year 2062, men will live longer than women.

**4.** Now, solve the inequality $0.200x + 68.94 > 0.106x + 77.01$ graphically.

   **a.** Use your graphing calculator to sketch a graph of $M(x) = 0.200x + 68.94$ and $W(x) = 0.106x + 77.01$ on the same coordinate axis.

   **b.** Determine the point of intersection of the two graphs using the intersect feature of your graphing calculator. What does the point represent in this situation?

To solve the inequality $M(x) > W(x)$ graphically, you need to determine the values of $x$ for which the graph of $M(x) = 0.200x + 68.94$ is above the graph of

$$W(x) = 0.106x + 77.01.$$

   **c.** Use the graph to solve $M(x) > W(x)$. How does your solution compare to the solution in Problem 3?

**5. a.** Write an inequality to determine the birth years of women whose life expectancy is at least 85.

   **b.** Solve the inequality numerically, using the table feature of your graphing calculator.

   **c.** Use your graphing calculator to solve this inequality graphically.

## Solving Inequalities in One Variable Algebraically

The process of solving an inequality in one variable algebraically is very similar to solving an equation in one variable algebraically. Your goal is to isolate the variable on one side of the inequality symbol. You isolate the variable in an **equation** by performing the same operations to both sides of the equation so as not to upset the **balance**. You isolate the variable in an **inequality** by performing the same operations to both sides so as not to upset the **imbalance**.

**6. a.** Write the statement "15 is greater than 6" as an inequality.

   **b.** Add 5 to each side of $15 > 6$. Is the resulting inequality a true statement? (That is, is the left side still greater than the right side?)

   **c.** Subtract 10 from each side of $15 > 6$. Is the resulting inequality a true statement?

   **d.** Multiply each side of $15 > 6$ by 4. Is the resulting inequality true?

   **e.** Multiply each side of $15 > 6$ by $-2$. Is the left side still greater than the right side?

   **f.** Reverse the direction of the inequality symbol in part e. Is the new inequality a true statement?

Problem 6 demonstrates two very important properties of inequalities.

> **Property 1:** If $a < b$ represents a true inequality, then if
>
>   **i.** the same quantity is added to or subtracted from both sides
>
> or
>
>   **ii.** both sides are multiplied or divided by the same *positive number*, then the resulting inequality remains a true statement and the direction of the inequality symbol remains the same.

For example, because $-4 < 10$, then

   **i.** $-4 + 5 < 10 + 5$ or $1 < 15$ is true;

   $-4 - 3 < 10 - 3$ or $-7 < 7$ is true.

   **ii.** $-4(6) < 10(6)$ or $-24 < 60$ is true;

   $\frac{-4}{2} < \frac{10}{2}$ or $-2 < 5$ is true.

> **Property 2:**   If $a < b$ represents a true inequality, then if both sides are multiplied or divided by the same *negative number*, then the inequality symbol in the resulting inequality statement must be reversed ($<$ to $>$ or $>$ to $<$) in order for the resulting statement to be true.

For example, because $-4 < 10$, then $-4(-5) > 10(-5)$ or $20 > -50$.

Because $-4 < 10$, then $\dfrac{-4}{-2} > \dfrac{10}{-2}$ or $2 > -5$.

Properties 1 and 2 will be true if $a < b$ is replaced by $a \leq b$, $a > b$, or $a \geq b$.

The following example demonstrates how properties of inequalities can be used to solve an inequality algebraically.

**Example 2**   *Solve* $3(x - 4) > 5(x - 2) - 8$.

SOLUTION

$$3(x - 4) > 5(x - 2) - 8 \qquad \text{Apply the distributive property.}$$

$$3x - 12 > 5x - 10 - 8 \qquad \text{Combine like terms on the right side.}$$

$$3x - 12 > 5x - 18$$

$$\underline{-5x \qquad\quad - 5x} \qquad \text{Subtract } 5x \text{ from both sides; the direction of the inequality symbol remains the same.}$$

$$-2x - 12 > -18$$

$$\underline{+ 12 \qquad + 12} \qquad \text{Add 12 to both sides; the direction of the inequality does not change.}$$

$$\dfrac{-2x}{-2} > \dfrac{-6}{-2} \qquad \text{Divide both sides by } -2; \text{ the direction is reversed!}$$

$$x < 3$$

Therefore, from Example 2, any number less than 3 is a solution to the inequality $3(x - 4) > 5(x - 2) - 8$. The solution set can be represented on a number line by shading all points to the left of 3:

The open circle at 3 indicates that 3 is *not* a solution. A closed circle indicates that the number beneath the closed circle *is* a solution. The arrow shows that the solutions extend indefinitely to the left.

7. Solve the inequality $0.200x + 68.94 > 0.106x + 77.01$ algebraically to determine the birth years in which men will be expected to live longer than women. How does your solution compare to the solutions determined numerically and graphically in Problems 3 and 4c?

## Compound Inequality

You have joined a health-and-fitness club. Your aerobics instructor recommends that to achieve the most cardiovascular benefit from your workout, you should maintain your pulse rate between a lower and upper range of values. These values depend on your age.

**8.** If the variable $a$ represents your age, then the lower and upper values for your pulse rate are determined by the following.

$$\text{lower value: } 0.72(220 - a)$$
$$\text{upper value: } 0.87(220 - a).$$

**a.** Determine your lower value.

**b.** Determine your upper value.

For the most cardiovascular benefit, a 20-year-old's pulse rate should be between 144 and 174. The phrase "between 144 and 174" means the pulse rate should be greater than 144 *and* less than 174. Symbolically, this combination or **compound inequality** is written as

$$144 < \text{pulse rate } and \text{ pulse rate} < 174.$$

This statement is written more compactly as $144 < \text{pulse rate} < 174$.

The numbers that satisfy this compound inequality can be represented on a number line as

Other commonly used phrases that indicate compound inequalities involving the word *and* are given in the following example.

### Example 3

| STATEMENT, WHERE $x$ REPRESENTS A REAL NUMBER | TRANSLATION TO A COMPOUND INEQUALITY |
|---|---|
| $x$ is greater than or equal to 10 and less than 20 | $10 \leq x < 20$ |
| $x$ is greater than 10 and less than or equal to 20 | $10 < x \leq 20$ |
| $x$ is from 10 to 20 inclusive | $10 \leq x \leq 20$ |

**9.** Recall that the life expectancy for men is given by the expression $0.200x + 68.94$, where $x$ represents the number of years since 1975. Use this expression to write a compound inequality that can be used to determine in what birth years men will be expected to live into their 80s.

The following example demonstrates how to solve a compound linear inequality algebraically and graphically.

**Example 4**    **a.** *Solve* $-4 < 3x + 5 \leq 11$ *using an algebraic approach.*

SOLUTION

Note that the compound inequality has three parts: left: $-4$, middle: $3x + 5$, and right: 11. To solve this inequality, isolate the variable in the middle part.

$$-4 < 3x + 5 \leq 11$$
$$\underline{-5 \qquad\quad -5 \quad -5} \qquad \text{Subtract 5 from each part.}$$
$$-9 < 3x \leq 6$$
$$-\frac{9}{3} < \frac{3x}{3} \leq \frac{6}{3} \qquad \text{Divide each part by 3.}$$
$$-3 < x \leq 2$$

The solution can be represented on a number line as follows.

**b.** *Solve* $-4 < 3x + 5 \leq 11$ *using a graphical approach.*

SOLUTION

First, graph each part of the inequality on the same coordinate axes.

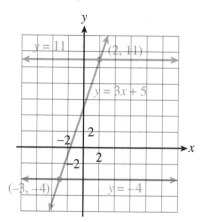

You need to determine values of $x$ for which the graph of $y_2 = 3x + 5$ is above the graph of $y_1 = -4$ and on or below the graph of $y_3 = 11$. Using the graphs, verify that the solution is $-3 < x \leq 2$.

**10. a.** Solve the compound inequality $80 \leq 0.200x + 68.94 < 90$ from Problem 9 to determine in what birth years men will be expected to live into their 80s.

**b.** Verify your results in part a by solving the compound inequality graphically. Use the window from Problem 4a.

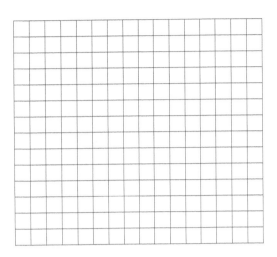

## Interval Notation

Interval notation is an alternative method to represent a set of real numbers described by an inequality. The **closed interval** $[-3, 4]$ represents all real numbers $x$ for which $-3 \leq x \leq 4$. The square brackets [ and ] indicate that the endpoints of the interval are included. The **open interval** $(-3, 4)$ represents all real numbers $x$ for which $-3 < x < 4$. Note that the parenthesis ( and ) indicate that the endpoints are not included. The interval $(-3, 4]$ is said to be **half-open** or **half-closed**. The interval is open at $-3$ (endpoint not included) and closed at 4 (endpoint included).

Suppose you want to represent the set of real numbers $x$ for which $x$ is greater than 3. The symbol $+\infty$ (positive infinity) is used to indicate **unboundedness** in the positive direction. Therefore, the interval $(3, +\infty)$ represents all real numbers $x$ for which $x > 3$. Note that $+\infty$ is always open.

The symbol $-\infty$ (negative infinity) is used to represent unboundedness in the negative direction. Therefore, the interval $(-\infty, 5]$ represents all real numbers $x$ for which $x \leq 5$.

**1.** In parts a–d, express each inequality in interval notation.

   **a.** $-5 \leq x \leq 10$   **b.** $4 \leq x \leq 8.5$  **c.** $x > -2$      **d.** $x \leq 3.75$

In parts e–h, express each of the following using inequalities.

   **e.** $(-6, 4)$         **f.** $(-\infty, 1.5)$     **g.** $(-2, 2)$        **h.** $(-3, +\infty)$

## SUMMARY
### Activity 3.4

1. The **solution set** of an inequality in one variable is the set of all values of the variable that satisfy the inequality.

2. The direction of an inequality is not changed when

   **i.** The same quantity is added to or subtracted from both sides of the inequality. Stated algebraically,

   If $a < b$, then $a + c < b + c$ and $a - c < b - c$.

   **ii.** Both sides of an inequality are multiplied or divided by the same positive number. If $a < b$, then $ac < bc$, and $\frac{a}{c} < \frac{b}{c}$, whenever $c > 0$.

3. The direction of an inequality is reversed if both sides of an inequality are multiplied by or divided by the same negative number. These properties can be written symbolically as

   **i.** If $a < b$, then $ac > bc$, where $c < 0$;

   **ii.** If $a < b$, then $\frac{a}{c} > \frac{b}{c}$, where $c < 0$.

   The two properties of inequalities above (Items 2 and 3) will still be true if $a < b$ is replaced by $a \leq b, a > b$, or $a \geq b$.

4. Inequalities such as $f(x) < g(x)$ can be solved using three different methods:

   **i.** A **numerical approach**, in which a table of input-output pairs is used to determine values of $x$ for which $f(x) < g(x)$;

   **ii.** A **graphical approach**, in which values of $x$ are located so that the graph of $f$ is below the graph of $g$;

   **iii.** An **algebraic approach**, in which the properties of inequalities are used to isolate the variable.

   Similar statements can be made for solving inequalities of the form $f(x) \leq g(x)$, $f(x) > g(x)$, and $f(x) \geq g(x)$.

## EXERCISES
### Activity 3.4

*In Exercises 1–6, translate the given statement into an algebraic inequality or compound inequality.*

1. To avoid an additional charge, the sum of the length, $l$, width, $w$, and depth, $d$, of a piece of luggage to be checked on a commercial airline can be at most 61 inches.

2. A PG-13 movie rating means that your age, $a$, must be at least 13 years for you to view the movie.

3. The cost, $C(A)$, of renting a car from company A is less expensive than the cost $C(B)$ of renting from company B.

**4.** The label on a bottle of film developer states that the temperature, $t$, of the contents must be kept between 68° and 77° Fahrenheit.

**5.** You are in a certain tax bracket if your taxable income, $i$, is over $24,650, but not over $59,750.

**6.** The range of temperature, $t$, on the surface of Mars is from 28°C to 140°C.

*Solve Exercises 7–14 graphically and algebraically.*

**7.** $3x > -6$

**8.** $3 - 2x \le 5$

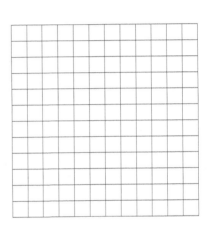

**9.** $x + 2 > 3x - 8$

**10.** $5x - 1 < 2x + 11$

**11.** $8 - x \geq 5(8 - x)$

**12.** $5 - x < 2(x - 3) + 5$

**13.** $\frac{x}{2} + 1 \leq 3x + 2$

**14.** $0.5x + 3 \geq 2x - 1.5$

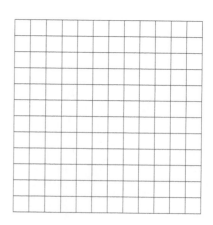

*Solve Exercises 15–16 graphically and algebraically.*

**15.** $1 < 3x - 2 < 4$

**16.** $-2 < \frac{x}{3} + 1 < 5$

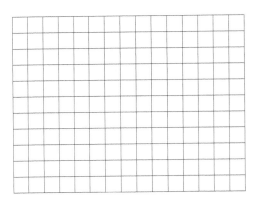

**17.** The consumption of cigarettes is declining. If $t$ represents the number of years since 1985, then the consumption, $C$, is modeled by

$$C = -14.25t + 598.69,$$

where $C$ represents the number of billions of cigarettes smoked per year.

**a.** Write an inequality that can be used to determine the first year in which cigarette consumption is less than 200 billion cigarettes per year.

**b.** Solve the inequality in part a using an algebraic as well as a graphical approach.

**18.** You contact two local rental companies and obtain the following information for the one-day cost of renting a truck:

Company 1: $40.95 per day plus $0.19 per mile

Company 2: $19.95 per day plus $0.49 per mile

Let $n$ represent the total number of miles driven in one day.

**a.** Write an expression to determine the total cost, $C$, of renting a truck for $n$ days from company 1.

**b.** Write an expression to determine the total cost, $C$, of renting a truck for $n$ days from company 2.

**c.** Use the expressions in parts a and b to write an inequality that can be used to determine for what number of miles it is less expensive to rent the truck from company 2.

**d.** Solve the inequality.

**19.** The sign on the elevator in a seven-story building states that the maximum weight it can carry is 1200 pounds. You need to move a large shipment of books to the sixth floor. Each box weighs 60 pounds.

**a.** Let $n$ represent the number of boxes placed in the elevator. If you weigh 150 pounds, write an expression that represents the total weight in the elevator. Assume that only you and the boxes are in the elevator.

**b.** Using the expression in part a, write an inequality that can be used to determine the maximum number of boxes that you can place in the elevator at one time.

**c.** Solve the inequality.

**20.** The following equation is used in meteorology to determine the temperature humidity index:

$$T = \tfrac{2}{5}(w + 80) + 15,$$

where $w$ represent the wet-bulb thermometer reading. For what values of $w$ would $T$ range from 70 to 75?

**21.** The temperature readings in the United States have ranged from a record low of $-79.8°F$ (Alaska, January 23, 1971) to a record high of $134°F$ (California, July 10, 1913).

**a.** If $F$ represents the Fahrenheit temperature, write a compound inequality that represents the interval of temperatures (in °F) in the United States.

**b.** Recall that Fahrenheit and Celsius degrees are related by the formula

$$F = 1.8C + 32.$$

Rewrite the compound inequality in part a to determine the temperature range in degrees Celsius.

c. Solve the compound inequality.

22. You are enrolled in a half-year wellness course. You achieved grades of 70, 86, 81, and 83 on the first four exams. The final exam counts the same as the four exams already given.

a. If $x$ represents the grade on the final exam, write an expression that represents your course average.

b. If your average is greater than or equal to 80 and less than 90, you will earn a B in the course. Using the expression from part a for your course average, write a compound inequality that must be satisfied to earn a B.

c. Solve the inequality.

**ACTIVITY 3.5**
Will Trees Grow?

While researching a term paper on global climate change, you discover a mathematical model that gives the relationship between temperature and amount of precipitation that is necessary for trees to grow. If $t$ represents the average annual temperature in °F, and $p$ represents the annual precipitation in inches, then

$$t \geq 35$$
$$5t - 7p < 70$$

Source: Miller and Thompson, *Elements of Meteorology*.

These inequalities form a **system of inequalities in two variables**. The solution of the system is the set of all ordered pairs of the form $(t, p)$ that make each of the inequalities in the system a true statement.

1. **a.** Will trees grow in a region in which the average annual temperature is 22°F and the annual precipitation is 30 inches?

**b.** Will trees grow if the average annual temperature is 55°F and the annual precipitation is 20 inches?

**c.** In Sydney, Australia, the average annual temperature is 64°F and the annual precipitation is 48 inches. Will trees grow in Sydney?

Actually, there are an infinite number of pairs of values for temperature $t$ and amount of precipitation $p$ for which trees will grow. Although it is not possible to list all the possible combinations, you can visualize all the solution pairs by graphing the solution set of the system. You will return to the Will Trees Grow? system later in this Activity.

## Solving a Linear Inequality in Two Variables by Graphing

To determine the solution set for a system of linear inequalities in two variables, you begin by graphing the solutions of each of the inequalities in the system. Problem 2 guides you through the process of graphing a linear equality.

**2. a.** To obtain the graph of $4x - 2y \geq 8$, first replace the inequality symbol $\geq$ with an equal sign and sketch a graph of the resulting equation.

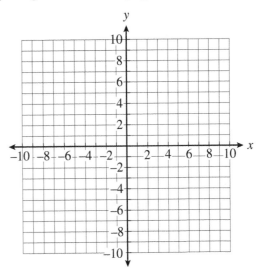

Note that the line $4x - 2y = 8$ divides the coordinate plane into three sets of points:

    **1.** Points on the line that satisfy the equation $4x - 2y = 8$

    **2.** Points below the line that satisfy the inequality $4x - 2y > 8$

    **3.** Points above the line that satisfy the inequality $4x - 2y < 8$.

A **half-plane** is a set of points on one side of a line. Therefore, the set of points above the line $4x - 2y = 8$ is a half-plane. The set of points below the line is also a half-plane. The solution set to a linear inequality will include all the points in one half-plane or the other.

    **b.** Select a point in the half-plane below the line $4x - 2y = 8$. Use this test point to determine if the points in the half-plane are in the solution set of the inequality $4x - 2y \geq 8$.

**c.** Determine if the points in the half-plane above the line $4x - 2y = 8$ are solutions to the inequality $4x - 2y \geq 8$.

**d.** Shade the half-plane in the graph in part a that contains the test point that makes the inequality $4x - 2y \geq 8$ a true statement.

Therefore, the graph of the solution of the inequality $4x - 2y \geq 8$ is the set of all points on the line $4x - 2y = 8$ and in the half-plane below the line $4x - 2y = 8$. The graph gives you a visual representation of the solution set.

**3.** Graph the solution to the linear inequality $2x + 3y < 6$.

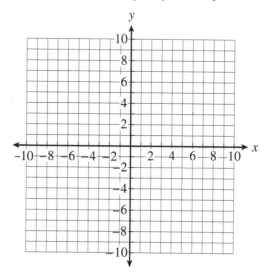

You may have discovered several patterns while graphing the inequalities in Problems 2 and 3. First, if the inequality symbol is $\leq$ or $\geq$, the points along the line are solutions to the inequality and the line is drawn solid. If the inequality symbol is $<$ or $>$, the corresponding line is drawn dashed, indicating that points along the line are not solutions to the inequality.

When the inequality **is written in slope-intercept** form (solved for $y$), another pattern is observed.

> **i.** $y < mx + b$ or $y \leq mx + b$ means the half-plane **below** the line $y = mx + b$ is shaded.
>
> **ii.** $y > mx + b$ or $y \geq mx + b$ means the half-plane **above** the line $y = mx + b$ is shaded.

**4.** Redo Problem 2 using the given patterns. Compare your results.

**5.** You can use the TI-83/84 Plus to graph a linear inequality such as $4x - 2y \geq 8$.

    **a.** Replace the inequality symbol with an equal sign and solve the corresponding equation $4x - 2y = 8$ for $y$.

    **b.** Enter the equation in part a into the calculator and show the graph in the standard window. Your screen should appear as follows:

    **c.** To shade the half-plane below the line, press $y =$ and move the cursor to the extreme left. Next press ENTER key as many times as necessary to change the icon to ◣. Then graph to obtain the following screen:

**6.** Use the graphing calculator to verify the results in Problem 3.

## Solving a System of Linear Inequalities by Graphing

Recall that the solution to a system of linear **equations** is the point of intersection of the graphs of each line in the system. The $(x, y)$ coordinates of the point of intersection makes each equation in the system a true statement. The solution to a system of linear **inequalities** such as

$$4x - 2y \geq 8$$
$$2x + 3y < 6$$

is the intersection of the solutions for each of the inequalities in the system. Therefore, to determine the solution set for a system of linear inequalities, you begin by graphing the solutions of each of the inequalities in the system.

**7. a.** Use the results from Problems 2 and 3 to graph the solution set of the inequalities $4x - 2y \geq 8$ and $2x + 3y < 6$ on the following coordinate system:

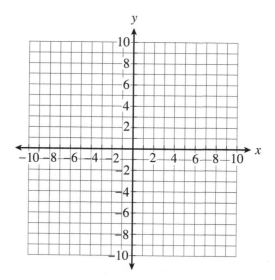

The solution of the system inequalities

$$4x - 2y \geq 8$$
$$2x + 3y < 6$$

is the intersection (if any) of all the solution regions of the inequalities in the system.

**b.** Graph the solution set of the system

$$4x - 2y \geq 8$$
$$2x + 3y < 6$$

on the coordinate system in part a.

**c.** Verify the results in part b using the graphing calculator. After solving each inequality for $y$, enter the corresponding equations in $Y_1$ and $Y_2$. Determine the intersection of the boundary lines using CALC feature. Shade the regions determined by each inequality. The solution set is that portion of the graph that is shaded twice. Your screen should appear as follows:

NOTE: The calculator does not draw dashed lines.

**8.** Solve each of the following systems of linear inequalities using a graphing approach. Verify using a graphing calculator.

**a.** $3x + 2y \geq 16$

$x - 2y \leq 0$

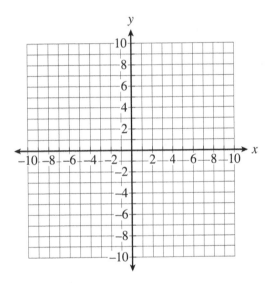

**b.** $y \leq -3x + 9$

$y \geq 2x - 3$

$x \geq 0$

$y \geq 0$

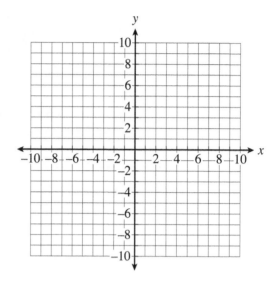

**c.** $y > 2x + 4$

$y \leq 2x - 6$

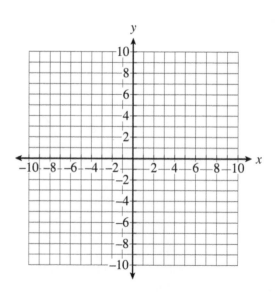

## Corner Points

The graph of the system of inequalities in Problem 8a is

$$3x + 2y \geq 16$$
$$x - 2y \leq 0$$

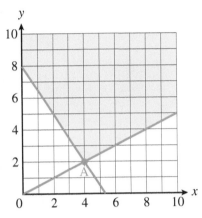

The point A of the intersection of the boundary lines of the shaded region is called a **corner point**.

**9. a.** Determine the coordinates of the corner point A in Problem 8a.

**b.** Is the corner point in part a solution of the given system of inequalities in Problem 8b? Explain.

**10.** By observing the boundary lines, determine if the corner point in Problem 7 is a solution to the system of inequalities.

**11.** Determine the corner points of the system in Problem 8b.

**12.** Return to the system of linear inequalities encountered in the Will the Trees Grow? situation:

$$t \geq 35$$
$$5t - 7p < 70,$$

where $t$ represents the average annual temperature in °F, and $p$ represents the annual precipitation in inches.

   **a.** Graph the given system of inequalities. Determine ordered pairs of the form $(t, p)$.

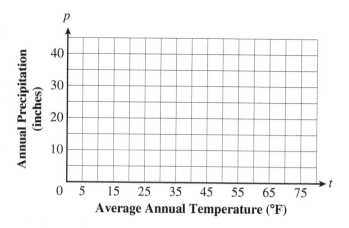

   **b.** Determine the corner point. What is the significance of the point in this situation?

c. Determine whether or not trees will grow in each of the following regions.

| REGION | AVERAGE TEMPERATURE (°F) | ANNUAL PRECIPITATION (INCHES) | (t, p) | CONCLUSION |
|---|---|---|---|---|
| Baghdad, Iraq | 73 | 6 | | |
| Fairbanks, Alaska | 29 | 14 | | |
| Lima, Peru | 66 | 1 | | |
| Aden, Yemen | | | | |

Now, go to additional regions (such as Aden, Yemen) and confirm whether trees will grow there (without artificial support) by inspecting the graph of the system and by direct substitution.

## SUMMARY
### Activity 3.5

1. An inequality of the form $Ax + By < C$, where $A$ and $B$ cannot both equal zero, is called a **linear inequality in two variables**. The symbol $<$ can be replaced by $>$, $\leq$ or $\geq$.

2. The solution set of a linear inequality in two variables $x$ and $y$ is the collection of all the ordered pairs $(x, y)$ whose coordinates satisfy the given inequality.

3. A **half-plane** is the set of all points on one side of a line.

4. To graph a linear inequality in two variables,
   i. Replace the inequality symbol with an equal sign and graph the resulting line. Draw a solid line if the inequality symbol is $\leq$ or $\geq$. If the inequality symbol is $<$ or $>$, draw a dashed line.
   ii. Select a test point not on the line and substitute its coordinates into the inequality. If the resulting statement is true, shade in the area on the same side of the line as the test point. If the resulting statement is false, shade in the area on the opposite side of the line as the test point.

5. Two or more linear inequalities in two variables make up a **system of linear inequalities**.

6. The solution set of a system of linear inequalities in two variables is the collection of all ordered pairs whose coordinates satisfy each linear inequality in the system.

7. To graph a system of linear inequalities in two variables,
   i. Graph each linear inequality in the system.
   ii. The graph of the system is the intersection (overlap) of the shaded areas representing the solutions of the linear inequalities in the system, and any solid line common to all the inequalities in the system.

8. The points determined by the intersection of the boundary lines of the graph of a system of linear inequalities are called **corner points**.

## EXERCISES
### Activity 3.5

*In Exercises 1–7, solve each of the systems of linear inequalities using a graphing approach. Verify using a graphing calculator.*

**1.**     $x \geq 0$

$y \geq 0$

$3x + 2y \leq 6$

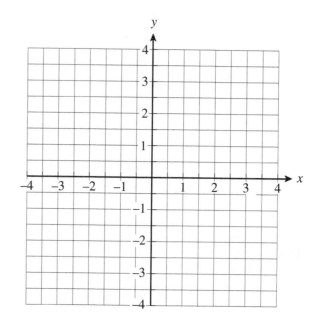

**2.**  $x + y \leq 5$

$2x + y \geq 4$

**3.** $y < x + 3$
$\phantom{3.}\ y \geq -2x + 6$

**4.** $-x + 2y \leq 10$
$\phantom{4.}\ 2x - y \geq -4$
$\phantom{4.}\quad\ y \leq 8$

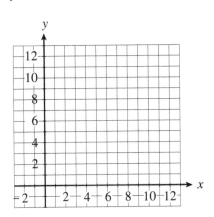

**5.** $2x - y \leq 0$
$\phantom{5.}\ 2x + y \geq 4$
$\phantom{5.}\ -2x + 3y \leq 12$

**6.** $x - 3y \leq 6$
$\phantom{6.}\ x - 3y > -6$

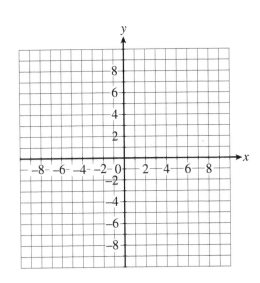

**7.** $x - 3y \geq 6$

$\quad x - 3y < -6$

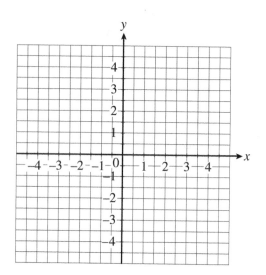

In Exercises 8–10, graph the given system of linear inequalities. Then, determine the corner points of the graph of the solution set.

**8.** $x \geq 1$

$\quad y \geq 0$

$\quad 2x + y \geq 4$

**9.** $y \geq 0$

$\quad y \leq 4$

$\quad x \geq 0$

$\quad x + y \leq 5$

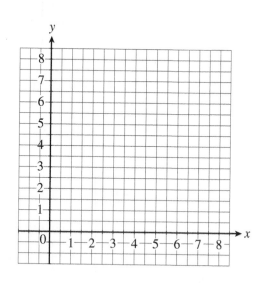

**10.** $3x - 5y \geq -10$

$\qquad x + y \geq 6$

$\qquad\qquad x \leq 5$

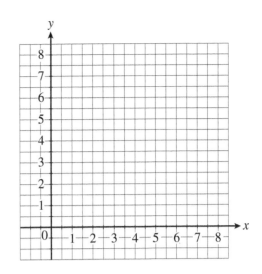

**11.** According to Miller and Thompson in their book *Elements of Meteorology*, grasslands will occur if the following system of inequalities is satisfied:

$$t \geq 35$$

$$5t - 7p \geq 70$$

$$3t - 35p \leq -140,$$

where $t$ represents the average annual temperature in °F, and $p$ represents the annual precipitation in inches.

**a.** Will grass grow in a region in which the average annual temperature is 40°F and the annual precipitation is 30 inches?

**b.** Graph the solution to the given system of linear inequalities.

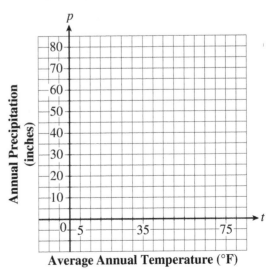

**c.** Determine the corner points.

**12.** The following mathematical model gives a relationship between a person's height and weight that is recommended for a healthy weight:

$$h > 0$$
$$w > 0$$
$$25h - 7w \leq 800$$
$$5h - w \geq 170,$$

where $h$ represents height in inches, and $w$ represents weight in pounds.

**a.** Your friend is 5 feet 7 inches tall and weighs 150 pounds. Is this a healthy weight for your friend? Explain.

**b.** According to the model, is 175 pounds a healthy weight for someone who is 6 feet tall? Explain.

**c.** Graph the solution set to the given system of linear inequalities. Use ordered pairs of the form $(w, h)$.

Weight (pounds)

**13.** The local university requires that students applying for admission must have a combined SAT verbal and math score of at least 1150. The college of arts and sciences has an additional requirement that the verbal score must be at least 550.

   **a.** Write a system of linear inequalities that gives the requirements (constraints) to be admitted to the college of arts and sciences.

   **b.** The maximum score on the verbal part of the SAT is 800. The maximum score on the math portion of the SAT is also 800. Write two linear inequalities that express the constraints on the SAT scores.

   **c.** The total system that describes the SAT requirements for admission to the college of arts and sciences is the combination of inequalities in parts a and b. Solve this system by graphing.

   **d.** Determine two different combinations of verbal and math scores that satisfy the admission requirements to the college of arts and sciences.

**14.** A course in graphics design is being offered in the evening at the local community college. Because of limited space in the lab, the course is limited to 16 students. In order for the college to cover expenses to run the course, at least $2800 must be received in tuition. The college charges $280 per student if you are a resident student (live in the county where the college is located). Students who live outside the county are charged $400 for the course.

   **a.** Could a combination of 10 in-county students and 8 out-of-county students enroll in the course? Explain.

**b.** Could a combination of 6 in-county students and 2 out-of-county students enroll in the course? Explain.

**c.** Let $x$ represent the number of in-county students enrolled in the course and $y$ represent the number of out-of-county students enrolled. Write a system of linear inequalities that describes the constraints (limitations or restrictions) placed on $x$ and $y$ in this situation.

**d.** Solve the system in part c by graphing.

**e.** Give one combination of students (number of in-county and number of out-of-county) that could enroll in the course so that the constraints on the numbers and what they paid are satisfied.

**f.** Write an equation that gives the total amount of tuition, denoted by $T$, in terms of $x$ and $y$.

In the next Activity, you will return to Exercise 14 and determine the specific combination of students (number of in-county and number of out-of-county) that satisfy the constraints in part c **and** maximize the amount of tuition received by the college.

**Activity 3.6**
Helping Hurricane
Victims

**OBJECTIVES**

1. Determine the objective function in a situation where a quantity is to be maximized or minimized.

2. Determine the constraints that place limitations on the quantities contained in the objective function.

3. Translate the constraints into a system of linear inequalities.

4. Use linear programming method to solve a problem in which a quantity is to be maximized or minimized subject to a set of constraints.

Food and clothing are being sent by commercial airplanes to hurricane victims in Florida. Each container of food is estimated to feed 12 people. Each container of clothing is intended to help 5 people. Organizers of the relief effort want to determine the number of containers of food and clothing that should be sent in each plane shipment that will maximize the number of victims helped.

1. If $x$ represents the number of containers of food and $y$ represents the number of containers of clothing, write an equation that expresses the number $N$ of victims to be helped in terms of $x$ and $y$.

The equation developed in Problem 1 is called the **objective function**. In this problem, you want to determine the maximum number of people that can helped. The objective function expresses the quantity to be maximized (or in other cases, minimized) in terms of two or more variables.

The commercial aircraft that are used to ship the containers have weight and volume restrictions. Such limitations are called **constraints**. Each constraint is translated into a linear inequality. All the constraints form a system of linear inequalities. When graphed the solutions to this system of inequalities is called the **feasible region**.

2. The weight and space restrictions imposed by the airlines are summarized as follows:

- The total weight of the supplies cannot exceed 19,000 pounds
- The total volume must be no more than 8,000 cubic feet

Each container of food weighs 50 pounds and occupies 20 cubic feet of space. Each container of clothing weighs 20 pounds and has a volume of 10 cubic feet.

   a. Write the plane's weight constraint as a linear inequality. Remember that $x$ represents the number of containers of food to be shipped and $y$ represents the number of containers of clothing.

   b. Write the plane's space restriction as a linear inequality.

   c. Additional restrictions on the number $x$ of containers of food and the number $y$ of containers of clothing is written as $x \geq 0$ and $y \geq 0$. Explain.

The hurricane victims relief situation can be summarized as follows:

If $N$ represents the number of victims that are helped,

   $x$ represents the number of containers of food per shipment,

   $y$ represents the number of containers of clothing per shipment,

then you want to maximize $N = 2x + 5y$ (objective function) subject to the following set of constraints:

$$50x + 20y \leq 19{,}000$$
$$20x + 10y \leq 8{,}000$$
$$x \geq 0$$
$$y \geq 0$$

## Linear Programming

Linear programming is a mathematical method used to determine a "best" way to attain a certain objective. Essentially, a linear programming problem consists of an objective function and a set of constraints (a system of linear inequalities). Historically, linear programming methods were developed during World War II by the United States Air Force to solve military problems. Applications included the development of efficient plans for air lifting supplies and personnel, effective deployment of aircraft, and "best" strategies for defense.

Since World War II, linear programming methods have been applied in such diverse areas as economics, engineering, manufacturing, agriculture, biology, and the social sciences. Other areas in which linear programming is heavily used include food blending, inventory management, finance management, planning advertisement campaigns, and business management to maximize income or minimize production costs.

Mathematicians can solve linear programming problems involving many variables using computers and sophisticated mathematical methods. The linear programming problems that you will encounter in this book involve two variables. You will solve them using a graphical method. This process is outlined in Problem 3.

**3. a.** Return to the hurricane victim relief situation. Graph the feasible region for the system of constraints given by

$$50x + 20y \leq 19{,}000$$
$$20x + 10y \leq 8{,}000$$
$$x \geq 0$$
$$y \geq 0$$

**b.** Determine the corner points of the feasible region in part a.

In a linear programming problem, the corner points of the feasible region are called **feasible points**.

**c.** Determine the value of the objective function $N = 12x + 5y$ for each of the corner points. Use the following table to help organize your work. The first row is completed.

| CORNER POINTS | x | y | N = 12x + 5y |
|---|---|---|---|
| (0, 0) | 0 | 0 | $N = 12(0) + 5(0) = 0$ |
| (0, 800) | | | |
| (380, 0) | | | |
| (300, 200) | | | |

If a maximum value for the number $N$ of hurricane victims to be helped exists, then the maximum must occur at one of the feasible points.

**d.** What is the maximum number of hurricane victims that can be helped per shipment?

You may have wondered why the maximum value for the objective function must occur at one of the corner points of the feasible region. To literally see it, look more closely at the objective function, which tells you how many people can be helped for a particular combination of clothing and food containers.

**4. a.** Suppose there were 3600 people that were helped. Determine one combination of clothing containers and food containers that would result in this number.

**b.** All the possible solutions to part a lie on the line defined by $3600 = 12x + 5y$. Graph this line with the feasible region. How many points on the line are feasible?

**c.** Now suppose 5000 people were helped. Is there a combination of clothing and food containers that would lead to this result? Support your answer by graphing $5000 = 12x + 5y$ with the feasible region.

If you were to graph more of the lines that result from letting $N$ equal some number between 3600 and 5000, you will see a family of parallel lines. As the number $N$ of people helped decreases from 5000, the lines get closer to the feasible region until finally one of the lines touches the corner point (300, 200). This line represents the solution to the problem, namely $N = 4600$.

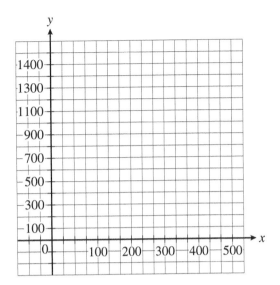

1. Linear programming is a method used to determine the maximum or minimum values of a quantity that are dependent upon variable quantities that are restricted.

2. A linear programming problem consists of an objective function and a set of constraints.

3. The **objective function** is expressed as an equation that describes a quantity to be maximized or minimized in terms of two or more variables.

4. The **constraints** are the limitations or restrictions placed on the variables that the quantity to be maximized (or minimized) depends. Each constraint is written as a linear inequality.

5. All the constraints form a system of linear inequalities. The graph of the solution set of this system is called the **feasible region**.

6. The corner points determined by the intersection of the boundary lines of the feasible region are called **feasible points**.

7. Solving a linear programming problem:

    1. Determine all the constraints and express as a system of linear inequalities.

    2. Determine an equation for the objective function.

    3. Graph the constraints and determine the feasible region.

    4. Determine the corner points of the feasible region.

    5. Determine the value of the objective function at each corner point (feasible point).

    6. The solution is determined by the feasible point that yields the maximum (or minimum) value of the objective function.

**EXERCISES**
Activity 3.6

1. Solve this linear programming problem by graphing the feasible region and testing the corner points to determine the maximum value for the objective function.

   Maximize $z = 5x + 5y$ with the constraints

   $2x + y \leq 8$

   $x + 3y \leq 9$

   $x \geq 0$

   $y \geq 0$

   | CORNER POINTS | x | y | Z = 5x + 5y |
   |---|---|---|---|
   |  |  |  |  |
   |  |  |  |  |
   |  |  |  |  |
   |  |  |  |  |

2. Solve this linear programming problem by graphing the feasible region and testing the corner points to determine the maximum value for the objective function.

   Maximize $z = 4x + y$ with the constraints   $4x - 3y \leq 20$

   $2x + y \leq 20$

   $x + 3y \leq 30$

   $x \geq 0$

   $y \geq 0$

   | CORNER POINTS | x | y | Z = 4x + y |
   |---|---|---|---|
   |  |  |  |  |
   |  |  |  |  |
   |  |  |  |  |
   |  |  |  |  |
   |  |  |  |  |

3. A course in graphics design is being offered in the evening at the local community college. Because of limited space in the lab, the course is limited to 16 students. In order for the college to cover expenses to run the course, at least $2800 must be received in tuition. The college charges $280 per student if you are a resident student (live in the county where the college is located). Students who live outside the county are charged $400 for the course.

   **a.** Identify the constraints.

**b.** Let $x$ represent the number of in-county students enrolled in the course and $y$ represent the number of out-of-county students enrolled. Write a system of linear inequalities that describes the constraints (limitations or restrictions) placed on $x$ and $y$ in this situation.

**c.** Graph the solution to the set of constraints in part b. Determine the corner points.

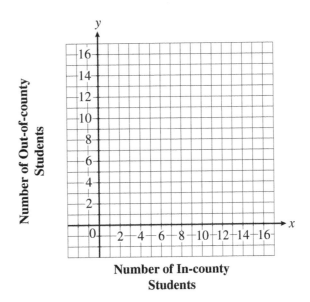

**Number of In-county Students**

**d.** The administration of the college wants to maximize the amount of tuition. Write an equation that gives the amount of tuition, denoted by $T$, received by the college for the graphics design course.

**e.** Complete the following table.

| CORNER POINT | x | y | T = 280x + 400y |
|---|---|---|---|
| (0, 7) | 0 | 7 | 280(0) + 400(7) = 2800 |
| (0, 16) | | | |
| (10, 0) | | | |
| (16, 0) | | | |

**f.** For what combination of students that could enroll in the course result in a maximum amount of tuition for the college. What is the maximum tuition for the course? Is this what you expected?

**4.** You have just inherited $15,000. After consulting with your parents, you decide to spend $3000 on a used car for transportation to school and your part-time job. The remaining $12,000 is to be invested for college in the following funds:

- a municipal bond fund having a 7% yield
- a local Credit Union CD (Certificate of Deposit) having a 5% yield
- a high-risk stock that should have a 12% return

In order to minimize risk, you decide to invest at most $2000 in the high-risk stock. For tax considerations, you decide to invest at least twice as much in the municipal bond (tax free) as in the Credit Union's CD.

**a.** Let $x$ represent the amount to be invested in bonds and $y$ represent the amount to be invested in CDs. Write an expression in terms of $x$ and $y$ that represents the amount to be invested in the high-risk stock.

**b.** The amount of money to be invested in each fund cannot be negative. Express this constraint using three linear inequalities.

**c.** In the statement of the problem, an additional constraint was placed upon the amount of money to be invested in the high-risk stock. Express this constraint as a linear inequality.

**d.** Express the remaining constraint on the amounts of money to be invested as a linear inequality.

**e.** List the complete set of constraints as a system of linear inequalities.

**f.** Graph the feasible region for the set of constraints in part e.

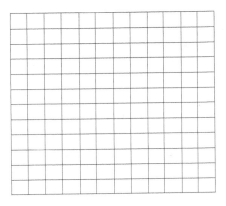

**g.** Determine the corner points.

**h.** You need to determine the amount of money to be invested in each fund in order to maximize the yield (return) after one year. Determine an equation for the yield $Y$ in terms of $x$ and $y$. The resulting equation defines the objective function.

**i.** Determine the value of the objective function for each of the corner points.

| CORNER POINT | $x$ | $y$ | $Y = -0.05x - 0.07y + 1440$ |
|---|---|---|---|
| | | | |
| | | | |
| | | | |
| | | | |

**j.** How much money should be invested in each fund to maximize your yield?

**5.** Your Key Club is sponsoring a program on drinking and driving for students and their parents. Admission is a $3 donation from each parent that attends and $2 donation from each student. The event will be held in the high school theater, which has a 300-seat capacity. The proceeds will be donated to a health fund for needy families.

**a.** If $x$ represents the number of parents that attend and $y$ represents the number of students that attend, write an equation that expresses the total amount $A$ of proceeds of the event in terms of $x$ and $y$. This equation represents the objective function.

**b.** Write the theater's seating capacity as a linear equality.

**c.** An additional requirement is that every two parents must bring at least one student. Write this restriction as a linear inequality in terms of $x$ and $y$.

**d.** Are there any additional restrictions on the values of $x$ and $y$? Explain.

**e.** Write the constraints of this situation as a system of linear inequalities.

**f.** Graph the feasible region of the set of constraints in part.

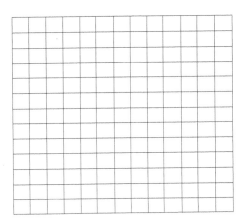

**g.** Determine the corner points of the solution set in part f.

**h.** Determine the value of the objective function $A = 3x + 2y$ for each of the corner points. Use the following table to organize your calculations.

| CORNER POINTS | x | y | $A = 3x + 2y$ |
|---|---|---|---|
|  |  |  |  |
|  |  |  |  |
|  |  |  |  |

**i.** Do you want to maximize or minimize the objective function in this situation? Explain.

**j.** How many parents and students should attend in order to maximize the amount of proceeds?

**6.** A 4-H club plans to grow Christmas trees as a class project. There is a 1200 square foot plot of land available at their school to grow balsam fir and Douglas fir trees. The profit for each balsam fir tree is $15 and for each Douglas fir is $18. A balsam fir requires 10 square feet of space and 6 pounds of fertilizer. A Douglas fir requires 12 square foot of space and 4 pounds of fertilizer. There are only 576 pounds of fertilizer available. Determine the number of each type of fir tree the club should grow to maximize their profit.

| CORNER POINTS | x | y | |
|---|---|---|---|
| | | | |
| | | | |
| | | | |
| | | | |

**ACTIVITY 3.7**
Healthy Burgers

Almost everyone has become more health conscious these days. Changes in eating styles have reflected efforts to improve nutrition. Awareness of fat, fiber and protein content of many foods is closely studied by consumers at the grocery store.

A local food processing company is planning a new line of meatless burgers composed of two new protein products. The two protein ingredients are

Megasoy, containing 6 grams of fiber and 8 grams of protein in each ounce, and Numyco, containing 6 grams of fiber and 4 grams of protein in each ounce.

The company wishes to minimize their cost while meeting protein and fiber constraints set by their marketing department for each package of burgers. Each package of burgers must contain at least 36 grams of fiber and at least 32 grams of protein.

1. The constraints in this problem are different from those in the Hurricane Relief activity. The fiber and protein content together must be **greater than**, rather than **less than**, a fixed amount. Translate the constraints into linear inequalities. Let $M$ and $N$ represent the number of ounces of Megasoy and Numyco, respectively, in each package of burgers.

2. **a.** Graph the feasible region for the system of constraints.

   **b.** As in previous problems, the feasible region in part a is entirely in the first quadrant, since $M \geq 0$ and $N \geq 0$. Describe how the feasible region in part a. is different from the feasible regions encountered in the previous activity.

   **c.** Determine all the corner points.

3. The objective function to be minimized is the cost of the two ingredients to be used in one package of burgers.

    a. If each ounce of Megasoy costs 9 cents and each ounce of Numyco costs 12 cents, write the equation for the objective function, and determine its value at each corner point.

| CORNER POINT | M | N | C = 9M + 12N |
|---|---|---|---|
|  |  |  |  |
|  |  |  |  |
|  |  |  |  |

    b. How many ounces of Megasoy and Numyco should be used to minimize the cost?

As you have seen, the feasible region for a linear programming problem can literally be any of the regions bounded by a collection of lines, even a region extending to infinity. The more constraints in a problem, the more linear boundaries, and hence more corner points that need to be checked.

## Efficient use of Energy

In the following problem, the Energy department wishes to set a standard for designing a new power plant that will minimize greenhouse gas emissions. Two sources of energy are considered, liquefied coal and a new biofuel. A facility can be designed to use both fuels. The design decision centers on how much of each fuel to use. The following table lists the properties of one unit of each type of fuel.

| FUEL | ENERGY PRODUCED (Kilowatts) PER UNIT | USEFUL BYPRODUCTS (Grams) PER UNIT | ESTIMATED COST (Dollars) PER UNIT | GREENHOUSE GAS EMISSION (Grams) PER UNIT |
|---|---|---|---|---|
| Liquefied Coal | 3.5 | 1.2 | 3.2 | 23.5 |
| Biofuel | 2.8 | 2.5 | 4.50 | 18.8 |

*Note:* A more realistic problem would involve many variables and be much more complex than this simplified scenario.

4. Translate each of the following constraints into a linear inequality. Let $C$ represent the number of units of liquefied coal and $B$ represent the number of units of biofuel. All constraints refer to the number of units used in one hour.

    a. The design must use at least 50 units of liquefied coal.

    b. The design must use at least 75 units of biofuel.

    c. The energy produced must be at least 800 Kilowatts.

    d. The useful byproducts must be at least 500 grams.

    e. The estimated cost must be no more than $1300.

**5.** Since there are five linear inequalities in this system, the feasible region may have as many as five corner points. Graph each of the five linear inequalities, shade the feasible region, and determine each of the corner points.

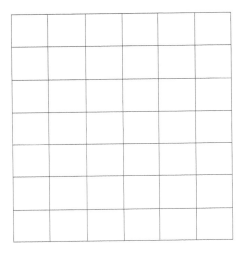

**6. a.** The objective function gives the greenhouse gas emitted by using any combination of liquefied coal and biofuel. Write the equation for the objective function and evaluate it for each corner point of the feasible region. Let $E$ represent the amount of greenhouse gas emitted.

**b.** Recommend which combination of the two fuels will minimize greenhouse gas emission.

As you should have discovered in Problem 6, sometimes two adjacent corner points will both provide the optimal solution. In such a case, there are actually many solutions. Every point on one side of the feasible region will result in the optimal solution. This happens when the family of parallel lines representing the objective function values are also parallel to the line representing one of the constraints. This is verified in Problem 7 for the power plant problem.

**7. a.** Determine the slope of the line resulting from replacing $E$ with the minimal value 5371.4 in the objective function.

**b.** Determine the slope of the line $3.5C + 2.8B = 800$ representing the boundary of the energy produced constraint. Compare your result with the slope in part a.

**SUMMARY**
Activity 3.7

1. A feasible region maybe be enclosed by a polygon or may be unbounded. The objective function may be minimized or maximized. In each case the solution will be at a corner point of the feasible region.

2. Sometimes, there may be many solutions, represented by the points between two corner points of the feasible region.

## EXERCISES
### Activity 3.7

1. For each set of constraints, graph the feasible region and identify the coordinates of each corner point.

   a. $3x + 5y \leq 90$

   $x + 2y \geq 20$

   $x \geq 5$

   $y \geq 0$

   b. $10x + y \geq 120$

   $5x + 3y \geq 180$

   $x \geq 0$

   $y \geq 0$

2. Solve each linear programming problem.

   a. Minimize $C = 15x + 12y$

   subject to:

   $3x + 5y \geq 50$

   $4x + y \geq 27$

   $x \geq$

   $y \geq 4$

| CORNER POINT | x | y | $C = 15x + 12y$ |
|---|---|---|---|
|  |  |  |  |
|  |  |  |  |

**b.** Minimize $F = 1.5g + 2.3t$
subject to:

$1.5g + 2.4t \geq 6.6$

$3.2g + 2.5t \geq 9.6$

$g \geq 0$

$t \geq 1.5$

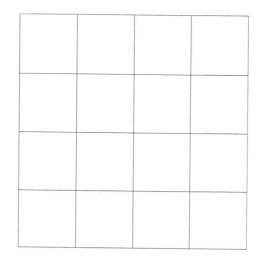

| CORNER POINT | $g$ | $t$ | $F = 1.5g + 2.3t$ |
|---|---|---|---|
|  |  |  |  |
|  |  |  |  |
|  |  |  |  |

**3.** It is possible that the constraints imposed by a situation will result in an empty feasible region.

**a.** Graph the following system of linear inequalities. Are there any possible solutions to the system?

$x + 2y \leq 10$

$2x + 3y \geq 5$

$x \geq 0$

$y \geq 6$

**b.** Normally it is possible to alter one of the constraints so there is a feasible region. Change one of the inequalities to create a feasible region.

**4.** A local company makes gourmet cat food by combining only two ingredients, referred to as brand $X$ and brand $Y$. The table describes the characteristics of a single pound of each brand.

| BRAND | X | Y |
|---|---|---|
| Cost ($ per pound) | $4.00 | $6.00 |
| Ounces of Protein (per pound) | 2 | 5 |
| Ounces of Fat (per pound) | 5 | 5 |
| Ounces of Fiber (per pound) | 8 | 2 |

Each five pound bag of cat food must contain at least 15 ounces of protein, 20 ounces of fat, and 16 ounces of fiber. The company wishes to determine the least expensive combination of brand $X$ and brand $Y$ that will satisfy all the requirements.

**a.** Write the objective function and the system of constraints. Let $x$ and $y$ represent the pounds of brand $X$ and brand $Y$, respectively that go into a five pound bag.

**b.** Graph the feasible region.

**c.** Determine the amount of both brands to use in a five pound bag that will minimize the cost.

**5.** An appliance manufacturer must ship at least 200 stoves to two warehouses on the Gulf coast, one in Galveston, Texas, the other in Mobile, Alabama. Each warehouse can hold as many as 160 stoves at one time. Galveston currently holds 40 stoves, while Mobile has 30 in the warehouse. It costs $18 to ship one stove to Galveston and $14 to ship one to Mobile. How many stoves should be shipped to each warehouse to minimize the cost of shipping? What is that minimum cost?

**PROJECT
ACTIVITY 3.8**
The Labor of
Recycling

**OBJECTIVE**

Solve a linear programming
problem with integer
solutions.

Dwindling natural resources and space for disposing of waste have become major problems in the 21st century. Recycling of basic containers, whether plastic, glass or metal, has become an important business in recent years. In designing your recycling business for efficiency, you need to know how best to allocate your equipment budget. A part of this process is determining how many of each major piece of equipment should be purchased. Sorting, cleaning, grinding and packaging recyclable material requires very specialized equipment.

For this project you need to decide how many glass recycling machines and plastic recycling machines to buy. Each machine has a maximum capacity of material that it can process. The glass recycling machine can process 3.2 tons of glass per hour. The plastic recycling machine can process 1.6 tons of plastic per hour.

The floor space available for the machines is limited, so you need to know that a glass recycling machine requires 180 square feet of floor space and a plastic recycling machine requires 205 square feet of floor space.

The cost for one glass recycling machine is $14,500 and the cost for one plastic recycling machine is $19,600.

1. Translate the following constraints into a system of linear inequalities. Let G represent the number of glass recycling machines and $P$ the number of plastic recycling machines.

   a. The facility needs to be able to process at least 10 tons of glass per hour.

   b. The facility needs to be able to process at least 7 tons of plastic per hour.

   c. The total floor space available for the machines is 3400 square feet.

   d. The budget for recycling machines is $300,000.

2. The objective function to be maximized is the total value of recycled material that can be processed in one hour. Assuming recycled glass has a value of $112 per ton and recycled plastic has a value of $235 per ton, write the equation for the value of the recycled material that is produced in one hour by $G$ glass recycling machines and $P$ plastic recycling machines (assuming all machines are working at full capacity).

3. Now graph the feasible region, determine the corner points, and determine the maximum value of the recycled material based upon the corner points.

| G | P | V = 358.4G + 376P |
|---|---|---|
|   |   |   |
|   |   |   |
|   |   |   |
|   |   |   |

4. Is the solution you determined in Problem 3 really feasible?

5. If you simply rounded the values for G and P in Problem 3, would you have a feasible solution? Check by substituting into each constraint inequality.

Since the number of machines of either type must be whole numbers (positive integers), when the coordinates of the corner points include decimal fractions they are actually not feasible, as is the case in this problem. In such a situation, only integer solutions are feasible. In other words, only the points with integer coordinates lying inside the feasible region are in fact feasible. The solution will be a point close to the optimal corner point, but close examination is required.

The graph in Problem 6 shows a part of the feasible region near the optimal corner point, with integer coordinate points plotted. Of the integer points shown, $(11, 7)$ is close, but not inside the feasible region.

6. Consider the five points that are in the feasible region. Determine the value of the objective function for each point. What is the number of each machine that should be bought to maximize the value of recyclable material?

| POINT | G | P | V = 358.4G + 376P |
|-------|---|---|-------------------|
| (11, 6) | | | |
| (11, 5) | | | |
| (12, 6) | | | |
| (12, 5) | | | |
| (13, 5) | | | |

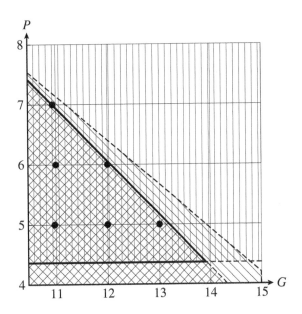

7. What is the maximum value of recyclables that can be processed in one hour? How does this compare to the value you got in Problem 3?

## Activities 3.1–3.8 What Have I Learned?

1. What is meant by a *solution to a system of linear equations*? How is a solution represented algebraically? Graphically?

2. Typically, a linear system of equations has one unique solution. Under what conditions is this not the case?

3. In this section, you solved $2 \times 2$ linear systems four ways. List them. Give an advantage of each approach.

4. Describe a procedure that will combine the following two linear equations in three variables into a single linear equation in two variables.

$$2x + 3y - 5z = 10$$
$$3x - 2y + 2z = 4.$$

5. Explain when the addition method would be more efficient to use than the substitution method as you solve a system of linear equations algebraically.

6. In solving an inequality, explain when you would change the direction of the inequality symbol.

**7. a.** Graph the solution set of the following system of linear inequalities.

$3x + y \geq 4$

$3x + y < 1$

**b.** Does the system in part a have a solution? Explain why or why not.

## Activities 3.1–3.8  How Can I Practice?

**1.** Solve the following systems both graphically and algebraically.

**a.** $x + y = -3$
$y = x - 5$

**b.** $x - 2y = -1$
$4x - 3y = 6$

**c.** $2x - 3y = 7$
$5x - 4y = 0$

**d.** $x - y = 6$
$y = x + 2$

**2.** Rewrite the systems in Exercise 1 in the form

$$y = ax + b$$
$$y = cx + d$$

and check your solutions numerically using the table feature of your graphing calculator.

**3.** Solve the following inequalities algebraically. Check your solutions graphically.

   **a.** $2.5x + 9.8 \geq 14.3$     **b.** $-3x + 14 < 32$     **c.** $-5 \leq 3x - 8 < 7$

**4.** You are going to help your grandmother create a garden of tulips and daffodils. She has space for approximately 80 bulbs. The florist tells you that tulips cost $0.50 per bulb and daffodils cost $0.75 per bulb. How many of each can you purchase if her budget is $52?

   **a.** Write the system of equations.

   **b.** Solve the system algebraically.

   **c.** Check your solution graphically using your graphing calculator.

**5.** You need some repair work done on your truck. Towne Truck charges $80 just to examine the truck and $30 per hour for labor costs. World Transport Co. charges $50 for the initial exam and $40 per hour for the labor.

   **a.** Write a cost equation for each company. Use $y$ to represent the total cost of doing the work and $x$ to represent the number of hours of labor.

**b.** Complete the table of values for the cost functions.

| x (NUMBER OF HOURS) | y, TOWNE TRUCK COST | y, WORLD TRANSPORT COST |
|---|---|---|
| 2 | | |
| 4 | | |
| 6 | | |
| 8 | | |

**c.** Graph the functions.

**d.** From the graph, determine after how many hours the costs will be equal. What will be the total cost?

**e.** Check your solution in part d by solving the system algebraically.

**f.** You think that you have a transmission problem that will take approximately 6 hours to fix. Determine from the graph which company you will hire for this job. Explain.

**6.** Translate each of the following into an inequality statement.

**a.** $x$ is greater than $-5$ and at most 6.

**b.** $x$ is less than $-5$ or x is at least 3.

**c.** $x$ is greater than or equal to $-3$ and less than 4.

**7.** You own a hot dog cart in New York City. Your monthly profit is determined from the expression $1.50x - 50$, where $x$ represents the number of hot dogs sold each month. The number 1.50 in the expression is the profit for each hot dog. The cost of leasing the hot dog stand is the number 50 in the expression $1.50x - 50$.

**a.** To ensure a profit of at least $2000 per month, approximately how many hot dogs do you have to sell? Write the inequality and solve.

**b.** Your profit has been fluctuating between $1500 and $2200 per month. Determine approximately between what two values your hot dog sales have to be to realize this range of profit. Write the inequality and solve.

8. The formula $A = P + Prt$ represents the value, $A$, of an investment of $P$ dollars at a yearly simple interest rate, $r$, for $t$ years.

   **a.** Write an equation to model the value, $A$, of an investment of $100 at 8% for $t$ years.

   **b.** Write an equation to model the value $A$ of an investment of $120 at 5% for $t$ years.

   **c.** Assuming $A$ has the same value, the equations in parts a and b form a system of two linear equations. Solve this system using an algebraic approach.

   **d.** Interpret your answer in part c.

9. Assuming equal costs, when warehouse workers use hand trucks to load a boxcar, it costs the management $40 for labor for each boxcar. After management purchases a forklift for $2000, it costs only $15 for labor to load each boxcar.

   **a.** Write an equation that models the cost, $C(n)$, of loading $n$ boxcars with a hand truck.

   **b.** Write an equation that models the total cost, $C(n)$, including the purchase price of the forklift, of loading $n$ boxcars with the forklift.

   **c.** The equations in parts a and b form a system of linear equations. Solve the system using an algebraic approach.

   **d.** Interpret your answer in part c in the context of the boxcar situation.

**10.** The sign on the elevator in a 10-story building states that the maximum weight the elevator can carry is 1500 pounds. As part of your work-study program, you need to move a large shipment of books to the sixth floor. Each box weighs 80 pounds.

**a.** Let $n$ represent the number of boxes that you place in the elevator. If you weigh 150 pounds, write an expression that represents the total weight, $w$, in the elevator. Assume that only you and the boxes are in the elevator.

**b.** Using the expression in part a, write an inequality that can be used to determine the maximum number of boxes that you can place in the elevator at one time.

**c.** Solve the inequality in part b.

**11.** The feasible region for a set of constraints is given as

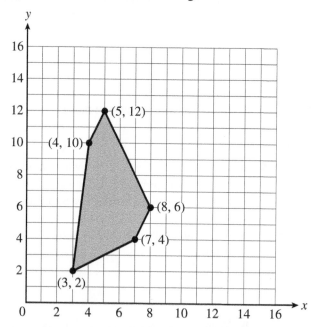

The feasible points are indicated in each corner of the graphed region.

**a.** If the objective function has equation $P = 3x + 2y$, complete the following table.

| CORNER POINT | x | y | P = 3x + 2y |
|---|---|---|---|
|  |  |  |  |
|  |  |  |  |
|  |  |  |  |
|  |  |  |  |
|  |  |  |  |

**b.** Determine the minimum value of the objective function.

**c.** Determine the maximum value of the objective function.

**12.** Solve the following systems of linear inequalities.

**a.** $y \geq \frac{1}{3}x - 2$

$y < -x + 3$

**b.** $x - y \leq 0$

$y \geq -3x + 9$

**13.** Determine the corner points of the solution set of the following system of linear inequalities.

$x \geq 0$

$x \leq 4$

$y \geq 0$

$x + 2y \leq 10$

**14.** Solve each of the following linear programming problems.

   **a.** Maximize the objective function: $I = 0.08x + 0.10y$ subject to the following constraints:

$x + y \leq 12{,}000$

$x \geq 1{,}000$

$y \geq 2{,}000$

| FEASIBLE POINT | $0.08x + 0.10y = 1$ |
|---|---|
|  |  |
|  |  |
|  |  |

**b.** Minimize the objective function: $C = 40x + 25y$
subject to the following constraints:

$$250x + 100y \geq 2000$$
$$100x + 50y \geq 900$$
$$x \geq 0$$
$$y \geq 0$$

| CORNER POINT | $40x + 25y = C$ |
|---|---|
|  |  |
|  |  |
|  |  |

**15.** You earn $7 per hour tutoring students in the Math Tutoring Center in your high school. In addition, you tutor after school for $10 per hour. The tutoring center requires that each student tutor at least three hours per week, but no more than eight hours per week. In order to have enough time to do your own homework, you decide to tutor no more than 20 hours per week.

**a.** Write the objective function that gives the total weekly earnings in terms of the number of hours tutoring.

**b.** List the constraints as a system of linear inequalities.

**c.** Graph the solution set for the set of constraints in part b.

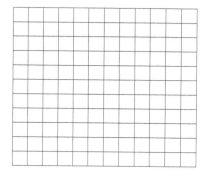

**d.** Determine the corner points.

**e.** Complete the following table to determine the number of hours that you should tutor in order to maximize your weekly earnings.

| CORNER POINT | x | y | T = 10x + 7y |
|---|---|---|---|
|  |  |  |  |
|  |  |  |  |
|  |  |  |  |
|  |  |  |  |

**f.** Determine the maximum weekly earnings.

# Summary

*The bracketed numbers following each concept indicate the activity in which the concept is discussed.*

| CONCEPT / SKILL | DESCRIPTION | EXAMPLE |
|---|---|---|
| **System of equations** [3.1] | Two equations that relate the same variables are called a system of equations. The solution of the system is the ordered pair(s) that satisfies the two equations. | For the system of equations $2x + 3y = 1$ $x - y = 3,$ the ordered pair $(2, -1)$ is a solution of the system because $x = 2, y = -1$ satisfy both equations. |
| **Graphical method for solving a system of linear equations** [3.1] | Graph both equations on the same coordinate system. If the two lines intersect, then the solution to the system is the coordinates of the point of intersection. |  |
| **Substitution method for solving a system of linear equations** [3.1] [3.3] | • Solve one equation for either variable, say $y$ as an expression in $x$.<br>• In the other equation, replace $y$ by the expression in $x$. (This equation should now contain only the variable $x$.)<br>• Solve this equation for $x$.<br>• Use this value of $x$ to determine $y$. | For the system of equations $2x + 3y = 11$ $y = x - 3$<br>• In the second equation, $y$ is already written as an expression in $x$.<br>• Rewrite the first equation $2x + 3(y) = 11$ as $2x + 3(x - 3) = 11.$<br>• Solve this equation for $x$: $2x + 3x - 9 = 11$ $5x = 20$ $x = 4$<br>• Solve for $y$: $y = x - 3$, so $y = 4 - 3 = 1.$ |
| **Consistent system** [3.1] | A linear system is consistent if there is at least one solution. | $y = 3x - 10$ $y = 5x + 14$ is a consistent system. |
| **Inconsistent system** [3.1] | A linear system is inconsistent if there is no solution. The lines are parallel. | $y = 2x + 1$ $y = 2x - 3$ |
| **Solution set of an inequality** [3.4] | The solution set of an inequality in one variable is the set of all values of the variable that satisfy the inequality. | $\{x \mid x \le 3\}$ is the solution set to the inequality $2x + 3 \le 9$. |
| **Solving inequalities: direction of inequality sign** [3.4] | **Property 1.** The direction of an inequality is not changed when<br>  i. the same quantity is added to or subtracted from both sides of the inequality. Stated algebraically, if $a < b$ then $a + c < b + c$ and $a - c < b - c.$ | For example, because $-4 < 10$, then<br>  i. $-4 + 5 < 10 + 5$ or $1 < 15$ is true<br>  $-4 - 3 < 10 - 3$ or $-7 < 7$ is true. |

ii. both sides of an inequality are multiplied or divided by the same positive number. If $a < b$ then

$ac < bc$, where $c > 0$ and $\dfrac{a}{c} < \dfrac{b}{c}$, where $c > 0$.

ii. $-4(6) < 10(6)$ or $-24 < 60$ is true;

$\dfrac{-4}{2} < \dfrac{10}{2}$ or $-2 < 5$ is true.

**Property 2.** The direction of an inequality is reversed if both sides of an inequality are multiplied by or divided by the same negative number. These properties can be written symbolically as:

i. if $a < b$, then $ac > bc$, where $c < 0$.

ii. if $a < b$, then $\dfrac{a}{c} > \dfrac{b}{c}$, where $c < 0$.

Properties 1 and 2 will still be true if $a < b$ is replaced by $a \le b$, $a > b$, or $a \ge b$.

Because $-4 < 10$, then $-4(-5) > 10(-5)$ or $20 > -50$.

Because $-4 < 10$, then $\dfrac{-4}{-2} > \dfrac{10}{-2}$ or $2 > -5$.

These properties will be true if $a < b$ is replaced by $a \le b$, $a > b$, or $a \ge b$.

| | | |
|---|---|---|
| **Solving inequalities of the form $f(x) < g(x)$** [3.4] | Inequalities of the form $f(x) < g(x)$ can be solved using three different methods.<br><br>**Method 1** is a numerical approach, in which a table of input-output pairs is used to determine values of $x$ for which $f(x) < g(x)$.<br><br>**Method 2** is a graphical approach, in which values of $x$ are located so that the graph of $f$ is below the graph of $g$.<br><br>**Method 3** is an algebraic approach, in which the two properties of inequalities are used to isolate the variable. | Solve $5x + 1 \ge 3x - 7$.<br><br><br>$(-4, -19)$<br><br>$5x + 1 \ge 3x - 7$<br>$2x \ge -8$<br>$x \ge -4$ |
| **A compound inequality** [3.4] | A compound inequality is a statement that involves more than 1 inequality symbol $<, >, \le, \ge$, or $\ne$ | $-3 < x + 7 \le 10$ |
| **Linear inequality in two variables** [3.5] | An inequality of the form, $Ax + By < C$, where $A$ and $B$ can not both equal zero, is a linear inequality in two variables. The symbol $<$ can be replaced by $>$, $\le$, or $\ge$. | $2x + 3y \le 10$ is a linear inequality in two variables. |

| | | |
|---|---|---|
| **Graph of a linear inequality in two variables** [3.5] | The graph is the collection all ordered pairs $(x, y)$ whose coordinates satisfy the given inequality. |  |
| | | All points on the solid line $y = -x + 3$ and above the line $y = -x + 3$ represent the graph of $x + y \geq 3$. |
| **Half-plane** [3.5] | A half-plane is the set of all points on one side of a line | All the points above the line $y = -x + 3$ represented in the shaded region in the graph above. |
| **System of linear inequalities in two variables** [3.5] | A system of linear inequalities consists of two or more linear inequalities. | $x + y \leq 5$ <br> $y \leq 2x - 6$ <br> $x \geq 0, y \geq 0$ <br> represents a system of linear inequalities. |
| **Graphing a system of linear inequalities in two variables** [3.5] | Step 1. Graph each linear inequality in the system. <br> Step 2. The graph of the system is the intersection of the shaded regions representing the solutions of the linear inequalities in the system, and any solid line common to all the inequalities in the system. | 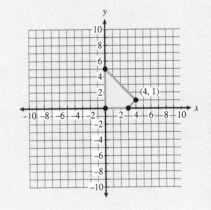 |
| **Corner points** [3.5] | The points determined by the intersection of the boundary lines of the graph of a system of linear inequalities are called corner points. | The corner points in the region above are $(0, 0)$, $(0, 5)$, $(3, 0)$, and $(4, 1)$. |
| **Linear programming** [3.6] | Linear programming is a method used to determine the maximum or minimum value of a quantity that is dependent upon variable quantities that are restricted. | |

| Linear programming problem [3.6] | A linear programming problem consists of an objective function and a set of constraints. | Objective function: $$c = 5x + 5y$$ Constraints: $$2x + y \leq 8$$ $$x + 3y \leq 9$$ $$x \geq 0, y \geq 0$$ |
|---|---|---|
| Objective function [3.6] | The objective function is given as an equation that describes a quantity to be maximized or minimized. | Objective function: $c = 5x + 5y$ Maximize the value c. |
| Constraints [3.6] | The constraints are the limitations or restrictions on the variables that the quantity to be maximized (or minimized) depends on. Each constraint is written as a linear inequality. All the constraints form a system of linear inequalities. | Maximize $c = 5x + 5y$ subject to the following constraints: $$2x + y \leq 8$$ $$x + 3y \leq 9$$ $$x \geq 0, y \geq 0$$ |
| Feasible region [3.6] | The feasible region is the graph of the solution set of the set of constraints. | |
| Feasible points [3.6] | The corner points determined by the intersection of the boundary lines of the feasible region are called feasible points. | The feasible points of the above region are (0, 0), (0, 3), (4, 0) and (3, 2). |
| Solution of a linear programming problem [3.6] | The solution to a linear programming problem is determined by the feasible point that yields the maximum (or minimum) value of the objective function. | (see table below) |

| CORNER POINTS | x | y | $C = 5x + 5y$ |
|---|---|---|---|
| (0, 0) | 0 | 0 | 0 |
| (0, 3) | 0 | 3 | 15 |
| (4, 0) | 4 | 0 | 20 |
| (3, 2) | 3 | 2 | 25 |

The maximum value of c is 25 when $x = 3$ and $y = 2$.

# Gateway Review

1. Which input value results in the same output value for $y_1 = 2x - 3$ and $y_2 = 5x + 3$?

2. Which point on the line given by $4x - 5y = 20$ is also on the line $y = x + 5$?

3. Solve the following system of two linear equations.

   $y = 2x + 8$

   $y = -3x + 3$

4. You sell centerpieces for $19.50 each. Your fixed costs are $500 per month, and each centerpiece costs $8 to produce.

   a. Let $n$ represent the number of centerpieces you sell. Write an equation to determine the cost, $C$.

   b. Write an equation to determine the revenue, $R$.

   c. What is your break-even point (cost = revenue)?

5. Suppose you wish to break even (in Exercise 4) by selling only 25 centerpieces. At what price would you need to sell each centerpiece?

6. Solve the system algebraically.

$$y = -25x + 250$$
$$y = 25x + 300$$

7. Use the addition method to solve the following system.

$$4m - 3n = -7$$
$$2m + 3n = 37$$

8. Solve the following system graphically and algebraically.

$$y = 6x - 7$$
$$y = 6x + 4$$

9. Consider the lines represented by the following pair of equations: $3x + 2y = 10$ and $x - 2y = -2$.

   **a.** Solve the system algebraically.

   **b.** Determine the point of intersection of the lines by solving the system graphically.

   **c.** Determine the point of intersection of the lines by solving the system using the tables feature of your calculator, if available.

10. Use your graphing calculator to estimate the solution to the following system. (Note: Both equations first must be written in the form $y = mx + b$.)

    $$342x - 167y = 418$$

    $$-162x + 103y = -575$$

    Use the window Xmin $= -10$, Xmax $= 0$,

    Xscl $= 2$, Ymin $= -28$, Ymax $= 0$, Yscl $= 2$.

11. Solve the systems of equations. Solve at least one algebraically and at least one graphically.

    **a.** $3x - y = 10$
           $5x + 2y = 13$

    **b.** $4x + 2y = 8$
           $x - 3y = -19$

    **c.** $2x + y = 10$
           $y = -2x + 13$

    **d.** $2x + 6y = 4$
           $x + 3y = 2$

12. The employees of a beauty salon order lunch two days in a row from the corner deli. Lunch on the first day consists of 5 small pizzas and 6 cookies for a total of $27. On the second day, 8 pizzas are ordered along with 4 cookies, totaling $39. To know how much money to pay, employees have to determine how much each pizza and each cookie cost. How much does the deli charge for each pizza and each cookie?

13. Solve the following inequalities algebraically.

    **a.** $2x + 3 \geq 5$
           **b.** $3x - 1 \leq 4x + 5$

14. The weekly revenue, $R(x)$, and cost, $C(x)$, generated by a product can be modeled by the following equations.

$$R(x) = 75x$$
$$C(x) = 50x + 2500$$

Determine when $R(x) \geq C(x)$ numerically, algebraically, and graphically.

| x | R(x) | C(x) |
|---|------|------|
| 0 | | |
| 50 | | |
| 100 | | |
| 150 | | |
| 200 | | |

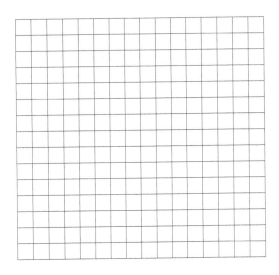

**15.** Graph the solution set for each of the following systems of linear inequalities:

**a.** $x + y \geq 10$
$x + y \leq 12$
$3y \leq x$
$x \geq 0$
$y \geq 0$

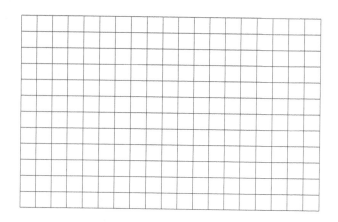

**b.** $x + y < 5$
$2x + y > 4$
$x > 0$
$y > 0$

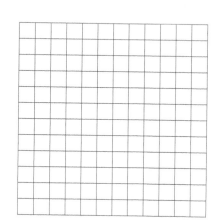

**16.** Solve the following linear programming problems.

**a.** Maximize the objective function: $C = 300x + 400y$ Subject to the following constraints:

$y \geq 1$
$x \geq 1$
$y \leq 4$
$x \leq 6$
$x + y \leq 8$

**b.** Minimize the objective function: $W = 2x + 1.5y$ Subject to the following constraints:

$$x + y \geq 100$$
$$y \geq 2x$$
$$x \geq 20$$

**17.** You are the assistant manager of a local retail store specializing in audio and video equipment. The manager has asked you to do a cost analysis to determine the number of DVD players to order for next month's sale. The manager has given you the following information on two models:

|  | SONY | PANASONIC |
|---|---|---|
| Profit to store | $40 | $60 |
| Wholesale Cost | $250 | $400 |

Due to contract obligations, the store must order at least 20 Panasonic models. The manager projects that the total profit on the sale of the two DVD models must be at least $4,800.

**a.** You need to determine how many of each DVD model to order in order to minimize the cost. Determine the objective function.

**b.** List the constraints as a system of linear inequalities.

**c.** Graph the solution set of the set of constraints in part b.

**d.** Determine the corner points.

**e.** Complete the following table to determine how many units of each model must be ordered in order to minimize the cost. What is the minimum cost?

| CORNER POINT | X | Y | C = 250X + 400Y |
|---|---|---|---|
|  |  |  |  |
|  |  |  |  |

# Problem Solving with Quadratic and Variation Function Models

**ACTIVITY 4.1**

The Amazing Property of Gravity

**OBJECTIVES**

1. Evaluate functions of the form $y = ax^2$.

2. Graph functions of the form $y = ax^2$.

3. Interpret the coordinates of points on the graph of $y = ax^2$ in context.

4. Solve an equation of the form $ax^2 = c$ graphically.

5. Solve an equation of the form $ax^2 = c$ algebraically by taking square roots.

Note: a ≠ 0 in objectives 1–5.

In the sixteenth century, scientists such as Galileo were experimenting with the physical laws of gravity. In a remarkable discovery, they learned that if the effects of air resistance are neglected, any two objects dropped from a height above earth will fall at exactly the same speed. That is, if you drop a feather and a brick down a tube whose air has been removed, the feather and brick will fall at the same speed. Surprisingly, the function that models the distance fallen by such an object in terms of elapsed time is a very simple one:

$$s = 16t^2,$$

where $t$ represents the number of seconds elapsed and $s$ represents distance (in feet) the object has fallen.

The function defined by $s = 16t^2$ indicates a sequence of two mathematical operations:

Start with a value for $t \rightarrow$ *square the value* $\rightarrow$ *multiply by 16* $\rightarrow$ to obtain values for $s$.

**1.** Use the given equation to complete the table.

| t (sec) | s (ft) |
|---------|--------|
| 0       |        |
| 1       |        |
| 2       |        |
| 3       |        |

**2. a.** How many feet does the object fall one second after being dropped?

**b.** How many feet does the object fall two seconds after being dropped?

**3. a.** Determine the average rate of change of distance fallen from time $t = 0$ to $t = 1$.

    **b.** What are the units of measurement of the average rate of change?

    **c.** Explain what the average rate of change indicates about the falling object.

**4.** Determine and interpret the average rate of change of distance fallen from time $t = 1$ to $t = 2$.

**5.** Is the function $s = 16t^2$ a linear function? Explain your answer.

**6. a.** If the object hits the ground after 5 seconds, determine the practical domain of the function.

    **b.** On the following grid, plot the points given in the table in Problem 1 and sketch a curve representing the distance function through the points.

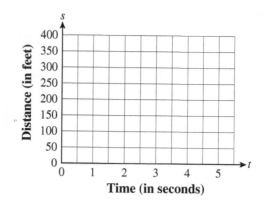

    **c.** Use your graphing calculator to verify the graph in part b. Your graph should resemble the one below.

**7. a.** Confirm that the point (2.5, 100) lies on the graph. What do the coordinates of this point indicate about the falling object?

**b.** Confirm that the point (4.5, 324) lies on the graph. What do the coordinates of this point indicate about the falling object?

**8.** Use the graph to estimate the amount of time it takes the object to fall 256 feet.

**9.** Use $s = 16t^2$ to write an equation to determine the amount of time it takes the object to fall 256 feet.

To solve the equation in Problem 9, you need to reverse the order of operations indicated by the function rule, replacing each operation by its inverse. Here, one of the operations is "square a number." The inverse of squaring is to take a square root.

Start with a value for $s$ → *divide by 16* → *take its square root* → to obtain $t$.

In particular, if $s = 256$ feet:

Start with 256 → *divide by 16* → *take its square root* → to obtain $t$.

$$256 \div 16 = 16 \qquad \sqrt{16} = 4 \qquad t = 4$$

Therefore, you can conclude that it takes four seconds for the object to fall 256 feet.

**10.** Reverse the sequence of operations indicated by $s = 16t^2$ to determine the amount of time it takes an object to fall 1296 feet, approximately the height of a 100-story building.

## Graph of a Parabola

Some interesting properties of the function defined by $s = 16t^2$ arise when you ignore the falling object context and consider just the algebraic rule itself.

Replace $t$ with $x$ and $s$ with $y$ and consider the general equation $y = 16x^2$. First, by ignoring the context, you can allow $x$ to take on a negative, positive, or zero value. For example, suppose $x = -5$. Then

$$y = 16(-5)^2 = 16 \cdot 25 = 400.$$

**11. a.** Use $y = 16x^2$ to complete the table.

| x | −4 | −3 | −2.5 | −2 | −1.5 | −1 | −0.5 | 0 | 0.5 | 1 | 1.5 | 2 | 2.5 | 3 | 4 |
|---|---|---|---|---|---|---|---|---|---|---|---|---|---|---|---|
| y |  |  |  |  |  |  |  | 0 |  | 16 |  | 64 |  | 144 |  |

**b.** What pattern (symmetry) do you notice from the table?

**12. a.** Sketch the graph of $y = 16x^2$ by using the table in Problem 11. Plot the points and then draw a curve through them. Scale the axes appropriately.

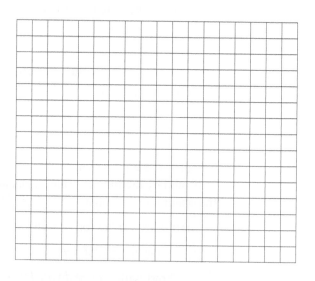

**b.** Use a graphing calculator to produce a graph of this function in the window $-5 \le x \le 5, -100 \le y \le 400$. Your graph should resemble the one below.

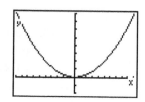

The U-shaped graph of $y = 16x^2$ is called a **parabola**.

**13. a.** The graph of the squaring function defined by $y = x^2$ is a parabola. How is the graph of $y = 16x^2$ related to the graph of $y = x^2$?

**b.** The graphs of $y = 16x^2$ and $y = x^2$ are both U-shaped. Is the graph of $y = 16x^2$ wider or narrower than the graph of $y = x^2$? Explain.

**c.** Is the graph of $y = 0.5x^2$ wider or narrower than the graph of $y = x^2$? Explain. Verify using a graphing calculator.

**d.** If $0 < a < 1$, then is the graph of $y = ax^2$ wider or narrower than the graph of $y = x^2$?

**e.** If $a > 1$, then is the graph of $y = ax^2$ wider or narrower than the graph of $y = x^2$?

## Solving Equations of the Form $ax^2 = c, a \neq 0$

**14. a.** In the table in Problem 11a, how many points on the graph of $y = 16x^2$ lie 256 units above the $x$-axis?

**b.** Identify the points. What are their coordinates?

The $x$-values of the points on the graph of $y = 16x^2$ that lie 256 units above the $x$-axis can be determined algebraically by solving the equation $256 = 16x^2$.

Example 1    *Solve the equation $16x^2 = 256$ algebraically.*

SOLUTION

**Step 1.**    Divide both sides by 16:

$$\frac{16x^2}{16} = \frac{256}{16} \text{ to obtain } x^2 = 16$$

**Step 2.**   Calculate the square root:

When $x$ is no longer restricted to positive (or nonnegative) values only, there are *two* square roots of 16, one denoted by $\sqrt{16}$ and the other denoted by $-\sqrt{16}$. These two square roots are often written in condensed form as $\pm\sqrt{16}$. Since $\sqrt{16} = 4$ and $-\sqrt{16} = -4$, the solutions to the equation $x^2 = 16$ are $x = \pm 4$.

The solution to $16x^2 = 256$ can be written in the following systematic manner.

$16x^2 = 256$

$\dfrac{16x^2}{16} = \dfrac{256}{16}$        Divide both sides by 16.

$x^2 = 16$          Simplify.

$x = \pm\sqrt{16}$        Take the positive and negative square roots.

or equivalently, $x = \pm 4$

**15. a.** How many points on the graph in Problem 12b lie 400 units above the $x$-axis?

    **b.** Identify the points. What are their coordinates?

    **c.** Set up the appropriate equation to determine the values of $x$ for which $y = 400$, and solve it algebraically.

**16.** Solve the following equations algebraically:

    **a.** $x^2 = 36$

    **b.** $2x^2 = 98$

    **c.** $3x^2 = 375$

    **d.** $5x^2 = 50$

**17. a.** Refer to the graph in Problem 12 to determine how many points on the graph of $y = 16x^2$ lie 16 units *below* the x-axis.

**b.** Set up an equation that corresponds to the question in part a.

**c.** How many solutions does this equation have? Explain.

**18.** What does the graph of $y = 16x^2$ (Problem 12) indicate about the number of solutions to the following equations? (You do not need to solve these equations.)

**a.** $16x^2 = 100$     **b.** $16x^2 = 0$     **c.** $16x^2 = -96$

**19.** Solve the following equations:

**a.** $5x^2 = 20$     **b.** $4x^2 = 0$     **c.** $3x^2 = -12$

---

### SUMMARY
**Activity 4.1**

**1.** The graph of a function of the form $y = ax^2$, $a \neq 0$, is a U-shaped curve and is called a **parabola**.

**2.** If $a > 0$, then the larger the value of $a$, the narrower the graph of $y = ax^2$.

**3.** An equation of the form $ax^2 = c$, $a \neq 0$, is solved algebraically by dividing both sides of the equation by $a$ and then taking the positive and negative square roots of both sides.

---

### EXERCISES
**Activity 4.1**

**1.** On the Earth's Moon, gravity is only one-sixth as strong as it is on Earth, so an object on the Moon will fall one-sixth the distance it would fall on Earth in the same time. This means that the gravity distance function for a falling object on the Moon is

$$s = \left(\frac{16}{6}\right)t^2 \text{ or } s = \frac{8}{3}t^2,$$

where $t$ represents time since the object is released, in seconds, and $s$ is the distance fallen, in ft.

    **a.** How far does an object on the Moon fall in three seconds?

    **b.** How long does it take an object on the Moon to fall 96 feet?

    **c.** Graph the Moon's gravity function on a properly scaled and labeled coordinate axis or on a graphing calculator for $t = 0$ to $t = 5$.

    **d.** Use the graph to estimate how long it takes an object on the Moon to fall 35 feet.

    **e.** Write an equation to determine the required time in part d. Solve the equation algebraically.

    **f.** How does your answer in part e compare to your estimate in part d?

**2. a.** The graphs of $y = x^2$, $y = \dfrac{1}{3}x^2$ and $y = 5x^2$ appear in the following graphing calculator screen. Match the equation with the graph.

**b.** Is the graph of $y = 0.75x^2$ wider or narrower than the graph of $y = 10x^2$? Verify using a graphing calculator.

**c.** Is the graph of $y = 10x^2$ wider or narrower than the graph of $y = 5x^2$?

**3.** Solve the following equations:

**a.** $5x^2 = 45$   **b.** $9x^2 = 0$

**c.** $-25x^2 = 100$   **d.** $x^2 = 5$

**e.** $2x^2 = 20$   **f.** $\frac{x^2}{2} = 32$

**4.** Solve the following by first writing the equation in the form $x^2 = c$:

**a.** $x^2 - 49 = 0$   **b.** $15 + c^2 = 96$   **c.** $3a^2 - 21 = 27$

In a right triangle, as shown in the following diagram, the side $c$ opposite the right angle is called the hypotenuse, and the other two sides $a$ and $b$ are called legs. The Pythagorean theorem states that in any right triangle, the lengths of the three sides are related by the equation $c^2 = a^2 + b^2$.

*Use the Pythagorean theorem to answer Exercises 5–6.*

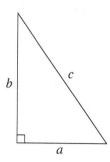

**5.** Determine the length of the hypotenuse in a right triangle with legs 5 inches and 12 inches.

**6.** One leg of a right triangle measures 8 inches and the hypotenuse 17 inches. Determine the length of the other leg.

**ACTIVITY 4.2**
Baseball and the
Sears Tower

**OBJECTIVES**

1. Identify functions of the form $y = ax^2 + bx + c$ as quadratic functions.

2. Explore the role of $a$ as it relates to the graph of $y = ax^2 + bx + c$.

3. Explore the role of $b$ as it relates to the graph of $y = ax^2 + bx + c$.

4. Explore the role of $c$ as it relates to the graph of $y = ax^2 + bx + c$.

Note: $a \neq 0$ in objectives 1–4.

Imagine yourself standing on the roof of the 1450-foot-high Sears Tower in Chicago. When you release and drop a baseball from the roof of the tower, *the ball's height above the ground, H* (in feet), can be modeled as a function of the time, *t* (in seconds), since it was dropped. This height function is defined by

$$H = -16t^2 + 1450.$$

**1. a.** Complete the following table:

| TIME, t (sec) | $H = -16t^2 + 1450$ |
|---|---|
| 0 | |
| 1 | |
| 2 | |
| 3 | |
| 4 | |
| 5 | |
| 6 | |
| 7 | |
| 8 | |
| 9 | |
| 10 | |

**b.** How far does the baseball fall during the first second?

**c.** How far does it fall during the second second?

**2.** Using the height function, $H = -16t^2 + 1450$, determine the average rate of change of $H$ with respect to $t$ over the given interval.

**a.** $0 \leq t \leq 1$ 　　　　　　　　**b.** $1 \leq t \leq 2$

**c.** Based on the results of parts a and b, do you believe that $H = -16t^2 + 1450$ is a linear function? Explain.

**3. a.** If the object hits the ground in approximately 9.5 seconds, what is the practical domain of the height function?

**b.** Determine the practical range of the height function.

**c.** On the following grid, plot the points in Problem 1 and sketch a curve representing the height function.

**d.** Is the graph of the height function the actual path of the object when the ball is dropped? Explain.

Some interesting properties of the function defined by $H = -16t^2 + 1450$ arise when you ignore the falling object context. Replace $H$ with $y$ and $t$ with $x$ and consider the general function defined by $y = -16x^2 + 1450$.

**4.** The graph of $y = -16x^2 + 1450$ can be obtained by performing three transformations on the graph of $y = x^2$. In parts a–c,

 **i.** Use a graphing calculator to sketch a graph resulting from the given transformation. Set the window parameters at Xmin $= -10$, Xmax $= 10$ and Ymin $= -1000$ and Ymax $= 1500$.

 **ii.** Write the equation of the graph.

 **a.** A vertical stretch of the graph of $y = x^2$ by a factor of 16.

 **b.** A reflection of the graph in part a over the $x$-axis.

**c.** A vertical shift of the graph in part b upward 1450 units.

**d.** The graph of $y = x^2$ is U-shaped and is said to open upward. The graph of $y = -16x^2 + 1450$ is also U-shaped. Does the graph open upward or open downward?

**5.** The graph of $y = -16x^2 + 1450$ (setting the window parameters at Xmin = $-10$ and Xmax = 10 and Ymin = $-50$ and Ymax = 1500) should appear as follows:

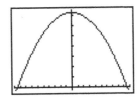

Describe the important features of the graph including the shape, symmetry, and intercepts.

The graph of $y = -16x^2 + 1450$ is a **parabola**. The graph of a parabola is a ∪-shaped figure that opens upward, ∪, or downward, ∩. Parabolas are graphs of a special category of functions called quadratic functions.

## Quadratic Function

### DEFINITION

Any function defined by an equation of the form $y = ax^2 + bx + c$ or $f(x) = ax^2 + bx + c$, where $a$, $b$, and $c$ represent real numbers and $a \neq 0$, is called a **quadratic function**. The dependent variable $y$ is defined by an expression having three terms: the **quadratic term**, $ax^2$, the **linear term**, $bx$, and the **constant term**, $c$. The numerical factors of the quadratic and linear terms, $a$ and $b$, are called the **coefficients** of the terms.

**Example 1**   *$y = -16x^2 + 100$ defines a quadratic function. The quadratic term is $-16x^2$. The linear term is $0x$, although it is not written as part of the expression defining $y$. The constant term is 100. The numbers $-16$ and 0 are the coefficients of the quadratic and linear terms respectively. Therefore, $a = -16$, $b = 0$, and $c = 100$.*

**6.** For each of the following quadratic functions, identify the value of $a$, $b$, and $c$:

| QUADRATIC FUNCTION | $a$ | $b$ | $c$ |
|---|---|---|---|
| $y = 3x^2$ | | | |
| $y = -2x^2 + 3$ | | | |
| $y = x^2 + 2x - 1$ | | | |
| $y = -x^2 + 4x$ | | | |

## The Constant Term $c$

Consider once again the height function $H = -16t^2 + 1450$ from the beginning of the activity.

**7. a.** What is the $H$-intercept of the graph?

**b.** What is the practical meaning of the $H$-intercept in this situation?

**c.** Predict what the graph of $H = -16t^2 + 1450$ would look like if the constant term 1450 were changed to 800. That is, the baseball is dropped from a height of 800 feet rather than 1450 feet. Verify your prediction by graphing $H = -16t^2 + 800$. What does the constant term tell you about the graph of the parabola?

In general, the constant term $c$ of a quadratic function $y = ax^2 + bx + c$ *always* indicates the *y*-intercept of the parabola. The *y*-intercept of any quadratic function is $(0, c)$.

**8.** Graph the parabolas defined by the following quadratic equations. Note the similarities and differences among the graphs, especially the *y*-intercepts. Be careful in your choice of a window.

**a.** $f(x) = 1.5x^2$

**b.** $g(x) = 1.5x^2 + 7$

**c.** $q(x) = 1.5x^2 + 4$

**d.** $s(x) = 1.5x^2 - 4$

## The Effects of the Coefficient *a*

**9. a.** Using transformations, describe how to obtain the graph of $y = 16x^2 + 1450$ from the graph of $y = x^2$.

**b.** Compare the transformations used to graph $y = 16x^2 + 1450$ to the transformations used to graph $y = -16x^2 + 1450$ (see Problem 4). What is different?

**c.** Graph the quadratic function defined by $g(x) = 16x^2 + 1450$ on the same screen as $y = -16x^2 + 1450$. Use the window settings Xmin $= -10$, Xmax $= 10$, Ymin $= -50$, and Ymax $= 3000$.

**d.** What effect does the sign of the coefficient of $x^2$ appear to have on the graph of the parabola?

**10.** Graph the functions $h(x) = -16x^2 + 100, f(x) = -6x^2 + 100$, and $g(x) = -40x^2 + 100$ in the same window. What effect does the magnitude of the coefficients of $x^2$ (namely, $|-16| = 16$, $|-6| = 6$, and $|-40| = 40$) appear to have on the graph of that particular parabola?

The results from Problems 9 and 10 regarding the effects of the coefficient *a* can be summarized as follows:

The graph of a quadratic function defined by $f(x) = ax^2 + bx + c$ is called a parabola.

- If $a > 0$, the parabola opens upward.
- If $a < 0$, the parabola opens downward.
- The magnitude of *a* affects the width of the parabola. The larger the absolute value of *a*, the narrower the parabola.

**11. a.** Does the graph of $y = -3x^2 + 2x - 1$ open upward or downward?

**b.** Is the graph of $h(x) = 0.3x^2$ wider or narrower than the graph of $f(x) = x^2$?

**c.** How do the output values of $h$ and the output values of $f$ compare for the same input value?

**d.** Is the graph of $g(x) = 3x^2$ wider or narrower than the graph of $f(x) = x^2$?

**e.** How do the output values of $g$ and $f$ compare for the same input value?

## The Effects of the Coefficient $b$

Assume for the time being that you are back on the roof of the 1450-foot Sears Tower. Instead of merely releasing the ball, suppose you *throw it down* with an initial velocity of 40 feet per second. Then the function describing its height above ground as a function of time is modeled by

$$H_{down} = -16t^2 - 40t + 1450.$$

If you tossed the ball up with an initial velocity of 40 feet per second, then the function describing its height above ground as a function of time is modeled by

$$H_{up} = -16t^2 + 40t + 1450.$$

**12.** Predict what features of the graphs of $H_{down}$ and $H_{up}$ have in common with $H = -16t^2 + 1450$.

**13. a.** Graph the three functions $H$, $H_{down}$, and $H_{up}$ using the same window setting.

**b.** What effect do the $-40t$ and $40t$ terms seem to have upon the graphs?

In general, if $b = 0$, the turning point of the parabola is located on the $y$-axis. If $b \neq 0$, the turning point will not be on the $y$-axis.

**14.** Set the window of your graphing calculator to Xmin = −8, Xmax = 8, Ymin = −20, and Ymax = 20, and graph the parabolas defined by the following quadratic equations. Note the differences among the graphs, paying careful attention to the effects of the signs of the coefficients $a$, $b$, and $c$ on the graph.

**a.** $y = x^2$

**b.** $y = x^2 - 4x$

**c.** $y = x^2 - 8x$

**d.** $y = x^2 + 6x$

**e.** $y = -x^2 + 6x$

**f.** $y = -x^2 - 8x$

**15.** Match each function with its corresponding graph below, and then verify using your graphing calculator.

**a.** $f(x) = x^2 + 4x + 4$    **b.** $g(x) = 0.2x^2 + 4$    **c.** $h(x) = -x^2 + 3x$

**i.**                        **ii.**                        **iii.**

---

**SUMMARY**
**Activity 4.2**

**1.** The function that has a parabola as its graph is called a **quadratic function**. The equation of a quadratic function with $x$ as the independent variable and $y$ as the dependent variable has the standard form

$$y = ax^2 + bx + c,$$

where $a$, $b$, and $c$ represent real numbers and $a \neq 0$.

**2.** The graph of a quadratic function is called a **parabola**.

3. For the quadratic function defined by $f(x) = ax^2 + bx + c$:
   - If $a > 0$, the parabola opens upward.
   - If $a < 0$, the parabola opens downward.

   The magnitude of $a$ affects the width of the parabola. The larger the absolute value of $a$, the narrower the parabola.

4. If $b = 0$, the turning point of the parabola is located on the y-axis. If $b \neq 0$, the turning point will not be on the y-axis.

5. The constant term, $c$, of a quadratic function $y = ax^2 + bx + c$ always indicates the y-intercept of the parabola. The y-intercept of any quadratic function is $(0, c)$.

## EXERCISES
### Activity 4.2

1. **a.** Complete the following table for $y = x^2$:

| x | y |
|---|---|
| −3 | |
| −2 | |
| −1 | |
| 0 | |
| 1 | |
| 2 | |
| 3 | |

**b.** Use the results of part a to sketch a graph $y = x^2$.

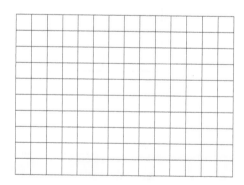

**c.** Use your graphing calculator to compare and check the information for parts a and b. Are the graphs the same?

**d.** What is the coefficient of the term $x^2$?

**e.** From the graph, determine the domain and range of the quadratic function.

**2. a.** Create a table similar to the one in Exercise 1a for $y = -x^2$.

| x | −3 | −2 | −1 | 0 | 1 | 2 | 3 |
|---|---|---|---|---|---|---|---|
| y | | | | | | | |

**b.** Sketch the graph of $y = -x^2$.

**c.** Use your graphing calculator to compare and check the information for parts a and b. Are the graphs the same?

**d.** What is the coefficient of the term $-x^2$?

**e.** How can the graph of $y = -x^2$ be obtained from the graph of $y = x^2$?

**3.** In each of the following functions defined by an equation of the form $y = ax^2 + bx + c$, identify the value of $a$, $b$, and $c$.

**a.** $y = -2x^2$

**b.** $y = \frac{2}{5}x^2 + 3$

**c.** $y = -x^2 + 5x$

**d.** $y = 5x^2 + 2x - 1$

**4.** Predict what the graph of each of the following quadratic functions will look like. Use your graphing calculator to verify your prediction.

**a.** $y = 3x^2 + 5$           **b.** $y = -2x^2 + 1$

    **c.** $y = 0.5x^2 - 3$

5. Graph the following pairs of quadratic functions and describe any similarities as well as any differences that you observe in the graphs:

    **a.** $f(x) = 3x^2, g(x) = -3x^2$          **b.** $h(x) = \frac{1}{2}x^2, f(x) = 2x^2$

    **c.** $g(x) = 5x^2, h(x) = 5x^2 + 2$          **d.** $f(x) = 4x^2 - 3, g(x) = 4x^2 + 3$

    **e.** $f(x) = 6x^2 + 1, h(x) = -6x^2 - 1$

6. Use your graphing calculator to graph the two functions $y_1 = 3x^2$ and $y_2 = 3x^2 + 2x - 2$.

    **a.** What is the vertical intercept of the graph of each function?

    **b.** Compare the two graphs to determine the effect of the linear term $2x$ and the constant term $-2$ on the graph of $y_1 = 3x^2$.

For Exercises 7–11, determine

    **a.** whether the parabola opens upward or downward and

    **b.** the $y$-intercept.

7. $y = -5x^2 + 2x - 4$            **8.** $y = \frac{1}{2}x^2 + x$

**9.** $y = 2v^2 + v + 3$          **10.** $y = 3x^2 + 10$

**11.** $y = -x^2 + 6x - 7$

**12.** Does the graph of $y = -2x^2 + 3x - 4$ have any $x$-intercepts? Explain.

**13. a.** Is the graph of $y = \dfrac{3}{5}x^2$ wider or narrower than the graph of $y = x^2$?

   **b.** For the same $x$-value, which graph would have a larger $y$-value?

**14.** Put the following in order from narrowest to widest.
   **a.** $y = 0.5x^2$          **b.** $y = 8x^2$          **c.** $y = -2.3x^2$

**15.** Use transformations of the graph of $y = x^2$ to obtain a graph of each of the following. Verify using a graphing calculator.
   **a.** $y = -0.5x^2$

   **b.** $y = 2x^2 + 3$

c. $y = -5x^2 - 2$

d. $y = x^2 + 2x + 1$   NOTE: $x^2 + 2x + 1 = (x + 1)^2$

**ACTIVITY 4.3**
The Shot Put

**OBJECTIVES**

1. Determine the vertex or turning point of a parabola.

2. Identify the vertex as a maximum or minimum.

3. Determine the axis of symmetry of a parabola.

4. Identify the domain and range.

5. Determine the y-intercept of a parabola.

6. Determine the x-intercept(s) of a parabola using technology.

7. Interpret the practical meaning of the vertex and intercepts in a given problem.

8. Identify the vertex from the standard form $y = a(x - h)^2 + k$ of the equation of a parabola.

Parabolas are good models for a variety of situations that you encounter in everyday life. Examples include the path of a golf ball after it is struck, the arch (cable system) of a bridge, the path of a baseball thrown from the outfield to home plate, the stream of water from a drinking fountain, and the path of a cliff diver.

Consider the 2000 men's Olympic shot put event, which was won by Finland's Arsi Harju with a throw of 69 feet $10\frac{1}{4}$ inches. The path of his winning throw can be approximately modeled by the quadratic function defined by

$$y = -0.015545x^2 + x + 6,$$

where $x$ is the horizontal distance in feet from the point of the throw and $y$ is the vertical height in feet of the shot above the ground.

1. **a.** After inspecting the equation for the path of the winning throw, which way do you expect the parabola to open? Explain.

   **b.** What is the y-intercept of the graph of the parabola? What practical meaning does this intercept have in this situation?

2. Use your graphing calculator to produce a plot of the path of the winning throw. Be sure to adjust your window settings so that all of the important features of the parabola (including x-intercepts) appear on the screen. Your graph should resemble the following.

3. From the graph, what are the appropriate values for $x$ (practical domain), and $y$ (practical range)?

4. Use the table feature of your graphing calculator to complete the following table:

| x | 10 | 20 | 30 | 40 | 50 |
|---|----|----|----|----|----|
| y |    |    |    |    |    |

## Vertex of a Parabola

An important feature of the graph of any quadratic function defined by $f(x) = ax^2 + bx + c$ is its **turning point**, also called the **vertex**. The turning point of a parabola that opens downward or upward is the point at which the parabola changes direction from increasing to decreasing or decreasing to increasing.

**5. a.** Use the results of Problem 4 to estimate the coordinates of the vertex of the shot put function.

**b.** Use the Trace feature of your graphing calculator to approximate the vertex of the shot put function.

**6.** The vertex is often very important in a situation. What is the significance of the coordinates of the turning point in this problem?

The coordinates of the vertex of a parabola having equation $y = ax^2 + bx + c$ can be determined from the values of $a$ and $b$ in the equation.

## DEFINITION

The **vertex** or turning point of a parabola having equation $y = ax^2 + bx + c$ has coordinates

$$\left(-\frac{b}{2a}, -\frac{b^2 - 4ac}{4a}\right),$$

where $a$ is the coefficient of the $x^2$ term and $b$ is the coefficient of the $x$ term.

Note that the $y$-coordinate of the vertex is determined by substituting the $x$-coordinate of the vertex into the equation of the parabola and evaluating the resulting expression.

**Example 1**   *Determine the vertex of the parabola defined by the equation $y = -3x^2 + 12x + 5$.*

SOLUTION

**Step 1.**   Determine the $x$-coordinate of the vertex by substituting the values of $a$ and $b$ into the formula $x = \frac{-b}{2a}$.

Because $a = -3$ and $b = 12$, you have

$$x = \frac{-(12)}{2(-3)} = \frac{-12}{-6} = 2.$$

**Step 2.**   The $y$-coordinate of the vertex can be determined two ways.

**i.** Substitute $a = -3$, $b = 12$, and $c = 5$ into the expression $-\frac{b^2 - 4ac}{4a}$ and evaluate as follows.

$$-\frac{12^2 - 4(-3)(5)}{4(-3)} = -\frac{144 + 60}{-12} = \frac{-204}{-12} = 17$$

**ii.** The $y$-value of the vertex is the corresponding output value for $x = 2$. Substituting 2 for $x$ in the equation, you have

$$y = -3(2)^2 + 12(2) + 5 = 17.$$

Therefore, the vertex is (2, 17).

Because the parabola in Example 1 opens downward ($a = -3 < 0$), the vertex is the high point (maximum) of the parabola as demonstrated by the following graph of the parabola.

**7.** Determine the vertex of the parabola defined by $y = -0.015545x^2 + x + 6$ (the shot put function).

Rather than using the Trace feature to approximate the vertex of the parabola in Example 1, you can determine the vertex by selecting the maximum option in the Calc menu of your graphing calculator. Follow the prompts to obtain the coordinates of the maximum point (vertex).

For further help with the TI-83/84 Plus, see Appendix A.

**8. a.** Use your graphing calculator to determine the vertex of the parabola having equation $y = -0.015545x^2 + x + 6$ (the shot put function).

**b.** How do the coordinates you determined using the formula (see Problem 7) compare with your results in part a?

**c.** What is the practical meaning of the coordinates of the vertex in this situation?

## Axis of Symmetry of a Parabola

> **DEFINITION**
>
> The **axis of symmetry** is a vertical line that divides the parabola into two symmetrical parts that are mirror images in the line.

Example 2    *Consider the parabola from Example 1 having equation $y = -3x^2 + 12x + 5$. The axis of symmetry of the parabola is $x = 2$. Note that the line of symmetry passes through the vertex of the parabola.*

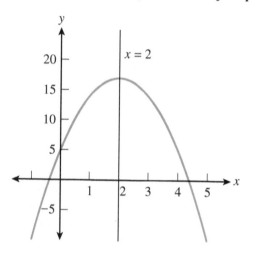

The vertex (turning point) of a parabola lies on the axis of symmetry. Since the $x$-value of the vertex is $x = \dfrac{-b}{2a}$, the equation of the axis of symmetry is

$$x = \frac{-b}{2a}.$$

**9.** What is the axis of symmetry of the shot put function?

## Intercepts of the Graph of a Parabola

The $y$-intercept of the graph of the parabola defined by $y = -3x^2 + 12x + 5$ (see Example 1) can be determined directly from the equation. If $x = 0$, then

$$y = -3(0)^2 + 12(0) + 5 = 5$$

and the $y$-intercept is $(0, 5)$.

In general, the $y$-intercept of the parabola defined by $y = ax^2 + bx + c$ is $(0, c)$.

Because the vertex (2, 17) of the parabola having equation $y = -3x^2 + 12x + 5$ is a point above the $x$-axis (the $y$-coordinate is positive) and the parabola opens downward, the parabola must intersect the $x$-axis in two places. This is verified by the following graph:

Appendix

The $x$-intercepts can be determined using the zero option in the Calc menu of the TI-83/84 Plus calculator (see Appendix A for details). Follow the prompts to obtain one $x$-intercept at a time. The screens should appear as follows:

**10. a.** Use the zero option of your graphing calculator to determine the $x$-intercept(s) for the shot put function having equation $y = -0.015545x^2 + x + 6$. The right most intercept appears in the following screen:

**b.** Is either $x$-intercept determined in part a significant to the problem situation? Explain.

The graph of $y = -0.0155x^2 + x + 6$ has two $x$-intercepts. Does the graph of every parabola have $x$-intercepts? Problems 11 and 12 will help answer this question.

**11. a.** Use the values of $a$, $b$, and $c$ to determine the coordinates of the vertex of the graph of $y = x^2 + 6x + 12$.

**b.** Use the $y$-coordinate of the vertex to determine if the vertex is above or below the $x$-axis.

**c.** Use the value of $a$ in $y = x^2 + 6x + 12$ to determine if the parabola opens upward or downward.

   **d.** Use the results from parts b and c to determine if the parabola has $x$-intercepts.

   **e.** Use your graphing calculator to verify your answer to part d.

**12. a.** Use the values of $a$, $b$, and $c$ to determine the coordinates of the vertex of the graph of $y = -x^2 + 8x - 21$.

   **b.** Use the $y$-coordinate of the vertex to determine if the vertex is above or below the $x$-axis.

   **c.** Use the value of $a$ in $y = -x^2 + 8x - 21$ to determine if the parabola opens upward or downward.

   **d.** Use the results from parts b and c to determine if the parabola has $x$-intercepts.

   **e.** Use your graphing calculator to verify your answer to part d.

If a parabola opens upward and the vertex is above the $x$-axis there are no $x$-intercepts. If a parabola opens downward and the vertex is below the $x$-axis, there are no $x$-intercepts.

**13. a.** Use your result from Problem 10 to determine the practical domain of the shot put function. How does this compare with your answer in Problem 3?

   **b.** Sketch the path of the winning throw of the shot put. Be sure to label all key points, including the vertex and intercepts.

**c.** From the graph of the winning throw, over what horizontal distance (*x*-interval) is the height of the shot put increasing?

**d.** Determine the *x*-interval over which the height of the shot put is decreasing.

**e.** What is the practical range?

**14.** Now consider the function $y = -0.015545x^2 + x + 6$ as a general function that is not restricted by the physical situation in the activity.

**a.** What is the domain of the general function?

**b.** Over what *x*-interval does the general function increase?

**c.** Over what *x*-interval does the general function decrease?

**d.** What is the range?

## Standard Form of an Equation of a Quadradic Function

**15. a.** Sketch a graph of the quadratic function defined by $y = 3x^2$.

**b.** The graph of $y = 3x^2$ is shifted horizontally 2 units to the right. Sketch a graph of the new function. Write the equation of the transformed graph.

**c.** On the same coordinate axis, shift the graph in part b vertically 5 units upward. Write the equation of this new graph.

**d.** What is the vertex of the original parabola having equation $y = 3x^2$ ?

**e.** What is the vertex of the transformed parabola in part c?

The shift of the graph of $y = 3x^2$ horizontally 2 units to the right, followed by a vertical shift 5 units upward, moved the vertex of the parabola from $(0, 0)$ to $(2, 5)$. The resulting equation of the new parabola, $y = 3(x - 2)^2 + 5$, represents another way of writing the equation of a quadratic function.

If $(h, k)$ represents the vertex of a parabola, then $y = f(x) = a(x - h)^2 + k$, $a \neq 0$, is another form of the equation of a quadratic function. This form is especially convenient because the vertex $(h, k)$ of the parabola is easily identified.

**16.** Determine the vertex of the graph of each of the following parabolas.

  **a.** $y = -2(x - 3)^2 + 4$

**b.** $y = 1.25(x + 4)^2 + 3$

**c.** $y = -3(x + 2)^2 - 4.5$

The sign of a in $y = f(x) = a(x - h)^2 + k$, as in $y = g(x) = ax^2$, determines the direction in which the parabola opens. If $a > 0$, then the parabola opens upward. If $a < 0$, the parabola opens downward.

**17. a.** Graph the quadratic function defined by $y = f(x) = 3(x - 1)^2 + 2$. Be sure to identify the vertex and y-intercept.

**b.** Graph the quadratic function defined by $y = g(x) = 3x^2 - 6x + 5$.

**c.** Compare the graphs in parts a and b.

**d.** Write the equation $y = 3(x - 1)^2 + 2$ in the form of $y = ax^2 + bx + c$. How does this equation campare to the equation of the parabola in part b?

## SUMMARY
### Activity 4.3

The following characteristics are commonly used in analyzing the quadratic function defined by $f(x) = ax^2 + bx + c, a \neq 0$, and its graph.

**1.** The **axis of symmetry** is a vertical line that separates the parabola into two mirror images. The equation of the vertical axis of symmetry is given by $x = \frac{-b}{2a}$.

2. The **vertex** (turning point) always falls on the axis of symmetry. The $x$-coordinate of the vertex is given by $\frac{-b}{2a}$. Its $y$-coordinate is determined by evaluating the function at this value. In other words, the $y$-coordinate of the vertex is given by $f\left(-\frac{b}{2a}\right)$.

3. If the parabola changes from increasing to decreasing at the turning point, then the vertex is a maximum point. If the parabola changes from decreasing to increasing at the turning point, then the vertex is a minimum point.

4. The **$y$-intercept**, the point where the parabola crosses the $y$-axis (that is, where its $x$-coordinate is zero), is always given by $(0, c)$.

5. The **$x$-intercept** is the point or points (if any) where the parabola crosses the $x$-axis (that is, where its $y$-coordinate is zero).

6. If a parabola opens upward and the vertex is above the $x$-axis there are no $x$-intercepts. If a parabola opens downward and the vertex is below the $x$-axis, there are no $x$-intercepts.

7. The **domain** of the general quadratic function is the set of all real numbers.

8. If the parabola opens upward, the **range** is all real numbers greater than or equal to the $y$-value of the vertex. If the parabola opens downward, the *range* is all real numbers less than or equal to the $y$-value of the vertex.

9. The equation of a quadratic function can be written in the form $y = f(x) = a(x - h)^2 + k$, where $(h, k)$ is the vertex and $a \neq 0$.

## EXERCISES
### Activity 4.3

For Exercises 1–8, determine the following characteristics of each quadratic function:

    **a.** the direction in which the graph opens

    **b.** the axis of symmetry

    **c.** the turning point (vertex); determine if maximum or minimum

    **d.** the $y$-intercept

**1.** $f(x) = x^2 - 3$

**2.** $g(x) = x^2 + 2x - 8$

**3.** $y = x^2 + 4x - 3$

**4.** $f(x) = 3x^2 - 2x$

**5.** $h(x) = x^2 + 3x + 4$

**6.** $g(x) = -x^2 + 7x - 6$

**7.** $y = 2x^2 - x - 3$

**8.** $f(x) = x^2 + x + 3$

For Exercises 9–16, use your graphing calculator to sketch the graphs of the functions and then determine each of the following:

    **a.** the coordinates of the $x$-intercepts for each function, if they exist

    **b.** the domain and range for each function

    **c.** the $x$-interval over which each function is increasing

    **d.** the $x$-interval over which each function is decreasing

**9.** $g(x) = -x^2 + 7x - 6$

**10.** $h(x) = 3x^2 + 6x + 4$

**11.** $y = x^2 - 12$

**12.** $f(x) = x^2 + 4x - 5$

**13.** $g(x) = -x^2 + 2x + 3$            **14.** $h(x) = x^2 + 2x - 8$

**15.** $y = -5x^2 + 6x - 1$            **16.** $f(x) = 3x^2 - 2x + 1$

**17.** You shoot an arrow straight into the air from a height of 5 feet with an initial velocity of 96 feet per second. The height, $h$, in feet above the ground, at any time, $t$ (in seconds), is modeled by

$$h = 5 + 96t - 16t^2.$$

     **a.** Determine the maximum height the arrow will attain.

     **b.** Approximately when will the arrow reach the ground?

     **c.** What is the significance of the $h$-intercept?

     **d.** What are the practical domain and practical range in this situation?

     **e.** Use your graphing calculator to determine the $t$-intercepts. Determine the practical meaning of these intercepts in this situation.

**18.** As part of a recreational waterfront grant, the city council plans to enclose a rectangular area along the waterfront of Lake Erie and create a park and swimming area. The budget calls for the purchase of 3000 feet of fencing. *Note:* There is no fencing along the lake.

     **a.** Draw a picture of the planned recreational area. Let $x$ represent the length of one of the two equal sides that are perpendicular to the water.

**b.** Write an expression that represents the width (side opposite the water) in terms of $x$. *Note:* You have 3000 feet of fencing.

**c.** Write an equation that expresses the area $A$ of this rectangular site as a quadratic function of $x$.

**d.** Determine the value of $x$ for which $A$ is a maximum.

**e.** What is the maximum area that can be enclosed?

**f.** What are the dimensions of the enclosed area?

**g.** Use your graphing calculator to graph the area function. What point on the graph represents the maximum area?

**h.** What is the $A$-intercept? Does this point have any practical meaning in this situation?

**i.** From the graph, determine the $x$-intercepts. Do they have any practical meaning in this situation? Explain.

**19.** The cost to produce metal statues for local parks is given by

$$C = 2x^2 - 120x + 2000,$$

where $x$ represents the number of statues produced and $C$ is the cost of producing them.

**a.** Use your graphing calculator to graph the cost function and determine the coordinates of the turning point.

**b.** Determine the vertex algebraically.

**c.** How do your answers in parts a and b compare?

**d.** Is the vertex a minimum or maximum point?

**e.** What is the practical meaning of the vertex in this situation?

**f.** What is the $C$-intercept? What is the practical meaning of this intercept?

20. You are manufacturing ceramic lawn ornaments. After several months, your accountant tells you that your profit $P$ can be modeled by

$$P = -0.002n^2 + 5.5n - 1200,$$

where $n$ is the number of ornaments sold each month.

**a.** Use your graphing calculator to produce a graph of this function. Use the table feature set at TblStart $= 0$ and $\Delta$Tbl $= 500$ to help you set your window. Include the $n$-intercepts and the vertex.

**b.** Determine the $n$-intercepts of the graph of the profit function.

**c.** Determine the practical domain of the profit function.

**d.** Determine the practical range of the profit function.

**e.** How many ornaments must be sold to maximize the profit?

**f.** Write the equation that must be solved to determine the number of ornaments that must be sold to produce a profit of $2300.

**g.** Solve the equation in part f graphically.

**ACTIVITY 4.4**
Per Capita
Personal Income

**OBJECTIVES**

1. Solve quadratic equations numerically.
2. Solve quadratic equations graphically.
3. Determine the zeros of a function using technology.

According to statistics from the U.S. Department of Commerce, the per capita personal income (or the average annual income) of each resident of the United States from 1960 to 2000 can be modeled by the equation

$$P = 15.1442x^2 + 98.7687x + 1831.6909,$$

where $P$ represents the per capita income and $x$ represents the number of years since 1960.

1. What is the practical domain for the model represented by the quadratic function?

2. Let $x = 0$ correspond to the year 1960. Use a graphing calculator to complete the following table of values for $x$, the number of years since 1960, and $P$, the per capita income. Round the output to the nearest dollar.

| YEAR | 1960 | 1965 | 1970 | 1975 | 1980 | 1985 | 1990 | 1995 | 2000 |
|------|------|------|------|------|------|------|------|------|------|
| $x$ | | | | | | | | | |
| P ($) | | | | | | | | | |

3. Sketch a graph of the function using a graphing calculator using the window Xmin = −5, Xmax = 45, Ymin = −2000, and Ymax = 35,000. The graph should appear as follows:

4. Estimate the per capita personal income in the year 1989 $(x = 29)$.

5. You want to determine in which year the per capita personal income reached $20,500. Write an equation to determine the value of $x$ when $P = 20,500$.

The equation in Problem 5 is called a **quadratic equation**. The standard form of a quadratic equation is $ax^2 + bx + c = 0$, $a \neq 0$. Examples of quadratic equations include $x^2 + 3x - 1 = 9$, $2x^2 - 4x + 1 = 0$, and $6x^2 = 18$.

One method of approximating a solution to an equation is numerical, using a table of appropriate data points. Example 1 demonstrates this method.

Example 1   *Solve the quadratic equation $x^2 + 3x - 1 = 9$ numerically (using tables of data).*

SOLUTION

Create a table in which $x$ is the input and $y = x^2 + 3x - 1$ is the output. The solution is the $x$-value corresponding to a $y$-value of 9.

```
Plot1 Plot2 Plot3
\Y1■X²+3X-1
\Y2■9■
\Y3=
\Y4=
\Y5=
\Y6=
\Y7=
```

| X | Y1 | Y2 |
|---|----|----|
| 1 | 3  | 9  |
| 2 | 9  | 9  |
| 3 | 17 | 9  |
| 4 | 27 | 9  |
| 5 | 39 | 9  |
| 6 | 53 | 9  |
| 7 | 69 | 9  |

X=1

Using the graphing calculator, the solution is $x = 2$.

**6.** Determine the solution to $20{,}500 = 15.1442x^2 + 98.7687x + 1831.6909$ numerically using a table of appropriate data points (see Problem 2). What is your approximation using this approach?

## Solving Quadratic Equations Graphically

A second method of solving the quadratic equation in Problem 5 is graphical, using a graphing calculator. Recall that you can solve the equation $15.1442x^2 + 98.7687x + 1831.6909 = 20{,}500$ by solving the following system of equations graphically:

$$y_1 = 15.1442x^2 + 98.7687x + 1831.6909$$
$$y_2 = 20{,}500$$

The expression for $y_1$ gives the per capita personal income in any given year. The value $y_2$ is the specific per capita personal income in which you are interested. The solution to the equation is the $x$-value for which $y_1 = y_2$. To do this, determine the point of intersection of these two graphs. If you use the intersect option under the Calc menu, the graph should appear as follows:

Another graphical method for solving the problem is to rearrange the quadratic equation

$$20{,}500 = 15.1442x^2 + 98.7687x + 1831.6909$$

so that the left-hand side is equal to zero. Subtracting 20,500 from each side, you have

$$0 = 15.1442x^2 + 98.7687x - 18{,}668.3091. \quad \text{(Equation 1)}$$

If you let $y = 15.1442x^2 + 98.7687x - 18{,}668.3091$, then the solution to the equation 1 is the $x$-value for which $y = 0$, if it exists. This is the $x$-value of the $x$-intercept of the graph, also called the **zero of the function**.

**7. a.** Use your graphing calculator to sketch a graph of
$$y = 15.1442x^2 + 98.7687x - 18{,}668.3091.$$

The screen should appear as follows:

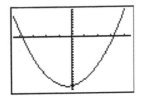

**b.** What are the $x$-intercepts of the new function defined by $y = 15.1442x^2 + 98.7687x - 18{,}668.3091?$

**c.** Using the results from part b, determine the solutions to the equation $20{,}500 = 15.1442x^2 + 98.7687x + 1831.6989$. Are both of the values relevant to our problem? Explain.

**8.** Describe two different ways to solve the equation $2x^2 - 4x + 3 = 2$ using a graphing approach. Solve the equation using each graphing method. How do your answers compare?

**SUMMARY**
**Activity 4.4**

**1.** A **quadratic equation** is an equation having standard form $ax^2 + bx + c = 0$, $a \neq 0$.

**2.** To solve $f(x) = n$ **numerically**, construct a table for $y = f(x)$, and determine the $x$-values that produce $n$ as $y$-value.

**3.** To solve $f(x) = n$ **graphically**:

   **a.** Graph $y_1 = f(x)$, graph $y_2 = n$, and determine the $x$-values of the points of intersection.

   **b.** Or graph $y = f(x) - n$, and determine the $x$-values of the $x$-intercepts of the graph (zeros of the function) using a graphing calculator.

In Exercises 1–4, solve the quadratic equation numerically (using tables of $x$- and $y$-values). Verify your solutions graphically.

**1.** $-4x = -x^2 + 12$

**2.** $x^2 + 9x + 18 = 0$

**3.** $2x^2 = 8x + 90$

**4.** $x^2 - x - 3 = 0$

In Exercises 5–8, solve the quadratic equation graphically using at least two different approaches. When necessary, give your solutions to the nearest hundredth.

**5.** $x^2 + 12x + 11 = 0$

**6.** $2x^2 - 3 = 2x$

**7.** $16x^2 - 400 = 0$

**8.** $4x^2 + 12x = -4$

In Exercises 9–12, solve the equation by using either a numeric or a graphic approach.

**9.** $x^2 + 2x - 3 = 0$

**10.** $x^2 + 11x + 24 = 0$

**11.** $x^2 - 2x - 8 = x + 20$

**12.** $x^2 - 10x + 6 = 5x - 50$

**13.** The stopping distance, $d$ (in feet), for a car moving at a velocity (speed) $v$ miles per hour is modeled by the equation

$$d = 0.04v^2 + 1.1v.$$

**a.** What is the stopping distance for a velocity of 55 miles per hour?

**b.** What is the speed of the car if it takes 200 feet to stop?

**14.** An international rule for determining the number, $n$, of board feet (usable finished lumber) in a 16-foot log is modeled by the equation

$$n = 0.22d^2 - 0.71d,$$

where $d$ is the diameter of the log in inches.

**a.** How many board feet can be obtained from a 16-foot log with a 14-inch diameter?

**b.** Sketch a graph of this function. What is the practical domain of this function?

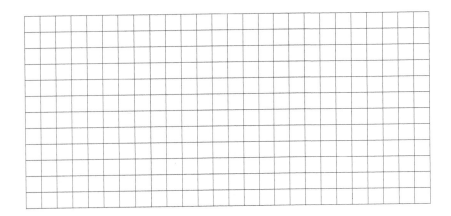

**c.** Use the graph to approximate the $d$-intercept(s). What is the practical meaning in this situation?

**d.** What is the diameter of a 16-foot log that has 200 board feet?

**ACTIVITY 4.5**
Sir Isaac Newton

**OBJECTIVES**

1. Factor expressions by removing the greatest common factor.

2. Factor trinomials using trial and error.

3. Use the zero-product principle to solve equations.

4. Solve quadratic equations by factoring.

Sir Isaac Newton XIV, a descendant of the famous physicist and mathematician, takes you to the top of a building to demonstrate a physics property discovered by his famous ancestor. He throws your math book straight up into the air. The book's distance, $s$, above the ground as a function of time, $x$, is modeled by

$$s = -16x^2 + 16x + 32.$$

**1.** When the book strikes the ground, what is the value of $s$?

**2.** Write the equation that you must solve to determine when the book strikes the ground.

The quadratic equation in Problem 2 can be solved by using a numerical or a graphical approach. However, an algebraic technique is efficient in this case and will give an exact answer. The algorithm is based on the algebraic principle known as the **zero-product principle**.

---

**Zero-Product Principle**

If $a$ and $b$ are any numbers and $a \cdot b = 0$, then either $a$ or $b$, or both, must be equal to zero.

---

Example 1　　*Solve the equation $x(x + 5) = 0$.*

SOLUTION

The two factors in this equation are $x$ and $x + 5$. The zero-product principle says one of these factors must equal zero. That is,

$$x = 0 \quad \text{or} \quad x + 5 = 0.$$

The first equation tells you that $x = 0$ is a solution. To determine a second solution, solve $x + 5 = 0$.

$$x + 5 = 0$$
$$\underline{-5 \quad -5}$$
$$x = -5$$

There are two solutions, $x = 0$ and $x = -5$.

Your graphing calculator verifies the solutions as follows.

**3.** Solve each of the following equations using the zero-product principle.

　　**a.** $3x(x - 2) = 0$ 　　　　　　　　**b.** $(2x - 3)(x + 2) = 0$

**c.** $(x + 2)(x + 3) = 0$

For the zero-product principle to be applied, one side of the equation must be zero. Therefore, at first glance, the zero-product principle can be used to solve the quadratic equation $3x^2 - 6x = 0$. However, a second condition must be satisfied. The nonzero side of the equation must be written as a product.

The process of writing an expression such as $3x^2 - 6x$ as a product is called factoring.

> **DEFINITION**
> Rewriting an expression as a product is called **factoring**.

## Factoring Common Factors

A **common factor** is a number or an expression that is a factor of each term of the entire expression. Whenever you wish to factor a polynomial, look first for a common factor.

> **PROCEDURE**
> **Removing a Common Factor from a Polynomial:** First, identify the common factor, and then apply the distributive property in reverse.

**Example 2**   *Given the binomial $3x + 6$, 3 is a common factor because 3 is a factor of both terms $3x$ and 6. Applying the distributive property in reverse, you write*

$$3x + 6 \text{ as } 3(x + 2).$$

You may always check the factored binomial by multiplying:

$$3(x + 2) = 3(x) + 3(2) = 3x + 6$$

When you look for a common factor, determine the largest or **greatest common factor** (or GCF). You can see that 3 is a common factor of $6x + 24$ because 3 is a factor of both 6 and 24. However, there is a larger common factor, 6. Therefore,

$$6x + 24 = 6(x + 4).$$

**Example 3**   *Given $6x^2 + 14x - 30$, you can see that 2 is a common factor. Is 2 the greatest common factor? Yes, because no larger number is a factor of every term.*

If you divide each term by 2, you obtain $3x^2 + 7x - 15$. The expression $6x^2 + 14x - 30$ can now be written in factored form as $2(3x^2 + 7x - 15)$. Check the factored trinomial by multiplying.

**Example 4** *Factor* $4x^3 - 8x^2 + 28x$.

SOLUTION

Four is a factor of each term, but $x$ is as well. Therefore, the greatest common factor is $4x$. You remove the GCF by dividing each term by $4x$. This leads to the factored form $4x(x^2 - 2x + 7)$.

You can check your factoring by applying the distributive property.

4. Factor the following polynomials by removing the greatest common factor.

    **a.** $9a^6 + 18a^2$                **b.** $21xy^3 + 7xy$

    **c.** $3x^2 - 21x + 33$          **d.** $4x^3 - 16x^2 - 24x$

## Factoring Trinomials

With patience, you can factor trinomials of the form $ax^2 + bx + c$ by trial and error, using the FOIL method in reverse.

---

PROCEDURE: **Factoring Trinomials by Trial and Error**

1. Remove the greatest common factor, GCF.

2. To factor the resulting trinomial into the product of two binomials, try combinations of factors for the first and last terms in two binomials.

3. Check the outer and inner products to match the middle term of the original trinomial.

    **a.** If the constant term, $c$, is positive, both of its factors are positive or both are negative.

    **b.** If the constant term is negative, one factor is positive and one is negative.

4. If the check fails, repeat steps 2 and 3.

---

**Example 5** *Factor* $6x^2 - 7x - 3$.

SOLUTION

**Step 1.** There is no common factor, so go to step 2.

**Step 2.** You could factor the first term, $6x^2$, as $6x(x)$ or as $2x(3x)$. The last term, $-3$, has factors $3(-1)$ or $-3(1)$. Try $(2x + 1)(3x - 3)$.

**Step 3.** The outer product is $-6x$. The inner product is $3x$. The sum is $-3x$, not $7x$. The check fails.

**Step 4.** Try $(2x - 3)(3x + 1)$. The outer product is $2x$. The inner product is $-9x$. The sum is $-7x$. It checks.

**5.** Factor the following trinomials.

  **a.** $x^2 - 7x + 12$                     **b.** $x^2 - 8x - 9$

  **c.** $x^2 + 14x + 49$               **d.** $25 + 10w + w^2$

## Solving Quadratic Equations by Factoring

The following example demonstrates the procedure for solving quadratic equations written in standard form, $ax^2 + bx + c = 0$, by factoring.

**Example 6**   *Solve the equation $3x^2 - 2 = -x$ by factoring.*

**Step 1.** Rewrite the equation in the form $ax^2 + bx + c = 0$ (called standard form).

$$3x^2 - 2 = -x$$
$$\underline{+\ x \qquad\qquad +\ x}$$
$$3x^2 + x - 2 = 0$$

**Step 2.** Factor the expression on the nonzero side of the equation.

$$(x + 1)(3x - 2) = 0$$

**Step 3.** Use the zero-product principle to set each factor equal to zero, and then solve each equation.

$$(x + 1)(3x - 2) = 0$$

| $x + 1 = 0$ | $3x - 2 = 0$ |
|---|---|
| $x = -1$ | $3x = 2$ |
| | $x = \frac{2}{3}$ |

Therefore, the solutions are $x = -1$ and $x = \frac{2}{3}$.

These solutions can be verified graphically as follows.

**6. a.** Returning to the math book problem from the beginning of this activity, solve the equation from Problem 2 by factoring.

    **b.** Are both solutions to the equation ($x = 2$ and $x = -1$) also solutions to the question, "At what time does the book strike the ground"? Explain.

**7. a.** You want to know at what time the book is 32 feet above the ground. Write a quadratic equation that represents this situation.

**b.** Solve the quadratic equation in part a by factoring.

**8.** Solve each of the following quadratic equations by factoring.

**a.** $2x^2 - x - 6 = 0$ **b.** $3x^2 - 6x = 0$

**c.** $x^2 + 4x = -x - 6$

**9.** Determine the zeros of the function defined by $f(x) = 2x^2 - 3x - 2$.

---

**SUMMARY**
**Activity 4.5**

**1.** To remove a **common factor** from a polynomial, first
   **a.** identify the common factor, and then
   **b.** apply the distributive property in reverse.

**2.** The **zero-product principle** says that if $ab = 0$ is a true statement, then either $a = 0$ or $b = 0$.

**3.** To factor trinomials of the form $ax^2 + bx + c$ by **trial and error**,
   **a.** remove the greatest common factor.
   **b.** try combinations of factors for the first and last terms in two binomials.
   **c.** check the outer and inner products to match the middle term of the original trinomial.

   • If the constant term, $c$, is positive, both factors of $c$ are positive or both are negative.

   • If the constant term is negative, one factor is positive and one is negative.

   **d.** If the check fails, repeat steps 3b and 3c.

**4.** To solve equations by **factoring,**

  **a.** use the addition principle to remove all terms from one side of the equation; this results in a polynomial being set equal to zero.

  **b.** combine like terms, and then factor the nonzero side of the equation.

  **c.** use the zero-product principle to set each factor containing a variable equal to zero, and then solve the equations.

  **d.** check your solutions in the original equation.

**EXERCISES**
**Activity 4.5**

*In Exercises 1–4, factor the polynomials by removing the GCF (greatest common factor).*

**1.** $12x^5 - 18x^8$

**2.** $14x^6y^3 - 6x^2y^4$

**3.** $2x^3 - 14x^2 + 26x$

**4.** $5x^3 - 20x^2 - 35x$

*In Exercises 5–13, completely factor the polynomials. Remember to look first for the GCF.*

**5.** $x^2 + x - 6$

**6.** $p^2 - 16p + 48$

**7.** $x^2 + 7xy + 10y^2$

**8.** $x^2 - 4x - 32$

**9.** $12 + 8x + x^2$

**10.** $2x^2 + 7x - 15$

**11.** $3x^2 + 19x - 14$

**12.** $8x^4 - 47x^3 - 6x^2$

**13.** $20b^4 - 65b^3 - 60b^2$

*In Exercises 14–21, solve each quadratic equation by factoring.*

**14.** $x^2 - 5x + 6 = 0$

**15.** $x^2 + 2x - 3 = 0$

**16.** $x^2 - x = 6$                **17.** $x^2 - 5x = 14$

**18.** $3x^2 + 11x - 4 = 0$         **19.** $3x^2 - 12x = 0$

**20.** $x^2 - 7x = 18$              **21.** $3x(x - 6) - 5(x - 6) = 0$

**22.** Your neighbors have just finished installing a new swimming pool at their home. The pool measures 15 feet by 20 feet. They would like to plant a strip of grass of uniform width around three sides of the pool, the two short sides and one of the longer sides.

**a.** Sketch a diagram of the pool and the strip of lawn, using $x$ to represent the width of the uniform strip.

**b.** Write an equation for the area, $A$, in terms of $x$ that represents the lawn area around the pool.

**c.** They have enough seed for 168 square feet of lawn. Write an equation that relates the quantity of seed to the area of the uniform strip of lawn.

**d.** Solve the equation in part c to determine the width of the uniform strip that can be seeded.

**ACTIVITY 4.6**
Ups and Downs

**OBJECTIVES**

1. Use the quadratic formula to solve quadratic equations.
2. Identify the solutions of a quadratic equation with points on the corresponding graph.
3. Determine the zeros of a function.

Suppose a soccer goalie punted the ball in such a way as to kick the ball as far as possible down the field. The height of the ball above the field as a function of time can be approximated by

$$y = -0.017x^2 + 0.98x + 0.33,$$

where $y$ represents the height of the ball (in yards) and $x$ represents the horizontal distance (in yards) down the field from where the goalie kicked the ball.

In this situation, the graph of $y = -0.017x^2 + 0.98x + 0.33$ is the actual path of the flight of the soccer ball. The graph of this function appears below:

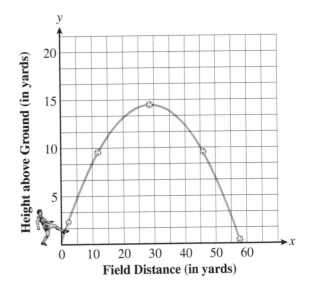

1. Use the graph to estimate how far downfield from the point of contact the soccer ball is 10 yards above the ground. How often during its flight does this occur?

2. **a.** Use $y = -0.017x^2 + 0.98x + 0.33$ to write the quadratic equation that arises in determining when the ball is 10 yards above the ground.

   **b.** Rewrite the equation in standard form and simplify if possible.

   **c.** What does the graph tell you about the number of solutions to this equation?

By some straightforward (but somewhat messy) algebraic manipulations, a quadratic equation can be turned into a formula that produces the solutions. This formula is called the **quadratic formula**.

---

**The Quadratic Formula**

For a quadratic equation in standard form, $ax^2 + bx + c = 0, a \neq 0$, the solutions are

$$x = \frac{-b \pm \sqrt{b^2 - 4 \cdot a \cdot c}}{2 \cdot a}.$$

The $\pm$ in the formula indicates that there are two solutions, one in which the terms in the numerator are added, and another in which the terms are subtracted.

---

When you use this formula, the quadratic equation *must* be in standard form so that the values (and signs) of the three coefficients $a$, $b$, and $c$ are correct. You also want to be careful when you key the expression into your calculator. The square root and quotient computations need to be done carefully; you often must include appropriate sets of parentheses.

**Example 1** *Use the quadratic formula to solve the quadratic equation $6x^2 - x = 2$.*

SOLUTION

$6x^2 - x - 2 = 0$      Write equation in standard form, $ax^2 + bx + c = 0$

$a = 6, b = -1, c = -2$      Identify $a$, $b$, and $c$.

$x = \dfrac{-(-1) \pm \sqrt{(-1)^2 - 4(6)(-2)}}{2(6)}$      Substitute for $a$, $b$, and $c$ in $x = \dfrac{-b \pm \sqrt{b^2 - 4ac}}{2a}$.

$x = \dfrac{1 \pm \sqrt{1 + 48}}{12} = \dfrac{1 \pm 7}{12}$

$x = \dfrac{1 + 7}{12} = \dfrac{2}{3}, x = \dfrac{1 - 7}{12} = \dfrac{-6}{12} = -\dfrac{1}{2}$

3. Use the quadratic formula to solve the quadratic equation in Problem 2b.

**4.** Solve $3x^2 + 20x + 7 = 0$ using the quadratic formula.

**5.** Determine the zeros of the function defined by $f(x) = -x^2 + 4x - 1$

**SUMMARY**
**Activity 4.6**

The solutions of a quadratic equation in standard form, $ax^2 + bx + c = 0, a \neq 0$, are

$$x = \frac{-b \pm \sqrt{b^2 - 4 \cdot a \cdot c}}{2 \cdot a}.$$

The $\pm$ symbol in the formula indicates that there are two solutions, one in which the terms in the numerator are added and one in which the terms are subtracted.

**EXERCISES**
**Activity 4.6**

Use the quadratic formula to solve the equations in Exercises 1–5.

**1.** $x^2 + 2x - 15 = 0$

**2.** $4x^2 + 32x + 15 = 0$

**3.** $-2x^2 + x + 1 = 0$

**4.** $2x^2 + 7x = 0$    **5.** $-x^2 + 10x + 9 = 0$

**6. a.** Determine the $x$-intercepts, if any, of the graph of $y = x^2 - 2x + 5$.

**b.** Sketch the graph of $y = x^2 - 2x + 5$ using your graphing calculator and verify your answer to part a.

**7.** The following data from the National Health and Nutrition Examination Survey indicate that the number of American adults who are overweight or obese is increasing.

| YEARS SINCE 1960, x | 1 | 12 | 18 | 31 | 39 |
|---|---|---|---|---|---|
| PERCENTAGE OF AMERICAN ADULTS WHO ARE OVERWEIGHT OR OBESE, P | 45 | 47 | 47 | 56 | 64.5 |

The function defined by $P = 0.017x^2 - 0.174x + 45.493$ can be used to model these data.

**a.** Determine the percentage of overweight or obese Americans in the year 2000.

**b.** Determine the year after 1960 when the model predicts that the percentage of overweight or obese Americans will first exceed 75%.

**c.** Verify your results in part b using a graphing calculator.

**8.** The height of a bridge arch located in the Thousand Islands is modeled by the function $y = -0.04x^2 + 28$, where $x$ is the distance, in feet, from the center of the arch and $y$ is the height of the arch.

**a.** Sketch a picture of this arch on a grid using the vertical axis as the center of the arch.

**b.** Determine the $y$-intercept. What is the practical meaning of this intercept in this situation?

**c.** Determine the $x$-intercepts algebraically using the quadratic formula.

**d.** Graph the function on your graphing calculator and check the accuracy of the intercepts you found in part c.

**e.** If the arch straddles the river exactly, how wide is the river?

**f.** A sailboat is approaching the bridge. The top of the mast measures 30 feet. Will the boat clear the bridge? Explain.

**g.** You want to install a flagpole on the bridge at an arch height of 20 feet. Write the equation that you must solve to determine how far to the right of center the arch height is 20 feet.

**h.** Solve the equation in part g using the quadratic formula. Use your graphing calculator to check your result.

**9.** The number, $n$ (in millions), of cellular phone subscribers in the United States from 1990 to 1999 is given in the following table:

| YEAR | 1990 | 1991 | 1992 | 1993 | 1994 | 1995 | 1996 | 1997 | 1998 | 1999 |
|---|---|---|---|---|---|---|---|---|---|---|
| NUMBER OF SUBSCRIBERS (millions) | 5.28 | 7.56 | 11.03 | 16.01 | 24.13 | 33.79 | 44.04 | 55.31 | 69.20 | 86.05 |

This data can be approximated by the quadratic model

$$y = 0.846x^2 + 1.32x + 5.20,$$

where $x = 0$ corresponds to the year 1990.

**a.** Use your graphing calculator to sketch a graph of the function.

**b.** Use the graph in part a to estimate the year in which there will be 120 million cellular phone subscribers.

**c.** Use the quadratic formula to answer part b. How does your answer compare to the estimate you obtained using a graphical approach?

**d.** How confident are you in your prediction? Explain.

You will return to the cellular phone situation in the exercises of Activity 4.7.

**ACTIVITY 4.7**
Air Quality in
Atlanta

**OBJECTIVES**

1. Determine quadratic regression models using the graphing calculator.

2. Solve problems using quadratic regression models.

The Air Quality Index, or AQI, measures how polluted the air is by measuring five major pollutants: ground-level ozone, particulate matter, carbon monoxide, sulfur dioxide, and nitrogen oxide. Based on the amount of each pollutant in the air, the AQI assigns a numerical value to air quality, as follows.

**Air Quality Index**

| | |
|---|---|
| 0–50 | Good |
| 51–100 | Moderate |
| 101–150 | Unhealthy for sensitive groups |
| 151–200 | Unhealthy |
| 201–300 | Very unhealthy |
| 301–500 | Hazardous |

Atlanta

**GEORGIA**

The following table indicates the number of days in which the AQI was greater than 100 in the city of Atlanta, Georgia.

| YEAR | 1990 | 1992 | 1994 | 1996 | 1998 | 1999 |
|---|---|---|---|---|---|---|
| NUMBER OF DAYS AQI >100, $n$ | 42 | 20 | 15 | 25 | 50 | 61 |

1. Sketch a scatterplot of the data. Let $t$ represent the number of years since 1990. Therefore, $t = 0$ corresponds to the year 1990. Does the data appear to be quadratic? Explain.

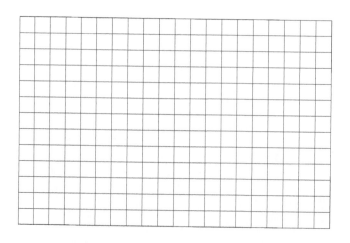

2. Use the regression feature of your graphing calculator to determine and plot a quadratic function that best fits these data. Your graph should appear as follows:

3. Do you believe that the quadratic regression model is a good model for the number of days the AQI exceeded 100 in Atlanta from 1990 to 1999?

The procedure used to develop the equation of a quadratic function that best fits a set of data is quite different from the least squares method used to develop a linear regression equation. Therefore, a correlation coefficient $r$ cannot be calculated for quadratic regression equations. However, some statisticians use a value called the coefficient of multiple determination, denoted by $R^2$, to measure the goodness of fit of a quadratic model.

The values of $R^2$ vary from 0 to 1. The closer to 1, the better the likelihood of a good fit of the quadratic regression equation to the data. The value of $R^2$ is calculated using the graphing calculator and appears on the same screen as the quadratic regression equation.

4. What is the value of $R^2$ for the quadratic function determined in Problem 2? Does the value confirm your answer in Problem 3?

5. What is the practical domain of this function?

6. a. Use the quadratic regression equation to estimate the number of days the AQI exceeded 100 in Atlanta in each of the following years.

    **i.** 1995            **ii.** 1988            **iii.** 2002

   b. Which, if any, of these estimates do you think is most reliable? Explain.

7. Estimate the years in which the number of days that the AQI exceeded 100 in Atlanta was less than or equal to 30 using:

   a. the given table (numerical method).

   **b.** the graph of the quadratic regression equation (graphical method).

8. Use the quadratic formula (the algebraic method) to estimate the year in which the number of days that the AQI exceeded 100 in Atlanta was equal to 17.

9. Estimate graphically the years between 1990 and 1999 when the number of days that the AQI exceeded 100 in Atlanta was greater than 25.

10. **a.** The number of days that the AQI exceeded 100 in Atlanta in 1997 was 31. Does this agree with the prediction from the quadratic regression model?

   **b.** Include the data for 1997 from part a in the original data set, and then recalculate the quadratic regression equation.

   **c.** Predict the number of days that the AQI exceeded 100 in Atlanta in 1997 from this new quadratic regression equation from part b. Are the results any better?

11. The following data from the National Health and Nutrition Examination Survey appear in Exercise 7 of Activity 4.6. The data indicate that the number of American adults who are overweight or obese is increasing.

| YEARS SINCE 1960, x | 1 | 12 | 18 | 31 | 39 |
|---|---|---|---|---|---|
| PERCENT OF OVERWEIGHT OR OBESE AMERICANS, P(x) | 45 | 47 | 47 | 56 | 64.5 |

   Use the regression feature of your graphing calculator to verify that this data can be modeled by the equation $P(x) = 0.017x^2 - 0.174x + 45.493$.

## SUMMARY
Activity 4.7

Parabolic data can be modeled by a **quadratic regression equation**.

## EXERCISES
### Activity 4.7

1. During one game, the Virginia Tech punter was called upon to punt the ball four times. On one of these punts, the punter struck the ball at his own 30-yard line. The height, $h$, of the ball above the field in feet as a function of time, $x$, in seconds can be partially modeled by the following table:

| $x$ | 0 | 0.6 | 1.2 | 1.8 | 2.4 | 3.0 |
|---|---|---|---|---|---|---|
| $h(x)$ | 2.50 | 28.56 | 43.10 | 46.12 | 37.12 | 17.60 |

a. Sketch a scatterplot of the data using your graphing calculator. Your screen should appear as follows:

b. Use your graphing calculator to obtain a quadratic regression function for these data. Round the values of $a$, $b$, and $c$ to four decimal places.

c. Graph the equation from part b on the same coordinate axes as the data points. Does the curve appear to be a good fit for the data? Explain.

d. In this model, what is the practical domain of the quadratic regression function?

e. Estimate the practical range of this model.

f. How long after the ball was struck did the ball reach 35 feet above the field? Explain.

g. How many results did you obtain for part f? Do you think you have all of the solutions? Explain.

2. Use the following data set to perform the tasks in parts a–e.

| $x$ | 0 | 3 | 6 | 9 | 12 |
|---|---|---|---|---|---|
| $y$ | 5 | 28 | 86 | 180 | 310 |

**a.** Determine an appropriate scale, and plot these points.

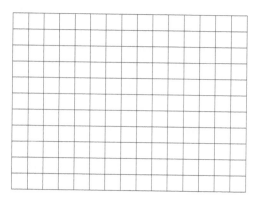

**b.** Use your graphing calculator to determine the quadratic regression equation for this data set.

**c.** Graph the regression equation on the same coordinate axes as the data points in part a.

**d.** Compare the predicted $y$-values with the $y$-values given in the table.

**e.** Predict the $y$-value for $x = 7$ and for $x = 15$.

**3.** The following table shows the stopping distance for a car at various speeds on dry pavement:

| SPEED (mph) | 25 | 35 | 45 | 55 | 65 | 75 |
|---|---|---|---|---|---|---|
| DISTANCE (ft) | 65 | 108 | 167 | 245 | 340 | 450 |

**a.** Use your graphing calculator to determine a quadratic regression equation that represents this data.

**b.** Use the regression equation to predict the stopping distance at 90 mph.

**c.** What speed would produce a stopping distance of 280 feet? (Round to the nearest tenth.) Explain how you arrived at your conclusion.

**4.** A downturn in the high-tech industry during the early 2000s has caused a similar downturn in computer science and engineering enrollments for new undergraduates. The following data from the Computing Research Association represents new enrollments in computer science and engineering from 1995 to 2001.

| YEARS SINCE 1995, x | 0 | 1 | 2 | 3 | 4 | 5 | 6 |
|---|---|---|---|---|---|---|---|
| NEW UNDERGRADS IN COMPUTER SCIENCE AND ENGINEERING (in thousands), N | 8.2 | 11.9 | 16.2 | 17.1 | 16.6 | 18.9 | 18.0 |

*Source:* Computer Research Associates

**a.** Sketch a scatterplot of the data using your graphing calculator. Your screen should appear as follows:

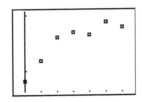

**b.** Use your graphing calculator to obtain a quadratic regression function for this data. Round the values of $a$, $b$, and $c$ to four decimal places.

**c.** Graph the equation from part b on the same coordinate axes as the data points. Does the curve appear to be a good fit for the data? Explain.

**d.** What does the regression equation predict for the new undergraduate enrollments in computer science and engineering in 2003? Does this seem reasonable?

**e.** Use the model to determine the year that new undergraduate computer science and engineering enrollments will drop below 15,000.

## Collecting and Analyzing Data

**5.** The number, $n$ (in millions) of cellular phone subscribers in the United States from 1990 to 1999 is given in the following table.

| YEAR | 1990 | 1991 | 1992 | 1993 | 1994 | 1995 | 1996 | 1997 | 1998 | 1999 |
|---|---|---|---|---|---|---|---|---|---|---|
| NUMBER IF SUBSCRIBERS (millions) | 5.28 | 7.56 | 11.03 | 16.01 | 24.13 | 33.79 | 44.04 | 55.31 | 69.20 | 86.05 |

**a.** In Exercise 9 of Activity 4.6, this data was approximated by the quadratic model: $y = 0.846x^2 + 1.32x + 5.20$, where $x = 0$ corresponds to the year 1990. Use a graphing calculator to determine a quadratic regression equation for the given data. How does the equation compare to the quadratic model given in Exercise 9? How good is the fit?

**b.** Use the model to predict the number of cellular phone subscribers in the year 2005.

**c.** Find a website on the Internet to determine the actual number of cell phone subscribers in the US in each year from 2000 to 2006. How good was your prediction in part b? Is it what you expected? Explain.

**d.** Sketch a scatterplot of the data you found in part c ( for years 2000–2006). Determine a new quadratic regression equation to predict the number of cellular phone subscribers in a given year. How good is the fit?

**e.** Use the regression equation in part d to predict the number of cellular subscribers in the year 2008. How confident are you in the prediction?

**6.** The shape of the main support cable in a suspension bridge is a parabola.

Use resources from the library or the Internet to determine specific dimensions, such as the distance between the main support columns, for one of the following bridges: Golden Gate Bridge, George Washington Bridge, of Verrazano Bridge.

Use the dimensions to develop points that lie on the graph of the main support cable of the bridge you selected. Draw a sketch of the support cable on graph paper. The orientation of the coordinate system, especially the origin, is very important. You will need at least three points that lie on the graph of the support cable in your drawing.

Use the points to determine a quadratic regression equation to represent the main support cable of the bridge. Use the model to determine the minimum distance from the cable to the highway.

Be prepared to give a presentation of your findings.

## Activities 4.1–4.7   What Have I Learned?

1. **a.** In order for the graph of the equation $y = ax^2 + bx + c$ to be a parabola, the value of the coefficient of $x^2$ cannot be zero. Explain.

   **b.** What is the vertex of the parabola having an equation of the form $y = ax^2$?

   **c.** Describe the relationship between the vertex and the $y$-intercept of the graph of $y = ax^2 + c$.

2. Determine if the vertex is a minimum point or a maximum point of $y = ax^2 + bx + c$ in each of the following situations.

   **a.** $a < 0$                    **b.** $a > 0$

3. **a.** What are the possibilities for the number of $y$-intercepts of a quadratic function?

   **b.** What are the possibilities for the number of $x$-intercepts of a parabola?

4. What is the relationship between the vertex and the $x$-intercept of the graph of $y = x^2 - 4x + 4$?

5. **a.** The vertex of a parabola is (3, 1). Using this information, complete the following table:

| x | 1 | 2 | 3 | 4 | 5 |
|---|---|---|---|---|---|
| y | 5 | 2 |   |   |   |

   **b.** If the vertex of a parabola is (2, 4), complete the following table:

| x | −2 | 0 | 2 | 4 | 6 |
|---|----|---|---|---|---|
| y | 0  | 3 |   |   |   |

6. The vertex of the parabola having equation $g(x) = x^2 + 2x - 8$ is $(-1,-9)$.

   **a.** The graph of $g$ is shifted vertically upward 5 units. Write the equation of the resulting graph.

   $$y = x^2 + 2x - 8 + 5 = x^2 + 2x - 3$$

   **b.** Determine the vertex of the graph in part a.

**c.** Compare the $y$-values of the vertex of the original parabola and the translated graph.

**7. a.** Given the following graph, explain why choices i, ii, and iii do not fit the curve:

    **i.** $f(x) = ax^2 + bx$ with $a > 0, b < 0$

    **ii.** $g(x) = ax^2 + c$ with $a < 0, c > 0$

    **iii.** $h(x) = ax^2 + bx + c$ with $a < 0, b > 0, c < 0$

**b.** What restrictions on $a$, $b$, and $c$ are necessary to fit $y = ax^2 + bx + c$ to this graph?

**8.** Review the steps in the following solution. Is the solution correct? Explain why or why not.

$$x^2 - 3x - 4 = 6$$
$$(x - 4)(x + 1) = 6$$
$$x - 4 = 6 \qquad x + 1 = 6$$
$$x = 10 \qquad\quad x = 5$$

*Recognizing the correspondence among situations, equations, and graphs is an important skill. Exercises 9–13 contain a description of a free-falling object where s is the distance an object is above the ground at time t. Match the description to the quadratic models. Then match each description (and equation) to the graph that represents the situation, selecting from graphs i–vii.*

**9.** A rock is thrown straight up with a velocity of 20 meters per second from a building that is 50 meters high.

**10.** A model rocket is shot straight up into the air from a launch pad at ground level with a velocity of 70 feet per second.

**11.** A telephone repairperson drops her vice grips from a 50-foot tower.

**12.** A ball is thrown directly upward with a velocity of 100 feet per second from a height of 6 feet above the ground on the moon.

**13.** A bundle of shingles is thrown straight down with a velocity of 50 feet per second from the roof of a building that is 50 feet high.

**a.** $s(t) = -16t^2 + 50$                  **b.** $s(t) = -4.9t^2 - 20t + 50$

**c.** $s(t) = -2.64t^2 + 100t + 6$       **d.** $s(t) = -16t^2 + 70t$

**e.** $s(t) = -16t^2 - 50t + 50$         **f.** $s(t) = -4.9t^2 + 20t + 50$

**g.** $s(t) = -16t^2 + 50t$

**i.**   $s(t)$

**ii.**   $s(t)$

**iii.**          $s(t)$

**iv.**            $s(t)$

**v.**           $s(t)$

**vi.**      $s(t)$

**vii.**     $s(t)$

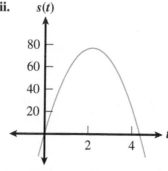

**Activities 4.1–4.7** How Can I Practice?

**1.** Complete the following table:

| EQUATION OF THE FORM $y = ax^2 + bx + c$ | VALUE OF $a$ | VALUE OF $b$ | VALUE OF $c$ |
|---|---|---|---|
| $y = 5x^2$ | | | |
| $y = \frac{1}{3}x^2 + 3x - 1$ | | | |
| $y = -2x^2 + x$ | | | |

For Exercises 2–7, determine the following characteristics for each graph:

    **a.** the direction in which the parabola opens

    **b.** the equation of the axis of symmetry

    **c.** the vertex; determine if maximum or minimum

    **d.** the $y$-intercept

**2.** $y = -2x^2 + 4$               **3.** $y = \frac{2}{3}x^2$

**4.** $f(x) = -3x^2 + 6x + 7$      **5.** $f(x) = 4x^2 - 4x$

**6.** $y = x^2 + 6x + 9$            **7.** $y = x^2 - x + 1$

For Exercises 8–11, use a graphing calculator to sketch the graph of each quadratic function, and then determine the following for each function.

    **a.** the coordinates of the $x$-intercepts (if they exist)

    **b.** the domain and range

    **c.** the $x$-interval over which the function is increasing

    **d.** the $x$-interval over which the function is decreasing

**8.** $y = -x^2 + 4$                    **9.** $y = x^2 - 5x + 6$

**10.** $y = -3x^2 - 6x + 8$            **11.** $y = 0.22x^2 - 0.71x + 2$

**12.** Use a graphing calculator to approximate the vertex of the graph of the parabola defined by the equation

$$y = -2x^2 + 3x + 25.$$

**13.** Completely factor the following polynomials.

    **a.** $9a^5 - 27a^2$           **b.** $24x^3 - 6x^2$

    **c.** $4x^3 - 16x^2 - 20x$       **d.** $5x^2 - 16x + 6$

    **e.** $x^2 - 5x - 24$           **f.** $y^2 + 10y + 25$

**14.** Determine one solution of the following quadratic equations numerically. That is, construct a table of $(x, y)$ ordered pairs, and estimate the value of $x$ that results in the required $y$-value.

    **a.** $5x^2 = 7$            **b.** $x^2 - 7x + 10 = 5$       **c.** $3x^2 - 5x = 2$

**a.**

| x | 1 | 1.1 | 1.2 | 1.3 | 1.4 | 1.5 |
|---|---|-----|-----|-----|-----|-----|
| y |   |     |     |     |     |     |

**b.**

| x | 0.5 | 0.6 | 0.7 | 0.8 | 0.9 | 1 |
|---|-----|-----|-----|-----|-----|---|
| y |     |     |     |     |     |   |

| c. | x | 0 | 1 | 2 | 3 | 4 | 5 |
|----|---|---|---|---|---|---|---|
|    | y |   |   |   |   |   |   |

15. Solve each of the equations from Exercise 14 using the quadratic formula. When necessary, round your solutions to the nearest tenth. Check your solutions by graphing.

16. Solve each of the following equations by factoring.

    **a.** $4x^2 - 8x = 0$            **b.** $x^2 - 6 = 7x + 12$

    **c.** $2x(x - 4) = -6$         **d.** $x^2 - 8x + 16 = 0$

    **e.** $x^2 - 2x - 24 = 0$       **f.** $y^2 - 2y - 35 = -20$

    **g.** $a^2 + 2a + 1 = 3a + 7$     **h.** $4x^2 + 4x - 3 = -3x - 1$

17. A fastball is hit straight up over home plate. The ball's height, $h$ (in feet), from the ground is modeled by

$$h = -16x^2 + 80x + 5,$$

where $t$ is measured in seconds.

    **a.** What is the maximum height of the ball above the ground?

**b.** Write an equation to determine how long will it take for the ball to reach the ground. Solve the equation using the quadratic formula. Check your solution by graphing.

**c.** Write the equation you would need to determine when the ball is 101 feet above the ground.

**d.** Solve the equation you determined in part c algebraically to determine the time it will take for the ball to reach a height of 101 feet. Verify your results graphically.

**18.** A suspension bridge (shown in the accompanying figure) is 100 meters long. The bridge is supported by cables attached to the tops of towers 35 meters high at each end of the bridge. The cables hang from the towers approximately in the shape of a parabola. The height, $h$ (in meters), of the cables above the surface of the roadway is modeled by

$$h = 0.01x^2 - x + 35,$$

where $x$ is the horizontal distance measured from the point where the tower and roadway meet.

**a.** Use your graphing calculator to examine the height function. What is the practical domain of this function?

**b.** What is the minimum distance of the cables from the roadway?

**19.** Use the following data set to perform the tasks in parts a–f:

| x | 0 | 1 | 3 | 5 | 7 | 8 |
|---|---|---|---|---|---|---|
| y | 10 | 4 | −18 | −54 | −107 | −145 |

**a.** Determine an appropriate scale and plot these points.

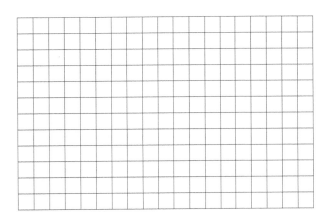

**b.** Use your graphing calculator to determine the quadratic regression equation for this data set.

**c.** Graph the regression equation on the same coordinate axes as the data points.

**d.** Compare the predicted outputs with the given outputs in the table.

**e.** What is the predicted output for $x = 4$ and for $x = 9$?

**f.** For what value of $x$ is $y = -40$? Use the quadratic formula.

**20.** The average miles per gallon (mpg) for U.S. cars has steadily increased since 1950. The following graphic gives the average miles per gallon for selected years.

PUMP YOU UP

**Average Miles per Gallon for Cars in the United States from 1950–2000**

| Year | Average mpg |
| --- | --- |
| 2000 | 22.0 |
| 1990 | 21.0 |
| 1980 | 15.5 |
| 1970 | 13.5 |
| 1960 | 13.4 |
| 1950 | 13.9 |

**a.** Draw a scatterplot of the data points, where $x$ represents the number of years since 1950.

**b.** Determine the equation of a quadratic function that best fits the data.

**c.** Use the regression equation to predict the average miles per gallon in the year 2010.

**d.** Use your model to determine the year when the average miles per gallon is 30.

**21.** Sketch a graph of each of the following pairs of functions. Describe the differences and the similarities in the graphs.

**a.** $y = 3x^2$, $y = 3x^2 + 5$

**b.** $y = 2x^2$, $y = -2x^2$

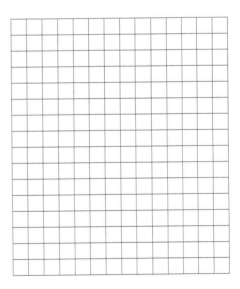

**c.** $y = 2x^2 + 1, y = 2x^2 - 4$

**d.** $y = 4x^2, y = 4(x - 1)^2$

**ACTIVITY 4.8**
A Thunderstorm

**OBJECTIVES**

1. Recognize the equivalent forms of the direct variation statement.
2. Determine the constant of proportionality in a direct variation problem.
3. Solve direct variation problems.

One of nature's more spectacular events is a thunderstorm. The skies light up, delighting your eyes, and seconds later your ears are bombarded with the boom of thunder. Because light travels faster than sound, during a thunderstorm you see the lightening before you hear the thunder. The formula

$$d = 1080t$$

describes the distance, $d$ in feet, you are from the storm's center if it takes $t$ seconds for you to hear the thunder.

1. Complete the following table for the model $d = 1080t$.

| $t$, IN SECONDS | 1 | 2 | 3 | 4 |
|---|---|---|---|---|
| $d$, IN FEET | | | | |

2. What does the ordered pair (3, 3240) from the above table mean in a practical sense?

3. As the value of $t$ increases, what happens to the value of $d$?

The relationship between time $t$ and distance $d$ in this situation is an example of **direct variation**. As $t$ increases, $d$ also increases.

**DEFINITION**

Two variables are said to **vary directly** if as the magnitude of one increases, the magnitude of the other does as well.

4. Graph the distance, $d$, as a function of time, $t$, using the values in Problem 1.

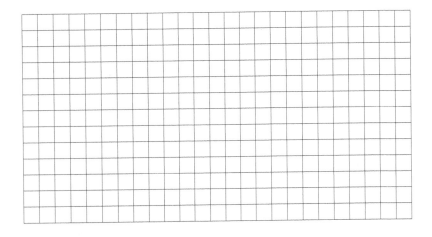

5. If the time it takes for you to hear the thunder after you see the lightning decreases, what is happening to the distance between you and the center of the storm?

---

If $x$ represents the independent variable and $y$ represents the dependent variable, then the following statements are equivalent.

a. $y$ varies directly as $x$

b. $y$ is directly proportional to $x$

c. $y = kx$ for some constant $k$.

The number represented by $k$ is called the constant of proportionality or constant of variation.

---

6. The amount of garbage, $G$, varies directly with the population, $P$. The population of Grand Prairie, Texas, is 0.13 million and creates 2.6 million pounds of garbage each week. Determine the amount of garbage produced by Houston with a population of 2 million.

a. Write an equation relating $G$ and $P$ and the constant of variation $k$.

b. Determine the value of $k$.

c. Rewrite the equation in part a using the value of $k$ from part b.

d. Use the equation in part c and the population of Houston to determine the weekly amount of garbage produced.

7. Use Problem 6 to outline a procedure to solve direct variation problems. Let $x$ represent the independent variable and $y$ represent the dependent variable.

a.

b.

c.

d.

Note that direct variations are not always increasing. For example, $y = -1.2x$ is a direct variation. From the graph it is clear that the function is decreasing.

This does not contradict the definition of a direct variation.

The relationship $y = -1.2x$ is still of the form $y = kx$ and as $x$ increases in value, the absolute value (the magnitude) of $y$ is increasing.

8. A worker's gross wages, $w$, vary directly as the number of hours the worker works, $h$. The following table shows the relationship between the wages and the hours worked.

| HOURS WORKED, h | 15 | 20 | 25 | 30 | 35 |
|---|---|---|---|---|---|
| WAGES, w | $172.50 | $230.00 | $287.50 | $345.00 | $402.50 |

a. Graph the gross wages, $w$, as a function of hours worked, $h$, using the values in the preceding table

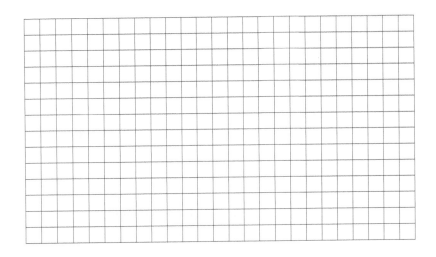

b. The relationship is defined by $w = kh$. Pick one ordered pair from the table and use it to determine the value of $k$.

c. What does $k$ represent in this situation?

d. Use the formula to determine the gross wages for a worker who works 40 hours.

Direct variation can involve higher powers of $x$, like $x^2$, $x^3$, or in general, $x^n$.

9. The power $P$ generated by a certain wind turbine varies directly as the square of the wind speed $w$. The turbine generates 750 watts of power in a 25 mph wind. Determine the power it generates in a 40 mph wind.

**SUMMARY**
Activity 4.8

1. Two variables are said to **vary directly** if as the magnitude of one increases, the magnitude of the other does as well.

2. The following statements are equivalent. The number represented by $k$ is called the **constant of proportionality or constant of variation.**

   **a.** $y$ varies directly as $x$

   **b.** $y$ is directly proportional to $x$

   **c.** $y = kx$ for some constant $x$

**EXERCISES**
Activity 4.8

1. The amount of sales tax, $s$, on any item is directly proportional to the list price of an item, $p$. The sales tax in your area is 8%.

   **a.** Write a formula that relates the amount of sales tax, $s$, to the list price, $p$, in this situation.

   **b.** Use the formula in part a to complete the following table:

   | LIST PRICE, $p$ | SALES TAX, $s$ |
   |---|---|
   | $10 | |
   | $20 | |
   | $30 | |
   | $50 | |
   | $100 | |

   **c.** Graph the sales tax, $s$, as a function of list price, $p$, using the values in the preceding table

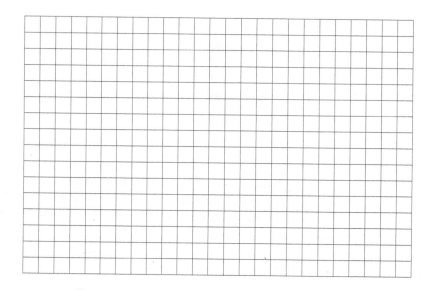

**d.** Determine the list price of an item for which the sales tax is $3.60.

2. The amount you tip a waiter, $t$, is directly proportional to the amount of the check, $c$.

  **a.** Assuming you tip your waiter 15% of the amount of the check, write a formula that relates the amount of the tip, $t$, to the amount of the check, $c$.

  **b.** Use the formula in part a to complete the following table.

| AMOUNT OF CHECK, $c$ | AMOUNT OF THE TIP, $t$ |
|---|---|
| $15 | |
| $25 | |
| $35 | |
| $50 | |
| $100 | |

  **c.** Graph the amount of the tip, $t$, as a function of the amount of the check, $c$, using the values in the preceding table.

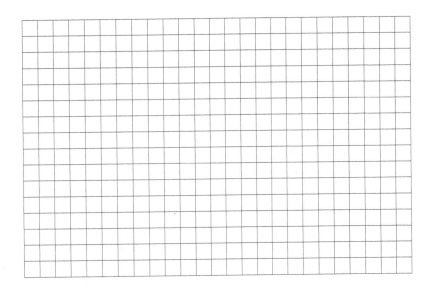

  **d.** A company has a policy that no tip can exceed $12.00 and still be reimbursed by the company. What is the maximum cost of a meal for which all of the tip will be reimbursed if the tip is 15% of the check?

**3.** The distance, $s$, that an object falls from rest varies directly as the square of the time, $t$, of the fall. A book dropped from the top of a building falls 144 feet in 3 seconds.

    **a.** Write a formula that relates the distance the book has fallen, $s$, in feet to the time, $t$, in seconds since it has been released.

    **b.** Use the formula in part a to complete the following table:

| TIME SINCE THE BOOK WAS RELEASED, $t$ | DISTANCE FALLEN, $s$ |
|:---:|:---:|
| 0.5 | |
| 1 | |
| 1.5 | |
| 2 | |
| 2.5 | |

    **c.** Graph the distance fallen, $s$, as a function of the time since the book was released, $t$, using the values in the preceding table.

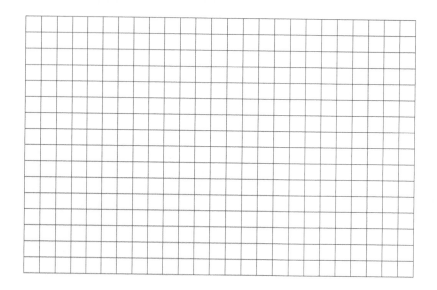

    **d.** Estimate the height of the building if it takes approximately 2.3 seconds for the book to hit the ground.

**4.** $y$ varies directly as $x$, $y = 25$ when $x = 5$. Determine $y$ when $x = 13$.

**5.** $y$ varies directly as $x$, $y = 7$ when $x = 21$. Determine $x$ when $y = 5$.

**6.** Given that $y$ varies directly as $x$, consider the following table:

| $x$ | 2 | 4 | 7 | | 12 |
|---|---|---|---|---|---|
| $y$ | 4 | 8 | | 20 | |

**a.** Determine a formula that relates $x$ and $y$.

**b.** Use the formula in part a to complete the table above.

**ACTIVITY 4.9**
The Power of
Power Functions

**OBJECTIVES**

1. Identify a direct variation function.

2. Determine the constant of variation.

3. Identify the properties of graphs of power functions defined by $y = kx^n$, where $n$ is a positive integer, $k \neq 0$.

4. Graph transformations of power functions.

You are traveling in a hot air balloon when suddenly your binoculars drop from the edge of the balloon's basket. At that moment, the balloon is maintaining a constant height of 500 feet. The distance of the binoculars from the edge of the basket is modeled by

$$s = 16t^2.$$

The following table gives the distance, $s$ (in feet), from the drop point at various times, $t$ (in seconds).

| $t$, TIME | 0 | 1 | 2 | 3 | 4 |
|---|---|---|---|---|---|
| $s$, DISTANCE | 0 | 16 | 64 | 144 | 256 |

As the input values (units of time) increase, the corresponding output values (units of distance) increase. Let us look more closely at how this increase takes place.

Because $s = 16t^2$, you can say that the output, $s$, varies directly as the square of the input, $t$. Therefore, as $t$ doubles in value from 1 to 2 or from 2 to 4, the corresponding output values become 4 times as large: increasing from 16 to 64 or 64 to 256.

**1. a.** As $t$ triples from 1 to 3, the corresponding $s$-values become _____ times as large.

   **b.** In general, if $y$ varies directly as the square of $x$, then when $x$ becomes $n$ times as large, the corresponding $y$-values become _____ times as large.

The volume, $V$, of a sphere is given by $V = \frac{4}{3}\pi r^3$. In this situation, you can say that the output, $V$, varies directly as the cube of the radius, $r$.

**2. a.** Complete the following table. Leave your answers for $V$ in terms of $\pi$.

| $r$ | 1 | 2 | 3 | 4 | 8 |
|---|---|---|---|---|---|
| $V$ | | | | | |

Note that as $r$-values double from 2 to 4 the corresponding $V$-values increase from $\frac{32}{3}\pi$ to $\frac{256}{3}\pi$.

   **b.** As $r$ doubles from 2 to 4 or from 4 to 8, the corresponding $V$-values become _____ times as large.

   **c.** In general, if $y$ varies directly as the cube of $x$, then when $x$ becomes $n$ times as large, the corresponding $y$-values become _____ times as large.

**d.** Sketch a graph of the volume function. What is the practical domain of this function?

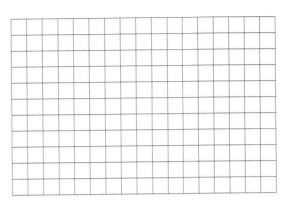

> **DEFINITION**
>
> The equation
>
> $$y = kx^n,$$
>
> where $k \neq 0$ and $n$ is a positive integer, defines a **direct variation** function in which $y$ varies directly as $x^n$. The constant, $k$, is called the **constant of variation** or the **constant of proportionality**.

**Example 1**  *The constant of variation, k, in the free-falling object situation defined by $s = 16x^2$ is 16.*

**3.** What is the constant of variation for the direct variation function defined by $V = \frac{4}{3}\pi r^3$?

In the falling binocular situation, you are given the direct variation equation. Suppose you only know that the distance, $s$, varies directly as the square of $x$ and one data pair. Are you able to determine the direct variation equation? Example 2 demonstrates the process discussed in Activity 4.8.

**Example 2**  *Let s vary directly as the square of t. If $s = 64$ when $t = 2$, determine the direct variation equation.*

SOLUTION

Because $s$ varies directly as the square of $t$, you have

$$s = kt^2,$$

where $k$ is the constant of variation. Substituting 64 for $s$ and 2 for $t$, you have

$$64 = k(2)^2 \quad \text{or} \quad 64 = 4k \quad \text{or} \quad k = 16.$$

Therefore, the direct variation equation is

$$s = 16t^2.$$

**4.** For each table, determine the pattern and complete the table. Determine the constant $k$ of variation and then write a direct variation equation for each table.

**a.** $y$ varies directly as $x$.

| x | 1 | 2 | 4 | 8 | 12 |
|---|---|---|---|---|----|
| y |   | 12 |  |   |    |

**b.** $y$ varies directly as $x^3$.

| x | 1 | 2 | 3 |
|---|---|---|---|
| y |   | 32 |  |

**c.** $y$ varies directly as $x$.

| x | 1 | 2 | 3 | 4 | 5 |
|---|---|---|---|---|---|
| y |   |   | 3 |   |   |

**5.** The length, $L$, of skid distance left by a car varies directly as the square of the initial velocity, $v$ (in miles per hour), of the car.

**a.** Write a general equation for $L$ as a function of $v$. Let $k$ represent the constant of variation.

**b.** Suppose a car traveling at 40 miles per hour leaves skid distance of 60 feet. Use this information to determine the value of $k$.

**c.** Use the function to determine the length of the skid distance left by the car traveling at 60 miles per hour.

## Power Functions

The direct variation functions that have equations of the form $y = kx^n$, where $n$ is a positive integer and $k \neq 0$, are also called **power functions**. The graphs of this family of functions are very interesting and are useful in problem solving.

6. Sketch a graph of each of the following power functions. Use a graphing calculator to verify the graph.

a. $y = x$

b. $y = x^2$

c. $y = x^3$

d. $y = x^4$

e. $y = x^5$

f. $y = x^6$

7. Each graph in Problem 6 has an equation of the form $y = x^n$, where $n$ is a positive integer.

a. What is the basic shape of the graph if

i. $n$ is even?

ii. $n$ is odd?

b. If $n$ is even, what happens to the graph as $n$ gets larger in value?

c. If $n$ is odd, is the function increasing or decreasing?

**8.** Use the patterns from Problem 7 in combination with graphing techniques you have learned previously to sketch a graph of each of the following without using a graphing calculator.

**a.** $y = x^2 + 1$

**b.** $y = -2x^4$

**c.** $y = 3x^8 + 1$

**d.** $y = -2x^5$

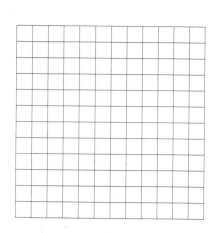

**e.** $y = x^{10}$

**f.** $y = 5x^3 + 2$

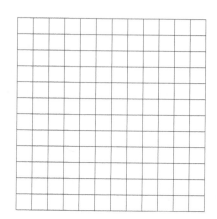

**SUMMARY**
**Activity 4.9**

1. The equation $y = kx^n$, where $k \neq 0$ and $n$ is a positive integer, defines a **direct variation function**. The constant, $k$, is called the **constant of variation**.

2. The direct variation functions that have equations of the form $y = kx^n$, where $n$ is a positive integer, are also called **power functions**.

   a. Power functions in which $n$ is even resemble parabolas. As $n$ increases in value, the graph flattens near the vertex.

   b. Power functions in which $n$ is odd resemble the graph of $y = kx^3$. If $k$ is positive, the graph is increasing. If $k$ is negative, the graph is decreasing.

**EXERCISES**
**Activity 4.9**

1. For each table, determine the pattern and complete the table. Then write a direct variation equation for each table.

   a. $y$ varies directly as $x$.

   | x | $\frac{1}{4}$ | 1 | 4 | 8 |
   |---|---|---|---|---|
   | y | | 8 | | |

   b. $y$ varies directly as $x^3$.

   | x | $\frac{1}{2}$ | 1 | 3 | 6 |
   |---|---|---|---|---|
   | y | | 1 | | |

2. The area, $A$, of a circle is given by the function $A = \pi r^2$, where $r$ is the radius of the circle.

   a. Does the area vary directly as the radius? Explain.

   b. What is the constant of variation $k$?

**3.** Assume that $y$ varies directly as the square of $x$, and that when $x = 2$, $y = 12$. Determine $y$ when $x = 8$.

**4.** The distance, $d$, that you drive at a constant speed varies directly as the time, $x$, that you drive. If you can drive 150 miles in 3 hours, how far can you drive in 6 hours?

**5.** The number of meters, $d$, that a skydiver falls before her parachute opens varies directly as the square of the time, $t$, that she is in the air. A skydiver falls 20 meters in 2 seconds. How far will she fall in 2.5 seconds?

*In Exercises 6–10, sketch a graph of the given power function. Verify your graphs using a graphing calculator.*

**6.** $y = -3x^2$

**7.** $y = x^4 + 1$

**8.** $y = -2x^5$

**9.** $f(x) = x^6$

**10.** $g(x) = 3x^3 - 3$

**11.** Determine the $x$-interval over which the function $f(x) = \frac{1}{2}x^4$ is increasing.

**12.** Does the function $g(x) = -\frac{1}{2}x^6$ have a maximum or a minimum point? Explain.

**13.** For $x > 1$, is the graph of $y = x^2$ rising faster or slower than the graph of $y = x^3$? Explain.

**14.** Is the graph of $y = \frac{3}{2}x^4$ wider or narrower than the graph of $y = x^4$?

**15.** How are the graphs of $y = -2x^3$ and $y = 2x^3 + 1$ different? How are the graphs similar?

**ACTIVITY 4.10**

Speed Limits

**OBJECTIVES**

1. Determine the domain and range of a function defined by $y = \frac{k}{x}$, where $k$ is a nonzero real number.

2. Determine the vertical and horizontal asymptotes of the graph of $y = \frac{k}{x}$.

3. Sketch a graph of functions of the form $y = \frac{k}{x}$.

4. Determine the properties of graphs having equation $y = \frac{k}{x}$.

The speed limit on the New York State Thruway is 65 miles per hour.

1. If you maintain an average speed of 65 miles per hour, how long will it take you to make a 200-mile trip on the thruway? Recall that *distance = rate · time*,

$$time = \frac{distance}{rate}.$$

2. Complete the following table, in which the input variable $r$ represents the average speed in miles per hour and the output variable $x$ represents the time in hours to complete a 200-mile trip.

| r (mph) | 20 | 30 | 40 | 50 | 60 | 70 | 80 |
|---------|----|----|----|----|----|----|----|
| t (hr.) |    |    |    |    |    |    |    |

3. Write an equation that defines travel time, $t$, as a function of the average speed, $r$.

4. As the average speed, $r$, increases, what happens to the travel time, $t$? What does this mean in practical terms?

5. During a winter storm, a combination of drifting snow and icy conditions reduces your average speed to almost a standstill. Complete the following table for a 200-mile trip on the New York State Thruway.

| r (mph) | 10 | 7 | 5 | 3 | 2 | 1 |
|---------|----|----|----|----|----|----|
| t (hr.) |    |   |   |   |   |   |

6. As the average speed $r$ gets closer to zero, what happens to the travel time $t$? Explain what this means in practical terms.

7. Can zero be used as an input value? Explain.

8. a. What is the practical domain of the function given in Problem 3?

**b.** Sketch a graph of this function using the table values in Problem 2 and 5.

**9. a.** What are the intercepts of the graph?

    **b.** Describe the relationship between the horizontal axis $(t = 0)$ and the graph of the function as the values of $r$ get very large.

In this situation, the horizontal line $t = 0$ is called a **horizontal asymptote**. A horizontal asymptote is a horizontal line that a graph approaches as the input values of $r$ get very large in a positive direction (or get very large in a negative direction).

    **c.** Describe the relationship between the vertical axis $(r = 0)$ and the graph of the function as the values of $r$ get close to zero.

In this situation, the vertical line $r = 0$ is called a **vertical asymptote**.

In general, a vertical asymptote is a vertical line, $x = a$, that the graph of a function defined by $y = f(x)$ becomes very close to but never touches. As the $x$-values get closer and closer to $x = a$, the $y$-values get larger and larger in magnitude. That is, the $y$-values become very large positive or very large negative values.

**10.** Using the graph in Problem 8, approximate your average speed if the 200-mile trip takes 5 hours.

## Functions Defined by $y = \frac{k}{x}$, where $k$ is a Nonzero Constant

The function rule $t = \frac{200}{r}$ gives the relationship between the average speed, $r$, the time, $t$, and the given value for distance (200). This function belongs to a family of functions having a general equation of the form $f(x) = \frac{k}{x}$, where $k$ represents some nonzero constant.

Example 1   *Examples of this type of function are $f(x) = \frac{1}{x}$, $g(x) = \frac{5}{x}$, and $h(x) = \frac{10}{x}$.*

**11. a.** What is the domain of functions $f$, $g$, and $h$ defined in Example 1?

**b.** Complete the following table.

| x | −20 | −10 | −5 | −1 | −0.5 | −0.1 | 0 | 0.1 | 0.5 | 1 | 5 | 10 | 20 |
|---|---|---|---|---|---|---|---|---|---|---|---|---|---|
| f(x) | | | | | | | | | | | | | |
| g(x) | | | | | | | | | | | | | |
| h(x) | | | | | | | | | | | | | |

**c.** Sketch graphs of $f$, $g$, and $h$ on the same coordinate system. Verify using your graphing calculator with window Xmin $= -5$, Xmax $= 5$, Ymin $= -25$, and Ymax $= 25$.

**12.** Using the table and graphs in Problem 11, answer each of the following questions.

    **a.** What happens to the $y$-values as the $x$-values increase in magnitude infinitely (without bound) in both the positive and negative directions?

    **b.** What is the horizontal asymptote for each graph?

    **c.** What happens to the $y$-values as the positive $x$-values get closer to zero?

    **d.** What happens to the $y$-values as the negative $x$-values get closer to zero?

    **e.** What is the vertical asymptote for each graph?

**13. a.** Do the graphs of $f$, $g$, or $h$ in Problem 11 have $x$- or $y$-intercepts?

    **b.** Do the functions $f$, $g$, and $h$ have a maximum function value or a minimum function value? Explain.

    **c.** Are any of the functions in problem 11 continuous? Explain.

**14. a.** Complete the following table, where $Q(x) = \dfrac{-1}{x}$.

| x | −10 | −5 | −1 | −0.5 | −0.1 | 0 | 0.1 | 0.5 | 1 | 5 | 10 |
|---|---|---|---|---|---|---|---|---|---|---|---|
| Q(x) | | | | | | | | | | | |

**b.** Sketch a graph of $Q$. Verify using your graphing calculator with window Xmin $= -4$, Xmax $= 4$, Ymin $= -4$, and Ymax $= 4$.

**c.** Add the graph of $f(x) = \dfrac{1}{x}$ to the grid in part b.

**d.** Describe how the graph of $Q(x) = \dfrac{-1}{x}$ can be obtained from the graph of $f(x) = \dfrac{1}{x}$.

**SUMMARY**
**Activity 4.10**

Functions defined by $f(x) = \dfrac{k}{x}$, where $k$ represents some nonzero constant, have the following properties.

**1.** The domain and the range consist of all real numbers except zero.

**2.** If $k > 0$, the graph of $f$ has the following general shape.

3. If $k < 0$, the graph of $f$ has the following general shape.

4. The vertical line $x = 0$ is the vertical asymptote.

5. The horizontal line $y = 0$ is the horizontal asymptote.

6. The graph does not intersect either axis (there are no intercepts).

7. There is no maximum or minimum $y$-value.

8. The function is not continuous at $x = 0$.

## EXERCISES
### Activity 4.10

1. You are a member of a group of distance runners who compete in races ranging in length from 5 to 25 kilometers. In these races, each runner who finishes is told his or her time. Given the time and the length of the race, you can calculate your average running speed.

   a. If you finish a 20-kilometer race in 1 hour 15 minutes, what is your average speed?

   b. Complete the following table for a 20-kilometer race.

| t (hr.) | 1.00 | 1.25 | 1.50 | 1.75 | 2.00 | 2.25 | 2.50 |
|---------|------|------|------|------|------|------|------|
| s (km/hr.) | | | | | | | |

   c. Write an equation that expresses the average speed, $s$, as a function of time $t$ in a 20-kilometer race.

   d.  i. What is the domain of the function?

      ii. What is the practical domain?

**iii.** Sketch a graph of the function using the practical domain.

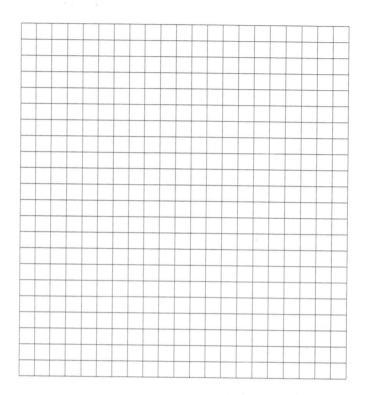

**e.** As the running time, $t$, gets longer, what happens to the average speed, $s$?

**f.** As the running time, $t$, is reduced (gets closer to zero), what happens to the average speed, $s$?

**2. a.** Sketch the graphs of the following pair of functions on the same coordinate system. Use labels or colors to differentiate the graphs. Verify your sketches using your graphing calculator.

$$f(x) = \frac{5}{x}, \qquad g(x) = \frac{-5}{x}$$

**b.** Describe how the graph of $g$ can be obtained from the graph of function $f$.

**3.** A commercial refrigerator has an initial cost, $C$, and a scrap value, $V$. If the life of the refrigerator is $N$ years, then the amount, $D$, that can be depreciated each year is modeled by the formula

$$D = \frac{C - V}{N}.$$

**a.** If the initial cost is $1400 and the scrap value is $200, write an equation for $D$ as a function of $N$.

**b.** Complete the following table.

| N | 1 | 2 | 3 | 6 | 12 | 24 |
|---|---|---|---|---|----|----|
| D |   |   |   |   |    |    |

**c.** Sketch a graph of the function.

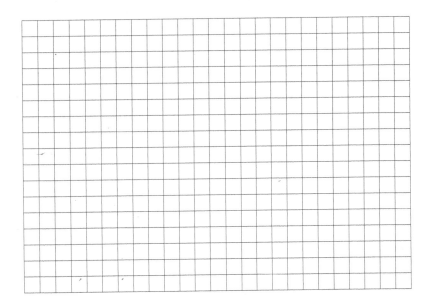

**d.** If the refrigerator is well constructed, it should have a long, useful life. Will an increase in the useful life of the refrigerator increase or decrease the amount, $D$, that can be depreciated each year? Explain.

4. The speed limit on Route 66 in Arizona is 75 miles per hour.

   a. If you maintain an average speed of 75 miles per hour, how long will it take you to make a 350-mile trip on Route 66?

   b. Write an equation that defines $t$ as a function of $r$, in which $r$ represents the average speed in miles per hour and $t$ represents the time in hours to complete the 350-mile trip.

   c. Complete the following table for the equation you determined in part b.

| INPUT, $r$, mph | 25 | 35 | 45 | 55 | 65 | 75 | 85 |
|---|---|---|---|---|---|---|---|
| OUTPUT, $t = f(r)$, hr. | | | | | | | |

   d. As your average speed increases, what happens to the time it takes to complete the trip?

   e. As your average speed for the trip gets closer to zero, what happens to the time it takes to complete the 350-mile trip?

   f. What is the practical domain?

   g. Sketch a graph.

   h. What are the vertical and horizontal asymptotes of the graph of the function?

**ACTIVITY 4.11**
Loudness of a
Sound

**OBJECTIVES**

1. Graph an inverse variation function defined by an equation of the form $y = \frac{k}{x^n}$, where $n$ is any positive integer, $x \neq 0$.

2. Describe the properties of graphs having equation $y = \frac{k}{x^n}$, $x \neq 0$.

3. Determine the vertical and horizontal asymptotes of the graphs of $y = \frac{k}{x^n}$.

4. Determine the constant of proportionality (also called the constant of variation).

The loudness (or intensity) of any sound is a function of the listener's distance from the source of the sound. In general, the relationship between the intensity $I$ and the distance $d$ can be modeled by an equation of the form

$$I = \frac{k}{d^2},$$

where $I$ is measured in decibels, $d$ is measured in feet, and $k$ is a constant determined by the source of the sound and the surroundings.

1. The intensity, $I$, of a human voice can be given by the formula $I = \frac{1500}{d^2}$. Complete the following table:

| $d$ (ft) | 0.1 | 0.5 | 1 | 2 | 5 | 10 | 20 | 30 |
|----------|-----|-----|---|---|---|----|----|----|
| $I$ (dB) |     |     |   |   |   |    |    |    |

2. **a.** What is the practical domain of the function?

**b.** Sketch a graph that shows the relationship between intensity of sound and distance from the source of the sound. Use the table in Problem 1 to help determine an appropriate scale.

3. As you move closer to the person speaking, what happens to the intensity of the sound?

4. As you move away from the person speaking, what happens to the intensity of the sound?

## Functions Defined by $y = \frac{k}{x^2}$, Where $k$ is a Nonzero Constant

The function defined by $I = \dfrac{1500}{d^2}$ belongs to a family of functions having an equation of the form $y = \dfrac{k}{x^2}$, where $k$ represents some nonzero constant.

Example 1   *Examples of this type of function are* $f(x) = \dfrac{1}{x^2}$ *and* $g(x) = \dfrac{10}{x^2}$.

**5. a.** What is the domain of functions $f$ and $g$ defined in Example 1?

**b.** Complete the following table:

| x | −20 | −10 | −5 | −1 | −0.5 | −0.1 | 0 | 0.1 | 0.5 | 1 | 5 | 10 | 20 |
|---|---|---|---|---|---|---|---|---|---|---|---|---|---|
| f(x) | | | | | | | | | | | | | |
| g(x) | | | | | | | | | | | | | |

**c.** Sketch the graphs of $f$ and $g$ on the same coordinate system. Verify your sketch using your graphing calculator.

**d.** Explain why no part of each graph appears below the *x*-axis.

**e.** What happens to the *y*-values as the *x*-values increase infinitely in the positive direction or decreases infinitely in the negative direction?

**f.** What happens to the *y*-values as the positive *x*-values get closer to zero?

**g.** What happens to the *y*-values as the negative *x*-values get closer to zero?

**h.** Do the functions have a maximum *y*-value or a minimum *y*-value?

**i.** Are the functions continuous?

**6.** Describe how the graphs of $y = \dfrac{1}{x}$ and $y = \dfrac{1}{x^2}$ are similar and how they are different.

**7. a.** Complete the following table:

| x | −20 | −10 | −5 | −1 | −0.5 | −0.1 | 0 | 0.1 | 0.5 | 1 | 5 | 10 | 20 |
|---|---|---|---|---|---|---|---|---|---|---|---|---|---|
| $g(x) = \dfrac{10}{x^2}$ | | | | | | | | | | | | | |
| $h(x) = \dfrac{-10}{x^2}$ | | | | | | | | | | | | | |

**b.** Sketch graphs of functions $g$ and $h$ on the same coordinate system. Use labels or different colors to differentiate the graphs. Verify your sketch using your graphing calculator.

**c.** Describe how to obtain the graph of function $h$ using the graph of function $g$.

**8.** Sketch a graph of $h(x) = \dfrac{1}{x^3}$. Is the graph similar to the graph of $f(x) = \dfrac{1}{x}$ or $g(x) = \dfrac{1}{x^2}$?

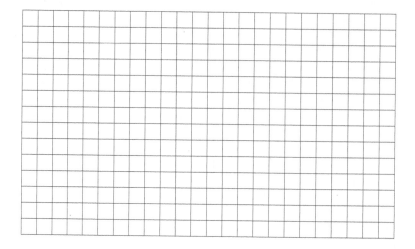

**9.** Sketch a graph $R(x) = \dfrac{1}{x^4}$. Is the graph similar to the graph of $f(x) = \dfrac{1}{x}$ or $g(x) = \dfrac{1}{x^2}$?

## Inverse Variation Functions

Functions defined by equations of the form $y = \dfrac{k}{x^n}$, where $k$ is a nonzero constant and $n$ is a positive integer, belong to the family of **inverse variation functions**.

Example 2   *For the inverse variation function given by $y = \frac{4}{x^2}$, $y$ varies inversely as $x^2$, or $y$ is inversely proportional to $x^2$. The number 4 is called the constant of variation or the constant of proportionality. The following table demonstrates that as $x$ doubles in value, the corresponding $y$-values are reduced by one-quarter.*

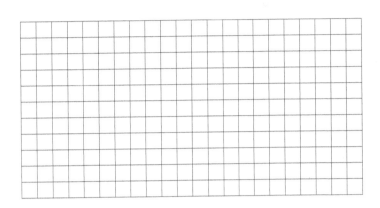

| $x$ | 2 | 4 | 8 | 16 |
|---|---|---|---|---|
| $y = \frac{4}{x^2}$ | 1 | $\frac{1}{4}$ | $\frac{1}{16}$ | $\frac{1}{64}$ |

**10.** For the function defined by $I = \dfrac{1500}{d^2}$ (see Problem 1), answer the following questions:

  **a.** $I$ varies inversely as what quantity?

  **b.** What is the constant of proportionality?

  **c.** If $d$ is doubled, what is the effect on $I$?

In many applications, the constant of proportionality, $k$, is unknown. The procedure for determining $k$ for an inverse variation is demonstrated in Example 3.

---

**Example 3** *y varies inversely as the square of x and y = 5 when x = 2. Determine the equation for y.*

SOLUTION

**Step 1.** Write the equation relating $x$ to $y$ using $k$ for the constant of proportionality.

$$y = \frac{k}{x^2}$$

**Step 2.** Substitute the given values of $x$ and $y$ ($y = 5$, $x = 2$) into the equation from Step 1.

$$5 = \frac{k}{2^2} \quad \text{or} \quad 5 = \frac{k}{4}$$

**Step 3.** Solve the equation in Step 2 for $k$.

$$5 \cdot 4 = \frac{k}{4} \cdot 4$$

$$20 = k$$

**Step 4.** Rewrite the equation from Step 1 by substituting the value of $k$ determined in Step 3.

$$y = \frac{20}{x^2}$$

---

**11.** In this activity, the relationship between the intensity, $I$, of a human voice and the distance, $d$, from the individual was given by $I = \frac{1500}{d^2}$, where $I$ is measured in decibels, $d$ is measured in feet, and 1500 is the constant of proportionality. The constant of proportionality depends on the source of the sound and the surroundings. If the source of the sound changes, the value of the constant of proportionality will also change.

**a.** The intensity of the sound made by a heavy truck 60 feet away is 90 decibels. Determine the constant of proportionality.

**b.** Write a formula for the intensity, $I$, of the sound made by a truck when it is $d$ feet away.

**c.** Use the formula from part b to determine the intensity of the sound made by the truck when it is 100 feet away.

**SUMMARY**
**Activity 4.11**

- Functions defined by equations of the form $y = \frac{k}{x^n}$, where $k$ is a positive integer, have the following properties.

  1. The domain and range consist of all real numbers except zero.

  2. The graph of $f$ has the following general shape:

     **a.** Where $k > 0$, and $n$ is an even integer.

     **b.** Where $k > 0$, and $n$ is an odd integer.

     **c.** Where $k < 0$, and $n$ is an even integer.

     **d.** Where $k < 0$, and $n$ is an odd integer.

  3. There are no $x$- or $y$-intercepts.

  4. There is no maximum or minimum $y$-value.

  5. The function is not continuous at $x = 0$.

- Functions defined by $y = \frac{k}{x^n}$ are called **inverse variation functions** in which

  1. $y$ is said to vary inversely as the $n$th power of $x$.

  2. $k$ is called the constant of variation or constant of proportionality.

1. Doctors sometimes use a patient's body-mass index to determine whether or not the patient should lose weight. The formula for the body-mass index, $B$, is

$$B = \frac{705w}{h^2},$$

where $w$ is the weight in pounds and $h$ is height in inches.

a. What is your body-mass index?

b. Suppose your friend weighs 170 pounds. Substitute this value into the body-mass index formula to obtain an equation for $B$ in terms of height.

c. What is the practical domain of the body-mass index function in part b?

d. Complete the following table using the formula for the body-mass index of a 170-pound person:

| $h$, HEIGHT IN INCHES | 60 | 64 | 68 | 72 | 76 | 80 |
|---|---|---|---|---|---|---|
| B | | | | | | |

e. Sketch a graph of the function defined by $B = \dfrac{119{,}850}{h^2}$. Use the data values in part d to help determine an appropriately scaled axis.

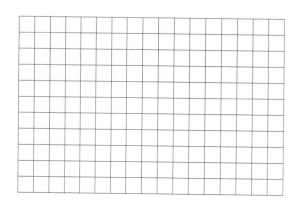

**f.** What happens to the body-mass index as height increases? Does this make sense in the context of the situation? Explain why or why not.

**g.** It is recommended that a person's body-mass index be between 19 and 25. Use the graph and the trace key on your calculator to approximate the values of $h$ for which $19 < B < 25$.

**2.** Sketch a graph of the functions $f(x) = \dfrac{3}{x^2}$ and $g(x) = \dfrac{-3}{x^2}$ on the same coordinate system. Describe how the graph of $g$ is related to the graph of $f$.

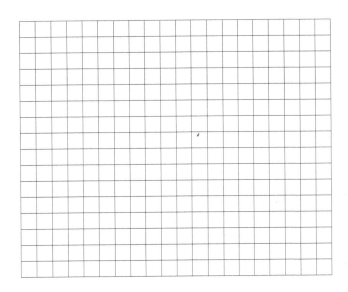

**3.** Match the following functions with the accompanying graphs.

**i.** $f(x) = \dfrac{10}{x^4}$

**ii.** $g(x) = \dfrac{100}{x^5}$

**iii.** $h(x) = \dfrac{-10}{x^3}$

**iv.** $F(x) = \dfrac{-1}{x^2}$

**a.**

**b.**

**c.**

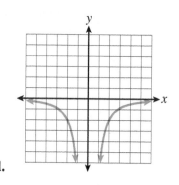

**d.**

4. Describe how the graphs of $y = \dfrac{1}{x^2}$ and $y = \dfrac{1}{x^3}$ are similar and how they are different.

5. Consider the family of functions of the form $y = \dfrac{k}{x^n}$, where $k$ is a nonzero constant and $n$ is a positive integer.

   **a.** What is the domain of the function?

   **b.** Use several different values of $k$ and $n$, where $k > 0$ and $n$ is an odd positive integer, to determine the general shape of the graph of $f$.

**c.** Use several different values of $k$ and $n$, where $k > 0$ and $n$ is an even positive integer, to determine the general shape of the graph of $f$.

**6.** How will the general shapes of the graphs in Exercise 5 change if $k < 0$?

**7.** If $y$ varies inversely as the cube of $x$, determine the constant of proportionality if $y = 16$ when $x = 2$.

**8.** For each inverse variation below, at least one ordered pair $(x, y)$ is given in the table. Use this ordered pair to determine the constant of proportionality. Then use the equation to complete the table.

**a.** $y$ varies inversely as $x$.

| x | y |
|---|---|
| $\frac{1}{2}$ | |
| 1 | 2 |
| 2 | |
| 6 | |

**b.** $y$ varies inversely as $x^3$.

| x | y |
|---|---|
| $\frac{1}{2}$ | |
| 1 | 8 |
| 2 | 1 |
| 6 | |

9. The amount of current, $I$, in a circuit varies inversely as the resistance $R$. A circuit containing a resistance of 10 ohms has a current of 12 amperes. Determine the current in a circuit containing a resistance of 15 ohms.

10. The intensity, $I$, of light varies inversely as the square of the distance, $d$, between the source of light and the object being illuminated. A light meter reads 0.25 unit at a distance of 2 meters from a light source. What will the meter read at a distance of 3 meters from the source?

11. You are investigating the relationship between the volume, $V$, and pressure, $P$, of a gas. In a laboratory, you conduct the following experiment: While holding the temperature of a gas constant, you vary the pressure and measure the corresponding volume. The data that you collect appears in the following table.

| P (psi) | 20 | 30 | 40 | 50 | 60 | 70 | 80 |
|---------|----|----|----|----|----|----|----|
| V (ft³) | 82 | 54 | 41 | 32 | 27 | 23 | 20 |

a. Sketch a graph of the data.

**b.** One possible model for the data is that $V$ varies inversely as the square of $P$. Does the data fit the model $V = \dfrac{k}{P^2}$? Explain.

**c.** Another possible model for the data is that $V$ varies inversely as $P$. Does $V = \dfrac{k}{P}$ model the data? Explain.

**d.** Predict the volume of the gas if the pressure is 65 pounds per square inch.

## Activities 4.8–4.11   What Have I Learned?

1. In a direct variation situation, as the value of the independent variable, $x$, increases, what happens to the value of the dependent variable, $y$?

2. In a hurricane, the wind pressure varies directly as the square of the wind velocity (speed). If the wind speed doubles in value, what change in the wind pressure do you experience?

3. Is the graph of $y = 3x^4$ narrower or wider than the graph of $y = x^2$? Explain.

4. In an inverse variation situation, as the value of independent variable, $x$, decreases, what happens to the value of the dependent variable, $y$?

5. Does an equation of the form $xy = k$ indicate a direct variation or an inverse variation situation? Explain.

6. Which of the following statements is not equivalent to the other two?

   a. $y$ varies directly as $x$

   b. $y = kx$ for some constant $k$

   c. $y = \dfrac{k}{x}$ for some constant $k$

7. For what values of $k$ will the graph of $y = \dfrac{k}{x}$ be in the second and fourth quadrants?

**Activities 4.8–4.11**    How Can I Practice?

1. $y$ varies directly as $x$ and $y = 21$ when $x = 6$. Determine the value of $y$ when $x = 14$.

2. $y$ varies inversely as $x$ and $y = 11$ when $x = 8$. Determine the value of $y$ when $x = 16$.

3. $y$ varies directly as $x^2$. When $x = 3$, $y = 45$. Determine $y$ when $x = 6$.

4. Recall if $d$ represents the distance (in feet) of the lightning from the observer, then $d$ varies directly as the time, $t$ (in seconds), it takes to hear the thunder. The relationship is modeled by

$$d = 1080t.$$

   a. As the time $t$ doubles (say from 3 to 6), the corresponding $d$-values _____ .

   b. What is the value of $k$, the constant of variation, in this situation? What significance does $k$ have in this problem?

5. The velocity, $v$, of a falling object varies directly to the time, $t$, of the fall. After three seconds, the velocity of the object is 60 feet per second. What will be its velocity after four seconds?

6. A propane gas bill varies directly as the amount of gas used. The bill for 56 gallons of propane was $184.80. What is the bill for 70 gallons of propane?

7. The time it takes to drive a certain distance varies inversely as the rate of travel. If it takes 6 hours at 48 miles per hour to drive the distance, how long would it take at 72 miles per hour?

**8.** The loudness of a speaker, measured in decibels, varies inversely as the square of the distance from the speaker. The loudness is 20 decibels when you are 10 feet from the speaker. Determine the loudness when you are 5 feet from the speakers.

**9.** Describe the relationship between the graphs of $f(x) = \dfrac{1}{x}$ and $g(x) = \dfrac{-1}{x}$.

**10.** Describe the relationship between the graphs of $f(x) = \dfrac{1}{x}$ and $g(x) = \dfrac{1}{x^3}$.

**11. a.** Suppose you are taking a trip of 145 miles. Assume that you drive the entire distance at a constant speed. Express your time to take this trip as a function of your speed.

   **b.** What is the practical domain of this function?

   **c.** Using the equation for the function, determine the domain.

**12.** The intensity of a light source varies inversely as the square of the distance from the light source. For a particular light the intensity measures 24 foot-candles at a distance of 12 feet from the source.

   **a.** Determine the equation that relates the intensity, $I$, to the distance from the light source, $s$, in this case.

   **b.** Use the equation in part a to complete the following table:

| DISTANCE FROM THE LIGHT SOURCE, $s$ | 2 | 3 | 4 | 6 | 8 | 12 |
|---|---|---|---|---|---|---|
| INTENSITY OF THE LIGHT, $I$ | | | | | | |

   **c.** Explain how this table indicates that the relationship between $s$ and $I$ is an inverse variation.

**d.** Graph the relationship between $I$ and $s$ using the last five pairs from the table in part b.

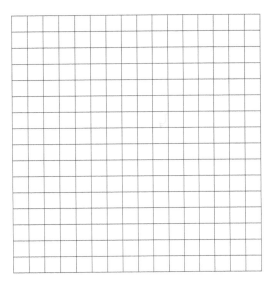

**e.** If the intensity from the light source in this case measures 6 foot-candles, how far are you from the light source?

# Summary

*The bracketed numbers following each concept indicate the activity in which the concept is discussed.*

| CONCEPT / SKILL | DESCRIPTION | EXAMPLE |
|---|---|---|
| **Parabola** [4.1] | A parabola is the U-shaped graph described by a function of the form $y = ax^2 + bx + c$. | 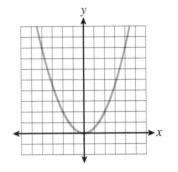 |
| **Solving an equation of the form** $ax^2 = c$ [4.1] | Solve an equation of this form algebraically by dividing both sides of the equation by $a$ and then taking the square root of both sides. | $2x^2 = 8$<br>$\dfrac{2x^2}{2} = \dfrac{8}{2}$<br>$x^2 = 4, x = \pm 2$ |
| **Quadratic function** [4.2] | The quadratic function with $x$ as the variable has the standard form $y = ax^2 + bx + c$, where $a$, $b$, and $c$ represent real numbers and $a \neq 0$. | $y = 2x^2 - 3x - 2$ |
| **Graph a quadratic function (a parabola)** [4.2] | For the quadratic function defined by $y = ax^2 + bx + c$; if $a > 0$, the parabola opens upward; if $a < 0$, the parabola opens downward. | The graph of $y = 2x^2 - 3x - 2$ is a parabola that opens upward. |
| **$y$-intercept of the graph of a quadratic function** [4.2] | The constant term $c$ of a quadratic function $y = ax^2 + bx + c$ always indicates the $y$-intercept of the parabola. The $y$-intercept of any quadratic function is $(0, c)$. | The vertical intercept of the graph of $y = 2x^2 - 3x - 2$ is $(0, -2)$. |
| **Axis of symmetry** [4.3] | The axis of symmetry of a parabola is a vertical line that separates the parabola into two mirror images. The equation of the vertical axis of symmetry is given by $x = \frac{-b}{2a}$. | See Example 2 in Activity 4.3. |
| **Vertex (turning point)** [4.3] | The vertex of a parabola defined by $y = ax^2 + bx + c$ is the point where the graph changes direction. It is given by $\left(\frac{-b}{2a}, f\left(-\frac{b}{2a}\right)\right)$. | See Example 1 in Activity 4.3. |
| **$x$-intercept(s)** [4.3] | An $x$-intercept is the point or points (if any) where the parabola crosses the $x$-axis (that is, where its $y$-coordinate is zero). | The $x$-intercepts of the parabola defined by $y = 2x^2 - 3x - 2$ are $(2, 0)$ and $(-0.5, 0)$. |

| | | |
|---|---|---|
| **Domain of the quadratic function** [4.3] | The domain of all quadratic functions is all real numbers. | The domain of $y = 2x^2 - 3x - 2$ is all real numbers. |
| **Range of the quadratic function** [4.3] | If the parabola opens upward, the range is $y \geq y$-value of vertex. If the parabola opens downward, the range is $y \leq y$-value of vertex. | The range of the parabola defined by $y = 2x^2 - 3x - 2$ is $y \geq \frac{-25}{8}$. |
| **Solving $f(x) = c$ graphically** [4.4] | Graph $y = f(x)$, graph $y = c$, and determine the $x$-values of the points of intersection. Or graph $y = f(x) - c$ and determine the $x$-intercepts. | See Example 1 in Activity 4.4. |
| **Greatest common factor (or GCF)** [4.5] | The GCF is the largest factor common to all terms in an expression. | The GCF of $3x^4 - 6x^3 + 18x^2$ is $3x^2$. |
| **Zero-product principle** [4.5] | If $a$ and $b$ are any numbers and $a \cdot b = 0$, then either $a$ or $b$, or both, must be equal to zero. | Example 1, Activity 4.5 |
| **Factoring trinomials by trial and error** [4.5] | To factor trinomials by trial and error, 1. remove the GCF. 2. try combinations of factors for the first and last terms in two binomials. 3. check the outer and inner products to match middle term of the original trinomial. 4. if the check fails, repeat steps 2 and 3. | Example 5, Activity 4.5 |
| **Solving quadratic equations by factoring** [4.5] | To solve a quadratic equation by factoring, 1. use the addition principle to remove all terms from one side of the equation. This results in a quadratic polynomial being set equal to zero. 2. combine like terms, and then factor the nonzero side of the equation. 3. use the zero-product principle to set each factor containing a variable equal to zero, and then solve the equations. 4. check your solutions in the original equation. | Example 6, Activity 4.5 |
| **Quadratic formula** [4.6] | $x = \dfrac{-b \pm \sqrt{b^2 - 4ac}}{2a}$ | |

| | | |
|---|---|---|
| **Solving a quadratic equation of the form $ax^2 + bx + c = 0$, $a \neq 0$, using the quadratic formula** [4.6] | To solve a quadratic equation of the form $ax^2 + bx + c = 0$, $a \neq 0$ using the quadratic formula $$x = \frac{-b \pm \sqrt{b^2 - 4ac}}{2a},$$ 1. Set the quadratic equation equal to zero. 2. Identify the coefficients $a$ and $b$ and the constant term $c$. 3. Substitute these values into the formula, and simplify. 4. Check your solutions. | Example 1, Activity 4.6. |
| **Direct variation** [4.8] | Two variables are said to vary directly if as the magnitude of one increases, the magnitude of the other does as well. | In the function $y = 2x$, $y$ varies directly as $x$. As $x$ increases in magnitude so does $y$. |
| **The constant of proportionality or constant of variation, $k$** [4.8] | The following statements are equivalent: a. $y$ varies directly as $x$ b. $y$ is directly proportional to $x$ c. $y = kx$ for some constant $k$ | In the direct variation function $y = 2x$, 2 is the constant of variation. |
| **Power functions** [4.9] | The direct variation function having an equation of the form $y = kx^n$, where $n$ is a positive integer, is also called a power function. | $y = 4x^3$ is a third-power function. |
| **Domain and range of $y = \frac{k}{x}$** [4.10] | The domain and range consist of all real numbers except zero. | $y = \frac{3}{x}$ |
| **Graph of $y = \frac{k}{x}$** [4.10] | The graph is in the first and third quadrants if $k > 0$ and in the second and fourth if $k < 0$. | $y = \frac{3}{x}$ |
| **Asymptotes of the graph of $y = \frac{k}{x}$** [4.10] | The $y$-axis, $x = 0$, is the vertical asymptote. The $x$-axis, $y = 0$, is the horizontal asymptote. | $y = \frac{3}{x}$ |

| | | |
|---|---|---|
| **Inverse variation function** [4.11] | An inverse variation function is a function defined by the equation $xy = k$ $\left(\text{or } y = \dfrac{k}{x}\right)$. When $k > 0$ and $x$ increases by a constant multiplicative factor $p$, the $y$ decreases by the multiplicative factor $\dfrac{1}{p}$. The value $x = 0$ is not in the domain of this function. | $y = \dfrac{360}{x}$ When $x = 4$, $y = \dfrac{360}{4} = 90$. If $x$ doubles to 8, $y$ is halved and becomes 45. |
| **Domain of $y = \dfrac{k}{x^n}$** [4.11] | The domain consists of all real numbers except zero. | $y = \dfrac{4}{x^3}$ |
| **Graph of $y = \dfrac{k}{x^n}$** [4.11] | The graphs will vary depending on the values of $k$ and $n$. | See the summary at the end of Activity 4.11. |
| **Asymptotes of the graph of $y = \dfrac{k}{x^n}$** [4.11] | The $y$-axis, $x = 0$, is the vertical asymptote. The $x$-axis, $y = 0$, is the horizontal asymptote. | $y = \dfrac{4}{x^3}$  |
| **Inverse variation functions** [4.11] | Functions defined by $y = \dfrac{k}{x^n}$ are called inverse variation functions in which $y$ is said to vary inversely as the $n$th power of $x$; $k$ is called the constant of variation. | For the function $y = \dfrac{4}{x^3}$, $y$ varies inversely as the cube of $x$, and 4 is the constant of variation. |

# Gateway Review

In Exercises 1–8, determine the following characteristics of each quadratic function by inspecting its equation.

    **a.** the direction in which the graph opens

    **b.** the equation of the axis of symmetry

    **c.** the vertex; maximum or minimum point

    **d.** the $y$-intercept

**1.** $y = x^2 + 2$                     **2.** $y = -3x^2$

**3.** $y = -3x^2 + 4$            **4.** $y = 2x^2 - x$

**5.** $y = x^2 + 5x + 6$        **6.** $y = x^2 - 3x + 4$

**7.** $y = x^2 - 2x + 1$        **8.** $y = -x^2 + 5x - 6$

In Exercises 9–15, sketch the graph of each quadratic function using your graphing calculator. Then determine each of the following using the graph.

    **a.** the coordinates of the $x$-intercepts; if they exist

    **b.** the domain and the range of the function

    **c.** the $x$-interval in which the function is increasing

    **d.** the $x$-interval in which the function is decreasing

**9.** $y = x^2 + 4x + 3$        **10.** $y = x^2 + 2x - 3$

**11.** $y = x^2 - 3x + 1$                                 **12.** $y = 2x^2 + 8x + 5$

**13.** $y = -2x^2 + 8$                                       **14.** $y = -3x^2 + 4x - 1$

**15.** $y = 4x^2 + 5$

*In Exercises 16–19, solve the quadratic equation numerically (using tables). Verify your solutions graphically.*

**16.** $x^2 + 4x + 4 = 0$                                  **17.** $x^2 - 5x + 6 = 0$

**18.** $3x^2 = 18x + 10$                                   **19.** $-x^2 = 3x - 10$

*In Exercises 20–21, solve the equation. Round your answer to the nearest tenth when necessary.*

**20.** $8x^2 = 10$                                               **21.** $5x^2 + 25x = -5$

**22.** Completely factor the following polynomials.

    **a.** $9a^5 - 27a^2$        **b.** $24x^3 - 6x^2$        **c.** $4x^3 - 16x^2 - 20x$

    **d.** $5x^2 - 16x + 6$     **e.** $x^2 - 5x - 24$      **f.** $t^2 + 10t + 25$

*In Exercises 23–27, solve each equation by factoring. Verify your answer graphically or by substitution of the solutions in the equations.*

**23.** $x^2 - 9 = 0$     **24.** $-x^2 + 36 = 0$     **25.** $x^2 - 7x + 12 = 0$

**26.** $x^2 - 6x = 27$        **27.** $x^2 = -x$

*In Exercises 28–32, write each of the equations in the form $ax^2 + bx + c = 0$. Then identify a, b, and c, and solve the equation using the quadratic formula. Verify your solutions by substitution.*

**28.** $x^2 + 5x + 3 = 0$     **29.** $2x^2 - x = -3$       **30.** $x^2 = 81$

**31.** $3x^2 + 5x = 12$                **32.** $2x^2 = 3x + 5$

**33.** For the quadratic function $f(x) = 2x^2 - 8x + 3$, determine the zeros of the function. First, approximate the zeros using your graphing calculator. Second, solve the equation using the quadratic formula. Approximate your answers to the nearest hundredth.

**34.** The height, $h$ (in feet), of a golf ball is a function of the time, $t$ (in seconds), it has been in flight. A golfer strikes a golf ball with an initial velocity of 80 feet per second. The flight path of the ball is a parabola. The approximate height of the ball above the ground is modeled by

$$h = -16t^2 + 80t.$$

**a.** Sketch a graph of the function. What is the practical domain in this situation?

**b.** Determine the vertex of the parabola. What is the practical meaning of this point?

**c.** What is the $h$-intercept, and what is its practical meaning in this situation?

**d.** Determine the $t$-intercepts. What is the significance of these intercepts?

**e.** What assumption are you making in this situation about the elevation of the spot where the ball is struck and the point where the ball lands?

**35.** To use the regression feature of your calculator to determine the equation of a parabola, you need three distinct points. The stream of water flowing out of a water fountain is in the shape of a parabola. Suppose you let the origin of a coordinate system correspond to the point where the water begins to flow out of the nozzle (see figure).

The maximum height of water stream occurs approximately 5 inches measured horizontally from the nozzle. The maximum height of the stream of water is measured to be approximately 6 inches.

**a.** What is the vertex of the parabola?

**b.** You already have two points that lie on the parabola. What are they? Use symmetry to obtain a third point.

**c.** Using these three points and the regression feature of your graphing calculator, determine the equation of the stream of water.

**36.** A fastball is hit straight up over home plate. The ball's height, $h$ (in feet), from the ground is modeled by

$$h(t) = -16t^2 + 80t + 5,$$

where $t$ is measured in seconds.

**a.** What is the maximum height of the ball above the ground?

**b.** How long will it take for the ball to reach the ground?

**37.** Safe automobile spacing, $S$ (in feet), is modeled by

$$S(v) = 0.03125v^2 + v + 18,$$

where $v$ is average velocity in feet per second.

**a.** Suppose a car is traveling at 44 feet per second. To be safe, how far should it be from the car in front of it?

**b.** If the car is following 50 feet behind a van, what is a safe speed for the car to be traveling? How fast is this in miles per hour (60 miles per hour ≈ 88 feet per second)?

**38.** $y$ varies directly as $x \cdot y = 88$ when $x = 16$. Determine the value of $x$ when $y = 77$.

**39.** $y$ varies inversely as $x \cdot y = 10$ when $x = 12$. Determine the value of $y$ when $x = 15$.

**40.** Determine which of the following graphs indicate direct variation and which indicate inverse variation. Explain your reasoning.

**a.**

**b.**

**c.**

**41.** The sales tax on an item varies directly as the cost of the item. The sales tax in your area is 7%. The sales tax on your item was $10.50. What was the cost of the item before the sales tax was applied?

**42.** County taxes vary directly with the assessed value of your property. Your 2008 tax bill indicated that you owed $1245 in taxes on your property assessed at $105,000.

   **a.** Determine the equation that relates the county tax due, $t$, to the assessed value of your property, $v$, in this case. Round $k$ to three decimal places.

   **b.** Use the equation in part a to complete the following table:

| ASSESSED VALUE OF YOUR PROPERTY, $v$ | 50,000 | 75,000 | 100,000 | 125,000 | 200,000 | 450,000 |
|---|---|---|---|---|---|---|
| AMOUNT OF COUNTY TAXES, $t$ | | | | | | |

   **c.** Explain how this table indicates that the relationship between $v$ and $t$ is a direct variation.

   **d.** Graph the relationship between $v$ and $t$ using the first five pairs from the table in part b.

   **e.** If the taxes on your property are $1164, what is the assessed value of your property.

**43.** According to the blueprint, the floor area of the stage in the new auditorium at your high school must be rectangular and equal to 1200 square feet. The width of the stage is key to all of the theater productions. Therefore, in this situation, the stage's depth is a function of its width.

   **a.** Let $d$ represent the depth and $w$ represent the width. Write an equation that expresses $d$ as a function of $w$.

**b.** Complete the following table using the equation from part a.

| w | 30 | 35 | 40 | 50 | 60 |
|---|----|----|----|----|----|
| d |    |    |    |    |    |

**c.** What happens to the depth as the width increases?

**d.** What happens if the width is 100 feet? Is this realistic? Explain.

**e.** Can the width be zero? Explain.

**f.** What do you think is the practical domain for this function?

**g.** What type of a function do you have in this situation?

**h.** What is the domain of the general function?

**i.** What is the vertical asymptote?

**j.** What is the horizontal asymptote? Explain in words how you determined it.

**44.** Sketch the following graphs without using your graphing calculator.

**a.** $f(x) = \dfrac{1}{x^2}$

**b.** $g(x) = \dfrac{-1}{x^3}$

**c.** Describe how the graphs are similar and how they are different.

**45. a.** If $y$ varies inversely as $x$, and $x = 10$ when $y = 12$, then determine the value of $y$ when $x = 30$.

**b.** The loudness, in decibels, of a stereo varies inversely to the square of the distance from the speaker to the person listening. If the loudness is 32 decibels at a distance of 4 feet, then what is the loudness when the listener is 10 feet from the speaker?

**46.** Determine the horizontal and vertical asymptotes and the intercepts of the graph of $f(x) = \dfrac{10}{x^3}$. Then graph the function.

# CHAPTER 5

# Modeling with Exponential and Logarithmic Functions

**OBJECTIVES**

1. Define growth factor.

2. Determine growth factors from percent increases.

3. Apply growth factors to problems involving percent increases.

4. Define decay factor.

5. Determine decay factors from percent decreases.

6. Apply decay factors to problems involving percent decreases.

To earn revenue (income), many state and local governments require merchants to collect sales tax on the items they sell. In several localities, the sales tax is assessed at as much as 8% of the selling price and is passed on directly to the purchaser.

1. Determine the total cost (including the 8% sales tax) to the customer of the following items. Include each step of your calculation in your answer.

   **a.** A greeting card selling for $1.50

   **b.** A DVD player priced at $300

Many people correctly determine the total costs for Problem 1 in two steps:

   • They first compute the sales tax on the item.

   • Then they add the sales tax to the selling price to obtain the total cost.

It is also possible to compute the total cost in one step by using the idea of a **growth factor**.

## Growth Factors

2. **a.** If a quantity increases by 50%, how does its new value compare to its original value? That is, what is the ratio of the new value to the original value? The first row of the following table is completed for you. Complete the remaining rows to confirm or discover your answer.

## A Matter of Values

| ORIGINAL VALUE | NEW VALUE (INCREASED BY 50%) | RATIO OF NEW VALUE TO ORIGINAL VALUE | | |
| --- | --- | --- | --- | --- |
| | | FRACTIONAL FORM | DECIMAL FORM | PERCENT FORM |
| 20 | 10 + 20 = 30 | $\frac{30}{20} = \frac{3}{2} = 1\frac{1}{2}$ | 1.50 | 150% |
| 50 | | | | |
| 100 | | | | |
| Your choice of an original value | | | | |

    **b.** Use the results from the preceding table to answer the question, "What is the ratio of the new value to the original value of any quantity that increases by 50%?" Express this ratio as a reduced fraction, a mixed number, a decimal and a percent.

**DEFINITION**

For any specified percent *increase*, no matter what the original value may be, the ratio of the new value to the original value is always the same. This ratio $\frac{\text{new value}}{\text{original value}}$ is called the **growth factor** associated with the specified percent increase.

The growth factor is most often written in decimal form. As you saw previously, the growth factor associated with a 50% increase is 1.50.

**PROCEDURE**

The growth factor is formed by adding the specified percent increase to 100% and then changing this percent into its decimal form.

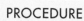
Example 1   *The growth factor corresponding to a 50% increase is*

$$100\% + 50\% = 150\%.$$

*If you change 150% to a decimal, the growth factor is* 1.50.

  **3.** Determine the growth factor of any quantity that increases by the given percent.

    **a.** 30%

**b.** 75%

**c.** 15%

**d.** 7.5%

**4.** A growth factor can always be written in decimal form. Explain why this decimal will always be greater than 1.

---

### PROCEDURE

When a quantity increases by a specified percent, its new value can be obtained by multiplying the original value by the corresponding growth factor. That is,

$$\text{original value} \cdot \text{growth factor} = \text{new value.}$$

---

**5. a.** Use the growth factor 1.50 to determine the new value of a stock portfolio that increased 50% over its original value of $400.

**b.** Use the growth factor 1.50 to determine the population of a town that has grown 50% over its previous size of 120,000 residents.

**6. a.** Determine the growth factor for any quantity that increases 20%.

**b.** Use the growth factor to determine this year's budget, which has increased 20% over last year's budget of $75,000.

**7. a.** Determine the growth factor of any quantity that increases 8%.

**b.** Use the growth factor to determine the total cost of each item in Problem 1.

In the previous problems, you were given an original (earlier) value and a percent increase and were asked to determine the new value. Suppose you are asked a "reverse" question: Sales in your small retail business have increased 20% over last year. This year you had gross sales receipts of $75,000. How much did you gross last year?

Using the growth factor 1.20, you can write

$$\text{original value} \cdot 1.20 = 75{,}000.$$

To determine last year's sales receipts, you divide both sides of the equation by 1.20.

$$\text{original value} = 75{,}000 \div 1.20.$$

Therefore, last year's sales receipts totaled $62,500.

---

**PROCEDURE**

When a quantity has *already* increased by a specified percent, its original value is obtained by dividing the new value by the corresponding growth factor. That is,

$$\text{new value} \div \text{growth factor} = \text{original value}.$$

---

**8.** You determined a growth factor for an 8% increase in Problem 7. Use it to answer the following questions.

**a.** The cash register receipt for your new coat, which includes the 8% sales tax, totals $243. What was the ticketed price of the coat?

**b.** The credit card receipt for your new sofa, which includes the 8% sales tax, totals $1620. What was the ticketed price of the sofa?

## Decay Factors

It's the sale you have been waiting for all season. Everything in the store is marked 40% off the original ticket price.

**9.** Determine the discounted price of a pair of sunglasses originally selling for $25.

Many people correctly determine the discounted price for Problem 9 in two steps:

• They first compute the actual dollar discount on the item.

• Then they subtract the dollar discount from the original price to obtain the sale price.

It is also possible to compute the sale price in one step by using the idea of a **decay factor**.

**10. a.** If a quantity decreases 20%, how does its new value compare to its original value? That is, what is the ratio of the new value to the original value? Complete the rows in the following table. The first row has been done for you. Notice that the new values are less than the originals, so the ratios of new values to original values will be less than 1.

## Up and Down

| ORIGINAL VALUE | NEW VALUE (DECREASED BY 20%) | RATIO OF NEW VALUE TO ORIGINAL VALUE | | |
| --- | --- | --- | --- | --- |
| | | FRACTIONAL FORM | DECIMAL FORM | PERCENT FORM |
| 20 | 16 | $\frac{16}{20} = \frac{4}{5}$ | 0.80 | 80% |
| 50 | | | | |
| 100 | | | | |
| Choose any value | | | | |

**b.** Use the results from the preceding table to answer the question, "What is the ratio of the new value to the original value of any quantity that decreases 20%?" Express this ratio in reduced-fraction, decimal, and percent forms.

### DEFINITION

For a specified percent *decrease*, no matter what the original value may be, the ratio of the new value to the original value is always the same. This ratio $\frac{\text{new value}}{\text{original value}}$ is called the **decay factor** associated with the specified percent decrease.

As you have seen, the decay factor associated with a 20% decrease is 80%. For calculation purposes, a decay factor is usually written in decimal form, so the decay factor 80% is expressed as 0.80.

### PROCEDURE

Note that a percent decrease describes the percent that has been *removed* (such as the discount taken off an original price), but the corresponding decay factor always represents the percent remaining (the portion that you still must pay). Therefore, a decay factor is formed by *subtracting* the specified percent decrease from 100% and then changing this percent into its decimal form.

Example 2   *The decay factor corresponding to a* 10% *decrease is*

$$100\% - 10\% = 90\%.$$

*If you change* 90% *to a decimal, the decay factor is* 0.90.

**11.** Determine the decay factor of any quantity that decreases by the following given percents:

a. 30%

b. 75%

c. 15%

d. 7.5%

Remember that multiplying the original value by the decay factor will always result in the amount remaining, not the amount that has been removed.

**12.** Explain why every decay factor will have a decimal format that is less than 1.

---

**PROCEDURE**

When a quantity *decreases* by a specified percent, its new value is obtained by multiplying the original value by the corresponding decay factor. That is,

$$\text{original value} \cdot \text{decay factor} = \text{new value}.$$

---

**13.** Use the decay factor 0.80 to determine the new value of a stock portfolio that has lost 20% of its original value of $400.

In the previous questions, you were given an original value and a percent decrease and were asked to determine the new (*smaller*) value. Suppose you are asked a "reverse" question: "Voter turnout in the local school board elections declined 40% from last year. This year only 3600 eligible voters went to the polls. How many people voted in last year's school board elections?"

Using the decay factor 0.60 you can write

$$\text{original value} \cdot 0.60 = 3600.$$

To determine last year's voter turnout, divide both sides of the equation by 0.60.

$$\text{original value} = 3600 \div 0.60$$

Therefore, last year 6000 people voted in the school board elections.

---

**PROCEDURE**

When a quantity has already *decreased* by a specified percent, its original value is obtained by dividing the new value by the corresponding decay factor. That is,

$$\text{new value} \div \text{decay factor} = \text{original value}.$$

**14. a.** You purchased a two-line answering machine and telephone on sale for $150. The discount was 40%. What was the original price?

**b.** Determine the original price of a Nordic Track treadmill that is on sale for $1140. Assume that the store has reduced all merchandise by 25%.

**SUMMARY**
**Activity 5.1**

1. When a quantity increases by a specified percent, the ratio $\frac{\text{new value}}{\text{original value}}$ is called the **growth factor**. The growth factor is formed by adding the specified percent increase to 100% and then changing this percent into its decimal form.

2. **a.** When a quantity increases by a specified percent, its new value can be obtained by multiplying the original value by the corresponding growth factor. So,

   original value · growth factor = new value.

   **b.** When a quantity has already increased by a specified percent, its original value can be obtained by dividing the new value by the corresponding growth factor. So,

   new value ÷ growth factor = original value.

3. When a quantity decreases by a specified percent, the ratio $\frac{\text{new value}}{\text{original value}}$ is called the **decay factor** associated with the specified percent decrease. The decay factor is formed by subtracting the specified percent decrease from 100%, and then changing this percent into its decimal form.

   **a.** When a quantity decreases by a specified percent, its new value can be obtained by multiplying the original value by the corresponding decay factor. So,

   original value · decay factor = new value.

   **b.** When a quantity has already decreased by a specified percent, its original value can be obtained by dividing the new value by the corresponding decay factor. So,

   new value ÷ decay factor = original value.

**EXERCISES**
**Activity 5.1**

1. Complete the following table:

| PERCENT INCREASE | 5% | | 15% | | 100% | 300% | |
|---|---|---|---|---|---|---|---|
| GROWTH FACTOR | | 1.35 | | 1.045 | | | 11.00 |

**2.** You are purchasing a new car. The price you negotiated with a car dealer in Virginia is $17,944, excluding sales tax. The local sales tax rate is 8.25%.

    **a.** What growth factor is associated with the sales tax rate?

    **b.** Use the growth factor to determine the total cost of the car.

**3.** The cost of first-class postage in the United States increased approximately 5.4% in January of 2006 to 39 cents. What was the pre-January cost of the first-class stamp? Round your answer to the nearest penny.

**4.** A state university in western Texas reported that its enrollment increased from 11,952 students in 2004–2005 to 12,144 students in 2005–2006.

    **a.** What is the ratio of the number of students in 2005–2006 to the number of students in 2004–2005?

    **b.** From your result in part a, determine the growth factor. Write it in decimal form to the nearest hundredth.

    **c.** By what percent did the enrollment increase?

**5.** The 2000 United States Census showed that from 1990 to 2000, Florida's population increased by 23.5%. Florida reported its population in 2000 to be 15,982,378. What was Florida's population in 1990?

**6.** In 1967, your parents bought a house for $26,000. The United States Bureau of Labor Statistics reports that, due to inflation, the cost of the same house in 2001 would be $138,563.

    **a.** What is the inflation growth factor of housing from 1967 to 2001?

    **b.** What is the inflation rate (percent increase to the nearest whole number percent) for housing from 1967 to 2001?

    **c.** In 2001, your parents sold their house for $245,000. What profit did they make in terms of 2001 dollars?

7. Your friend plans to move from Lubbock to Houston. She earns $50,000 a year in Lubbock. How much must she earn in Houston to maintain the same standard of living if the cost of living in Houston is 35% higher?

8. You decide to invest $3000 in a one-year certificate of deposit that earns an annual percentage yield of 5.05%. How much will your investment be worth in a year?

9. Your company is moving you from the United States to one of the other countries listed in the following table. For each country, the table lists the cost of goods and services that would cost $100 in the United States.

### Over There

| COUNTRY | COST OF GOODS AND SERVICES ($) | GROWTH FACTOR IN COST OF LIVING | PERCENT INCREASE IN SALARY |
|---|---|---|---|
| United States | 100 | | |
| Argentina | 140 | | |
| Australia | 114 | | |
| Belgium | 127 | | |
| Canada | 105 | | |
| Saudi Arabia | 131 | | |
| Singapore | 126 | | |

a. Determine the growth factor for each cost in the table, and list it in the third column.

b. Determine the percent increase in your salary that would allow you the same cost of living as you have in the United States. List the percent increase in the fourth column of the table.

c. You earn a salary of $45,000 in the United States. What would your salary have to be in Argentina for you to maintain the same standard of living?

10. Complete the following table:

| PERCENT DECREASE | 5% | | 15% | | 12.5% |
|---|---|---|---|---|---|
| DECAY FACTOR | | 0.45 | | 0.94 | |

11. You wrote an eight-page article that will be published in a journal. The editor has asked you to revise the article and reduce the number of pages to six. By what percent must you reduce the length of your article?

**12.** In 1995, the state of California recorded 551,226 live births. In 2000, the number of live births dropped to 531,285. For the five-year period from 1995 to 2000, what is the decay factor for live births? What is the percent decrease (also called the decay rate)?

**13.** A car dealer will sell you a car you want for $18,194, which is just $200 over the dealer invoice price (the price the dealer pays the manufacturer for the car). You tell him that you will think about it. The dealer is anxious to meet his monthly quota of sales, so he calls the next day to offer you the car for $17,994 if you agree to buy it tomorrow. You decide to accept the deal.

**a.** What is the decay factor associated with the decrease in the price to you? Write your answer in decimal form to the nearest thousandths.

**b.** What is the percent decrease of the price, to the nearest tenth of a percent?

**c.** The sales tax is 6.5%. How much did you save on sales tax by taking the dealer's second offer?

**14.** Your company is moving you from the United States to one of the other countries listed in the following table. For each country, the table lists the cost of goods and services that would cost $100 in the United States.

| COUNTRY | COST OF GOODS AND SERVICES ($) | DECAY FACTOR IN COST OF LIVING | PERCENT DECREASE IN COST OF LIVING |
|---|---|---|---|
| United States | 100 | | |
| Colombia | 83 | | |
| Hungary | 80 | | |
| India | 93 | | |
| Indonesia | 98 | | |
| Poland | 100 | | |
| South Africa | 87 | | |

**a.** Determine the decay factor for each cost in the table, and list it in the third column.

**b.** Determine the percent decrease in the cost of living for each country compared to living in the United States. List the percent decrease in the fourth column of the table.

**c.** You earn a salary of $45,000 in the United States. If you move to South Africa, what salary will you need for the cost of living there?

**d.** How much of your salary is available to save if you move to Hungary and your salary remains at $45,000?

15. You need a fax machine but plan to wait for a sale. Yesterday, the model you want was reduced by 30%. It originally cost $129.95. Use the decay factor to determine the sale price of the fax machine.

16. You are on a weight-reducing diet. Your doctor advises you that losing 10% of your body weight will significantly improve your health.

   **a.** You weigh 175 pounds. Determine and use the decay factor to calculate your goal weight to the nearest pound.

   **b.** After six months, you reach your goal weight. However, you still have more weight to lose to reach your ideal weight range, which is 125–150 pounds. If you lose 10% of your new weight, will you be in your ideal weight range? Explain.

17. Aspirin is typically absorbed into the bloodstream from the duodenum (the beginning portion of the small intestine). In general, 75% of a dose of aspirin is eliminated from the bloodstream in an hour. A patient is given a dose of 650 milligrams. How much aspirin remains in the patient after one hour?

18. Airlines often encourage their customers to book online by offering a 5% discount on their ticket. You are traveling from Dallas to San Diego. A fully refundable fare is $558.60. A restricted, nonrefundable fare is $273.60. Determine and use the decay factor to calculate the cost of each fare if you book online.

**ACTIVITY 5.2**

Take an
Additional
20% Off

## Cumulative Discounts

### OBJECTIVES

1. Define consecutive growth and decay factors.

2. Determine a consecutive growth or decay factor from two or more consecutive percent changes.

3. Apply consecutive growth and/or decay factors to solve problems involving percent changes.

Your friend arrives at your house. Today's newspaper contains a 20%-off coupon at Old Navy. The $100 jacket she had been eyeing all season was already reduced by 40%. She clipped the coupon, drove to the store, selected her jacket, and walked up to the register. The cashier brought up a price of $48; your friend insisted that the price should have been only $40. The store manager arrived and re-entered the transaction, and, again, the register displayed $48. Your friend left without purchasing the jacket and drove to your house to tell you her story.

**1.** How do you think your friend calculated a price of $40?

**2.** You grab a pencil and start your own calculation. First, you determine the ticketed price that reflects the 40% reduction. At what price is Old Navy selling the jacket? Explain how you calculated this price.

**3.** To what price does the 20%-off coupon apply?

**4.** Apply the 20% discount to determine the final price of the jacket.

You are now curious: could you justify a better price by applying the discounts in the reverse order? That is, applying the 20% off coupon, followed by a 40% reduction. You start a new set of calculations.

**5.** Starting with the list price, determine the sale price after taking the 20% reduction.

**6.** Apply the 40% discount to the intermediate sale price.

**7.** Which sequence of discounts gives a better sale price?

The important point to remember here is that when multiple discounts are given, they are always applied sequentially, one after the other—never all at once.

In the following example, you will see how to use decay factors to simplify calculations such as the ones above.

Example 1   *A stunning $2000 gold and diamond necklace you saw was far too expensive to even consider. However, over several weeks you tracked the following successive discounts: 20% off list; 30% off marked price; and an additional 40% off every item. Determine the selling price after each of the discounts is taken.*

SOLUTION

To calculate the first reduced price, apply the decay factor corresponding to a 20% discount. Recall that you form a decay factor by subtracting the 20% discount from 100% to obtain 80%, or 0.80 as a decimal. Apply the 20% reduction by multiplying the original price by the decay factor.

The first sale price $= \$2000 \cdot 0.80$; the selling price is now $1600.

In a similar manner, determine the decay factor corresponding to a 30% discount by subtracting 30% from 100% to obtain 70%, or 0.70 as a decimal. Apply the 30% reduction by multiplying the already discounted price by the decay factor.

The second sale price $= \$1600 \cdot 0.70$; the selling price is now $1120.

Finally, determine the decay factor corresponding to a 40% discount by subtracting 40% from 100% to obtain 60%, or 0.60 as a decimal. Apply the 40% reduction by multiplying the most current discounted price by the decay factor.

$\$1120 \cdot 0.60$; the final selling price is $672.

You may have noticed that it is possible to calculate the final sale price from the original price using a single chain of multiplications:

$\$2000 \cdot 0.80 \cdot 0.70 \cdot 0.60 = \$672$

The final sale price is $672.

**8.** Use the chain of multiplications in Example 1 to determine the final sale price of the necklace if the discounts are taken in the reverse order (40%, 30%, and 20%).

**You can form a single decay factor** that represents the cumulative effect of applying the three consecutive percent decreases; the single decay factor is the *product* of the three decay factors.

In Example 1, the effective decay factor is given by the product $0.80 \cdot 0.70 \cdot 0.6$, which equals 0.336 (or 33.6%). The effective discount is calculated by subtracting the decay factor (in percent form) from 100%, to obtain 66.4%. Therefore, the effect of applying 20%, 30%, and 40% consecutive discounts is identical to a single discount of 66.4%.

**9. a.** Determine a single decay factor that represents the cumulative effect of consecutively applying Old Navy's 40% and 20% discounts.

**b.** Use this decay factor to determine the effective discount on your friends's jacket.

**10. a.** Determine a single decay factor that represents the cumulative effect of consecutively applying discounts of 40% and 50%.

   **b.** Use this decay factor to determine the effective discount.

## Cumulative Increases

Your fast-food franchise is growing faster than you had ever imagined. Last year you had 100 employees statewide. This year you opened several additional locations and increased the number of workers by 30%. With demand so high, next year you will open new stores nationwide and plan to increase your employee roll by an additional 50%.

To determine the projected number of employees next year, you can use growth factors to simplify the calculations.

**11. a.** Determine the growth factor corresponding to a 30% increase.

   **b.** Apply this growth factor to calculate your current workforce.

**12. a.** Determine the growth factor corresponding to a 50% increase.

   **b.** Apply this growth factor to your current workforce to determine the projected number of employees next year.

**13.** Starting from last year's workforce of 100, write a single chain of multiplications to calculate the projected number of employees.

**You can form a single growth factor** that represents the cumulative effect of applying the two consecutive percent increases; the single growth factor is the *product* of the two growth factors.

In Problem 13, the effective growth factor is given by the product $1.30 \cdot 1.50$, which equals 1.95 (an increase of 95%), nearly double the number of employees last year.

## What Goes Up Often Comes Down

You purchased $1000 of a recommended stock last year and watched gleefully as it rose quickly by 30%. Unfortunately, the economy turned downward, and your stock recently fell 30% from last year's high. Have you made or lost money on your investment? The answer might surprise you. Find out by solving the following sequence of problems.

**14. a.** Determine the growth factor corresponding to a 30% increase.

**b.** Determine the decay factor corresponding to a 30% decrease.

You can form a single factor that represents the cumulative effect of applying the consecutive percent increase and decrease—the single factor is the *product* of the growth and decay factors. In this example, the effective factor is given by the product $1.30 \cdot 0.70$, which equals 0.91.

**15.** Does 0.91 represent a growth factor or a decay factor? How can you tell?

**16. a.** What is the current value of your stock?

**b.** What is the cumulative effect (as a percent change) of applying a 30% increase followed by a 30% decrease?

**17.** What is the cumulative effect if the 30% decrease had been applied first, followed by the 30% increase?

## SUMMARY
### Activity 5.2

1. The cumulative effect of a sequence of percent changes is the *product* of the associated growth or decay factors. For example,

   **a.** To calculate the effect of consecutively applying 20% and 50% increases, form the respective growth factors and multiply. The effective growth factor is
   $$1.20 \cdot 1.50 = 1.80,$$
   which represents an effective increase of 80%.

   **b.** To calculate the effect of applying a 25% *increase* followed by a 20% *decrease*, form the respective growth and decay factors, and then multiply them. The effective factor is $1.25 \cdot 0.80 = 1.00$, which indicates neither growth nor decay. That is, the quantity has returned to its original value.

2. The cumulative effect of a sequence of percent changes is the same, regardless of the order in which the changes are applied. For example, the cumulative effect of applying a 20% *increase* followed by a 50% *decrease* is equivalent to having first applied the 50% *decrease*, followed by the 20% *increase*.

1. A $300 suit is on sale for 30% off. You present a coupon at the cash register for an additional 20% off.

   a. Determine the decay factor corresponding to each percent decrease.

   b. Use these decay factors to determine the price you paid for the suit.

2. Your union has just negotiated a three-year contract containing annual raises of 3%, 4%, and 5% during the term of contract. Your current salary is $42,000. What will you be earning in three years?

3. You anticipated a large demand for a popular toy and increased your inventory of 1600 by 25%. You sold 75% of your inventory. How many toys remain?

4. You deposit $2000 in a five-year certificate of deposit that pays 4% interest compounded annually. Determine to the nearest dollar, your account balance when your certificate comes due.

5. Budget cuts have severely crippled your department over the last few years. Your operating budget of $600,000 has decreased 5% in each of the last three years. What is your current operating budget?

6. When you became a manager, your $60,000 annual salary increased 25%. You found the new job too stressful and requested a return to your original job. You resumed your former duties at a 20% reduction in salary. How much more are you making at your old job after the transfer and return?

**ACTIVITY 5.3**
Inflation

Exponential Growth

**OBJECTIVES**

1. Recognize an exponential function as a rule for applying a growth factor or a decay factor.

2. Graph exponential functions from numerical data.

3. Recognize exponential functions from equations.

4. Graph exponential functions using technology.

Inflation means that a current dollar will buy less in the future. According to the U.S. Consumer Price Index, the inflation rate for 2005 was 4%. This means that a one-pound loaf of white bread that cost a dollar in January 2005 cost $1.04 in January 2006. The change in price is usually expressed as an annual percentage rate, known as the inflation rate.

1. **a.** At the current inflation rate of 4%, how much will a $20 pair of shoes cost next year?

   **b.** Assume that the rate of inflation remains at 4% next year. How much will the shoes cost in the year following next year?

2. If you assume that inflation increases somewhat and remains 5% per year for the next decade, you can calculate the cost of a currently priced $8 pizza for each of the next ten years. Complete the following table. Round to the nearest cent.

| YEARS FROM NOW, $t$ | COST OF PIZZA, $c(t)$, $ |
|:---:|:---:|
| 0 | |
| 1 | |
| 2 | |
| 3 | |
| 4 | |
| 5 | |
| 6 | |
| 7 | |
| 8 | |
| 9 | |
| 10 | |

3. Plot the data from Problem 2 on appropriately scaled and labeled axes. Use the variable $t$, years from now, as the independent variable and $c(t)$, the cost of pizza, as the dependent variable.

4. Determine the average rate of change of the cost of the pizza in the first year (from $t = 0$ to $t = 1$), the fifth year (from $t = 4$ to $t = 5$), and the tenth year (from $t = 9$ to $t = 10$). Explain what these results mean for the cost of pizza over the next ten years.

To complete the table in Problem 2, you could calculate each cost value by multiplying the previous output by 1.05, the inflation's growth factor (see Activity 5.1). Thus, to obtain the cost after ten years, you would multiply the original cost, $8, by 1.05, a total of ten times. Symbolically, you write $8(1.05)^{10}$. Therefore, you can model the cost of pizza algebraically as

$$c(t) = 8(1.05)^t,$$

where $c(t)$ represents the cost and $t$ represents the number of years from now.

> DEFINITION
>
> When the independent variable of a function appears as an exponent of the growth factor, the function, in this case $c(t) = 8(1.05)^t$, is called an **exponential function**.

5. **a.** Under a constant annual inflation rate of 5%, what will a pizza cost after twenty years?

**b.** Use the cost function to calculate the cost of a pizza after five years.

**6. a.** A graph of the function $c(t) = 8(1.05)^t$ is shown below in a window for $t$ between $-20$ and $20$ and $c(t)$ between $0$ and $20$. Use the same window to graph this function on a graphing calculator.

**b.** Use the trace or table feature of the calculator to examine the coordinates of some points on the graph. Does your plot of the numerical data in Problem 3 agree with the graph shown here?

**c.** Is the entire graph in part a really relevant to the original problem? Explain.

**d.** Resize your window to include only the first quadrant from $x = 0$ to $x = 20$ and $y = 0$ to $y = 20$. Regraph the function.

**7. a.** How many years will it take for the price of a pizza to double? Explain how you determined your answer.

**b.** How many years will it take for the price of a pizza to triple? Explain how you find your answer.

## Exponential Decay

You have just purchased an automobile for $16,000. Much to your dismay, you have just learned that you should expect the value of your car to depreciate by 15% per year!

**8.** What is the decay factor (see Activity 5.1) for the yearly depreciation rate 15%?

**9.** Use the decay factor from Problem 8 to determine the car's values for the years given in the table. Record your results in the table.

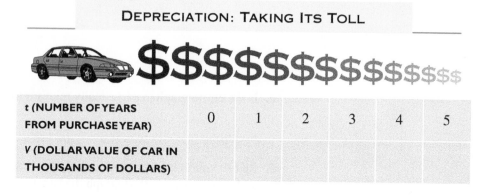

| DEPRECIATION: TAKING ITS TOLL | | | | | | |
|---|---|---|---|---|---|---|
| *t* (NUMBER OF YEARS FROM PURCHASE YEAR) | 0 | 1 | 2 | 3 | 4 | 5 |
| *V* (DOLLAR VALUE OF CAR IN THOUSANDS OF DOLLARS) | | | | | | |

In Problem 9, you could calculate the value of the car in any given year by multiplying the previous year's value by 0.85, the depreciation decay factor. Thus, to obtain the retail value after 5 years, you could multiply the original value by 0.85 a total of five times as follows:

$$16(0.85)(0.85)(0.85)(0.85)(0.85) \approx 7.1 \text{ thousand or } \$7100$$

or equivalently in exponential form,

$$16(0.85)^5 \approx \$7100$$

Therefore, you can model the value of the car, *V*, algebraically by the formula

$$V = 16(0.85)^t,$$

where *t* represents the number of years you own the car and *V* represents the car's value in thousands of dollars.

**10.** Determine the value of the car in 6 years.

11. Graph the depreciation formula for the car's value, $V = 16(0.85)^t$, as a function of the time from the year of purchase. Use the following grid or a graphing calculator. Extend your graph to include 10 years from the date of purchase.

12. How long will it take for the value of the car to decrease to half its original value? Explain how you determined your answer.

## SUMMARY
**Activity 5.3**

An **exponential function** is a function in which the independent variable appears as an exponent of the growth factor [for example, $c = 8(1.05)^t$] or a decay factor [for example, $V = 16(.85)^t$].

## EXERCISES
**Activity 5.3**

1. **a.** Complete the following table, in which $f(x) = \left(\frac{1}{2}\right)^x$ and $g(x) = 2^x$.

| x | −2 | −1 | 0 | 1 | 2 |
|---|---|---|---|---|---|
| f(x) | | | | | |
| g(x) | | | | | |

**b.** Use the points in part a to sketch a graph of the given functions $f$ and $g$ on the same coordinate axes. Compare the graphs. List the similarities and differences.

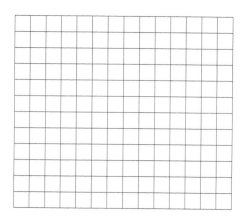

**c.** Use a graphing calculator to graph the functions $f(x) = \left(\frac{1}{2}\right)^x$ and $g(x) = 2^x$ given in part a in the window Xmin $= -2$, Xmax $= 2$, Ymin $= -2$, and Ymax $= 5$. Compare to the graphs you obtained in part b.

**2.** Suppose the inflation rate is 7% per year and remains the same for the next seven years.

**a.** Complete the following table for the cost of a pair of sneakers that costs $45 now. Round to the nearest cent:

| $t$, YEARS FROM NOW | 0 | 1 | 2 | 3 | 4 | 5 | 6 | 7 |
|---|---|---|---|---|---|---|---|---|
| $c(t)$, COST OF SNEAKERS ($) | 45 | | | | | | | |

**b.** Determine the growth factor for a 7% inflation rate.

**c.** If the yearly inflation rate remains at 7%, what exponential function would you use to determine the cost of $45 sneakers after $t$ years?

**d.** What would be the cost of the sneakers in ten years if the inflation rate stayed at 7%?

**3.** An exponential function may be increasing or decreasing. Determine which is the case for each of the following functions. Explain how you determined each answer.

**a.** $y = 5^x$                                     **b.** $y = \left(\frac{1}{2}\right)^x$

**c.** $y = 1.5^t$                                     **d.** $y = 0.2^p$

**4. a.** Evaluate the functions in the following table for the input values, $x$:

| INPUT $x$ | 0 | 1 | 2 | 3 | 4 | 5 |
|---|---|---|---|---|---|---|
| $g(x) = 3x$ | | | | | | |
| $f(x) = 3^x$ | | | | | | |

**b.** Compare the functions $f(x) = 3^x$ and $g(x) = 3x$ from $x = 0$ to $x = 5$ by comparing the output values in the table.

**c.** Compare the graphs of the functions $f$ and $g$ that are shown in the following window. Approximate the interval in which the exponential function $f$ grows slower than the linear function $g$ and the interval where it grows faster.

**d.** Compare the rate of increase of the functions $f(x) = 3^x$ and $g(x) = 3x$ from $x = 0$ to $x = 5$ by calculating the average rate of change for each function from $x = 0$ to $x = 5$. Determine which function grows faster on average in the given interval.

**5. a.** For investment purposes, you recently bought a house for $100,000 in a neighborhood where the price of houses has been rising $10,000 a year. If the rise in housing prices continues in the same manner, how much will your investment be worth in a year and in two years?

**b.** You decided to buy a second investment house, again for $100,000 but in another area. Here the prices have been rising at a rate of 10% a year. If this rate of increase continues, how much will your investment be worth in a year and in two years?

**c.** Which investment will give you the better return?

**6.** As a radiology specialist you use the radioactive substance iodine-131 to diagnose conditions of the thyroid gland. Iodine-131 decays (loses radiation energy and changes to a nonradioactive form of iodine) at the rate of 8.3 percent per day. Your hospital currently has a 20-gram supply.

**a.** What is the decay factor for the decay of the iodine?

**b.** Use the decay factor from part a to determine the number of grams remaining for the days listed in the following table. Record your results in the table to the nearest hundredth.

| t (NUMBER OF DAYS STARTING FROM A 20-GRAM SUPPLY OF IODINE-131) | 0 | 4 | 8 | 12 | 16 | 20 | 24 |
|---|---|---|---|---|---|---|---|
| N, NUMBER OF GRAMS OF IODINE-131 REMAINING FROM A 20-GRAM SUPPLY | 20.00 | | | | | | |

**c.** Write an exponential decay formula for $N$, the number of grams of iodine-131 remaining, in terms of $t$, the number of days from the current supply of 20 grams.

**d.** Determine the number of grams of iodine-131 remaining from a 20-gram supply after 2 months (60 days).

**e.** Graph the decay formula for iodine-131, $N = 20(0.917)^t$ as a function of the time $t$ (days). Use appropriate scales and labels on the following grid or an appropriate window on a graphing calculator.

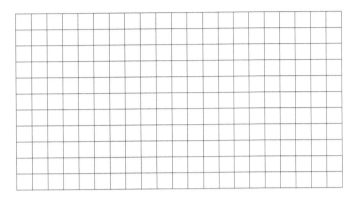

**f.** How long will it take for iodine-131 to decrease to half its original value? Explain how you determined your answer.

**ACTIVITY 5.4**

The Summer Job

**OBJECTIVES**

1. Determine the growth or decay factor of an exponential function.

2. Identify the properties of the graph of an exponential function defined by $y = b^x$ where $b > 0$ and $b \neq 1$.

3. Graph exponential functions using transformations.

Your brother will be attending college in the fall, majoring in mathematics. On July 1, he goes to your neighbor's house looking for summer work to help pay for college expenses. Your neighbor is interested since he needs some odd jobs done. Your brother can start right away and will work all day July 1 for 2 cents. This gets your neighbor's attention, but you wonder if there is a catch. Your brother says that he will work July 2 for 4 cents, July 3 for 8 cents, July 4 for 16 cents, and so on for *every* day of the month of July.

*For Problems 1–2, assume that the neighbor hires your brother.*

**1. a.** Complete the following table.

| DAY IN JULY (INPUT) | PAY IN CENTS (OUTPUT) |
|---|---|
| 1 | |
| 2 | |
| 3 | |
| 4 | |
| 5 | |
| 6 | |
| 7 | |
| 8 | |

**b.** Do you notice a pattern in the output values? Describe how you can obtain the pay on a given day knowing the pay on the previous day.

**c.** Use what you discovered in part b to determine the pay on July 9.

**2. a.** The pay on any given day can be written as a power of 2. Write each pay entry in the output column of the table in Problem 1 as a power of 2. For example, $2 = 2^1, 4 = 2^2$.

**b.** Let n represent the number of days worked. Write an equation for the daily pay, $P(n)$, (in cents) as a function of $n$, the number of days worked. Note that the number of days worked is the same as the July date.

**c.** Use the equation from part b to determine how much your brother will earn on July 20. That is, determine the value of $P(n)$ when $n = 20$. What are the units of measurement of your answer?

**d.** How much will he earn on July 31? Be sure to indicate the units of your answer.

Therefore, it was not a good idea for the neighbor to hire your brother! This situation demonstrates the growth power of exponential functions.

3. **a.** Determine the average rate of change of $P(n)$ as $n$ increases from $n = 3$ to $n = 4$. What are the units of measurement of your answer?

   **b.** Determine the average rate of change of $P(n)$ as $n$ increases from $n = 7$ to $n = 8$. Include units in your answer.

   **c.** Is the function linear? Explain.

4. **a.** What is the practical domain of the function defined by $P(n) = 2^n$?

   **b.** Sketch a scatterplot of ordered pairs of the form $(n, P(n))$ from July 1 to July 10 on appropriately scaled and labeled axes.

The function defined by $P(n) = 2^n$ gives the relationship between the pay $P(n)$ (in cents) and the given July date, $n$, worked. This function belongs to a family of **exponential functions**.

If $x$ represents the independent variable and $y$ represents the dependent variable, then some **exponential functions** can be defined by equations of the form $y = b^x$, where the base $b$ is a constant such that $b$ is a positive number not equal to 1 ($b > 0$ and $b \neq 1$). As discussed in Activity 5.3, the base $b$ is a growth or decay factor.

Example 1    *Some examples of exponential functions are*

$$g(x) = 10^x, \text{ where } b = 10, h(x) = (1.08)^x, \text{ where } b = 1.08,$$

$$V(x) = \left(\frac{1}{2}\right)^x, \text{ where } b = \frac{1}{2}, \text{ and } T(x) = (0.75)^x, \text{ where } b = 0.75.$$

## Graphs of Increasing Exponential Functions

Because $n$ in $P(n) = 2^n$ (the summer job situation) represents a given day in July, the practical domain (whole numbers from 1 to 31) limits the investigation of the exponential function.

**5. a.** Consider the general function defined by $f(x) = 2^x$. Use a graphing calculator to sketch a graph of this function. Use the window $Xmin = -10$, $Xmax = 10$, $Ymin = -2$, and $Ymax = 10$. Your screens should appear as follows:

**b.** Because the graph of the general function $f(x) = 2^x$ is continuous (it has no holes or breaks), what appears to be the domain of the function $f$? What is the range of the function $f$?

**c.** Determine the $y$-intercept of the graph of $f$ by substituting 0 for $x$ in the equation $y = 2^x$ and solving for $y$.

**d.** Is the function $f$ increasing or decreasing?

### DEFINITION

If the base $b$ of an exponential function defined by $y = b^x$ is greater than 1, then $b$ is the **growth factor**. The graph of $y = b^x$ is increasing if $b > 1$. For each increase of 1 of the value of $x$, $y$ increases by a factor of $b$.

**Example 2**   *The base 2 of $f(x) = 2^x$ is the growth factor because each time the input, x, is increased by 1, the output is multiplied by 2.*

**6.** Identify the growth factor, if any, for the given function.

**a.** $y = 1.08^x$

**b.** $h(x) = 0.8^x$

**c.** $y = 8x$

**d.** $g(x) = 10^x$

**7.** Return to the graph of $f(x) = 2^x$.

   **a.** Does the graph of $f(x) = 2^x$ appear to have an $x$-intercept?

   **b.** Use your calculator to complete the following table.

| $x$ | $-1$ | $-2$ | $-4$ | $-6$ | $-8$ | $-10$ |
|---|---|---|---|---|---|---|
| $f(x) = 2^x$ | | | | | | |

      *Note:* By definition, $b^{-n} = \dfrac{1}{b^n}$. Therefore, $2^{-1} = \dfrac{1}{2^1} = 0.5$, $2^{-4} = \dfrac{1}{2^4} = 0.0625$ and $2^{-10} = \dfrac{1}{2^{10}} \approx 0.000977$.

   **c.** As the values of the input variable $x$ decrease, what happens to the output values?

   **d.** Use the trace feature of your graphing calculator to trace the graph of $f(x) = 2^x$ for $x < 0$. What appears to be the relationship between the graph of $y = 2^x$ and the $x$-axis when $x$ becomes more negative?

---

**DEFINITION**

A horizontal axis having equation $y = 0$ is called a **horizontal asymptote** of the graph of a function defined by $y = b^x$, where $b > 0$ and $b \neq 1$. The graph of the function gets closer and closer to the $x$-axis ($y = 0$) as the input gets farther from the origin, in the negative direction.

---

**Example 3**   *The $x$-axis is the horizontal asymptote of $y = 3^x$ and $y = 7^x$ because, as $x$ gets more negative, the graph gets closer and closer to the $x$-axis. See the graph that follows.*

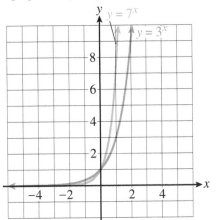

**8. a.** Complete the following table.

| $x$ | $-3$ | $-2$ | $-1$ | $0$ | $1$ | $2$ | $3$ | $4$ | $5$ |
|---|---|---|---|---|---|---|---|---|---|
| $f(x) = 2^x$ | | | | | | | | | |
| $g(x) = 10^x$ | | | | | | | | | |

**b.** Sketch the graph of the functions $f$ and $g$ on your graphing calculator. Use the window $\mathrm{Xmin} = -5$, $\mathrm{Xmax} = 5$, $\mathrm{Ymin} = -2$, and $\mathrm{Ymax} = 9$.

**c.** Use the results from parts a and b to describe how the graphs of $f(x) = 2^x$ and $g(x) = 10^x$ are similar and how they are different. Be sure to include domain, growth factor, $x$- and $y$-intercepts, and horizontal asymptotes. Also discuss whether the graph of $g$ increases faster or slower than the graph of $f$.

**9.** Sketch a graph of the given transformation of the graph of $y = 2^x$. Indicate any intercepts. Then, write the equation of the transformed graph. Verify the graph using a graphing calculator.

**a.** reflection of the graph across the $x$-axis.

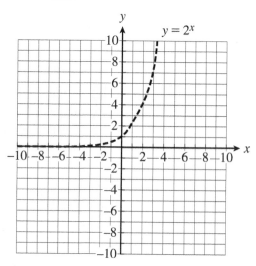

**b.** vertical stretch of the graph by a factor of 5.

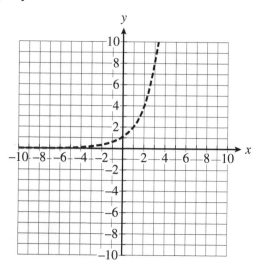

**c.** horizontal shift of the graph 3 units to the right.

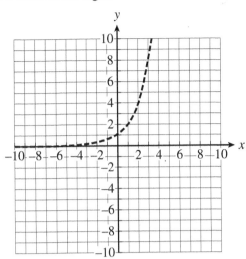

**d.** vertical shift of the graph 3 units upward.

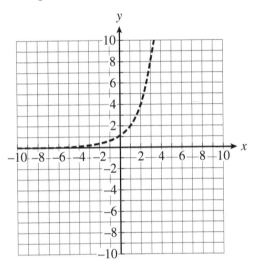

**e.** What is the equation of the horizontal asymptote in part d?

**10.** Describe in words how the graph of $y = 2^x$ is transformed by each equation.

**a.** $y = 0.5 \cdot 2^x$

**b.** $y = 2^{x+1}$

**c.** $y = 2^x + 1$

**d.** $y = -3 \cdot 2^x$

## Graphs of Decreasing Exponential Functions

**11. a.** Complete the following table.

| $x$ | | −3 | −2 | −1 | 0 | 1 | 2 | 3 | 4 | 5 |
|---|---|---|---|---|---|---|---|---|---|---|
| $y = \left(\frac{1}{2}\right)^x$ | | | | | | | | | | |

**b.** Describe how you can obtain the $y$-value for $x = 6$, using the $y$-value for $x = 5$.

**c.** Sketch the graph of $y = \left(\dfrac{1}{2}\right)^x$. Verify your sketch using your graphing calculator.

**d.** What are the domain and range of the exponential function?

**e.** Determine the $y$-intercept of the graph.

**f.** Is the function defined by $y = \left(\dfrac{1}{2}\right)^x$ increasing or decreasing?

---

**DEFINITION**

If the base $b$ of an exponential function $y = b^x$ is between 0 and 1, then $b$ is the **decay factor**. The graph of $y = b^x$ is decreasing if $0 < b < 1$. For each increase of 1 of the value of the input, the output decreases by a factor of $b$.

Example 4  *The base $\frac{1}{2}$ in the function $y = \left(\frac{1}{2}\right)^x$ is the decay factor because each time x is increased by 1, the output value is multiplied by $\frac{1}{2}$.*

**12.** Identify the decay factor, if any, for the function defined by the given equation.

**a.** $y = 0.98^x$

**b.** $h(x) = 1.8^x$

**c.** $y = 0.8x$

**d.** $g(x) = \left(\dfrac{2}{7}\right)^x$

**13.** Return to the graph of $y = \left(\dfrac{1}{2}\right)^x$.

**a.** Does the graph of $y = \left(\dfrac{1}{2}\right)^x$ have an x-intercept?

**b.** Complete the following table.

| x | 1 | 3 | 5 | 7 | 10 |
|---|---|---|---|---|----|
| $y = \left(\frac{1}{2}\right)^x$ | | | | | |

**c.** As the values of the input variable x get larger, what happens to the y-values?

**d.** Does the graph of $y = \left(\dfrac{1}{2}\right)^x$ have a horizontal asymptote? Explain.

**14.** Describe in words how the graph of $y = \left(\dfrac{1}{2}\right)^x$ is transformed. Sketch a graph of the given equation and verify using a graphing calculator.

**a.** $y = \left(\dfrac{1}{2}\right)^x - 2$

**b.** $y = \left(\dfrac{1}{2}\right)^{x+1}$

**c.** $y = -2\left(\dfrac{1}{2}\right)^{x}$

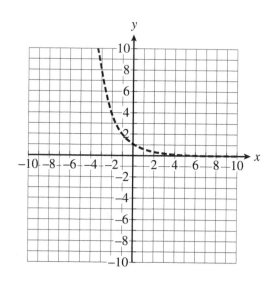

**15. a.** For each of the following exponential functions, identify the base, $b$, and determine whether the base is a growth or decay factor. Graph each function on your graphing calculator, and complete the table below.

| FUNCTION | BASE, B | GROWTH OR DECAY FACTOR | X-INTERCEPT | Y-INTERCEPT | HORIZONTAL ASYMPTOTE | INCREASING OR DECREASING |
|---|---|---|---|---|---|---|
| $h(x) = (1.08)^x$ | | | | | | |
| $T(x) = (0.75)^x$ | | | | | | |
| $f(x) = (3.2)^x$ | | | | | | |
| $r(x) = \left(\frac{1}{4}\right)^x$ | | | | | | |

**b.** Without graphing, how might you determine which of the functions in part a increase and which decrease? Explain.

16. Examine the output pattern to determine which of the following data sets is linear and which is exponential. For the linear set, determine the slope. For the exponential set, determine the growth or decay factor.

a.

| x | −2 | −1 | 0 | 1 | 2 | 3 | 4 |
|---|---|---|---|---|---|---|---|
| y | −8 | −4 | 0 | 4 | 8 | 12 | 16 |

b.

| x | −2 | −1 | 0 | 1 | 2 | 3 | 4 |
|---|---|---|---|---|---|---|---|
| y | $\frac{1}{16}$ | $\frac{1}{4}$ | 1 | 4 | 16 | 64 | 256 |

17. Determine the decay factor of the function represented by the data, and complete the table.

| x | −2 | −1 | 0 | 1 | 2 |
|---|---|---|---|---|---|
| f(x) | 16 | 4 | | | |

## SUMMARY
**Activity 5.4**

Functions defined by equations of the form $y = b^x$, where $b > 0$ and $b \neq 1$, are called **exponential functions** and have the following properties.

1. The domain is all real numbers.

2. The range is $y > 0$.

3. If $0 < b < 1$, the function is decreasing and has the following general shape.

In this case, $b$ is called the **decay factor**.

**4.** If $b > 1$, the function is increasing and has the following general shape.

In this case, $b$ is called the **growth factor**.

**5.** The $y$-intercept is $(0, 1)$.

**6.** The graph does not intersect the horizontal axis. There is no $x$-intercept.

**7.** The line $y = 0$ (the $x$-axis) is a **horizontal asymptote**.

**8.** The function is continuous.

## EXERCISES
### Activity 5.4

**1. a.** Complete the following tables.

| $x$ | $-3$ | $-2$ | $-1$ | 0 | 1 | 2 | 3 |
|---|---|---|---|---|---|---|---|
| $h(x) = 5^x$ | | | | | | | |

| $x$ | $-3$ | $-2$ | $-1$ | 0 | 1 | 2 | 3 |
|---|---|---|---|---|---|---|---|
| $g(x) = \left(\frac{1}{5}\right)^x$ | | | | | | | |

**b.** Sketch graphs of $h$ and $g$ on the following grid.

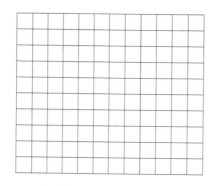

**c.** Use the tables and graphs in parts *a* and *b* to complete the following table.

| FUNCTION | BASE, *b* | GROWTH OR DECAY FACTOR | *x*-INTERCEPT | *y*-INTERCEPT | HORIZONTAL ASYMPTOTE | INCREASING OR DECREASING |
|---|---|---|---|---|---|---|
| $h(x) = 5^x$ | | | | | | |
| $g(x) = \left(\frac{1}{5}\right)^x$ | | | | | | |

**2. a.** Complete the following table.

| *x* | −3 | −2 | −1 | 0 | 1 | 2 | 3 |
|---|---|---|---|---|---|---|---|
| $f(x) = 3^x$ | | | | | | | |
| $g(x) = x^3$ | | | | | | | |
| $h(x) = 3x$ | | | | | | | |

**b.** Sketch a graph of each of the given functions *f*, *g*, and *h*.

**c.** Describe any similarities or differences that you observe in the graphs.

**3.** Using your graphing calculator, investigate the graphs of the following families (groups) of functions. Describe any relationships within each family, including domain and range, growth or decay factors, vertical and horizontal intercepts, and asymptotes. Identify the functions as increasing or decreasing.

**a.** $f(x) = \left(\frac{3}{4}\right)^x$, $g(x) = \left(\frac{4}{3}\right)^x$

**b.** $f(x) = 10^x, g(x) = -10^x$

**c.** $f(x) = 3^x, g(x) = \left(\frac{1}{3}\right)^x$

**4.** Determine which of the following data sets are linear and which are exponential. For the linear sets, determine the slope. For the exponential sets, determine the growth factor or the decay factor.

**a.**

| x | −2 | −1 | 0 | 1 | 2 | 3 | 4 |
|---|----|----|---|---|---|---|---|
| y | $\frac{1}{9}$ | $\frac{1}{3}$ | 1 | 3 | 9 | 27 | 81 |

**b.**

| x | −2 | −1 | 0 | 1 | 2 | 3 | 4 |
|---|----|----|---|---|---|---|---|
| y | 2 | 2.5 | 3 | 3.5 | 4 | 4.5 | 5 |

**c.**

| x | −2 | −1 | 0 | 1 | 2 | 3 | 4 |
|---|----|----|---|---|---|---|---|
| y | 0.75 | 1.5 | 3 | 6 | 12 | 24 | 48 |

**d.**

| x | −2 | −1 | 0 | 1 | 2 | 3 | 4 |
|---|----|----|---|---|---|---|---|
| y | 6.25 | 2.5 | 1 | 0.4 | 0.16 | .064 | .0256 |

**5.** Assume that $y$ is an exponential function of $x$.

**a.** If the growth factor is 1.08, then complete the following table.

| x | 0 | 1 | 2 | 3 |
|---|---|---|---|---|
| y | 23.1 | | | |

**b.** If the decay factor is 0.75, then complete the following table.

| x | 0 | 1 | 2 | 3 |
|---|---|---|---|---|
| y | 10 | | | |

**6. a.** Would you expect $f(x) = 3^x$ to increase faster or slower than $g(x) = 2.5^x$ for $x > 0$? Explain. (*Hint:* You may want to use your graphing calculator for help.)

**b.** Would you expect $f(x) = \left(\frac{1}{2}\right)^x$ to decrease faster or slower than $g(x) = (0.70)^x$ for $x > 0$? Explain.

7. Determine the domain and range of each of the following functions.

**a.**

**b.**

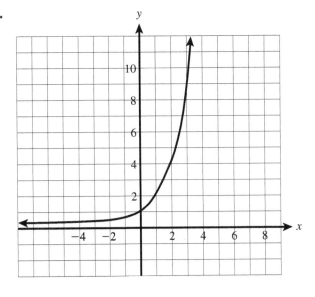

8. Take a piece of paper from your notebook. Let $x$ represent the number of times you fold the paper in half and $f(x)$ represent the number of sections the paper is divided into after the folding.

**a.** Complete the table of values.

| x | 0 | 1 | 2 | 3 | 4 | 5 |
|---|---|---|---|---|---|---|
| f(x) | | | | | | |

**b.** If you could fold the paper 8 times, how many individual sections will there be on the paper?

**c.** Does this data represent an exponential function? Explain.

**d.** What is the practical domain and range in this situation?

In 9–13, match the graphs with its equation.

**9.** $y = 3^x$          **10.** $y = 3^{x+2}$          **11.** $y = 2 \cdot 3^x$

**12.** $y = -3^x$          **13.** $y = 3^{-x}$

**a.**

**b.**

**c.**

**d.**

**e.**

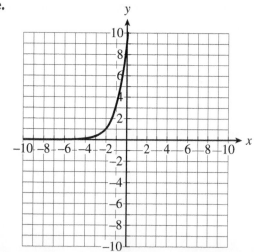

**14.** Sketch a graph of each of the following equations. Verify using a graphing calculator. Identify if the graph is increasing or decreasing.

    **a.** $y = 5^x$                             **b.** $y = \left(\dfrac{4}{5}\right)^x$

    **c.** $y = (2.5)^x$                        **d.** $y = (0.65)^x$

**15.** In parts a–f, graph the function defined by the given equation. Using transformations, describe how the graph is related to the graph of $y = 4^x$. Verify the graph using a graphing calculator.

**a.** $y = 4^{x+2}$

**b.** $y = -4^x$

**c.** $y = 4^{-x}$

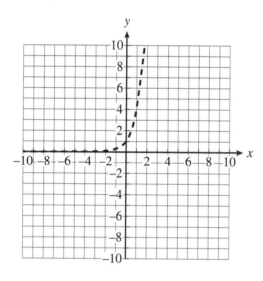

**d.** $y = 3 \cdot 4^x$

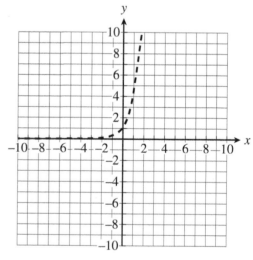

**e.** $y = \dfrac{1}{3} \cdot 4^x$

**f.** $y = 4^x + 2$

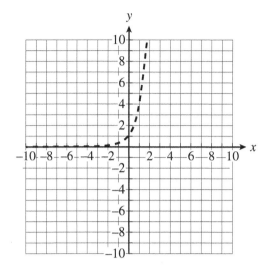

**16.** The graph of $y = -3 \cdot 2^x - 2$ is the result of three transformations of the graph of $y = 2^x$. Perform the transformations on the graph of $y = 2^x$, one at a time, until the graph of $y = -3 \cdot 2^x - 2$ is obtained. Verify using a graphing calculator.

**ACTIVITY 5.5**

Cellular Phones

**OBJECTIVES**

1. Determine the growth and decay factor for an exponential function represented by a table of values or an equation.

2. Graph exponential functions defined by $y = ab^x$, where $a \neq 0$, $b > 0$ and $b \neq 1$.

3. Identify the meaning of $a$ in $y = ab^x$ as it relates to a practical situation.

4. Determine the doubling and halving time.

During a meeting, you hear the familiar ring of a cell phone. Without hesitation, several of your friends reach into their jacket pockets, brief cases, and purses to receive the anticipated call. Although sometimes annoying, cell phones have become part of our way of life.

The following table shows the rapid increase in the number of cellular phone users (figures are approximate) in the late 1990s. Note that the independent variable (year) increases in steps of one unit (year).

## Calling All Cells

| YEAR | NUMBER OF CELLULAR PHONES AS OF JAN. I (in millions) |
|------|------|
| 1996 | 44.248 |
| 1997 | 55.312 |
| 1998 | 69.140 |
| 1999 | 86.425 |
| 2000 | 108.031 |

1. Is this a linear function? How do you know?

2. **a.** Evaluate the indicated ratios to complete the following table:

| No. of phones in 1997 / No. of phones in 1996 | No. of phones in 1998 / No. of phones in 1997 | No. of phones in 1999 / No. of phones in 1998 | No. of phones in 2000 / No. of phones in 1999 |
|------|------|------|------|
| | | | |

**b.** What do you notice about the values of the table?

In an exponential function with base $b$, equally spaced $x$-values yield $y$-values whose successive ratios are constant. If the $x$-values increase by increments of 1, the common ratio is the base $b$. If $b > 1$, $b$ is the growth factor; if $0 < b < 1$, $b$ is the decay factor.

3. **a.** Does the relationship in the table preceding Problem 1 represent an exponential function? Explain.

**b.** What is the growth factor?

**c.** As a consequence of the result found in part b, you can start with 44.248, the number of cellular phone users in 1996, and obtain the number of cellular phone users in 1997 by multiplying by the growth factor, $b = 1.25$. You can then determine the number of cellular phone users in 1998 by multiplying the number of cellular phone users in 1997 by $b$, and so on. Verify this with your calculator. Note that because the exponential function is a mathematical model, the results will vary slightly from the actual number of phones given in the table preceding Problem 1.

Once you know the growth factor ($b = 1.25$), you can determine the equation that gives the number of phones as a function of $t$, the number of years since 1996. Note that $t = 0$ corresponds to 1996, $t = 1$ to 1997, and so on.

**4. a.** Complete the table.

| $t$ | CALCULATION FOR THE NUMBER OF CELL PHONES | EXPONENTIAL FORM | NUMBER OF CELL PHONES (IN MILLIONS) |
|---|---|---|---|
| 0 | 44.248 | $44.248(1.25)^0$ | 44.248 |
| 1 | (44.248)1.25 | $44.248(1.25)^1$ | |
| 2 | | | |
| 3 | | | |

**b.** Use the pattern in the preceding table to help you write the equation of the form $N = a \cdot b^t$, where $N$ represents the number of cell phones (in millions) in use at time $t$, the number of years since 1996.

**c.** What is the practical domain of the function $N$?

**d.** Graph the function $N$ on your graphing calculator, and then sketch the result below on an appropriately scaled and labeled axis.

**e.** Using transformations, describe how the graph in part d is related to the graph of the increasing function $N = (1.25)^t$.

**f.** Determine the $N$-intercept of the graph of $N$ by substituting 0 for $t$. What is the practical meaning of the vertical intercept in this situation?

**g.** What does the value of $a$ in the equation in part b represent?

> **DEFINITION**
>
> Many exponential functions can be represented symbolically by $y = a \cdot b^x$, where $a$ is the value of $y$ when $x = 0$ and $b$ is the growth or decay factor. If the $x$-variable of $y = a \cdot b^x$ represents time, then the coefficient $a$ is called the initial value.

Example 1   *The exponential function defined by $y = 5 \cdot 2^x$ has y-intercept $(0, 5)$ and growth factor $b = 2$. The exponential function defined by $y = \frac{1}{2}(0.75)^x$ has y-intercept $\left(0, \frac{1}{2}\right)$ and decay factor $b = 0.75$.*

**5.** Use the function defined by $N = 44.248(1.25)^t$ to estimate the number of cell phone users in 2005. Do you think this is a good estimate? Explain.

**6. a.** Use the graph of the exponential function $N = 44.248(1.25)^t$ and the trace or table feature of your graphing calculator to estimate the number of years it takes for the number of cell phone users to double from 44.248 million to 88.496 million.

**b.** Estimate the time necessary for the number of cell phone users to double from 88.496 million to 176.992 million. Verify your estimate using your calculator.

**c.** How long will it take for any given number of cell phone users to double?

> **DEFINITION**
>
> The **doubling time** of an exponential function is the time it takes for an output to double. The doubling time is determined by the growth factor and remains the same for all output values.

**Example 2** *The balance B(t), in dollars, of an investment account is defined by $B(t) = 5500(1.12)^t$, where t is the number of years. The initial value for this function is $5500. Determine the value of t when the balance is doubled or equal to $11,000.*

SOLUTION

If you use the table feature of your calculator, the doubling time is estimated at 6.1 years (see the following calculator graphic). The intersect feature on the graphing calculator shows the doubling time to be 6.12 years to the nearest hundredth.

## Decreasing Exponential Functions

You sold your used car and have just purchased a new car for $26,000. You have just learned that you should expect the value of your car to depreciate by 30% per year! The following table shows the book value of the car for the next several years, where *V* is the value in thousands of dollars:

**DEPRECIATION: TAKING ITS TOLL**

| t (year) | 0 | 1 | 2 | 3 | 4 |
|---|---|---|---|---|---|
| V (in thousands of dollars) | 26 | 18.2 | 12.7 | 8.9 | 6.2 |

The values of the independent variable, *t*, are incremented by 1, and a value of the *V* is obtained by multiplying the previous value by a constant factor. This is another example of an exponential function. However, because the value of the car is decreasing, the constant factor is a *decay factor* and its value will be between 0 and 1.

**7. a.** Calculate the decay factor, *b*, in this situation. Show the calculations you perform to determine the factor.

**b.** You can now start with 26, the initial value of the car (in thousands of dollars), and obtain the value after one year by multiplying by the decay factor, $b = 0.70$. The value of the car after two years is the value of the car after one year times the decay factor. Verify this on your calculator, and compare your results with the entries in the graphic prior to Problem 7.

**8. a.** Complete the following table:

| T | CALCULATION OF THE VALUE OF THE CAR | EXPONENTIAL FORM | VALUE, $V = a \cdot b^t$ (in thousands of dollars) |
|---|---|---|---|
| 0 | 26 | $26(0.70)^0$ | 26 |
| 1 | $26 \cdot 0.70$ | $26(0.70)^1$ | |
| 2 | | | |
| 3 | | | |

**b.** Use the pattern in the preceding table to help you write an equation of the form $V = a \cdot b^t$, where $V$ represents the value of the car as a function of time, $t$.

**c.** What is the practical domain of this function?

**d.** Graph this function on your graphing calculator, and sketch the result below on an appropriate scaled and labeled set of axes. Note that the graph is a vertical stretch of the graph of the decreasing function defined by $V = (0.70)^t$

**e.** Determine the $V$-intercept of the graph by substituting 0 for the input $t$. What is the practical meaning of the intercept in this situation?

**9. a.** Use your graphing calculator to estimate the number of years it takes to halve the value of the automobile from $26,000 to $13,000.

**b.** Estimate the time necessary to halve the value from $13,000 to $6500. Verify your answer using your graphing calculator.

**c.** How long will it take for any specific value of the car to halve?

> DEFINITION
>
> The **half-life** of an exponential function is the time it takes for a $y$-value to decay by one-half. The half-life is determined by the decay factor and remains the same for all $y$-values.

**10.** Homemade chocolate chip cookies lose their freshness over time. Let the taste quality be 1 when the cookies are fresh. The taste quality decreases according to the function:

$$y = 0.8^x,$$

where $x$ is the number of days since the cookies were baked.

Determine when the taste quality will be one-half of its value. Use the intersect feature of your calculator to determine when $y$ is $\frac{1}{2}$ of 1 or 0.5.

**SUMMARY**
**Activity 5.5**

1. For **exponential functions** defined by $y = ab^x$, $a$ is the value of $y$ when $x = 0$ (sometimes called the initial value), and $b$ is the growth or decay factor.

2. The $y$-intercept of these functions is $(0, a)$.

3. In an exponential function, equally spaced $x$-values yield $y$-values whose successive ratios are constant. If the $x$-values increase by one unit, then
   a. the constant ratio is the **growth factor** if the $y$-values are increasing.
   b. the constant ratio is the **decay factor** if the $y$-values are decreasing.

4. The **doubling time** of an increasing exponential function is the time it takes for $y$-values to double. The doubling time is set by the growth factor and remains the same for all $y$-values.

5. The **half-life** of a decreasing exponential function is the time it takes for $y$-values to decay by one-half. The half-life is determined by the decay factor and remains the same for all $y$-values.

1. The population of Russia in selected years can be approximated by the following table.

| YEAR | 1995 | 1996 | 1997 | 2000 |
|---|---|---|---|---|
| POPULATION (in millions) | 148.0 | 147.6 | 146.9 | 146.0 |

   **a.** Let 1995 correspond to $t = 0$. Let $b$ be the ratio between the population of Russia in 1996 and 1995. Determine an exponential function of the form $y = a \cdot b^t$ to represent the population of Russia symbolically. Round to four decimal places.

   **b.** Does the function in part a give an accurate value of the population of Russia in 2000? Explain.

2. Without using your graphing calculator, match each graph with its equation. Then check your answer using a graphing calculator.

   **a.** $f(x) = 0.5(0.73)^x$     **b.** $g(x) = 3(1.73)^x$     **c.** $h(x) = -2(1.73)^x$

**i.**

**ii.**

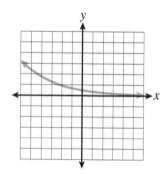

**iii.**

3. Which of the following tables represent exponential functions? Indicate the growth or decay factor for the data that is exponential.

a.

| x | 0 | 1 | 2 | 3 | 4 |
|---|---|---|---|---|---|
| y | 0 | 2 | 16 | 54 | 128 |

b.

| x | 0 | 1 | 2 | 3 | 4 |
|---|---|---|---|---|---|
| y | 1 | 4 | 16 | 64 | 256 |

c.

| x | 1 | 2 | 3 | 4 | 5 |
|---|---|---|---|---|---|
| y | 1750 | 858 | 420 | 206 | 101 |

4. **a.** Sketch a graph of $f(x) = 2^x$ and $g(x) = 3 \cdot 2^x$ on the same coordinate axis.

**b.** Describe how the graphs of $f$ and $g$ are similar and how they are different.

5. If $f(x) = 3 \cdot 4^x$, determine the exact value of each of the following, when possible. Otherwise, use your calculator to approximate the value to the nearest hundredth.

**a.** $f(-2)$                      **b.** $f\left(\frac{1}{2}\right)$

**c.** $f(2)$                         **d.** $f(1.3)$

**6.** In 1995, the U.S. emitted approximately 1400 million tons of carbon into the atmosphere. This represented about one-fourth of the world total. The U.S. emissions were increasing at about 1.3% per year. If $t$ represents the number of years since 1995 and $A(t)$ represents the amount of carbon (in millions of tons) emitted in a given year, then $A(t) = 1400(1.013)^t$.

**a.** What is the initial amount of U.S. carbon emissions?

**b.** Complete the following table:

| t, NUMBER OF YEARS SINCE 1995 | 0 | 1 | 2 | 3 | 4 | 5 |
|---|---|---|---|---|---|---|
| A(t), AMOUNT OF U.S. CARBON EMISSIONS (in millions of tons) | | | | | | |

**c.** Determine the growth factor for carbon emissions.

**d.** Sketch a graph of this exponential equation. Use $0 \le t \le 25$ and $0 \le A(t) \le 2500$.

**e.** Use the equation $A(t) = 1400(1.013)^t$ to determine the amount of carbon emission in 2010. Include the units of measurement in your answer.

**f.** Use the graph and trace features of your graphing calculator to approximate the year in which carbon emissions in the U.S. will exceed 2000 million tons.

**7.** Chlorine is used to disinfect swimming pools. The chlorine concentration should be between 1.5 and 2.5 parts per million (ppm). On sunny, hot days, 30% of the chlorine dissipates into the air or combines with other chemicals. The chlorine concentration, $A(x)$, (in parts per million) in a pool after $x$ sunny days can be modeled by

$$A(x) = 2.5(0.7)^x.$$

**a.** What is the initial concentration of chlorine in the pool?

**b.** Complete the following table:

| x | 0 | 1 | 2 | 3 | 4 | 5 |
|------|---|---|---|---|---|---|
| A(x) |   |   |   |   |   |   |

**c.** Sketch a graph of the chlorine function.

**d.** What is the chlorine concentration in the pool after three days?

**e.** Approximate graphically and numerically the number of days before chlorine should be added.

**8.** In the 1990s, there was a growing national increase in the number of investment clubs. An investment club is a group of people who meet on a regular basis to invest in the stock market. By joining a club, members are able to share in a diverse portfolio and therefore reduce the risk of losing money.

The following table shows the rapid growth in the number of clubs from 1990 to 1996 (figures for the number of clubs are approximate). Note that the independent variable (year) increases in steps of one unit.

| YEAR | NUMBER OF CLUBS AS OF JAN. I |
|------|------------------------------|
| 1990 | 5820 |
| 1991 | 7180 |
| 1992 | 8860 |
| 1993 | 10,930 |
| 1994 | 13,480 |
| 1995 | 16,630 |
| 1996 | 20,510 |

**a.** Does the relationship in the table represent an exponential function? Explain.

**b.** What is the initial number of investment clubs?

**c.** What is the growth factor?

**d.** Determine the equation that gives the number of clubs $N$ as a function of $t$, the number of years since 1990. Note that $t = 0$ corresponds to 1990.

**e.** Graph the function.

**f.** What is the $N$-intercept? What is the practical meaning of this intercept in this situation?

**g.** Use the equation to estimate the number of clubs in 2000. Do you think this is a good estimate? Explain.

**h.** Use the graph of the exponential function and the trace or table feature of your graphing calculator to estimate the number of years it takes for the number of clubs to double from 5820 to 11,640.

**i.** How long will it take for any given number of clubs to double?

**ACTIVITY 5.6**
*Population Growth*

**OBJECTIVES**

1. Determine annual growth or decay rate of an exponential function represented by a table of values or an equation.

2. Graph an exponential function having equation $y = a(1 + r)^x$.

According to the 2000 U.S. census, the city of Charlotte, North Carolina, had a population of approximately 541,000.

**1. a.** Assuming that the population increases at a constant rate of 3.2%, determine the population of Charlotte (in thousands) in 2001.

**b.** Determine the population of Charlotte (in thousands) in 2002.

**c.** Divide the population in 2001 by the population in 2000, and record this ratio.

**d.** Divide the population in 2002 by the population in 2001, and record this ratio.

**e.** What do you notice about the ratios in parts c and d? What do these ratios represent?

Linear functions represent quantities that change at a constant average rate (slope). Exponential functions represent quantities that change at a constant ratio, expressed as a percent.

**Example 1** *Population growth, sales and advertising trends, compound interest, spread of disease, and concentration of a drug in the blood are examples of quantities that increase or decrease at a constant rate expressed as a percent.*

**2.** Let $t$ represent the number of years since 2000 ($t = 0$ corresponds to 2000). Use the results from Problem 1 to complete the following table:

| t, Years (since 2000) | 0 | 1 | 2 | 3 | 4 | 5 |
|---|---|---|---|---|---|---|
| P, population (in thousands) | 541 | | | | | |

Charlotte

Once you know the growth factor, $b$, and the initial value, $a$, you can write the exponential equation. In this situation, the initial value is 541, the population, in 1000s, in 2000 ($t = 0$). The growth factor is $b = 1.032$.

**b.** Write the exponential equation, $P = a \cdot b^t$, for the population of Charlotte.

**3. a.** Write the growth rate, $r = 3.2\%$, as a decimal.

**b.** Add 1 to the decimal form of the growth rate $r$.

The growth factor, $b$, is determined from the growth rate, $r$, by writing $r$ in decimal form and adding 1: $b = 1 + r$.

**Example 2**   *Determine the growth factor, b, for a growth rate of r = 8%.*

SOLUTION

$$r = 8\% = 0.08, b = 1 + r = 1 + 0.08 = 1.08$$

**c.** Solve the equation for the growth factor, $b = 1 + r$, for $r$.

The growth rate, $r$, is determined from the growth factor, $b$, by subtracting 1 from $b$ and writing the result in percent form.

**Example 3**   *Determine the growth rate, r, for a growth factor of b = 1.054.*

SOLUTION

$$r = b - 1 = 1.054 - 1 = 0.054 = 5.4\%$$

The growth rate is 5.4%

**4. a.** Complete the following table:

| $t$ | CALCULATION FOR POPULATION (in thousands) | EXPONENTIAL FORM | P, POPULATION (in thousands) |
|---|---|---|---|
| 0 | 541 | $541(1.032)^0$ | 541 |
| 1 | (541)1.032 | $541(1.032)^1$ | |
| 2 | (541)(1.032)(1.032) | | |
| 3 | | | |

**b.** Use the pattern in the table in part a to help you write an equation for $P$, the population of Charlotte (in thousands), using $t$, the number of years since 2000, as the independent variable.

The equation $P = 541(1.032)^t$ has the general form $P = P_0(1 + r)^t$, where $r$ is the annual **growth rate**, $(1 + r)$ is the **growth factor** or the base, $b$, of the exponential function, $t$ is the time in years, and $P_0$ is the initial value, the population when $t = 0$.

## Example 4

a. *Determine the growth factor and the growth rate of the function defined by* $y = 250(1.7)^x$.

SOLUTION

The growth factor $1 + r$ is the base 1.7. To determine the growth rate, solve the equation $1 + r = 1.7$ for $r$.

$$r = 0.7 \text{ or } 70\%$$

b. *If the growth rate of a function is 5%, determine the growth factor.*

SOLUTION

If $r = 5\%$ or 0.05, the growth factor is $1 + r = 1 + 0.05 = 1.05$.

5. a. Determine the growth factor in the Charlotte population function $P = 541(1.032)^t$.

 b. Determine the growth rate. Express your answer as a percent.

6. a. Using the function defined by $P = 541(1.032)^t$, determine the population of Charlotte in 2006. That is, determine $P$ when $t = 6$.

 b. Graph the population function with a graphing calculator. Set the window to Xmin $= -50$, Xmax $= 100$, Ymin $= 0$, and Ymax $= 13,000$. The graph should appear as follows:

 c. Determine $P$ when $t = 0$. What is the graphical and the practical meaning of this number?

**7. a.** Use the population model to predict Charlotte's population in 2010.

   **b.** Verify your prediction on the graph.

**8. a.** Use the graph to estimate when Charlotte's population will reach 700,000, assuming it continues to grow at the same rate. Remember, $P$ is the number of thousands.

   **b.** Evaluate $P$ when $t = 32$ and describe what it means.

**9.** Use the population model to estimate the population of Charlotte in 2002 and in 2020. In which prediction are you more confident? Why?

**10. a.** Assuming the growth rate remains constant, how long will it take for Charlotte to double its 2000 population?

   **b.** Explain how you reached your conclusion in part a.

## Waste-Water Treatment Facility

You are working at a waste-water treatment facility. You are presently treating water contaminated with 18 micrograms of pollutant per liter. Your process is designed to remove 20% of the pollutant during each treatment. Your goal is to reduce the pollutant to less than 3 micrograms per liter.

**11. a.** What percent of pollutant present at the start of a treatment remains at the end of the treatment?

   **b.** The concentration of pollutant is 18 micrograms per liter at the start of the first treatment. Use the result of part a to determine the concentration of pollutant at the end of the first treatment.

**c.** Complete the following table. Round the results to the nearest hundredth.

| n, NUMBER OF TREATMENTS | 0 | 1 | 2 | 3 | 4 | 5 |
|---|---|---|---|---|---|---|
| C, CONCENTRATION OF POLLUTANT, IN µg/l, AT THE END OF THE nTH TREATMENT | 18 | 14.4 | | | | |

**d.** Write an equation for the concentration, $C$, of the pollutant as a function of the number of treatments, $n$.

The equation $C = 18(0.80)^n$ has the general form $C = C_0(1 - r)^n$, where $r$ is the **decay rate**, $(1 - r)$ is the **decay factor** or the base of the exponential function, $n$ is the number of treatments, and $C_0$ is the initial value, the concentration when $n = 0$.

## Example 5

**a.** *Determine the decay factor and the decay rate of the function defined by* $y = 123(0.43)^x$.

SOLUTION

The decay factor $1 - r$ is the base, 0.43. To determine the decay rate, solve the equation $1 - r = 0.43$ for $r$.

$$r = 0.57 \text{ or } 57\%$$

**b.** *If the decay rate of a function is 5%, determine the decay factor.*

SOLUTION

If $r = 5\%$ or 0.05, the decay factor is $1 - r = 1 - 0.05 = 0.95$.

**12. a.** If the decay rate is 2.5%, what is the decay factor?

**b.** If the decay factor is 0.76, what is the decay rate?

**13. a.** Use the function defined by $C = 18(0.8)^n$ to predict the concentration of contaminants at the waste-water treatment facility after seven treatments.

**b.** Sketch a graph of the concentration function on a graphing calculator. Use the table in Problem 11c to set a window. Does the graph look like you expected it would? Explain.

**c.** What is the $C$-intercept? What is the practical meaning of the intercept in this situation?

**d.** Reset the window of your graphing calculator to Xmin $= -5$, Xmax $= 15$, Ymin $= -10$, and Ymax $= 50$. Does the graph have a horizontal asymptote? Explain what this means in this situation.

**14.** Use the table or trace feature of a graphing calculator to estimate the number of treatments necessary to bring the concentration of pollutant below 3 micrograms per liter.

## SUMMARY
### Activity 5.6

1. **Exponential functions** are used to describe phenomena that grow or decay by a constant percent rate over time.

2. If $r$ represents the **annual growth rate**, the exponential function that models the quantity, $P$, can be written as

$$P = P_0(1 + r)^t,$$

where $P_0$ is the initial amount, $t$ represents the number of elapsed years, and $1 + r$ is the growth factor.

3. If $r$ represents the **annual decay rate**, the exponential function that models the amount remaining can be written as

$$P = P_0(1 - r)^t,$$

where $1 - r$ is the decay factor.

## EXERCISES
### Activity 5.6

1. Determine the growth and decay factors and growth and decay rates in the following table.

| GROWTH FACTOR | GROWTH RATE | DECAY FACTOR | DECAY RATE |
|---|---|---|---|
| 1.02 | | 0.77 | |
| | 2.9% | | 68% |
| 2.23 | | 0.953 | |
| | 34% | | 19.7% |
| 1.0002 | | 0.9948 | |

**2.** The 2000 U.S. Census reports the populations of Bozeman, Montana, as 27,509 and Butte, Montana, as 32,370. Since the 1990 census, Bozeman's population has been increasing at approximately 1.96% per year. Butte's population has been decreasing at approximately 0.29% per year. Assume that the growth and decay rates stay constant.

   **a.** Let $P$ represent the population $t$ years after 2000. Determine the exponential functions that model the populations of both cities.

   **b.** Use the population models to predict the populations of both cities in 2005.

   **c.** Estimate the number of years necessary for the population of Bozeman, Montana, to double.

   **d.** Using the table and/or graphs of these functions, predict when the populations will be equal.

**3.** You have just taken over as the city manager of a small city. The personnel expenses were $8,500,000 in 2006. Over the past five years, the personnel expenses have increased at a rate of 3.2% annually.

   **a.** Assuming that this rate continues, write an equation describing personnel costs, $C$, in millions of dollars, where $t = 0$ corresponds to 2006.

   **b.** Sketch a graph of this function up to the year 2016 ($t = 10$).

   **c.** What are your projected personnel costs in the year 2011?

   **d.** What is the $C$-intercept? What is the practical meaning of the intercept in this situation?

   **e.** In what year will the personnel expenses be double the 2006 personnel expenses?

4. According to the U.S. Bureau of the Census, the population of the United States from 1930 to 2000 can be modeled by $P = 120.6 \cdot 1.0125^t$, where $t$ represents the number of years since 1930.

   a. Sketch a graph of the U.S. population model from 1930 to 2000.

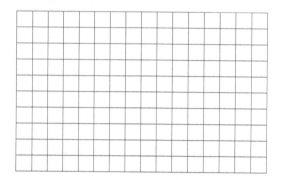

   b. Determine the annual growth rate and the growth factor from the equation.

   c. Use the population equation to determine the population (in millions) of the U.S. in 2000. How does your answer compare to the actual population of 281.4 million?

5. You have recently purchased a new truck for $20,000, by arranging financing for the next five years. You are curious to know what your new truck will be worth when the loan is completely paid off.

   a. Assuming that the value depreciates at a constant rate of 15%, write an equation that represents the value $V$ of the truck $t$ years from now.

   b. What is the decay rate in this situation?

   c. What is the decay factor in this situation?

   d. Use the equation from part a to estimate the value of your truck five years from now.

   e. Use the trace and table features of a graphing calculator to check your results in part d.

   f. Use the trace or table features of a graphing calculator to determine when your truck will be worth $10,000.

**ACTIVITY 5.7**
Time Is Money

**OBJECTIVES**

1. Distinguish between simple and compound interest.

2. Apply the compound interest formula to determine the future value of a lump-sum investment earning compound interest.

3. Apply the continuous compounding formula $A = Pe^{rt}$.

Congratulations, you have inherited $20,000! Your grandparents suggest that you save half of the inheritance for a "rainy day."

**1. a.** Suppose the $10,000 is deposited in a bank at 6.5% annual interest. What is the interest earned after one year?

**b.** Suppose you left the money in the account for 10 years. Can the total amount of interest on your investment be calculated by multiplying your answer in part a by 10? What assumption are you making if you said yes?

Recall that for **simple interest** on an investment, the interest earned during the first period does not earn interest for the rest of the life of the investment. Therefore, at 6.5% simple annual interest, the $10,000 would earn a total interest of $10,000(0.065)(10) = \$6,500$.

The interest paid on savings accounts in most banks is **compound interest**. The interest earned for each period is added to the previous principal before the next interest calculation is made. Simply stated, interest earns interest.

For example, if you deposit $10,000 in the bank at 6.5%, the balance after one year is

$$10,000 + 0.065(10,000) = 10,000 + 650 = 10,650.$$

The interest, $650, earned during the year becomes part of the new balance. At the end of the second year, your balance is

$$10,650 + 0.065(10,650) = 10,650 + 692.25 = 11,342.25.$$

Note that you made interest on the original deposit, plus interest on the first year's interest. In this situation, we say that interest is compounded. Usually, the compounding occurs at fixed intervals (typically at the end of every year, quarter, month, or day). In this example, interest is compounded annually.

If interest is compounded, then the current balance is given by the formula

$$A = P\left(1 + \frac{r}{n}\right)^{nt},$$

where $A$ is the current balance or compound amount in the account,
$P$ is the principal (the original amount deposited),
$r$ is the annual interest rate (in decimal form),
$n$ is the number of times per year that interest is compounded, and
$t$ is the time in years the money has been invested.

The given formula for the compound amount $A$ is called the **compound interest formula**.

Example 1   *You invest $2000 at 8% compounded quarterly. How much money do you have after five years?*

SOLUTION

The principal is $2000; so $P = 2000$. The annual interest rate is 8%; so $r = 0.08$. Interest is compounded quarterly; that is, four times per year, so $n = 4$. The money is invested for five years; so $t = 5$. Substituting numbers for the variables in the preceding formula, you have

$$A = 2000(1 + \tfrac{0.08}{4})^{4 \cdot 5} = \$2971.89.$$

The amount $A = \$2971.90$ in Example 1 is called the **future value** of the investment.

2. **a.** Suppose you deposit $10,000 in an account that has a 6.5% annual interest rate and whose interest is compounded annually ($n = 1$). Substitute the appropriate values for the variables into the compound interest formula to verify that the balance $A$ at the end of the second year is $11,342.25.

   **b.** Use the compound interest formula to complete the following table:

| t, YEAR | 0 | 1 | 2 | 3 | 4 |
|---|---|---|---|---|---|
| A, BALANCE | 10,000.00 | 10,650.00 | 11,342.25 | | |

3. **a.** Suppose you deposit the $10,000 into an account that has the same interest rate of 6.5%, with compounding quarterly ($n = 4$) rather than annually ($n = 1$). Write a new formula for your balance, $A$, as a function of time.

   **b.** What would be your balance after the first year?

   **c.** Use the table feature of your calculator to determine the balance at the end of each year for the specified years in the table in Problem 4. Record the values in the table under $n = 4$ (compounded quarterly).

4. Now deposit your $10,000 into a 6.5% account with *monthly* compounding ($n = 12$) and then in an account with *daily* compounding ($n = 365$). Use your graphing calculator and the appropriate formula to complete the following table.

| COMPARISON OF $10,000 PRINCIPAL IN 6.5% APR ACCOUNTS WITH VARYING COMPOUNDING PERIODS | | | |
|---|---|---|---|
| t | n = 4 | n = 12 | n = 365 |
| 0 | | | |
| 5 | | | |
| 10 | | | |
| 15 | | | |
| 20 | | | |
| 25 | | | |
| 30 | | | |
| 35 | | | |
| 40 | | | |

5. In Problem 4, you calculated the balance on a deposit of $10,000 at an annual interest rate of 6.5% that was compounded at different intervals. After 40 years, which account has the higher balance? Does this seem reasonable? Explain.

## Continuous Compounding

You could extend compounding to every hour or every minute or even every second. However, compounding more frequently than every hour does not increase the balance very much.

To discover why this happens, take a closer look at the exponential functions from Problems 2–4.

$$n = 1: \quad A = 10{,}000\left(1 + \frac{0.065}{1}\right)^{1 \cdot t} = 10{,}000[(1 + 0.065)^1]^t$$

$$n = 4: \quad A = 10{,}000\left(1 + \frac{0.065}{4}\right)^{4 \cdot t} = 10{,}000\left[\left(1 + \frac{0.065}{4}\right)^4\right]^t$$

$$n = 12: \quad A = 10{,}000\left(1 + \frac{0.065}{12}\right)^{12 \cdot t} = 10{,}000\left[\left(1 + \frac{0.065}{12}\right)^{12}\right]^t$$

$$n = 365: \quad A = 10{,}000\left(1 + \frac{0.065}{365}\right)^{365 \cdot t} = 10{,}000\left[\left(1 + \frac{0.065}{365}\right)^{365}\right]^t$$

Can you discover a pattern in the form of the underlined expressions?

Each formula can be expressed as $A = 10{,}000b^t$, where $b = \left(1 + \frac{0.065}{n}\right)^n$ for $n = 1, 4, 12$, and $365$. The number $b$ is called the **growth** factor, and $n$ is the number of compounding periods per year.

**Example 2** *If $n = 4$ in the formula $b = \left(1 + \frac{0.065}{n}\right)^n$, then $b = \left(1 + \frac{0.065}{4}\right)^4 = 1.06660$. The number $1.06660$ is the growth factor.*

**6.** Determine the value of $b$ in the following table, where $b = \left(1 + \frac{0.065}{n}\right)^n$. Round to five decimal places.

| $n$, NUMBER OF COMPOUNDING PERIODS | 1 | 4 | 12 | 365 |
|---|---|---|---|---|
| $b$, GROWTH FACTOR | | | | |

The growth rate is the percentage by which the balance grows by in 1 year. It is called the **effective yield**, $r_e$. Notice that as the number of compounding periods increases, the effective yield increases. This means that with the same annual interest rate (APR), your investment will earn more with more compounding periods.

PROCEDURE

**To Calculate the Effective Yield**

**1.** Determine the growth factor $b = \left(1 + \dfrac{r}{n}\right)^n$.

**2.** Subtract 1 from $b$ and write the result as a decimal.

$$r_e = b - 1 = \left(1 + \frac{r}{n}\right)^n - 1$$

**Example 3** *Determine the effective yield for an annual percentage rate (APR) of 4.5% compounded monthly.*

SOLUTION

$r = 4.5\% = 0.045, \ n = 12$

$$r_e = b - 1 = \left(1 + \frac{r}{n}\right)^n - 1 = \left(1 + \frac{0.045}{12}\right)^{12} - 1 = 1.04594 - 1 = 0.04594$$

$r_e = 4.594\%$

**7. a.** If interest is compounded hourly, then $n = 365 \cdot 24 = 8760$. Compute the growth factor, $b$, for compounding hourly, using an APR of 6.5%.

**b.** Determine the effective yield associated with each of the growth factors in the following table.

| $n$ | 1 | 4 | 12 | 365 |
|---|---|---|---|---|
| **GROWTH FACTOR, $b$** | 1.065 | 1.0666 | 1.06697 | 1.06715 |
| **EFFECTIVE YIELD $r_e$** | | | | |

**c.** Write a sentence comparing the growth factor $b$ for compounding hourly, $n = 8760$, to that for daily compounding, $n = 365$.

If the compounding periods become shorter and shorter (compounding every hour, every minute, every second), $n$ gets larger and larger. If you consider the period to be so short that it's essentially an instant in time, you have what is called **continuous compounding**. Some banks use this method for compounding interest.

The compound interest formula $A = P\left(1 + \frac{r}{n}\right)^{nt}$ is no longer used when interest is compounded continuously. The following develops a formula for continuous compounding.

**Step 1.** Rewrite the given formula as indicated using properties of exponents.

$$A = P\left(1 + \frac{r}{n}\right)^{nt} = P\left[\left(1 + \frac{r}{n}\right)^{n/r}\right]^{rt}, \text{ since } \frac{n}{r} \cdot rt = nt$$

**Step 2.** Let $\frac{n}{r} = x$. It follows that $\frac{r}{n} = \frac{1}{x}$. Note that as $n$ gets very large, the value of $x$ also gets very large.

**Step 3.** Substituting $x$ for $\frac{n}{r}$ and $\frac{1}{x}$ for $\frac{r}{n}$, in the rewritten formula in step 1, you have

$$A = P\left[\left(1 + \frac{r}{n}\right)^{n/r}\right]^{rt} = P\left[\left(1 + \frac{1}{x}\right)^{x}\right]^{rt}.$$

**8. a.** Now take a closer look at the expression $\left(1 + \frac{1}{x}\right)^{x}$. Enter $\left(1 + \frac{1}{x}\right)^{x}$ into your calculator as a function of $x$. Display a table that starts at 0 and is incremented by 100. The results are displayed below.

**b.** In the table of values, why is there an error at $x = 0$?

**c.** Scroll down in the table and describe what happens to the output, $\left(1 + \frac{1}{x}\right)^{x}$, as the input, $x$, gets very large.

The letter $e$ is used to represent the number that $\left(1 + \frac{1}{x}\right)^x$ approaches as $x$ gets very large. This notation was devised by mathematician Leonhard Euler (1707–1783). Euler used the letter $e$ to denote this number. The number is irrational and its decimal representation never ends and never repeats.

**9.** The number e is a very important number in mathematics. Find it on your calculator, and write its decimal approximation below. How does this approximation compare to the result in Problem 8a?

You are now ready to complete the compound interest formula for continuous compounding. Substituting $e$ for $\left(1 + \frac{1}{x}\right)^x$ in $A = P\left[\left(1 + \frac{1}{x}\right)^x\right]^{rt}$, you obtain the continuous compounding formula

$$A = Pe^{rt},$$

where $A$ is the current amount, or balance, in the account;

   $P$ is the principal;

   $r$ is the annual interest rate (annual percentage rate in decimal form);

   $t$ is the time in years that your money has been invested; and

   $e$ is the base of the continuously compounded exponential function.

**Example 4**   *You invest $100 at a rate of 4% compounded continuously. How much money will you have after 5 years?*

SOLUTION

The principal is $100, so $P = 100$. The annual interest rate is 4%, so $r = 0.04$. The money is invested for 5 years, so $t = 5$. Because interest is compounded continuously, you use the formula for continuous compounding as follows.

$$A = 100e^{0.04 \cdot 5} = \$122.14$$

**10. a.** Calculate the balance of your $10,000 investment in 10 years with an annual interest rate of 6.5% compounded continuously.

The formula used for the preceding result was $A = 10{,}000e^{0.065t}$. Comparing $A = 10{,}000e^{0.065t}$ with $A = 10{,}000b^t$ shows that the growth factor is $b = e^{0.065}$.

   **b.** Determine the growth factor in this situation.

   **c.** What is the effective yield of an annual interest rate of 6.5% compounded continuously?

**11. a.** Historically, investments in the stock market have yielded an average rate of 11.7% per year. Suppose you invest $10,000 in an account at an 11% annual interest rate that compounds continuously. Use the formula $A = Pe^{rt}$ to determine the balance after 35 years.

**b.** What is the balance after 40 years?

**c.** Your grandfather claimed that $10,000 could grow to more than half a million dollars by retirement time (40 years). Is your grandfather correct in his claim?

## SUMMARY
### Activity 5.7

**1.** The formula for **compounding interest** is $A = P\left(1 + \frac{r}{n}\right)^{nt}$, where

A is the current balance or compound amount in the account,
P is the principal (the original amount deposited),
r is the annual interest rate (in decimal form),
n is the number of times per year that interest is compounded, and
t is the time in years the money has been invested.

**2.** The formula for **continuous compounding** is $A = Pe^{rt}$.

**3.** If the number of **compounding periods** is large, $A = P\left(1 + \frac{r}{n}\right)^{nt}$ is approximated by $A = Pe^{rt}$.

## EXERCISES
### Activity 5.7

**1.** You inherit $25,000 and deposit it into an account that earns 4.5% annual interest compounded quarterly.

**a.** Write an equation that gives the amount of money in the account after $t$ years.

**b.** How much money will be in the account after 10 years?

**c.** You want to have approximately $65,000 in the bank when your first child begins college. Use your graphing calculator to determine in how many years you will reach this goal.

**d.** If the interest were to be compounded continuously at 4.5%, how much money would be in the account after 10 years?

**e.** Use your graphing calculator to determine in how many years you would reach your goal of $65,000, if the interest is compounded continuously.

**f.** Should you look for an investment account that will be compounded continuously?

2. You deposit $2000 in an account that earns 5% annual interest compounded monthly.

   **a.** What will be your balance after 2 years?

   **b.** Estimate how long it would take for your investment to double.

   **c.** Identify the annual growth rate and the growth factor.

3. Your friend deposits $1900 in an account that earns 6% compounded continuously.

   **a.** What will be her balance after 2 years?

   **b.** Estimate how long it will take for your friend's investment to double.

4. You are 25 years old and begin to work for a large company that offers you two different retirement options.

   **Option 1.** You will be paid a lump sum of $20,000 for each year you work for the company.

   **Option 2.** The company will deposit $10,000 into an account that will pay you 12% annual interest compounded monthly. When you retire, the money will be given to you.

   Let *A* represent the amount of money you will have for retirement after *t* years.

   **a.** Write an equation that represents option 1.

   **b.** Write an equation that represents option 2.

   **c.** Use your graphing calculator to sketch a graph of the two options on the same axis. Your screen should appear as follows:

**d.** If you plan to retire at age 65, which would be the better plan? Explain.

**e.** If you decide to retire at age 55, which would be the better plan? Explain.

**f.** Use your graphing calculator to determine at what age it would not make a difference which plan you choose.

5. The compound interest formula that gives the balance in an account with a principal of $1500 that earns interest at the rate of 4.8% compounded monthly is $A = 1500 \cdot \left(1 + \dfrac{0.048}{12}\right)^{12t}$. Compare this formula to the exponential equation $A = 1500 \cdot b^t$.

   **a.** What takes the place of $b$ in the compound interest formula?

   **b.** What is the value of the growth factor $b$?

   **c.** What is the effective yield?

6. The compound interest formula that gives the balance in an account with a principal of $1500 that earns interest at the rate of 4.8% compounded continuously is $A = 1500 \cdot e^{0.048t}$. Compare this formula to the exponential equation $A = 1500 \cdot b^t$.

   **a.** What takes the place of $b$ in the compound interest formula?

   **b.** What is the value of the growth factor $b$?

   **c.** What is the effective rate?

**PROJECT ACTIVITY 5.8**

Continuous Growth and Decay

**OBJECTIVES**

1. Discover the relationship between the equations of exponential functions defined by $y = ab^t$ and the equations of continuous growth and decay exponential functions defined by $y = ae^{kt}$.

2. Solve problems involving continuous growth and decay models.

3. Graph base $e$ exponential functions using transformations.

The U.S. Bureau of the Census reported that the U.S. population on April 1, 2000, was 281,421,906. The U.S. population on April 1, 2001, was 284,236,125.

1. Assuming exponential growth, the U.S. population $y$ can be modeled by the equation $y = ab^t$, where $t$ is the number of years since April 1, 2000. Therefore, $t = 0$ corresponds to April 1, 2000.

 a. What is the initial value, $a$?

 b. Determine the annual growth factor, $b$, for the U.S. population.

 c. What is the annual growth rate?

 d. Write the equation for the U.S. population as a function of $t$.

The U.S. population did not remain constant at 281,421,906 from April 1, 2000, to March 31, 2001, and then jump to 284,236,125 on April 1, 2001. The population grew continuously throughout the year. The exponential function used to model continuous growth is the same function used to model continuous compounding for an investment.

Recall from Activity 4.7 that the formula for continuous compounding is $A = Pe^{rt}$, where $A$ (output) is the amount of the investment, $P$ is the initial principal, $r$ is the compounding rate, $t$ (input) is time, and $e$ is the constant irrational number. When this function is used more generally, it is written as

$$y = ae^{kt}, \text{ where}$$

 $A$ has been replaced by $y$, the output;

 $P$ replaced by $a$, the initial value; and

 $r$ replaced by $k$, the continuous growth rate.

Now, the exponential growth model for the U.S. population determined in Problem 1d, written in the form $y = ab^t$, can be rewritten equivalently in the continuous growth form, $y = ae^{kt}$. Since $y$ represents the same output value in each case, $ab^t = ae^{kt}$. Since $a$ represents the same initial value in each model, it follows that $b^t = e^{kt}$.

2. a. Notice that $e^{kt}$ can be written as $(e^k)^t$. How are $b$ and $e^k$ related?

 b. Set the value of $b$ determined in Problem 1 ($b = 1.01$) equal to $e^k$ and solve for $k$, the continuous growth rate. Solve the equation graphically by entering $Y_1 = e^x$ and $Y_2 = 1.01$. Use the window Xmin = 0, Xmax = 0.02, Ymin = 1, and Ymax = 1.02.

 c. Rewrite the U.S. population function from Problem 1 ($y = 281,421,906(1.01)^t$) in the form $y = a \cdot e^{kt}$.

Notice that an annual growth rate of $r = 0.01 = 1\%$ is equivalent to a continuous growth rate of $k = 0.00995 = 0.995\%$.

> Whenever growth is continuous at a constant rate, the exponential model used to describe it is $y = ae^{kt}$, where $k$ is the constant continuous growth rate, $a$ is the amount present initially (when $t = 0$) and $e$ is the constant irrational number approximately equal to 2.718.

## Example 1

a. Rewrite the equation $y = 42(1.23)^t$ into a continuous growth equation of the form $y = ae^{kt}$.

SOLUTION

$$1.23 = e^k, k = 0.207, y = 42e^{0.207t}$$

b. What is the continuous growth rate?

SOLUTION

$$0.207 = 20.7\%$$

c. What is the initial amount present (when $t = 0$)?

SOLUTION

$$42$$

Now, consider a situation which involves continuous decay at a constant percentage rate. Tylenol (acetaminophen) is metabolized in your body and eliminated at the rate of 24% per hour. You take two Tylenol tablets (1000 milligrams) at 12 noon.

3. Assume that the amount of Tylenol in your body can be modeled by an exponential function $Q = ab^t$, where $t$ is the number of hours from 12 noon.

   a. What is the initial value, $a$, in this situation?

   b. Determine the decay factor, $b$, for the amount of Tylenol in your body.

   c. Write an exponential equation for the amount of Tylenol in your body as a function of $t$.

Of course, the amount of Tylenol in your body does not decrease suddenly by 24% at the end of each hour; it is metabolized and eliminated continuously. The equation $y = ae^{kt}$ can also be used to model a quantity that decreases at a continuous rate. Recall in Problem 2a, you compared $y = ab^t$ to $y = ae^{kt}$ and established that $b = e^k$.

4. a. The value of $b$ for the Tylenol equation is 0.76. Set $b = 0.76$ equal to $e^k$ and solve for $k$ graphically as in Problem 2b. Use the window Xmin $= -1$, Xmax $= 0$, Ymin $= 0$, and Ymax $= 1$.

**b.** Write the equation for the amount of Tylenol in your body, $Q = 1000(0.76)^t$, in the form $Q = ae^{kt}$.

Notice that the value of $k$ in Problem 4 is negative. Whenever $0 < b < 1$, then $b$ is a decay factor and the value of $k$ will be negative. A decreasing exponential function written in the form $y = ae^{kt}$ will have $k < 0$, and $|k|$ is the continuous rate of decrease.

> For exponential decrease (decay) at a continuous constant rate, the model $y = ae^{kt}$ is used, where $k < 0$, $|k|$ is the constant continuous decrease (decay) rate, $a$ is the amount present initially, when $t = 0$, and $e$ is the constant irrational number approximately equal to 2.718.

## Example 2

**a.** Rewrite the decay equation $y = 12.5(0.83)^t$ as a function of the form $y = ae^{kt}$.

SOLUTION

$$0.83 = e^k, k = -0.186, y = 12.5e^{-0.186t}$$

**b.** What is the continuous percentage rate of decay?

SOLUTION

$$0.186 = 18.6\%$$

**c.** What is the initial amount present when $t = 0$?

SOLUTION

$$12.5$$

## Graphs of Exponential Functions Having Base $e$

**5.** Consider the exponential function defined by $y = e^x$.

**a.** What is the domain of the function?

**b.** Is this function increasing or decreasing? Explain.

**c.** Complete the following table. If necessary, round the $y$-values to the nearest two decimal places.

| $x$ | −3 | −2 | −1 | 0 | 1 | 2 | 3 | 4 | 5 |
|-----|----|----|----|---|---|---|---|---|---|
| $y = e^x$ | | | | | | | | | |

**d.** Sketch a graph of $y = e^x$. Verify using a graphing calculator.

**e.** What is the horizontal asymptote?

**f.** What is the range of the function?

**g.** What are the intercepts of the graph?

**h.** Is the function continuous over its domain?

**6.** In parts a–f, graph the function defined by the given equation. Using transformations, describe how the graph is related to the graph of $y = e^x$. Verify using a graphing calculator.

**a.** $y = -e^x$ 　　　　　　　　　　　　　　**b.** $y = e^{x+2}$

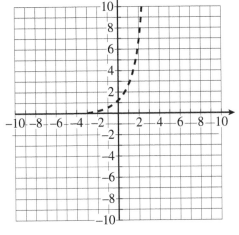

**c.** $y = e^x + 2$

**d.** $y = 2e^x$

**e.** $e^{-x}$

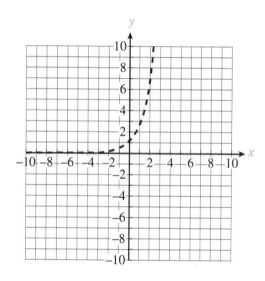

**f.** $y = -0.5e^x + 1$

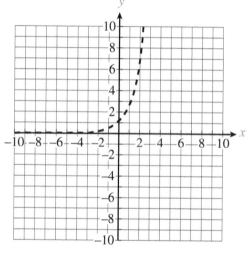

**7.** A vertical shift of the graph of $y = e^x$ changes the horizontal asymptote.

**a.** What is the equation of the horizontal asymptote of the graph of $y = e^x + 2$ (see Problem 6c)?

**b.** What is the equation of the horizontal asymptote of the graph of $y = e^x - 2$?

8. The graph of an increasing exponential function has the shape represented below.

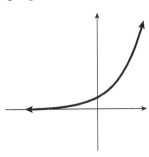

   a. If the equation for the preceding graph is written as $y = ab^x$, what do you know about the values of $a$ and $b$?

   b. If the equation for the preceding graph is written as $y = ae^{kx}$, what do you know about the values of $a$ and $k$?

9. The graph of a decreasing exponential function has the shape represented below.

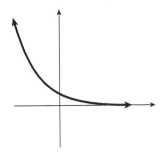

   a. If the equation for the preceding graph is written as $y = ab^x$, what do you know about the values of $a$ and $b$?

   b. If the equation for the preceding graph is written as $y = ae^{kx}$, what do you know about the values of $a$ and $k$?

10. Identify the given exponential function as increasing or decreasing. In each case give the initial value and rate of increase or decrease.

   a. $P = 2500e^{0.04t}$

   b. $Q = 400(0.86)^t$

   c. $A = 75(1.032)^t$

   d. $R = 12e^{-0.12t}$

**SUMMARY**
Activity 5.8

1. When a quantity increases or decreases continuously at a constant rate, the amount present at time $t$ can be modeled by $y = ae^{kt}$, where $a$ is the initial quantity at $t = 0$. If the quantity is increasing, then $k > 0$ and $k$ is the continuous rate of increase. If the quantity is decreasing, then $k < 0$ and $|k|$ is the continuous rate of decrease.

2. The graph of an increasing exponential function of the form $y = ab^x$ or $y = ae^{kt}$, where $a > 0$ and $b > 1$ or $k > 0$ will be shaped like

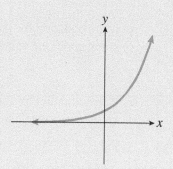

3. The graph of a decreasing exponential function of the form $y = ab^x$ or $y = ae^{kt}$, where $a > 0$ and $0 < b < 1$ or $k < 0$ will be shaped like

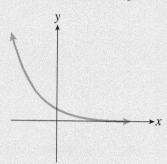

**Notation**

The function $y = ae^{kt}$ may be written in other forms, such as $y = y_0 e^{kt}$, where the initial value is $y_0$ ($y$ sub zero) or $Q = Q_0 e^{kt}$, where the initial value is $Q_0$ ($Q$ sub zero).

**EXERCISES**
Activity 5.8

1. In 2004, Charlotte, North Carolina, was ranked twentieth in population of all the U.S. cities. The population of Charlotte has been increasing steadily and the exponential function defined by $f(x) = 397.4(1.03)^x$ models this population from 1990 to 2004, where $x$ represents the number of years since 1990 and $f(x)$ represents the total population in thousands. (*Source:* U.S. Bureau of the Census.)

   **a.** Is this an increasing or decreasing exponential function? Explain.

   **b.** Determine the annual growth or decreasing (decay) rate from the model.

c. According to the model, what is the initial value? What does the initial value mean in this situation?

d. The equation for continuous growth is $y = ae^{kt}$. Set the value of $b$ in your model equal to $e^k$, and use your graphing calculator to determine the value for $k$ graphically. This will be the continuous growth or decay rate.

e. Rewrite the population function in the form of $y = ae^{kt}$.

f. Use the function from part e and predict the population of Charlotte in 2010.

2. The table shows the smoking prevalence among U.S. male adults (18 years and over) as a percent of the population.

## Where There's Smoke

| SMOKING PREVALENCE AMONG U.S. MALE ADULTS | | | | | | | |
|---|---|---|---|---|---|---|---|
| Year | 1955 | 1965 | 1970 | 1980 | 1990 | 2000 | 2002 |
| Years since 1955 | 0 | 10 | 15 | 25 | 35 | 45 | 47 |
| % of population | 56.9 | 51.9 | 44.1 | 37.6 | 28.4 | 25.7 | 25.2 |

*Source:* The U.S. Center for Disease Control and Prevention.

This data can be modeled by an exponential function $p(t) = 58.8(0.98)^t$, where $t$ equals the number of years since 1955 and $p$ is the smoking prevalence among male adults as a percent of the U.S. population.

a. Is this an increasing or decreasing exponential function? Explain.

**b.** Sketch a graph of the function using the data in the table. Does the graph reinforce your answer in part a?

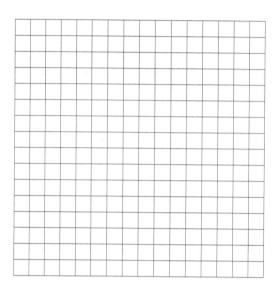

**c.** Determine the growth or decreasing (decay) rate from the model.

**d.** According to the model, what is the initial value?

**e.** The equation for the continuous growth or decay is $y = ae^{kt}$. Set the value of $b$ in your model equal to $e^k$, and use your graphing calculator to determine the value for $k$ graphically. This will be the continuous growth or decay rate.

**f.** Rewrite the smoking function in the form of $y = ae^{kt}$.

**g.** Use the function from part f and determine the percent of males in the U.S. population that will be smoking in 2006.

**3.** Identify the given exponential function as increasing or decreasing. In each case give the initial value and rate of increase or decrease.

   **a.** $R(t) = 33(1.097)^t$

   **b.** $f(x) = 97.8e^{-0.23x}$

    c. $S = 3250(0.73)^t$

    d. $B = 0.987e^{0.076t}$

4. Sketch a graph of each of the following and verify using your graphing calculator.

    a. $y = 20e^{0.08x}$             b. $f(x) = 10e^{-0.3x}$

    c. Compare the two graphs. Include shape, direction, and initial values.

5. Strontium 90 is a radioactive material that decays according to the function defined by $y = y_0e^{-0.0244t}$, where $y_0$ is the amount present initially and $t$ is time in years.

    a. If there are 20 grams of strontium 90 present today, how much will be present in 20 years?

    b. Use the graph of the function to approximate how long it will take for 20 grams to decay to 10 grams, 10 grams to decay to 5 grams, and 5 grams to decay to 2.5 grams. The length of time is called the *half-life*. In general, a half-life is the time required for half of a radioactive substance to decay.

    c. Identify the annual decay rate and the decay factor.

6. When drugs are administered into the bloodstream, the amount present decreases continuously at a constant rate. The amount of a certain drug in the bloodstream is modeled by the function $y = y_0 e^{-0.35t}$, where $y_0$ is the amount of the drug injected (in milligrams) and $t$ is time (in hours).

   a. Suppose that 10 milligrams are injected at 10:30 A.M., how much of the drug is still in the bloodstream at 2:00 P.M.?

   b. If another dose needs to be administered when there is 1 milligram of the drug present in the bloodstream, approximately when should the next dose be given (to the nearest quarter hour)?

7. The amount of credit-card spending from Thanksgiving to Christmas has increased by 14% per year since 1987. The amount, $A$, in billions of dollars of credit-card spending during the holiday period in a given year can be modeled by

$$A = f(x) = 36.2e^{0.14x},$$

   where $x$ represents the number of years since 1987.

   a. How much was spent using credit cards from Thanksgiving to Christmas in 1996?

   b. Sketch a graph of the credit-card function.

   c. What is the $A$-intercept of the graph? What is the practical meaning of the intercept in this situation?

   d. Determine, graphically and numerically, the year when credit-card spending reached 75 billion dollars.

   e. What is the doubling time?

8. *E. coli* bacteria are capable of very rapid growth, doubling in number approximately every 49.5 minutes. The number, $N$, of *E. coli* bacteria per milliliter after $x$ minutes can be modeled by the equation

$$N = 500,000e^{0.014x}.$$

a. What is the initial number of bacteria per milliliter?

b. How many *E. coli* bacteria would you expect after 99 minutes? (*Hint:* There will be two doublings.) Verify your estimate using the equation.

c. Use a graphing or numerical approach to determine the elapsed time when there would be 20,000,000 *E. coli* bacteria per milliliter.

## ACTIVITY 5.9
Bird Flu

**OBJECTIVES**

1. Determine the equation of an exponential function that best fits the given data.
2. Make predictions using an exponential regression equation.
3. Determine whether a linear or exponential model best fits the data.

In 2005, the avian flu, also known as bird flu, received international attention. Although there were very few documented cases of the avian flu infecting humans worldwide, world health organizations including the Centers for Disease Control in Atlanta expressed concern that a mutant strain of the bird flu virus capable of infecting humans would develop and produce a worldwide pandemic.

The infection rate (the number of people that any single infected person will infect) and the incubation period (the time between exposure and the development of symptoms) of this flu cannot be known precisely but they can be approximated by studying the infection rates and incubation periods of existing strains of the virus.

A very conservative infection rate would be 1.5 and a reasonable incubation period would be about 15 days or roughly half of a month. This means that the first infected person could be expected to infect 1.5 people in about 15 days. After 15 days, that person cannot infect anyone else. This assumes that the spread of the virus is not checked by inoculation or vaccination.

So the total number of infected people 0.5 months after the first person was infected would be 2.5, the sum of the original infected person and the 1.5 newly infected people. During the second half-month the 1.5 newly infected people would infect $1.5 \times 1.5 = 2.25$ new people. This means you have 2.25 people to add to the 2.5 people previously infected, or approximately 5 people infected with bird flu at the end of the first month.

The following table represents the total number of people who could be infected with a mutant strain of bird flu over a period of five months.

| MONTHS SINCE THE FIRST PERSON WAS INFECTED | 0 | 0.5 | 1 | 1.5 | 2 | 2.5 | 3 | 3.5 | 4 | 4.5 | 5 |
|---|---|---|---|---|---|---|---|---|---|---|---|
| NUMBER OF NEWLY INFECTED | | 1.5 | 2.25 | 3.375 | 5 | | | | | | |
| TOTAL NUMBER OF PEOPLE INFECTED | 1 | 2.5 | 5 | 8 | 13 | | | | | | |

1. Complete the table above. Round each value to the nearest whole person.

2. Let $t$ represent the number of months since the first person was infected and $N$ represent the total number of people infected with the bird flu virus. Create a scatterplot of the data below.

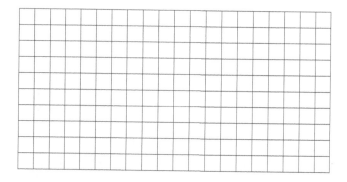

**3.** Does the scatterplot indicate a linear relationship between $t$ and $N$? Explain.

**4. a.** Use your calculator to model the data with an exponential function. Use option 0: ExpReg in the STAT CALC menu to determine an exponential function that best fits the given data. Record that model below. Round $a$ and $b$ to the nearest 0.001.

    **b.** Sketch a graph of the exponential model using your calculator and add it to the scatterplot in Problem 2.

    **c.** What is the practical domain of this function?

    **d.** What is the $N$-intercept of the graph? How does it compare to the actual initial value ($t = 0$) from the table?

**5. a.** Use the exponential model to determine the total number of infected people one year after the initial infection ($t = 12$) provided the virus is unchecked. Round your result to the nearest whole person.

    **b.** Use the exponential function to write an equation that can be used to determine when the virus will first infect 2,000,000 people.

    **c.** Solve the equation in part b using a graphing approach. Use the intersect feature of your calculator; the screen containing the solution should resemble the following:

    **d.** Interpret the meaning of your solution in part c.

## Increasing Exponential Model

According to the U.S. Department of Education, the number of college graduates increased significantly during the twentieth century. The following table gives the number (in thousands) of college degrees awarded from 1900 through 2000:

## College Bound

| YEAR | NUMBER OF COLLEGE GRADUATES (thousands) |
|------|------------------------------------------|
| 1900 | 30 |
| 1910 | 54 |
| 1920 | 73 |
| 1930 | 127 |
| 1940 | 223 |
| 1950 | 432 |
| 1960 | 530 |
| 1970 | 878 |
| 1980 | 935 |
| 1990 | 1017 |
| 2000 | 1180 |

**6.** Let $t$ represent the number of years since 1900 ($t = 0$ corresponds to 1900, $t = 10$ to 1910, etc). Let $N$ represent the number of college graduates (in thousands) at time $t$. Sketch a scatterplot of the given data on your graphing calculator. Your scatterplot should appear as seen to the left.

**7. a.** Use a graphing calculator to determine the equation of an exponential function that best fits the given data.

**b.** Sketch a graph of the exponential model using a graphing calculator.

**c.** What is the practical domain of this exponential function?

**d.** What is the $N$-intercept of the graph? How does it compare to the actual initial value ($t = 0$) from the table?

**8. a.** What is the base of the exponential model? Is the base a growth or decay factor? How do you know?

**b.** What is the annual growth rate?

**9. a.** Use the exponential model to determine the number of college graduates in 2010 ($t = 110$).

**b.** Use the exponential model to write an equation that can be used to determine the year in which there will be 2 million college graduates. Remember that the number of college graduates is measured in thousands.

**c.** Solve the equation in part a using a graphing approach. Use the intersect feature of your graphing calculator; the screen containing the solution should appear as follows.

**10.** What is the doubling time for your exponential model? That is, approximately how many years will it take for a given number of college graduates to double?

## Decreasing Exponential Model

Students in U.S. public schools have had much greater access to computers in recent years. The following table shows the number of students per computer in selected years:

| YEAR | 1983 | 1984 | 1985 | 1987 | 1989 | 1992 | 1995 | 1999 |
|---|---|---|---|---|---|---|---|---|
| NUMBER OF STUDENTS PER COMPUTER | 125 | 75 | 50 | 32 | 22 | 16 | 10 | 5.7 |

**11. a.** Use your graphing calculator to determine the equation of an exponential function that models the given data. Let the independent variable, $t$, represent the number of years since 1983.

**b.** Sketch a graph of the exponential model using your graphing calculator.

**c.** What is the base of the exponential model? Is the base a growth or decay factor? How do you know?

**d.** What is the annual decay rate?

**e.** Does the graph have a horizontal asymptote? What is the practical meaning of this asymptote in the context of the situation?

## EXERCISES
### Activity 5.9

**1.** The total amount of money spent on health care in the United States is increasing at an alarming rate. The following table gives the total national health care expenditures in billions of dollars in selected years from 1975 through 2003.

## Billions for Health

| YEAR | 1975 | 1980 | 1985 | 1990 | 1995 | 2000 | 2003 |
|---|---|---|---|---|---|---|---|
| TOTAL SPENT (BILLIONS OF DOLLARS) | 129.8 | 245.8 | 426.5 | 695.6 | 990.2 | 1309.9 | 1679.9 |

*Source:* National Center for Health Statistics.

**a.** Would the data in the preceding table be better modeled by a linear model, $y = mx + b$, or an exponential model, $y = ab^x$? Explain.

**b.** Sketch a scatterplot of this data.

**c.** Does the graph reinforce your conclusion in part a? Explain.

**d.** Use a graphing calculator to determine the exponential regression equation that best fits the health care data in the preceding table. Let your input, $t$, represent the number of years since 1975.

**e.** Using the regression equation from part d, determine the predicted total health care expenditures for the year 1995.

**f.** According to the exponential model, what is the growth factor for the total health care costs per year?

**g.** What is the growth rate?

**h.** According to the exponential model, in what year did the total heath care costs first exceed $1 trillion?

**i.** What is the doubling time for your exponential model?

**2. a.** Consider the following data set for the variables $x$ and $y$:

| $x$ | 5 | 8 | 11 | 15 | 20 |
|---|---|---|---|---|---|
| $y$ | 70.2 | 50.7 | 35.1 | 22.6 | 9.5 |

Plot these points on the following grid:

**b.** Use your graphing calculator to determine both a linear regression and an exponential regression model of the data. Record the equations for these models here.

**c.** Which model appears to fit the data better? Explain.

**d.** Use the better model to determine $y$ when $x = 13$ and $y$ when $x = 25$.

   **e.** For the exponential model, what is the decay factor?

   **f.** What does it mean that the decay factor is between 0 and 1?

   **g.** What is the half-life for the exponential model?

**3.** Use the graph of $y = 5 \cdot 2^x$ as a check, and summarize the properties of the exponential function $y = a \cdot b^x$, where $a > 0$.

   **a.** What is the domain?

   **b.** What is the range?

   **c.** When is $y = a \cdot b^x$ positive?

   **d.** When is $y = a \cdot b^x$ negative?

   **e.** What is the $y$-intercept of the graph of $y = a \cdot b^x$?

**4.** The number of transistors that can be placed on a single chip has grown significantly between 1970 and 2004. The following table gives the number of transistors (in millions) that can be placed on a specific chip in a given year.

| YEAR | X, NUMBER OF YEARS SINCE 1970 | CHIP | TRANSISTORS (IN MILLIONS) |
|---|---|---|---|
| 1971 | 1 | 4004 | 0.0023 |
| 1986 | 16 | 386DX | 0.275 |
| 1989 | 19 | 486DX | 1.2 |
| 1993 | 23 | Pentium | 3.3 |
| 1995 | 25 | P6 | 5.5 |
| 1997 | 27 | Pentium II | 7.5 |
| 1999 | 29 | Pentium III | 9.5 |
| 2000 | 30 | Pentium IV | 42 |
| 2004 | 34 | Pentium IV Prescott | 125 |

*Source:* Intel

   **a.** Use a graphing calculator to determine an exponential regression model of the data. Let the independent variable $x$ represent the number of years since 1970.

   **b.** Assuming the rate of growth continues, approximate the number of transistors that can be placed on a chip in 2012?

## Collecting and Analyzing Data

**5.** You need to find some real-world data that appears to be increasing exponentially. Newspapers, magazines, scientific journals, almanacs, and the Internet are good resources. Once the data has been obtained, model the data by an exponential function defined by $y = ab^x$. Explain why an exponential function would best represent the data. Be sure to describe the meaning of $a$ and $b$ in the exponential model in terms of the situation. Make a prediction about the dependent variable $y$ for a specific value of the independent variable $x$. Describe the reliability of this prediction.

**What Have I Learned?**

1. **a.** Think of an example, or find one in a newspaper or magazine or on the Internet, and use it to show how to determine the growth factor associated with a percent increase. For instance, you might think of or find growth factors associated with yearly interest rates for a saving account.

   **b.** Show how you would use the growth factor to apply a percent increase twice, then three times.

2. Current health research shows that losing just 10% of body weight produces significant health benefits, including a reduced risk for a heart attack. Suppose a relative who weighs 199 pounds begins a diet to reach a goal weight of 145 pounds.

   **a.** Use the idea of a decay factor to show your relative how much he will weigh after losing the first 10% of his body weight.

   **b.** Explain to your relative how he can use the decay factor to determine how many times he has to lose 10% of his body weight to reach his goal weight of 145 pounds.

3. Consider a linear function defined by $g(x) = mx + b$, $m \neq 0$, and an exponential function defined by $f(x) = a \cdot b^x$. Explain how you can determine from the equation whether the function is increasing or decreasing.

4. Suppose you have an exponential function of the form $f(x) = a \cdot b^x$, where $a > 0$ and $b > 0$ and $b \neq 1$. By inspecting the graph of $f$, can you determine if $b > 1$ or if $0 < b < 1$? Explain.

5. You are given a function defined by a table, and the *x*-values are in increments of 1. By looking at the table, can you determine whether or not the function can be approximated by an exponential model? Explain.

6. Explain the difference between growth rate and growth factor.

7. An exponential function $y = a \cdot b^x$ passes through the point $(0, 2.6)$. What can you conclude about the values of $a$ and $b$?

8. You have just received a substantial tax refund of $P$ dollars. You decide to invest the money in a CD for 2 years. You have narrowed your choices to two banks. Bank A will give you 6.75% interest compounded quarterly. Bank B offers you 6.50% compounded continuously. Where do you deposit your money? Explain.

9. Explain why the base in an exponential function cannot equal 1.

**Activities 5.1–5.9   How Can I Practice?**

1. A suit with an original price of $300 was marked down 30%. You have a coupon good for an additional 20% off.

   **a.** What is the suit's final cost?

   **b.** What is the equivalent percent discount?

2. The Ford Motor Company released its Taurus sales figures for the month of October in 2001. Dealers sold a total of 28,000 new Taurus automobiles, a decrease of 14% from the same month in 2001. Approximately, how many 2001 Taurus cars were sold?

3. You are planning to purchase a new car and have your eye on a specific model. You know that new car prices are projected to increase at a rate of 4% per year for the next few years.

   **a.** Write an equation that represents the projected cost, $C$, of your dream car $t$ years in the future, given that it costs $17,000 today.

   **b.** Identify the growth rate and the growth factor.

   **c.** Use your equation in part a to project the cost of your car three years from now.

   **d.** Use your graphing calculator to approximate how long it will take for your dream car to cost $30,000, if the price continues to increase at 4% per year.

4. Without using your graphing calculator, match the graph with its equation.

   **a.** $g(x) = 2.5(0.47)^x$        **b.** $h(x) = 1.5(1.47)^x$

i.

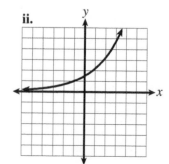

ii.

**5.** Explain the reasons for your choices in Problem 4.

**6.** Complete the following tables representing exponential functions. Round calculations to two decimal places whenever necessary.

**a.**

| x | 0 | 1 | 2 | 3 | 4 |
|---|---|---|---|---|---|
| y | 2.00 | 5.10 | | | |

**b.**

| x | 0 | 1 | 2 | 3 | 4 |
|---|---|---|---|---|---|
| y | 3.50 | 2.10 | | | |

**c.**

| x | 0 | 1 | 2 | 3 | 4 |
|---|---|---|---|---|---|
| y | $\frac{1}{6}$ | 6 | | | |

**7.** Write the equation of the exponential function that represents the data in each table in Problem 6.

**a.**                    **b.**                    **c.**

**8.** Without graphing, classify each of the following functions as increasing or decreasing, and determine $f(0)$. (Use your graphing calculator to verify.)

**a.** $f(x) = 1.3(0.75)^x$

**b.** $f(x) = 0.6(1.03)^x$

**c.** $f(x) = 3\left(\frac{1}{5}\right)^x$

**9. a.** Given the following table, do you believe that it can be approximately modeled by an exponential function?

| x | 0 | 1 | 2 | 3 | 4 | 5 | 6 |
|---|---|---|---|---|---|---|---|
| y | 2 | 5 | 12.5 | 31.3 | 78.1 | 195.3 | 488.3 |

**b.** If you answered yes to part a, what is the constant ratio of successive $y$-values?

**c.** Determine an exponential equation that models this data.

**10. a.** Complete the following tables.

| x | −3 | −2 | −1 | 0 | 1 | 2 | 3 |
|---|---|---|---|---|---|---|---|
| $h(x) = 4^x$ | | | | | | | |

| x | −3 | −2 | −1 | 0 | 1 | 2 | 3 |
|---|---|---|---|---|---|---|---|
| $g(x) = \left(\frac{1}{4}\right)^x$ | | | | | | | |

**b.** Sketch graphs of *h* and *g* on the following grid.

**c.** Use the tables and graphs in part a and b to complete this table.

| FUNCTION | BASE, b | GROWTH OR DECAY FACTOR | x-INTERCEPT | y-INTERCEPT | HORIZONTAL ASYMPTOTE | INCREASING OR DECREASING |
|---|---|---|---|---|---|---|
| $h(x) = 4^x$ | | | | | | |
| $g(x) = \left(\frac{1}{4}\right)^x$ | | | | | | |

**11.** Your starting salary for a new job is $22,000 per year. You are offered two options for salary increases:

    Plan 1: an annual increase of $1000 per year or

    Plan 2: an annual percentage increase of 4% of your salary.

Your salary is a function of the number of years of employment at your job.

**a.** Write an equation to determine the salary *S* after *x* years on the job using plan 1; using plan 2;

**b.** Complete the following table using the equations from part a:

| x | 0 | 1 | 3 | 5 | 10 | 15 |
|---|---|---|---|---|---|---|
| S, PLAN 1 | | | | | | |
| S, PLAN 2 | | | | | | |

**c.** Which plan would you choose? Explain.

**12.** You deposited $10,000 in an account that pays 12% annual interest compounded monthly.

    **a.** Write an equation to determine the amount, $A$, you will have in $t$ years.

    **b.** How much will you have in 5 years?

    **c.** Use your graphing calculator to determine in how many years your investment will double.

    **d.** Write an equation to determine the amount, $A$, you will have in $t$ years if the interest is compounded continuously.

    **e.** Use the equation in part d to determine how much you will have in 5 years. Compare your answer to your answer in part b.

**13.** The number of victims of a flu epidemic is increasing at a continuous rate of 7.5% per week.

    **a.** If 2000 people are currently infected, write an exponential model of the form $N = N_0 e^{rt}$, where $e$ is an irrational number having decimal approximation $e \approx 2.71$, and

        $N$ is the number of victims in thousands,

        $N_0$ is the initial number infected in thousands,

        $r$ is the weekly percent rate expressed as a decimal, and

        $t$ is the number of weeks.

    **b.** Use the exponential model to predict the number of people infected after eight weeks.

    **c.** Sketch the graph of the flu function using your graphing calculator.

    **d.** Use a graphing approach to predict when the number of victims of the flu will triple.

**14.** You are a college freshman and have a credit card. You immediately purchase a stereo system for \$415. Your credit limit is \$500. Let's assume that you make no payments and purchase nothing more and there are no other fees. The monthly interest rate is 1.18%.

    **a.** What is your initial credit card balance?

    **b.** What is the growth rate of your credit card balance?

    **c.** What is the growth factor of your credit card balance?

    **d.** Write an exponential function to determine how much you will owe (represented by $y$) after $x$ months with no more purchases or payments.

    **e.** Use your graphing calculator to graph this function. What is the $y$-intercept?

    **f.** What is the practical meaning of this intercept in this situation?

    **g.** How much will you owe after ten months? Use the table feature on your graphing calculator to determine the solution.

    **h.** When you reach your credit limit of \$500, the bank will expect a payment. How long do you have before you will have to start paying the money back? Use the trace feature on your graphing calculator to approximate the solution.

**15.** You are working part-time for a computer company while going to high school. The following table shows the hourly wage, $w(t)$, in dollars, that you earn as a function of time, $t$. Time is measured in years since the beginning of 2003 when you started working.

| TIME, $t$, YEARS, SINCE 2003 | 0 | 1 | 2 | 3 | 4 | 5 |
|---|---|---|---|---|---|---|
| HOURLY WAGE, $w$, (\$) | 12.50 | 12.75 | 13.01 | 13.27 | 13.53 | 13.81 |

    **a.** Calculate the ratios of the $w$-values to determine if the data in the table is exponential. Round each ratio to the nearest hundredth.

    **b.** What is the growth factor?

    **c.** Write an exponential equation that models the data in the table.

    **d.** What percent raise did you receive each year?

**e.** For approximately how many years will you have to work for the company in order for your hourly wage to double? (Assume you will receive the same percentage increase each year.)

**16.** The number of farms in the U.S. has declined from 1940 to 2000, as the data in the following table shows. The data is estimated from National Agricultural Statistics Service, U.S. Department of Agriculture.

| YEAR | 1940 | 1950 | 1960 | 1970 | 1980 | 1990 | 2000 |
|------|------|------|------|------|------|------|------|
| NUMBER OF FARMS, IN MILLIONS | 6.2 | 5.8 | 4 | 3 | 2.5 | 2.2 | 2 |

**a.** Make a scatterplot of this data.

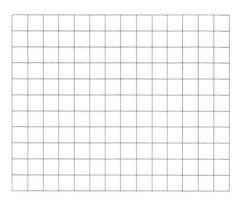

**b.** Does the scatterplot show that the data would be better modeled by a linear model or by an exponential model? Explain.

**c.** Use a graphing calculator to determine the exponential regression equation that best fits the U.S. farm data. Let $x$ represent the number of years since 1940.

**d.** Use the regression equation to predict the total number of farms in the U.S. in 2010.

**e.** According to your exponential model, what is the decay factor for the total number of farms in the U.S.?

**f.** What is the decay rate?

**g.** Use a graphing calculator to determine the halving time for your exponential model.

**ACTIVITY 5.10**

The Diameter of Spheres

**OBJECTIVES**

1. Define logarithm.

2. Write an exponential statement in logarithmic form.

3. Write a logarithmic statement in exponential form.

4. Determine log and ln values using a calculator.

Spheres are all around you (pardon the pun). You play sports with spheres like baseballs, basketballs, and golf balls. You live on a sphere. Earth is a big ball in space, as are the other planets, the Sun, and the Moon. All spheres have properties in common. For example, the formula for the volume, $V$, of any sphere is $V = \frac{4}{3}\pi r^3$, and the formula for the surface area, $S$, of any sphere is $S = 4\pi r^2$ where $r$ represents the radius of the sphere.

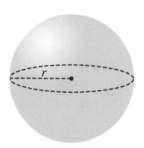

However, not all spheres are the same size. The following table gives the diameter, $d$, of some spheres you all know. Recall that the diameter, $d$, of a sphere is twice the radius, $r$.

| SPHERE | DIAMETER, $d$, IN METERS |
|---|---|
| Golf ball | 0.043 |
| Baseball | 0.075 |
| Basketball | 0.239 |
| Moon | 3,476,000 |
| Earth | 12,756,000 |
| Jupiter | 142,984,000 |

If you want to determine either the volume or surface area of any of the spheres in the preceding table, the diameter of the given sphere would be the $x$-value and would be referenced on the horizontal axis. But how would you scale this axis?

**1. a.** Plot the values in the first three rows of the table. Scale the axis starting at 0 and incrementing by 0.02 meter.

**b.** Can you plot the values in the last three rows of the table on the same axis? Explain.

**2. a.** Plot the values in the last three rows of the table on a different axis. Scale the axis starting at 0 and incrementing by 10,000,000 meters.

**b.** Can you plot the values in the first three rows of the table on the axis in part a? Explain.

**b.** Can you plot the values in the first three rows of the table on the axis in part a? Explain.

## Logarithmic Scale

**3.** There is a way to scale the axis so that you can plot all the values in the table on the same axis.

   **a.** Starting with the leftmost tick mark, give the first tick mark a value of 0.01 meter. Write 0.01 as a power of 10 as follows: $0.01 = \dfrac{1}{100} = \dfrac{1}{10^2} = 10^{-2}$ meter. Give the next tick mark a value of 0.1, written as $10^{-1}$ meter. Continue in this way by giving each consecutive tick mark a value that is one power of 10 greater than the preceding tick mark.

$10^{-2}$   $10^{-1}$

   **b.** Complete the following table by writing all of the diameters from the preceding table in scientific notation.

| SPHERE | DIAMETER, $d$, IN METERS | $d$, IN SCIENTIFIC NOTATION |
|---|---|---|
| Golf ball | 0.043 | |
| Baseball | 0.075 | |
| Basketball | 0.239 | |
| Moon | 3,476,000 | |
| Earth | 12,756,000 | |
| Jupiter | 142,984,000 | |

   **c.** To plot the diameter of a golf ball, notice that 0.043 meter is between $10^{-2} = 0.01$ meter and $10^{-1} = 0.1$ meter. Now using the axis in part a, plot 0.043 meter between the tick mark labeled $10^{-2}$ and $10^{-1}$ meter, closer to the tick mark labeled $10^{-2}$ meter.

   **d.** To plot the diameter of Earth, notice that 12,756,000 meters is between $10^7 = 10,000,000$ meters and $10^8 = 100,000,000$ meters. Now plot 12,756,000 meters between the tick marks labeled $10^7$ and $10^8$ meters, closer to the tick mark labeled $10^7$.

   **e.** Plot the remaining data in the same way by first determining between which two powers of 10 the number lies.

The scale you used to plot the diameter values is a *logarithmic* or *log scale*. The tick marks on a logarithmic scale are usually labeled with just the exponent of the powers of 10.

**4. a.** Rewrite the axis from Problem 3a by labeling the tick marks with just the exponents of the powers of 10.

**b.** The axis looks like a standard axis with tick marks labeled $-2, -1, 0, 1$, etc. However, it is quite different. Describe the difference between this log scale and a standard axis labeled in the same way. Focus on the values between consecutive tick marks.

> **DEFINITION**
>
> The exponents used to label the tick marks of the preceding axis are **logarithms** or simply **logs**. Since these are exponents of powers of 10, the exponents are logs **base** 10, known as **common logarithms** or common logs.

**Example 1**

    **a.** *The common logarithm of $10_b^3$ is the exponent to which 10 must be raised to obtain a result of $10_b^3$. Therefore, the common log of $10_b^3$ is 3.*

    **b.** *The common log of $10_b^{-2}$ is $-2$.*

    **c.** *The common log of $100 = 10^2$ is 2.*

**5.** Determine the common log of each of the following.

    **a.** $10^{-1}$                  **b.** $10^4$                  **c.** 1000

    **d.** 100,000                **e.** 0.0001

## Logarithmic Notation

Remember that a logarithm is an exponent. The common log of $x$ is an exponent, $y$, to which the base, 10, must be raised to get result $x$. That is, in the equation $10^y = x$, $y$ is the logarithm. Using log notation $\log_{10} x = y$. Therefore, $\log_{10} 10{,}000 = \log_{10} 10^4 = 4$.

**Example 2**

| $x$, THE NUMBER | $y$, THE EXPONENT TO WHICH THE BASE, 10, MUST BE RAISED TO GET $x$ | LOG NOTATION $\log_{10} x = y$ |
|:---:|:---:|:---:|
| $10_b^3$ | 3 | $\log_{10} 10^3 = 3$ |
| $10^{-2}$ | $-2$ | $\log_{10} 10^{-2} = -2$ |
| $100$ | 2 | $\log_{10} 100 = 2$ |

When using logs base 10, the notation $\log_{10}$ is shortened by dropping the 10. Therefore,

$$\log_{10} 10^3 = \log 10^3 = 3; \log_{10} 100 = \log 100 = 2$$

**6.** Determine each of the following:

**a.** $\log 10^{-1}$  **b.** $\log 10^4$  **c.** $\log 1000$

**d.** $\log 100,000$  **e.** $\log 0.0001$

## Bases for Logarithms

The logarithmic scale for the diameter of spheres situation was labeled with the exponents of powers of 10. Using 10 as the base for logarithms is common since the number 10 is the base of our number system. However, other numbers could be used as the base for logs. For example, you could use exponents of powers of 5 or exponents of powers of 2.

### Example 3

*Base-5 logarithms: The log base 5 of a number, x, is the exponent to which the base, 5, must be raised to obtain x. For example,*

**a.** $\log_5 5^4 = 4$

**b.** $\log_5 125 = \log_5 5^3 = 3$

**c.** $\log_5 \frac{1}{25} = \log_5 5^{-2} = -2$

*Base-2 logarithms: The log base 2 of a number, x, is the exponent to which 2 must be raised to obtain x. For example,*

**a.** $\log_2 2^5 = 5$

**b.** $\log_2 16 = \log_2 2^4 = 4$

**c.** $\log_2 \frac{1}{8} = \log_2 2^{-3} = -3$

In general, a statement in logarithmic form is $\log_b x = y$, where $b$ is the base of the logarithm, $x$ is a power of $b$, and $y$ is the exponent. The base $b$ for a logarithm can be any positive number except 1.

**7.** Determine each of the following.

**a.** $\log_4 64$  **b.** $\log_2 \frac{1}{16}$

**c.** $\log_3 9$  **d.** $\log_3 \frac{1}{27}$

The examples and problems so far in this activity demonstrate the following property of logarithms.

**Property of Logarithms**

For any base $b$ $(b > 0, b \neq 1)$, $\log_b b^n = n$.

8. Determine each of the following:

a. $\log 1$

b. $\log_5 1$

c. $\log_{\frac{1}{2}} 1$

d. $\log 10$

e. $\log_5 5$

f. $\log_{1/2} \left(\frac{1}{2}\right)$

9. a. Referring to Problem 8a–c, write a general rule for $\log_b 1$.

b. Referring to Problem 8d–f, write a general rule for $\log_b b$.

**Property of Logarithms**

In general, $\log_b 1 = 0$ and $\log_b b = 1$, where $b > 0, b \neq 1$

## Natural Logarithms

Because the base of a log can be any positive number except 1, the base can be the number $e$. Many applications involve the use of log base $e$. Log base $e$ is called the **natural** log and has the following special notation:

$$\log_e x \text{ is written as } \ln x, \text{ read simply as el-n-}x.$$

Example 4

a. $\ln e^2 = \log_e e^2 = 2$

b. $\ln \frac{1}{e^4} = \ln e^{-4} = -4$

10. Evaluate the following.

a. $\ln e^7$

b. $\ln \left(\frac{1}{e^3}\right)$

c. $\ln 1$

d. $\ln e$

e. $\ln \sqrt{e}$

## Logarithmic and Exponential Forms

Because logarithms are exponents, logarithmic statements can be written as exponential statements, and exponential statements can be written as logarithmic statements.

For example, in the statement $3 = \log_5 125$, the base is 5, the exponent (logarithm) is 3, and the result is 125. This relationship can also be written as the equation $5^3 = 125$.

> In general, the logarithmic equation $y = \log_b x$ is equivalent to the exponential equation $b^y = x$.

**Example 5**   *Rewrite the exponential equation $e^{0.5} = x$ as an equivalent logarithmic equation.*

SOLUTION:

In the equation $e^{0.5} = x$, the base is $e$, the result is $x$, and the exponent (logarithm) is 0.5. Therefore, the equivalent logarithmic equation is $0.5 = \log_e x$, or $0.5 = \ln x$.

**11.** Rewrite each exponential equation as a logarithmic equation and each log equation as an exponential equation.

    **a.** $3 = \log_2 8$          **b.** $\ln e^3 = 3$          **c.** $\log_2 \frac{1}{16} = -4$

    **d.** $6^3 = 216$          **e.** $e^1 = e$          **f.** $3^{-2} = \frac{1}{9}$

## Logarithms and the Calculator

The numbers whose logarithms you have been working with have been exact powers of the base. However, in many situations, you have to evaluate a logarithm where the number is not an exact power of the base. For example, what is log 20 or ln 15? Fortunately, the common log (base 10) and the natural log (base $e$) are on your calculator.

**12.** Use your calculator to evaluate the following.

    **a.** log 20                              **b.** ln 15

    **c.** $\ln \frac{1}{}$                              **d.** log 0.02

    **e.** Use a calculator to check your answers to Problems 6 and 10.

**13. a.** Use a calculator to complete the following table. Confirm the placement of the diameter values on the log-scaled axis.

| SPHERE | DIAMETER, $d$, IN METERS | $d$, IN SCIENTIFIC NOTATION | log($d$) |
|---|---|---|---|
| Golf ball | 0.043 | $4.3 \times 10^{-2}$ | |
| Baseball | 0.075 | $7.5 \times 10^{-2}$ | |
| Basketball | 0.239 | $2.39 \times 10^{-1}$ | |
| Moon | 3,476,000 | $3.476 \times 10^{6}$ | |
| Earth | 12,756,000 | $1.2756 \times 10^{7}$ | |
| Jupiter | 142,984,000 | $1.4298 \times 10^{8}$ | |

**b.** Plot the values from the log column in the preceding table on the following axis.

**c.** Compare the preceding plot with the plot in Problem 3a and comment.

**SUMMARY**
**Activity 5.10**

**1.** The notation for logarithms is $\log_b x = y$, where $b$ is the base of the log, $x$ is the resulting power of $b$, and $y$ is the exponent. The base $b$ can be any positive number except 1; $x$ can be any positive number. The range of $y$ values includes all real numbers.

**2.** The notation for **common logarithm** or base-10 logarithms is $\log_{10} x = \log x$.

**3.** The notation for the **natural logarithm** or base $e$ logarithm is $\log_e x = \ln x$.

**4.** The **logarithmic equation** $y = \log_b x$ is equivalent to the **exponential equation** $b^y = x$.

**5.** If $b > 0$ and $b \neq 1$,

   **a.** $\log_b 1 = 0$

   **b.** $\log_b b = 1$

   **c.** $\log_b b^n = n$

**EXERCISES**
**Activity 5.10**

**1.** Use the definition of logarithm to determine the exact value of each of the following.

   **a.** $\log_2 32$        **b.** $\log_3 27$        **c.** $\log 0.1$

**d.** $\log_2 \left( \frac{1}{64} \right)$          **e.** $\log_5 1$          **f.** $\log_{1/2} \left( \frac{1}{4} \right)$

**g.** $\log_7 \sqrt{7}$          **h.** $\log_{100} 10$          **i.** $\log 1$
     $\left( \textit{Hint: } \sqrt{7} = 7^{1/2} \right)$

**j.** $\log_2 1$      **k.** $\ln e^5$      **l.** $\ln \left( \frac{1}{e^2} \right)$      **m.** $\ln 1$

2. Evaluate each common logarithm without the use of a calculator.

     **a.** $\log \left( \dfrac{1}{1000} \right) =$ _____          **b.** $\log \left( \dfrac{1}{100} \right) =$ _____

     **c.** $\log \left( \dfrac{1}{10} \right) =$ _____          **d.** $\log 1 =$ _____

     **e.** $\log 10 =$ _____          **f.** $\log 100 =$ _____

     **g.** $\log 1000 =$ _____          **h.** $\log \sqrt{10}$ _____

3. Rewrite the following equations in logarithmic form.

     **a.** $3^2 = 9$          **b.** $\sqrt{121} = 11$    (*Hint:* First rewrite $\sqrt{121}$
                                                in exponential form.)

     **c.** $4^t = 27$          **d.** $b^3 = 19$

4. Rewrite the following equations in exponential form.

     **a.** $\log_3 81 = 4$          **b.** $\frac{1}{2} = \log_{100} 10$

     **c.** $\log_9 N = 12$          **d.** $y = \log_7 x$

     **e.** $\ln \sqrt{e} = \frac{1}{2}$          **f.** $\ln \left( \frac{1}{e^2} \right) = -2$

5. Estimate between what two integers the solutions for the following equations fall. Then solve each equation exactly by changing it to log form. Use your calculator to approximate your answer to three decimal places.

     **a.** $10^x = 3.25$      **b.** $10^x = 590$      **c.** $10^x = 0.0000045$

**ACTIVITY 5.11**
Walking Speed
of Pedestrians

**OBJECTIVES**

1. Determine the inverse of the exponential function.

2. Identify the properties of the graph of a logarithmic function.

3. Graph the natural logarithmic function using transformations.

On a recent visit to Boston, you notice that people seem rushed as they move about the city. Upon returning to school, you mention this observation to your psychology teacher. The instructor refers you to a psychology study that investigates the relationship between the average walking speed of pedestrians and the population of the city. The study cites statistics presented graphically as follows.

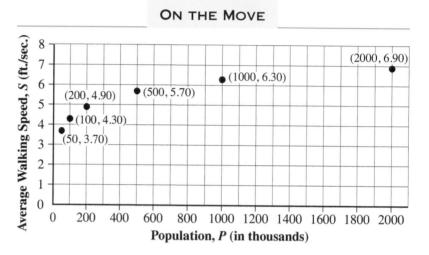

ON THE MOVE

**1. a.** Does the data appear to be linear? Explain.

**b.** Does the data appear to be exponential? Explain.

This data is actually logarithmic. Situations that can be modeled by logarithmic functions will be the focus of this and the following activity.

## Introduction to the Logarithmic Function

The logarithmic function base $b$ is defined by $y = \log_b x$, where

    **i.** $b$ represents the base of the log ($b > 0, b \neq 1$),

    **ii.** $x$ is the input and represents a power of the base $b$ ($x$ is also called the argument), and $y$ is the output and is the exponent needed on the base $b$ to obtain $x$.

**2. a.** Evaluate $\log_{10}(-100)$ using your calculator. What do you observe? Does it seem reasonable? Explain.

**b.** Is it possible to determine $\log(0)$?

**c.** What is the domain for the function defined by $y = \log x$?

**d.** What is the range? Remember, the output $y$ is an exponent.

**3.** The exponential function defined by $f(x) = 10^x$ has a special relationship with the corresponding logarithmic function defined by $g(x) = \log_{10} x = \log x$.

**a.** Complete the following tables for $f(x) = 10^x$ and $g(x) = \log x$.

| x | $f(x) = 10^x$ |
|---|---|
| −2 | |
| −1 | |
| 0 | |
| 1 | |
| 2 | |

| x | $g(x) = \log x$ |
|---|---|
| 0.01 | |
| 0.1 | |
| 1 | |
| 10 | |
| 100 | |

**b.** Compare the input and output values for functions $f$ and $g$.

**c.** Sketch the graphs of Y1 $= 10^x$ and Y2 $= \log_{10} x$ using your graphing calculator. Use the window Xmin $= -4$, Xmax $= 4$, Ymin $= -3$, and Ymax $= 3$. Your screen should appear as follows.

**d.** Graph $y = x$ on the same coordinate axes as functions $f$ and $g$. Describe in a sentence or two the symmetry you observe in the graphs of $f$ and $g$.

The functions defined by $f(x) = 10^x$ and $g(x) = \log x$ are *inverse functions*. The inverse function interchanges the domain and range of the original function. Also, the graph of an inverse function is the reflection of the original function about the line $y = x$. Therefore, the results in Problem 3 demonstrate that $f(x) = 10^x$ and $g(x) = \log x$ are inverse functions.

You can determine the equation of the inverse function by interchanging the input ($x$-values) and the output ($y$-values) in the given equation for the function and solving the new equation for $y$.

**Example 1**   *Determine the equation of the inverse of the function defined by $y = 5^x$.*

SOLUTION

| **Step 1.** | Interchange the $x$ and $y$ variables. | $x = 5^y$ |
|---|---|---|
| **Step 2.** | Solve the resulting equation for $y$ by writing the statement in logarithmic notation. | $y = \log_5 x$ |

**4.** Use the algebraic approach demonstrated in Example 1 to verify that $y = \log x$ is the inverse of $y = 10^x$.

Problems 2, 3, and 4 illustrate the following properties of the common logarithmic function.

---

**Properties of the Common Logarithmic Function $f(x) = \log x$**

**1.** The domain of $f$ is the set of all positive real numbers $(x > 0)$.
**2.** The range of $f$ is all real numbers.
**3.** $f$ is the inverse of the function defined by $g(x) = 10^x$.

---

## The Graph of the Natural Logarithmic Function

**5. a.** Using your calculator, complete the following table. Round your answers to three decimal places.

| $x$ | 0.1 | 0.5 | 1 | 5 | 10 | 20 | 50 |
|---|---|---|---|---|---|---|---|
| $y = \ln x$ | | | | | | | |

**b.** Sketch a graph of $y = \ln x$.

**c.** Verify your graph in part b using a graphing calculator. Using the window $\text{Xmin} = -1$, $\text{Xmax} = 4$, $\text{Ymin} = -2.5$, and $\text{Ymax} = 2.5$, your screen should appear as follows.

**d.** What are the domain and range of the function defined by $y = \ln x$?

**e.** Determine the intercepts of the graph.

**f.** Does the graph of $y = \ln x$ have a horizontal asymptote? Explain.

**g.** Is the natural log function continuous for $x > 0$ ?

**h.** Complete the following table using your calculator. Round your answers to the nearest tenth.

| $x$ | 1 | 0.5 | 0.25 | 0.1 | 0.01 | 0.001 |
|---|---|---|---|---|---|---|
| $y = \ln x$ | | | | | | |

**i.** As the $x$-values take on values closer and closer to 0, what happens to the corresponding $y$-values?

The $y$-axis is a vertical asymptote of the graph.

### DEFINITION

A **vertical asymptote** is a vertical line, $x = a$, that the graph of a function becomes very close to but never touches. As the $x$-values get closer and closer to $x = a$, the $y$-values get larger and larger in magnitude. That is, the $y$-values become very large positive or very large negative values.

**Example 2**   *The vertical asymptote of the graphs of $y = \log x$ and $y = \ln x$ is the vertical line $x = 0$.*

**6. a.** Graph $y = e^x$, $y = \ln x$, and $y = x$ on the same set of coordinate axes using the window Xmin $= -7.5$, Xmax $= 7.5$, Ymin $= -5$, and Ymax $= 5$. Describe the symmetry that you observe.

**b.** Use an algebraic approach to determine the inverse of the exponential function defined by $y = e^x$.

**7.** Sketch a graph of each of the following equations. Using transformations, describe the relationship between the graph and the graph of $y = \ln x$. Verify the graph using a graphing calculator.

**a.** $y = -\ln x$

**b.** $y = \ln(x + 3)$

 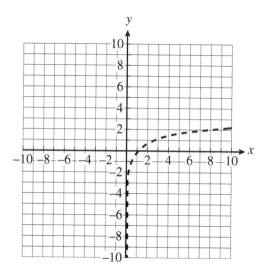

**c.** $y = \ln(-x)$

**d.** $y = \ln x + 3$

 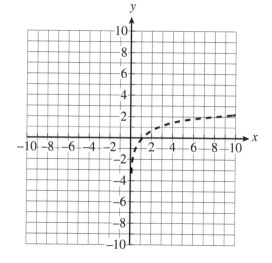

**e.** $y = 2 \ln x$                                    **f.** $y = 3 - 2\ln x$

                         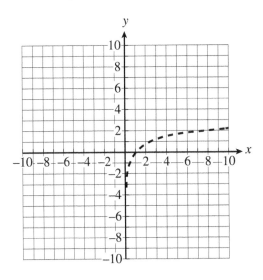

**8.** A horizontal shift of the graph of $y = \ln x$ changes the vertical asymptote.

   **a.** What is the equation of the vertical asymptote of the graph of $y = \ln(x + 3)$ (see Problem 7b)?

   **b.** What is the equation of the vertical asymptote of the graph of $y = \ln(x - 2)$?

---

**SUMMARY**
**Activity 5.11**

**1.** Properties of the log function defined by $y = \log x$.

   **a.** The domain of $f$ is $x > 0$.

   **b.** The range of $f$ is all real numbers.

   **c.** $f$ is the inverse of the function defined by $g(x) = 10^x$.

**2.** The graph of a logarithmic function defined by $y = \log_b x$, where $b > 1$, resembles the following graph, and the function

   **a.** is increasing for all $x > 0$

   **b.** has an $x$-intercept of $(1, 0)$

   **c.** has no $y$-intercept

   **d.** is continuous for $x > 0$.

**e.** has a vertical asymptote of $x = 0$, the $y$-axis

3. The **natural logarithmic function** is defined by

$$y = \ln x = \log_e x.$$

4. The graph of the natural logarithmic function $y = \ln x$

   **a.** is increasing for all $x > 0$

   **b.** has an $x$-intercept of $(1, 0)$

   **c.** has a vertical asymptote of $x = 0$, the $y$-axis

5. The natural logarithmic function is continuous over its domain, $x > 0$.

6. You can determine the equation of the inverse of the function by interchanging the input ($x$-values) and the output ($y$-values) in the given equation for the function and solving the new equation for $y$.

---

## EXERCISES
### Activity 5.11

1. Using the graph of $y = \log x$ as a check, summarize the following properties of the common logarithmic function.

   **a.** What is the domain?

   **b.** What is the range?

   **c.** For what values of $x$ is $\log x$ positive?

   **d.** For what values of $x$ is $\log x$ negative?

   **e.** For what values of $x$ does $\log x = 0$?

**f.** For what values of $x$ does $\log x = 1$?

**g.** For what values of $x$ is the function increasing?

**2. a.** Complete the following table using your calculator. Round your answers to the nearest tenth.

| x | 0.001 | 0.01 | 0.1 | 0.25 | 0.5 | 1 |
|---|-------|------|-----|------|-----|---|
| y = log x | | | | | | |

**b.** As the positive $x$-values take on values closer and closer to 0, what happens to the corresponding $y$-values?

**c.** Determine the vertical asymptote of the graph of $y = \log x$.

**3.** The exponential function defined by $y = 2^x$ has an inverse. Determine the equation of the inverse function. Write your answer in logarithmic form.

**4.** Using the graph of $y = \ln x$ as a check, summarize the following properties of the natural logarithmic function.

**a.** What is the domain?

**b.** What is the range?

**c.** For what values of $x$ is $\ln x$ positive?

**d.** For what values of $x$ is $\ln x$ negative?

**e.** For what values of $x$ does $\ln x = 0$?

**f.** For what values of $x$ does $\ln x = 1$?

**5.** Sketch a graph of each of the following equations. Using transformations, describe the relationship between the graph and the graph of $y = \log x$.

**a.** $y = 3\log x$

**b.** $y = \log(-x)$

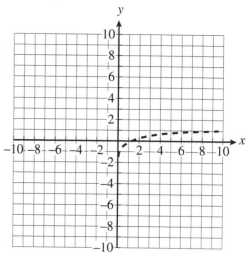

**c.** $y = -\log x$

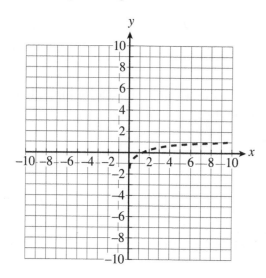

**d.** $y = \log(x + 2)$

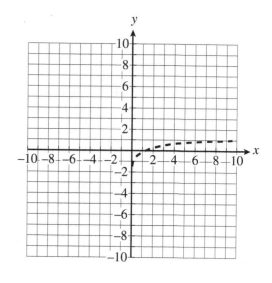

**e.** $y = 5 + \log x$                                                          **f.** $y = 3\log(x - 1)$

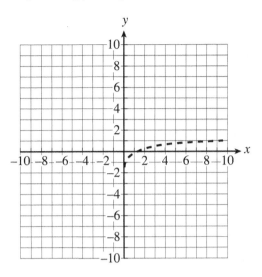

**6.** The life expectancy for a piece of equipment is the number, $n$, of years for the equipment to depreciate to a known salvage value, $V$. The life expectancy, $n$, is given by the formula

$$n = \frac{\log V - \log C}{\log (1 - r)},$$

where $C$ is the initial cost of the piece of equipment and $r$ is the annual rate of depreciation expressed as a decimal. If a computer costs \$34,000 and has a salvage value of \$1000, what is the life expectancy if the annual rate of depreciation is 40%?

**7.** The first two-year college, Joliet Junior College in Chicago, was founded in 1901. The number of two-year colleges grew rapidly, especially during the 1960's. Since then, the growth has lessened. The number y of two-year colleges in the United States can be modeled by

$$y = 513 + 175.6 \ln x,$$

where $x$ represents the number of years since 1960 (that is, $x = 0$ corresponds to 1960, $x = 1$ to 1961, etc.)

**a.** Determine the number of two-year colleges in the year 2000 ($x = 40$).

**b.** Approximate the number of two-year colleges in the year 2010.

**ACTIVITY 5.12**

Walking Speed
of Pedestrians,
continued

**OBJECTIVES**

1. Compare the average rate
of change of increasing
logarithmic, linear, and
exponential functions.

2. Determine the regression
equation of a natural
logarithmic function having
equation $y = a + b \ln x$ that
best fits a set of data.

In Activity 5.11 you looked at a psychology study that investigated the relationship
between the average walking speed of pedestrians and the population of the city.
Graphically the data was presented as follows.

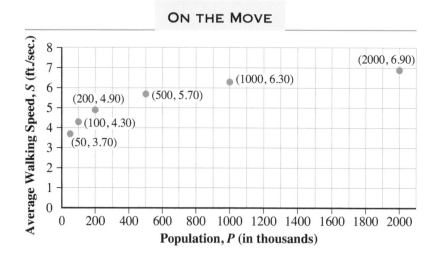

**1. a.** Does the data appear to be logarithmic? Explain.

**b.** Use the data in the graph to complete the following table.

| POPULATION, P (in thousands) | 50 | 100 | 200 | 500 | 1000 | 2000 |
|---|---|---|---|---|---|---|
| AVERAGE WALKING SPEED, S | | | | | | |

The natural logarithmic function can be used to model a variety of scientific and
natural phenomena. The natural logarithmic function is so prevalent that on most
graphing calculators it has its own built-in regression finder.

**2. a.** Use a graphing calculator and the table in Problem 1b to produce a scatterplot of the average walking speed data.

**b.** Use the regression feature of your calculator to produce a natural logarithmic
curve that approximates the data in the table. Use option 9 from the STAT
CALC menu.

The LnReg option will generate a regression equation of the form $y = a + b \ln x$. Round $a$ and $b$ to the nearest thousandth, and record the function below.

**c.** Enter the function from part b into your graphing calculator. Verify visually that this function is a good model for your data.

**d.** What is the practical domain of this function?

**e.** Use the function from part b to predict the average walking speed in Boston, population 589,121. (*Note: P* is in thousands (589.121 thousands).)

**f.** Use the model to predict the average walking speed in New York City, population 8,008,278.

**3. a.** If the average walking speed in a certain city is 5.2 feet per second, write an equation that can be used to estimate the population $P$ of the city.

**b.** Solve the equation using a graphical approach.

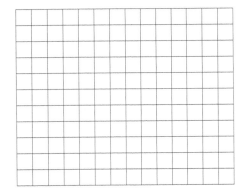

## Comparing the Average Rate of Change of Logarithmic, Linear, and Exponential Functions

**4. a.** Complete the following table using the function defined by $S = 0.303 + 0.868 \ln P$.

| P, POPULATION (thousands) | 10 | 20 | 150 | 250 |
|---|---|---|---|---|
| S, AVERAGE WALKING SPEED (ft./sec.) | | | | |

**b.** Determine the average rate of change of $S$ as the population increases from

    **i.** 10 to 20 thousand

    **ii.** 20 to 150 thousand

    **iii.** 150 to 250 thousand

**c.** What can you say in general about the average rate of change in the walking speed as the population increases?

You should have discovered that the average rate of change in this situation is always positive. This means that the walking speed increases as the population increases. Nevertheless, in general, the increase gets smaller as the population increases. This is characteristic of logarithmic functions.

In general, as the $x$-value of a logarithmic function with $b > 1$ increases, the $y$-value increases at a slower rate (the graph becomes less steep).

**5.** Complete the following statements by describing the rate at which the output values change.

    **a.** For an increasing linear function, as the input variable increases, the output

    ————————————

    **b.** For an increasing exponential function, as the input increases, the output

    ————————————

    **c.** For an increasing logarithmic function, as the input increases, the output

    ————————————

**6.** Consider the graphs of

    **i.** $f(x) = e^x$

    **ii.** $h(x) = x$

    **iii.** $g(x) = \ln x$

using the window Xmin $= -7.5$, Xmax $= 7.5$, Ymin $= -5$, and Ymax $= 5$.

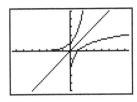

    **a.** Which of the functions are increasing?

    **b.** Which of the functions are decreasing?

    **c.** As the input values get larger, which of the functions grows fastest?

    **d.** As the input values get larger, which of the functions grows most slowly?

    **e.** Do any of these functions have a horizontal asymptote?

    **f.** Do any of these functions have a vertical asymptote?

    **g.** Compare the domains of these functions.

    **h.** Compare the ranges of these functions.

Problem 6 illustrates some of the relationships between $f(x) = b^x$, where $b > 1$, $g(x) = \log_b x$, where $b > 1$, and $y = mx + b$, where $m > 0$.

## Application

    **7.** You are working on the development of an "elastic" ball for the IBF Toy Company. The question you are investigating is, "If the ball is launched straight up, how far has it traveled vertically when it hits the ground for the 10th time?"

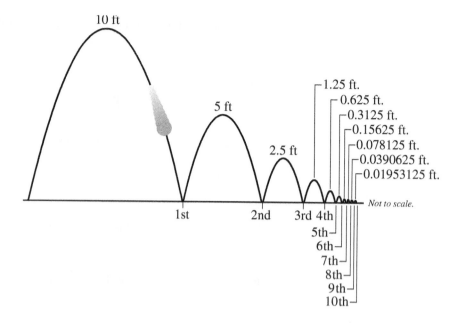

Your launcher will project the ball 10 feet into the air. This means it will travel 20 feet (10 feet up and 10 down) before it hits the ground the first time. Assuming that the ball returns to 50% of its previous height, it will rebound 5 feet and travel 10 feet before it hits the ground again. The following table summarizes this situation.

| N, times the ball hits the ground | 1 | 2 | 3 | 4 | 5 | 6 |
|---|---|---|---|---|---|---|
| Distance traveled since last time (ft.) | 20 | 10 | 5 | 2.5 | 1.25 | 0.625 |
| T, Total distance traveled (ft.) | 20 | 30 | 35 | 37.5 | 38.75 | 39.375 |

a. Using the window Xmin = 0, Xmax = 7, Ymin = 0, and Ymax = 45, a plot of N versus T should resemble the following.

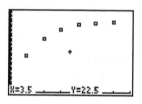

b. Do the table and scatterplot indicate the data is linear, exponential, or logarithmic?

c. Use your graphing calculator to produce linear, exponential, and natural log regression equations for the given data.

**d.** Graph each equation and visually determine which of the regression models best fits the data.

**e.** Use the equation of best fit to predict the total distance traveled by the ball when it hits the ground for the 10th time.

## SUMMARY
### Activity 5.12

**1.** As the input of a logarithmic function increases, the output increases at a slower rate (the graph becomes less steep).

**2.** The relationships among the graphs $f(x) = b^x$, where $b > 1$, $g(x) = \log_b x$, where $b > 1$, and $y = mx + b$, where $m > 0$, are identified in the following table.

| GRAPHS | INCREASING OR DECREASING | GROWTH RATE | HORIZONTAL OR VERTICAL ASYMPTOTE | DOMAIN | RANGE |
|---|---|---|---|---|---|
| $f(x) = b^x$, $b > 1$ | increasing | fastest | horizontal asymptote | all real numbers | $y > 0$ |
| $g(x) = \log_b x$, $b > 1$ | increasing | slowest | vertical asymptote | $x > 0$ | all real numbers |
| $y = mx + b$, $m > 0$ | increasing | constant | none | all real numbers | all real numbers |

## EXERCISES
### Activity 5.12

**1.** The following data from the Centers for Disease Control and Prevention indicates the reported rates, $R$, in rates per 100,000 people from 1985 to 2002 of a certain infectous disease. Let $t$ represent the number of years since 1985.

| YEARS, $t$, SINCE 1985 | 1 | 3 | 5 | 9 | 13 | 15 | 17 |
|---|---|---|---|---|---|---|---|
| REPORTED RATES: U.S. (rate per 100,000 population), $R$ | 40 | 90 | 160 | 200 | 250 | 260 | 288 |

**a.** Plot the points on the following grid.

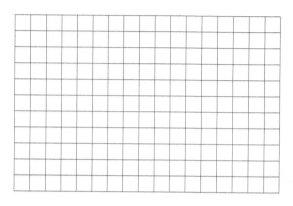

**b.** Does the scatterplot indicate that the data is logarithmic? Explain.

**c.** Determine the natural log regression equation. Record the regression equation below, and add a sketch of the regression curve to the scatterplot in part a.

**d.** Is the graph a good fit of the data?

**e.** Use your model to predict the reported rate of infections per 100,000 people in 2010.

**2. a.** Consider a data set for the variables $x$ and $y$.

| $x$ | 1 | 4 | 7 | 10 | 13 |
|-----|-----|-----|-----|-----|-----|
| $f(x)$ | 3.0 | 4.5 | 5.0 | 5.2 | 5.8 |

Plot these points on the following grid.

**b.** Does the scatterplot indicate the data is more likely linear, exponential, or logarithmic? Explain.

   **c.** Use your graphing calculator to determine a logarithmic regression model that represents this data.

   **d.** Use your model to determine $f(11)$ and $f(20)$.

**3.** The following data was collected during an experiment in science class. The table shows the yield $y$ of a substance (in milligrams) after $x$ minutes of a chemical reaction.

| MINUTES, $x$ | 1 | 2 | 3 | 4 | 5 | 6 | 7 | 8 |
|---|---|---|---|---|---|---|---|---|
| YIELD, $y$ (in milligrams) | 1.5 | 7.4 | 10.2 | 13.4 | 15.8 | 16.3 | 18.2 | 18.3 |

   **a.** Produce a scatterplot of the chemical reaction data.

   **b.** Use the regression feature of a calculator to obtain a natural logarithmic model and a linear model that approximates the data in the table. Graph each equation on the scatterplot in part a.

   **c.** Determine which model best fits the data.

**4.** The barometric pressure, $P$, in inches of mercury at a distance $x$ miles from the eye of a moderate hurricane can be modeled by

$$P = f(x) = 0.48 \ln (x + 1) + 27.$$

   **a.** Determine $f(0)$. What is the practical meaning of the value in this situation?

**b.** Sketch a graph of this function.

**c.** Describe how air pressure changes as you move away from the eye of the hurricane.

5. The formula $R = 80.4 - 11 \ln x$ is used to approximate the minimum required ventilation rate, $R$, as a function of the air space per child in a public school classroom. The rate $R$ is measured in cubic feet per minute, and $x$ is measured in cubic feet.

**a.** Sketch a graph of the rate function for $100 \leq x \leq 1500$.

**b.** Determine the required ventilation rate if the air space per child is 300 cubic feet.

6. You have recently accepted a job working in the coroner's office of a large city. Because of the large numbers of homicides, it has been very difficult for the coroners to complete all of their work. Your job is, in part, to assist them in the paperwork. On one particular day, you are working on a case in which you are attempting to establish the time of death.

The coroner tells you that to establish the time of death, he uses the formula

$$t = 4 \ln \frac{98.6 - T_s}{T_b - T_s},$$

where $t$ is the number of hours the victim has been dead,

$T_b$ represents the temperature of the body when discovered, and

$T_s$ represents the temperature of his surroundings.

The coroner also tells you that the thermostat was set at 68°F in the apartment in which the body was found and that the victim's body temperature was 78°F.

a. Using the preceding formula, determine the number of hours the victim has been deceased. Use your calculator to approximate your answer to one decimal place.

b. If the body was discovered at 10:07 P.M., what do you estimate for the time of death?

7. The following formula can be used to determine the time $t$ it takes for an investment to double or triple in value:

$$t = \frac{\ln m}{n \ln\left(1 + \dfrac{r}{n}\right)},$$

where
- $m$ represents the number of times the investment is to grow in value ($m = 2$ is double, $m = 3$ is triple),
- $r$ is the annual interest rate expressed as a decimal,
- $n$ is the number of corresponding compounding periods per year.

a. How many years will it take an investment to double if you are receiving an annual rate of 5.5% compounded quarterly ($n = 4$)?

b. How many years will it take the investment in part a to triple in value?

c. Suppose the interest on the investment in part a was compounded monthly ($n = 12$). How long will it take the value to double?

## Collecting and Analyzing Data

8. The cost of a gallon of gas has increased dramatically over the past few years. In the spring of 2008, it was speculated that the price of a gallon of regular unleaded gasoline would soon exceed $4.00 per gallon.

Go to the website www.fueleconomy.gov to obtain the average price for one gallon of regular unleaded gasoline in the U.S. in each year from 1986 through 2007.

a. Beginning with 1986, make a scatterplot of the data collected. Let the independent variable represent the average price (in cents) of one gallon of regular unleaded gasoline and the dependent variable represent the number of years since 1986. Describe any patterns you observe.

b. Determine a logarithmic regression equation for the data.

c. How well does the logarithmic model in part b fit the date? Explain.

d. Predict the year in which the average price of one gallon of regular unleaded gasoline will reach $4.00 per gallon.

e. How reliable is this prediction? Explain.

**ACTIVITY 5.13**
The Elastic Ball

**OBJECTIVES**

1. Apply the log of a product property.
2. Apply the log of a quotient property.
3. Apply the log of a power property.
4. Discover change of base formula.

You are continuing your work on the development of the elastic ball. You are still investigating the question, "If the ball is launched straight up, how far has it traveled vertically when it hits the ground for the 10th time?" However, your supervisor tells you that you cannot count the initial launch distance. You must calculate only the rebound distance.

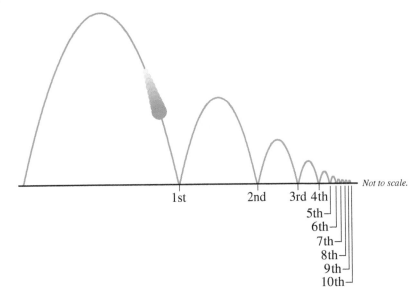

Using some physical properties, timers, and your calculator, you collect the following data.

| N, NUMBER OF TIMES THE BALL HITS THE GROUND | 1 | 2 | 3 | 4 | 5 | 6 |
|---|---|---|---|---|---|---|
| T, TOTAL REBOUND DISTANCE (ft.) | 0 | 9.0 | 13.5 | 16.3 | 18.7 | 21.0 |

1. Does the data seem reasonable? Explain.

2. Use your graphing calculator to construct a scatterplot of the data with N as the input and T as the output. Using a window of Xmin = 0, Xmax = 7, Ymin = 0, and Ymax = 25, your graph should resemble the following.

3. Do you believe the data can be modeled by a logarithmic function? Explain.

**4.** This data can be modeled by $T = 26.75 \log N$. Use a graphing calculator to verify visually that this is a reasonable model for the given data.

**5. a.** Using the log model, complete the following table. Round values to the nearest hundredth.

| N | 2 | 5 | 10 |
|---|---|---|---|
| T = 26.75 log N | | | |

**b.** What is the sum of the $T$-values for $N = 2$ and $N = 5$? How is that related to the $T$-value for $N = 10$?

**c.** Using the results from part b, how could you determine the total rebound distance after 10 bounces?

The results from Problem 5 can be written as follows.

$$\underbrace{26.75}_{} \quad = \quad \underbrace{8.05}_{} \quad + \quad \underbrace{18.70}_{}$$

$$26.75 \log 10 \quad = \quad 26.75 \log 2 \quad + \quad 26.75 \log 5$$
$$26.75 \log (2 \cdot 5) \quad = \quad 26.75 \log 2 \quad + \quad 26.75 \log 5$$

Dividing both sides by 26.75, you have

$$\log (2 \cdot 5) = \log 2 + \log 5.$$

This result illustrates an important property of logarithms.

**Property of the Logarithm of a Product**

If $A > 0, B > 0$, then $\log_b (A \cdot B) = \log_b A + \log_b B$, where $b > 0, b \neq 1$.

Expressed verbally, this property states that the logarithm of a product is the sum of the individual logarithms.

Example 1

**a.** $\log_2 32 = \log_2 (4 \cdot 8) = \log_2 4 + \log_2 8 = 2 + 3 = 5.$

**b.** $\log (5st) = \log (5) + \log (s) + \log (t)$

**c.** $\ln (xy) = \ln x + \ln y$

**6.** Use the property of the logarithm of a product to write the following as the sum of two or more logarithms.

**a.** $\log_b (7 \cdot 13)$  **b.** $\log_3 (xyz)$

**c.** log 15

**d.** ln $(3xy)$

**7.** Write the following as the logarithm of a single expression.

**a.** $\ln a + \ln b + \ln c$

**b.** $\log_4 3 + \log_4 9$

## Logarithm of a Quotient

Consider the following table from Problem 5.

| N | 2 | 5 | 10 |
|---|---|---|---|
| T = 26.75 log N | 8.05 | 18.70 | 26.75 |

This table also indicates that the rebound distance after this ball has hit the floor twice (8.05 ft.) is the total rebound distance when the ball has hit the ground 10 times (26.75 ft.) minus the total rebound distance when the ball has hit the ground 5 times (18.70 ft.).

This can be written as

$$
\begin{array}{ccccc}
8.05 & = & 26.75 & - & 18.70 \\
26.75 \log 2 & = & 26.75 \log 10 & - & 26.75 \log 5 \\
\log 2 & = & \log 10 & - & \log 5.
\end{array}
$$

Substituting $\log \left(\frac{10}{5}\right)$ for log 2, you have

$$\log \left(\tfrac{10}{5}\right) = \log 10 - \log 5.$$

This suggests another important property of logarithms. The property is demonstrated further in Problem 8.

**8. a.** Complete the following table. Round your answers to the nearest thousandth.

| x | Y1 = log($\frac{x}{4}$) | Y2 = log x − log 4 |
|---|---|---|
| 1 | | |
| 5 | | |
| 10 | | |
| 23 | | |

**b.** Is the expression $\log \left(\frac{x}{4}\right)$ equivalent to log x − log 4? Explain.

**c.** Sketch the graph of $y = \log \left(\frac{x}{4}\right)$ and $y = \log x - \log 4$ using a graphing calculator. What do the graphs suggest about the relationship between $\log \left(\frac{x}{4}\right)$ and log x − log 4?

**Property of the Logarithm of a Quotient**

If $A > 0, B > 0$, then $\log_b\left(\frac{A}{B}\right) = \log_b A - \log_b B$, where $b > 0, b \neq 1$.

Expressed verbally, this property states that the logarithm of a quotient is the difference of the logarithm of the numerator and the logarithm of the denominator.

Example 2

a. $\log_3\left(\frac{81}{27}\right) = \log_3 81 - \log_3 27 = 4 - 3 = 1$

   Note that $\log_3\left(\frac{81}{27}\right) = \log_3(3) = 1$.

b. $\log\left(\frac{2x}{y}\right) = \log(2x) - \log(y) = \log 2 + \log x - \log y$

c. $\ln\left(\frac{x^2}{5}\right) = \ln(x^2) - \ln(5)$

9. Use the properties of logarithms to write the following as the sum or difference of logarithms.

   a. $\log_6 \frac{17}{3}$
   
   b. $\ln \frac{x}{23}$
   
   c. $\log_3 \frac{2x}{y}$
   
   d. $\log \frac{3}{2z}$

10. Write the following expressions as the logarithm of a single expression.

    a. $\log x - \log 4 + \log z$
    
    b. $\log x - (\log 4 + \log z)$

11. a. Use a graphing calculator to sketch the graphs of $y = \log x + \log 4$ and $y = \log(x + 4)$.

    b. How do these graphs compare?

    c. What do the graphs suggest about the relationship between $\log(A + B)$ and $\log A + \log B$?

## Logarithm of a Power

Before calculators, logarithms were used to help in computing products and quotients of numbers. More importantly, logarithms were used to compute powers such as $734.21^3$ and $\sqrt{0.0761} = (0.0761)^{1/2}$. In such a case, the first step was to take the logarithm of the power and rewrite the resulting expression. To determine how to rewrite $\log 734.21^3$, you can investigate the expression $\log x^3$.

**12. a.** Complete the following table. Round to the nearest thousandth.

| x | Y1 = log x³ | Y2 = 3 log x |
|---|---|---|
| 2 | | |
| 7 | | |
| 15 | | |

**b.** Sketch the graphs of $y = \log x^3$ and $y = 3 \log x$ using your graphing calculator.

**c.** What do the results of part a and part b demonstrate about the relationship between $\log x^3$ and $3 \log x$?

The results in Problem 12 illustrate another property of logarithms.

**Property of the Logarithm of a Power**

If $A > 0$ and $p$ is any real number, then $\log_b A^p = p \cdot \log_b A$, where $b > 0, b \neq 1$. In words, the property states that the logarithm of a power is equivalent to the exponent times the logarithm of the base.

Example 3

**a.** $\log_3 9^2 = 2 \log_3 9 = 2 \cdot 2 = 4$

**b.** $\log_5 x^4 = 4 \log_5 x$

**c.** $\ln (xy)^7 = 7 \ln (xy)$

**d.** $\ln x^{1/4} = \frac{1}{4} \ln x$

**e.** $\log \sqrt{63} = \log 63^{1/2} = \frac{1}{2} \log 63$

**13.** Use the properties of logarithms to write the given logarithms as the sum or difference of two or more logarithms, or as the product of a real number and a logarithm. All variables represent positive numbers.

**a.** $\log_3 x^{1/2}$

**b.** $\log_5 x^3$

**c.** $\ln t^2$

**d.** $\log \sqrt[3]{50}$  (*Hint:* $\sqrt[3]{50} = 50^{1/3}$)

    **e.** $\log_5 \frac{x^2 y^3}{z}$                                    **f.** $\log_3 \frac{3x^2}{y^3}$

**14.** Write each of the following as the logarithm of a single expression with coefficient 1.

    **a.** $2 \log_3 5 + 3 \log_3 2$                   **b.** $\frac{1}{2} \log x^4 - \frac{1}{2} \log y^5$

    **c.** $3 \log_b 10 - 4 \log_b 5 + 2 \log_b 3$     **d.** $3 \ln 4 - (4 \ln 5 + 2 \ln 3)$

Using the properties of logarithms to solve exponential equations algebraically will be investigated in the next activity.

## Change of Base Formula

Because most graphing calculators only have the log base 10 (log) and the log base $e$ (ln) keys, you cannot graph a logarithmic function such as $y = \log_2 x$ directly. Consider the following argument to rewrite the expression $\log_2 x$ as an equivalent expression using log base 10.

By definition of logs, $y = \log_2 x$ is the same as $x = 2^y$. Taking the log base 10 of both sides of the second equation, $x = 2^y$, you have

$$\log x = \log 2^y.$$

Using the property of the log of a power, $\log x = y \log 2$. Solving for $y$, you have

$$y = \frac{\log x}{\log 2}.$$

Therefore, the equation $y = \log_2 x$ is equivalent to $y = \frac{\log x}{\log 2}$.

**15.** To graph $y = \log_2 x$, enter $\log(X) / \log(2)$ for Y1 in your graphing calculator. Your graph should resemble the following.

**16. a.** Write $y = \log_6 x$ as an equivalent equation using base 10.

    **b.** Use the result from part a to graph $y = \log_6 x$.

**c.** What is the domain of the function?

**d.** What is the $x$-intercept of the graph?

The formula you used in Problems 15 and 16 for graphing log functions of different bases is a special case of the formula

$$\log_b x = \frac{\log_a x}{\log_a b}, \text{ where } a > 0, \neq 1$$

This is often called the **change of base formula**, where $b > 0$ and $b \neq 1$.

The change of base formula is used to change from base $b$ to base $a$. Because most calculators have log base 10 (log) and log base $e$ (ln) keys, you usually convert to one of those bases. For those bases,

$$\log_b x = \frac{\log x}{\log b} \text{ or } \log_b x = \frac{\ln x}{\ln b}.$$

Example 4    *Change the equation $y = \log_5 x$ to an equivalent equation in base 10 and/or base e.*

$$y = \log_5 x = \frac{\log x}{\log 5} \text{ or } y = \log_5 x = \frac{\ln x}{\ln 5}$$

**17.** Use each of the change of base formulas to determine $\log_4 1024$.

    **a.** Using base 10:                 **b.** Using base $e$

    **c.** How do the results in parts a and b compare?

## SUMMARY
### Activity 5.13

**Properties of the Logarithmic Function**

If $A > 0, B > 0, b > 0$, and $b \neq 1$, then

**1.** $\log_b (A \cdot B) = \log_b A + \log_b B$

**2.** $\log_b \left(\dfrac{A}{B}\right) = \log_b A - \log_b B$

**3.** $\log_b (x + y) \neq \log_b x + \log_b y$

**4.** $\log_b A^p = p \log_b A$

**5.** You can use the calculator to change logarithms in base $b$ to common or natural logarithms by

$$\log_b x = \frac{\log x}{\log b} \text{ or } \log_b x = \frac{\ln x}{\ln b}.$$

1. Use the preceding properties of logarithms to write the following as a sum or difference of two or more logarithms.

   **a.** $\log_b (3 \cdot 7)$

   **b.** $\log_3 (3 \cdot 13)$

   **c.** $\log_7 \frac{13}{17}$

   **d.** $\log_3 \frac{xy}{3}$

2. Write the following expressions as the logarithm of a single number.

   **a.** $\log_3 5 + \log_3 3$

   **b.** $\log 25 - \log 17$

   **c.** $\log_5 x - \log_5 5 + \log_5 7$

   **d.** $\ln (x + 7) - \ln x$

3. **a.** Sketch the graphs of $y = \log (2x)$ and $y = \log x + \log 2$ on your graphing calculator.

   **b.** Are you surprised by the results? Explain.

4. **a.** Sketch the graphs of $y = \log \left(\frac{3}{x}\right)$ and $y = \log x - \log 3$ on your graphing calculator.

   **b.** Are you surprised by your results? Explain.

   **c.** If your graphs in part a are not identical, can you modify the second function to make the graphs identical? Explain.

5. You have been hired to handle the local newspaper advertising for a large used car dealership in your community. The owner tells you that your predecessor in this position used the formula

$$N(A) = 7.4 \log A$$

to decide how much to spend on newspaper advertising over a 2-week period. The owner admitted that he didn't know much about the formula except that $N(A)$ represented the number of cars that the owner could expect to sell, and $A$ was the amount of money that was spent on local newspaper advertising. He also indicated that the formula seemed to work well. You can purchase small ads in the local paper for $15 per day, larger ads for $50 per day, and giant ads for $750 per day.

a. How many cars do you expect to sell if you purchase one small ad?

b. To understand the relationship between the amount spent on advertising and the number of cars sold, you set up a table. Complete the following table.

| AD COST, A | EXPECTED CAR SALES, N(A) |
|---|---|
| 15 | |
| 50 | |
| 750 | |

c. How do the expected car sales from one small ad and one larger ad compare to the expected car sales from just one giant ad?

d. Are the results in the previous table above consistent with what you know about the properties of logarithms? Explain.

e. What are you going to advise the owner regarding the purchase of a giant ad?

6. Use the properties of logarithms to write the given logarithms as the sum or difference of two or more logarithms or as the product of a real number and a logarithm. Simplify, if possible. All variables represent positive numbers.

a. $\log_3 3^5$

b. $\log_2 2^x$

**c.** $\log_b \dfrac{x^3}{y^4}$

**d.** $\ln \dfrac{\sqrt[3]{x}\sqrt[4]{y}}{z^2}$

**e.** $\log_3 (2x + y)$

7. Write each of the following as the logarithm of a single expression with coefficient 1.

  **a.** $2\log_2 7 + \log_2 5$

  **b.** $\frac{1}{4}\log x^3 - \frac{1}{4}\log z^5$

  **c.** $2\ln 10 - 3\ln 5 + 4\ln z$

  **d.** $\log_5 (x + 2) + \log_5 (x + 1) - 2\log_5 (x + 3)$

8. Given that $\log_a x = 6$ and that $\log_a y = 25$, determine the numeric value of each of the following.

  **a.** $\log_a \sqrt{y}$

  **b.** $\log_a x^3$

  **c.** $3 + \log_a x^2$

  **d.** $\log_a \dfrac{x^2 y}{a}$

9. Use the change of base formula and your calculator to determine a decimal approximation of each of the following to the nearest ten thousandth.

  **a.** $\log_7 5$

  **b.** $\log_6 \sqrt{15}$

  **c.** $\log_{13} 47$

  **d.** $\log_5 \sqrt[3]{31}$

10. The formula

$$P = f(t) = 95 - 30\log_2 t$$

gives the percentage, $P$, of students who could recall the important content of a class-room presentation as a function of time, $t$, where $t$ is the number of days that have passed since the presentation was given.

**a.** Sketch a graph of the function.

**b.** After 3 days, what percentage of the students will remember the important content of the presentation?

**c.** According to the model, after how many days do only half $(P = 50)$ of the students remember the important features of the presentation? Use a graphing approach.

**ACTIVITY 5.14**

Prison Growth

**OBJECTIVE**

1. Solve exponential equations both graphically and algebraically.

Your sister is a criminal justice major at the local community college. The following statistics appeared in one of her required readings relating to the inmate population of U.S. federal prisons.

| YEAR | 1975 | 1979 | 1986 | 1990 | 1994 | 1998 | 2000 | 2003 |
|---|---|---|---|---|---|---|---|---|
| TOTAL SENTENCED POPULATION, $P_T$ (in thousands) | 20.1 | 21.5 | 31.8 | 47.8 | 76.2 | 95.5 | 112.3 | 158.0 |

She asks you to help analyze the prison growth situation for a project in her criminology course.

1. Although the years in the table are not evenly spaced, you notice that each of the populations seems to grow rather slowly at first and more quickly later. Do you think the data will be better modeled by linear or exponential functions?

2. Let $t$ represent the number of years since 1970. Use a graphing calculator to produce a scatterplot of the total inmate population, $P$. Your screen should appear as follows.

3. Use a graphing calculator to determine the regression equation of an exponential function that best represents the total inmate population, $P$. Remember that the input variable is $t$, the number of years since 1970. In your regression equation, $P = ab^t$, round the value for $a$ to two decimal places and the value for $b$ to three decimal places. Write your model below.

4. Use a graphing calculator to visually check how well the equation in Problem 3 fits the data. Using the window Xmin $= -3$, Xmax $= 40$, Ymin $= -5$, and Ymax $= 200$, your graph should resemble the following.

5. Use the exponential regression model from Problem 3 to determine the total federal prison inmate population in 2010.

**6. a.** Using your model from Problem 3, write an equation that can be used to determine the year in which the total federal inmate population, $P$, is 180,000. Remember, the population in the model is given in thousands.

**b.** Solve the equation in part a using a graphing approach. Your screen should resemble the following. What is the equation of the horizontal line in the graph?

To solve the equation $11.36(1.080)^t = 180$ for $t$ using an algebraic approach, you need to remove $t$ as an exponent. The following problem guides you through this process. As you will discover, logarithms are essential in this algebraic approach.

**7.** Solve $11.36(1.086)^t = 180$ for $t$ using an algebraic approach.

**a.** Isolate the exponential factor $(1.080)^t$ on one side of the equation.

**b.** Take the log (or ln) of each side of the equation in part a.

**c.** Apply the appropriate property of logarithms on the left side of the equation to remove $t$ as an exponent.

**d.** Solve the resulting equation in part c for $t$.

**e.** How does your solution in part d compare to the estimate obtained graphically in Problem 6b?

## Radioactive Decay

Radioactive substances, such as uranium-235, strontium-90, iodine-131, and carbon-14, decay continuously with time. If $P_0$ represents the original amount of a radioactive substance, then the amount $P$ present after a time $t$ (usually measured in years) is modeled by

$$P = P_0 e^{kt},$$

where $k$ represents the rate of continuous decay.

Example 1   *One type of uranium decays at a rate of 0.35% per day. If 40 pounds of this uranium is available today, how much will be available after 90 days?*

SOLUTION

The uranium decays at a constant rate of $0.35\% = 0.0035$ per day. The initial amount, the amount available on the first day, is 40 pounds, so the equation for the amount available after $t$ days is

$$P = 40e^{-0.0035t}.$$

To determine the amount available after 90 days, let $t = 90$. The amount available 90 days from now is

$$P = 40e^{-.0035(90)} = 29.2 \text{ lb.}$$

8. Strontium-90 decays continuously at a constant rate of 2.4% per year. Therefore, the equation for the amount $P$ of strontium-90 after $t$ years is

$$P = P_0 e^{-0.024t}.$$

   a. If 10 grams of strontium-90 are present initially, determine the number of grams present after 20 years.

   b. How long will it take for the given quantity to decay to 2 grams?

   c. How long would it take for the given amount of strontium-90 to decay to one-half of its original size (called its half-life)? Round to the nearest whole number.

   d. Do you think that the half-life of strontium-90 is 29 years regardless of the initial amount? Answer part c using $P_0$ as the initial amount. (*Hint:* Find $t$ when $P = \frac{1}{2}P_0$.)

**SUMMARY**
Activity 5.14

To solve exponential equations of the form $ab^x = c$, where $a > 0, b > 0, b \neq 1$, and $c > 0$:

1. Isolate the exponential factor on one side of the equation.

2. Take the log (or ln) of each side of the equation.

3. Apply the property $\log b^x = x \log b$ to remove the variable $x$ as an exponent.

4. Solve the resulting equation for the variable.

**EXERCISES**
Activity 5.14

1. The number of arrests for a certain crime in New York City has increased dramatically. The number of arrests can be modeled by

$$N(t) = 0.37(1.77)^t,$$

where $N(t)$ represents the number of arrests in thousands and $t$ represents the number of years since 1990.

a. How many arrests were made in 2000?

b. According to the model, in what year were there 50,000 arrests?

2. The U.S. Department of Transportation recommended that states adopt a 0.08% blood-alcohol concentration as the legal measure of drunk driving. Medical research has shown that as the concentration of alcohol in the blood increases, the risk of having a car accident increases exponentially. The risk, $R$, expressed as a percentage, is modeled by

$$R(x) = 6e^{12.77x},$$

where $x$ is the blood-alcohol concentration, expressed as a percent.

a. What is the risk of having a car accident if your blood-alcohol concentration is 0.08% ($x = 0.08$)?

b. What blood-alcohol concentration has a corresponding 25% risk of a car accident?

**3.** In 1990, the International Panel on Climate Change projected the following future amounts of carbon dioxide (in parts per million or ppm) in the atmosphere.

| YEAR | 1990 | 2000 | 2075 | 2175 | 2275 |
|---|---|---|---|---|---|
| AMOUNT OF CARBON DIOXIDE (ppm) | 353 | 375 | 590 | 1090 | 2000 |

**a.** Use a graphing calculator to create a scatterplot of the data. Let $t$ represent the number of years since 1990 and $A(t)$ represent the amount of carbon dioxide (in ppm) in the atmosphere. Do the carbon dioxide levels appear to be growing exponentially?

**b.** Use a graphing calculator to determine the regression equation of an exponential model that best fits the data.

**c.** Use the model in part b to determine in what year the 1990 carbon dioxide level is expected to double.

**d.** Verify your result in part c graphically.

*In Exercises 4–9, solve each equation using an algebraic approach. Verify your answers graphically.*

**4.** $2^x = 14$

**5.** $3^{2x} = 8$

**6.** $1000 = 500(1.04)^t$

**7.** $e^{0.05t} = 2$ (*Hint:* Take the natural log of both sides.)

**8.** $2^{3x+1} = 100$

**9.** $e^{-0.3t} = 2$

**10. a.** Iodine-131 disintegrates at a continuous constant rate of 8.6% per day. Determine its half-life. Use the model

$$P = P_0 e^{-0.086t},$$

where $t$ is measured in days. Round your answer to the nearest whole number.

**b.** If dairy cows eat hay containing too much iodine-131, their milk will be unsafe to drink. Suppose that hay contains 5 times the safe level of iodine-131. How many days should the hay be stored before it can be fed to dairy cows?
(*Hint:* Find $t$ when $P = \frac{1}{5}P_0$.)

**11. a.** In 1969 a report written by the National Academy of Sciences (U.S.) estimated that Earth could reasonably support a maximum world population of 10 billion. The world's population was approximately 3.6 billion and growing continuously at 2% per year. If this growth rate remained constant, in what year would the world population reach 10 billion, referred to as Earth's carrying capacity? Use the model

$$P = P_0 e^{kt},$$

where $P$ is the population (in billions), $P_0 = 3.6$, $k = 0.02$, and $t$ is the number of years since 1969.

**b.** According to your growth model, when would this 1969 population double?

**c.** The world population in 1995 was approximately 5.7 billion. How does this compare with the population predicted by your growth model in part a?

**d.** The growth rate in 1995 was 1.5%. Assuming this growth rate remains constant, determine when Earth's carrying capacity will be reached. Use the model $P = P_0 e^{kt}$.

## Collecting and Analyzing Data

**12.** The combined populations of China and India currently represent 38% of the world's population. Go to the United Nations' Population Database website http://esa.un.org/unpp to obtain the population of each country for every five years from 1960 to 2005.

**a.** Beginning with 1960, make a scatterplot of the data from each country's population. Let the independent variable represent the number of years since 1960 and the dependent variable represent the population of the country in billions. Describe any patterns you observe.

**b.** Determine whether a linear, exponential, or logarithmic function best fits each set of data. Explain.

**c.** Determine a regression equation for each set of population data. Which country has the larger rate of increase in population?

**d.** Sketch the graph of each regression equation on the appropriate scatterplot in part a.

**e.** Predict the population of each country in 2010.

**f.** Determine the year in which the population of each country should reach 1.5 billion.

**g.** Use the intersect feature of a graphing calculator to estimate the year when the populations of China and India will be equal.

**ACTIVITY 5.15**

Frequency and Pitch

**OBJECTIVE**

1. Solve logarithmic equations both graphically and algebraically.

Raising a musical note one octave has the effect of doubling the pitch, or frequency, of the sound. However, you do not perceive the note to sound "twice as high," as you might predict. Perceived pitch is given by the function

$$P(f) = 2410 \log (0.0016f + 1),$$

where $P$ is the perceived pitch in mels (units of pitch) and $f$ is the frequency in hertz.

1. Let frequency (input) vary in value from 10 to 100,000 hertz, and let the perceived pitch (output) vary from 0 to 6000 mels. Graph this equation on your graphing calculator, using the following window: Xmin = 0, Xmax = 100,000, Ymin = 0, and Ymax = 6000.

2. What is the perceived pitch, $P$, for the input value 10,000 hertz?

3. a. Write an equation that can be used to determine what frequency, $f$, gives an output value of 2000 mels.

   b. Solve the equation in part a using a graphing approach.

To determine the exact answer in Problem 3, you can use an algebraic approach. The following problem guides you through this process.

4. Solve the equation $2410 \log (0.0016f + 1) = 2000$ using an algebraic approach.

   a. Solve the equation for $\log (0.0016f + 1)$. That is, isolate the log on one side of the equation.

   b. The equation in part a is now in the form $\log_b N = E$, where $b = 10$, $N = 0.0016x + 1$, and $E = \frac{2000}{2410}$. Write the equation from part a in exponential form, $b^E = N$.

**c.** In exponential form, the equation in part a should be

$$0.0016f + 1 = 10^{2000/2410}.$$

Solve this equation for $f$. Of course, you will need to approximate a value of $10^{2000/2410}$ using your calculator.

**d.** How does your answer to part c compare to your answer to Problem 3b?

**5. a.** Use an algebraic approach to determine the frequency, $f$, that produces a perceived pitch of 3000 mels.

**b.** Verify your answer in part a using a graphing approach.

**6.** The formula $W = 0.35 \ln P + 2.74$ is a model for the average walking speed, $W$, in feet per second for a resident of a city with population $P$, measured in thousands.

**a.** Determine the walking speed of a resident of a small city having a population of 500,000.

**b.** If the average walking speed of a resident is 4.5 feet per second, what is the population of the city? Round your answer to the nearest thousand.

**SUMMARY**
**Activity 5.15**

**To solve a logarithmic equation algebraically,**

**Step 1.** Rewrite the equation in the form $\log_b (f(x)) = c$, where $b > 0$, $b \neq 1$, $c > 0$, and $f(x) > 0$.

**Step 2.** Rewrite the resulting equation from step 1 in exponential form, $f(x) = b^c$.

**Step 3.** Solve the resulting equation from step 2 algebraically.

**Step 4.** Check the solutions in the original equation.

*In Exercises 1–6, solve each equation using an algebraic approach. Then verify your answer using a graphical approach.*

**1.** $\log_2 x = 5$

**2.** $\ln x = 10$

**3.** $3 \log_5 (x + 2) = 5$

**4.** $\log_5 (x - 4) = 2$

**5.** $20 = 3.5 \ln x$

**6.** $4 + 1.75 \ln x = 31$

**7.** Stars have been classified into magnitude according to their brightness. Stars in the first six magnitudes are visible to the naked eye; those of higher magnitudes are visible only through a telescope. The magnitude, $m$, of the faintest star that is visible with a telescope having lens diameter $d$, in inches, is modeled by

$$m = 8.8 + 5.1 \log d.$$

What is the highest magnitude of a star that is visible with the 200-inch telescope at Mount Palomar, California?

**8.** Coal consumption in the United States can be modeled by the equation

$$A(x) = 4.95 + 4.67 \ln x,$$

where $x$ is the number of years since 1970, and $A(x)$ is the amount of coal consumed in quadrillions of British thermal units or quads. According to the model, in what year will the consumption of coal in the United States reach 30 quads?

**9.** The acidity or alkalinity of any solution is determined by the concentration of hydrogen ions, $[H^+]$, in the substance, measured in moles per liter (mol/l). Acidity (or alkalinity) is measured on a pH scale, using the model

$$pH = -\log [H^+].$$

The pH scale ranges from 0 to 14. Values below 7 have progressively greater acidity; values greater than 7 are progressively more alkaline. Normal unpolluted rain has a pH of about 5.6. The acidity of rain over the northeastern United States, caused primarily by sulfur dioxide emissions, has had very damaging effects. One of the most acidic rainfalls on record had a pH of 2.4. What was the concentration of hydrogen ions?

10. The Richter scale is a well-known method of measuring the magnitude of an earthquake in terms of the amplitude, $A$ (height), of its shock waves. The magnitude of any given earthquake is given by

$$m = \log\left(\frac{A}{A_0}\right),$$

where $A_0$ is a constant representing the amplitude of an average earthquake.

a. The magnitude of the 1906 San Francisco earthquake was 8.3 on the Richter scale. Write an equation that gives the amplitude, $A$, of the San Francisco earthquake in terms of $A_0$.

b. An earthquake with a magnitude of 5.5 will begin to cause serious damage. Write an equation that gives the amplitude, $A$, of a serious-damage earthquake in terms of $A_0$.

c. Determine the ratio of the amplitude of the San Francisco earthquake to the amplitude of a serious-damage (magnitude 5.5) earthquake. What is the significance of this number?

## Activities 5.10–5.15   What Have I Learned?

1. A logarithm is an exponent. Explain how this fact relates to the following properties of logarithms.

   a. $\log_b (x \cdot y) = \log_b x + \log_b y$

   b. $\log_b \frac{x}{y} = \log_b x - \log_b y$

   c. $\log_b x^n = n \cdot \log_b x$

2. You have $20,000 to invest. Your broker tells you that the value of shares of mutual fund A has been growing exponentially for the past 2 years and that shares of mutual fund B have been growing logarithmically over the same period. If you make your decision based solely on the past performances of the funds, in which fund would you choose to invest? Explain.

3. Study the following graphs showing various types of functions you have encountered in this course.

   a.

   b.

   c.

   d.

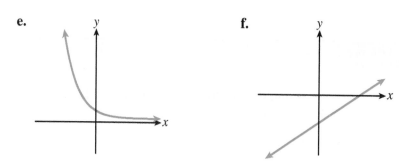

*Complete the following table with respect to the preceding graphs.*

| DESCRIPTION | GRAPH LETTER | GENERAL EQUATION |
|---|---|---|
| Constant function | | |
| Linearly decreasing function | | |
| Logarithmically increasing function | | |
| Exponentially decreasing function | | |
| Exponentially increasing function | | |
| Linearly increasing function | | |

4. The graph of $y = \log_b x$ will never be located in the second or third quadrants. Explain.

5. What function would you enter into Y1 on your graphing calculator to graph the function $y = \log_4 x$?

6. What values of $x$ cannot be inputs in the function $y = \log_b (3x - 2)$?

7. What is the relationship between the functions $y = \log x$ and $y = 10^x$? How are the graphs related?

**Activities 5.10–5.15**   How Can I Practice?

1. Write each equation in logarithmic form.

   **a.** $4^2 = 16$          **b.** $0.0001 = 10^{-4}$          **c.** $3^{-4} = \frac{1}{81}$

2. Write each equation in exponential form.

   **a.** $\log_2 32 = 5$          **b.** $\log_5 1 = 0$

   **c.** $\log_{10} 0.001 = -3$          **d.** $\ln e = 1$

3. Solve each equation for the unknown variable.

   **a.** $\log_4 x = -3$          **b.** $\log_b 32 = 5$          **c.** $\log_5 125 = y$

4. **a.** Complete the table of values for the function $f(x) = \log_4 x$.

| $x$ | 0.25 | 0.5 | 1 | 4 | 16 | 64 |
|---|---|---|---|---|---|---|
| $f(x)$ | | | | | | |

   **b.** Sketch a graph of the function, $f$.

   **c.** Use a graphing calculator to check your result in parts a and b.

   **d.** Determine the $x$-intercept.

   **e.** What is the domain of the function?

   **f.** What is the range?

   **g.** Is the function increasing or decreasing?

   **h.** Does the graph have a vertical or horizontal asymptote?

   **i.** Use your graphing calculator to determine $f(32)$.

   **j.** Use your graphing calculator to determine $x$ when $f(x) = 3.25$.

5. Write each of the following as a sum, difference, or multiple of logarithms. Assume that $x$, $y$, and $z$ are all greater than 0.

   **a.** $\log_b \frac{xy^2}{z}$

   **b.** $\log_3 \frac{\sqrt{x^3 y}}{z}$

   **c.** $\log_5 \left( x\sqrt{x^2 + 4} \right)$

   **d.** $\log_4 \sqrt[3]{\frac{xy^2}{z^2}}$

6. Rewrite the following as the logarithm of a single quantity.

   **a.** $\log x + \frac{1}{3}\log y - \frac{1}{2}\log z$

   **b.** $3 \log_3 (x + 3) + 2 \log_3 z$

   **c.** $\frac{1}{3}\log_3 x - \frac{2}{3}\log_3 y - \frac{4}{3}\log_3 z$

7. Use the change of base formula and your calculator to approximate the following.

   **a.** $\log_5 17$

   **b.** $\log_{13} \sqrt[3]{41}$

8. Solve each of the following using an algebraic approach.

   **a.** $25 + 3 \ln x = 10$

   **b.** $1.5 \log_4 (x - 1) = 7$

**9.** Solve the following algebraically. Check your solutions using graphs or tables.

   **a.** $3^x = 17$

   **b.** $42 = 3e^{1.7x}$

**10.** The following table shows per capita health care expenditures (in dollars) in the United States from 1988 to 1993.

| YEAR | 1988 | 1989 | 1990 | 1991 | 1992 | 1993 |
|---|---|---|---|---|---|---|
| EXPENDITURE ($) | 2201 | 2422 | 2688 | 2902 | 3144 | 3331 |

   **a.** Plot these points on the following grid.

   **b.** The logarithmic model that fits this data is $y = f(x) = 2090 + 630 \ln x$, where $y$ represents the per capita health care expenditures and $x$ is the number of years since 1987. Add a sketch of this model to the grid in part a.

   **c.** Use this model to predict the per capita health care expenditures in 2005.

   **d.** Use the model in part c to predict in what year health care expenditures will reach $3500. Use a graphing approach.

   **e.** Write the equation that you would solve to determine the answer to part d.

   **f.** Solve the equation in part e algebraically, and compare your result with your answer in part d.

**11.** Sketch a graph of each of the following equations. Using transformations, describe how the graph is related to either the graph of $y = \ln x$ or the graph of $y = \log x$.

**a.** $y = 3 \ln x$

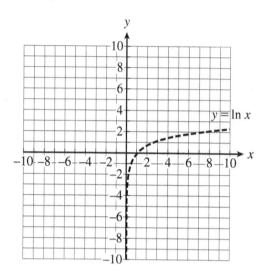

**b.** $y = 4 + 2 \log x$

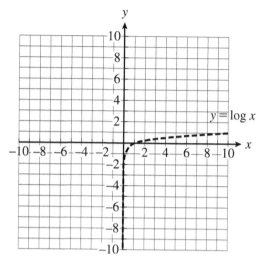

**c.** $y = -0.25 \ln x$

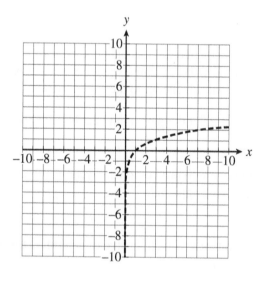

**d.** $y = 4.5 + 1.5 \ln x$

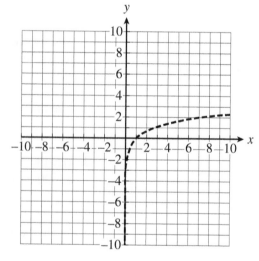

**e.** $y = 3 \log (x + 5)$

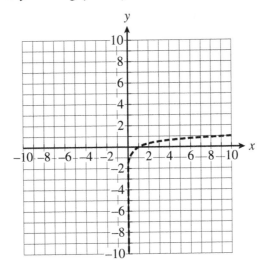

# Summary

*The bracketed numbers following each concept indicate the activity in which the concept is discussed.*

| CONCEPT / SKILL | DESCRIPTION | EXAMPLE |
|---|---|---|
| **Growth factor** [5.1] | When a quantity increases by a specified percent, the ratio of its new value to the original value is called the growth factor associated with the specified percent increase.<br><br>The growth factor is formed by adding the specified percent increase to 100% and then changing this percent into its decimal form. | To determine the growth factor associated with a 25% increase, add 25% to 100% to obtain 125%. Change 125% into a decimal to obtain the growth factor 1.25. |
| **Applying a growth factor to an original value** [5.1] | original value $\times$ growth factor = new value | A \$120 item increases by 25%. Its new value is \$120 $\times$ 1.25 = \$150. |
| **Applying a growth factor to a new value** [5.1] | new value $\div$ growth factor = original value | An item has already increased by 25% and is now worth \$200. Its original value was \$200 $\div$ 1.25 = \$160. |
| **Decay factor** [5.1] | When a quantity decreases by a specified percent, the ratio of its new value to the original value is called the *decay factor* associated with the specified percent decrease.<br><br>The decay factor is formed by subtracting the specified percent decrease from 100%, and then changing this percent into its decimal form. | To determine the decay factor associated with a 25% decrease, subtract 25% from 100%, to obtain 75%.<br><br>Change 75% into a decimal to obtain the decay factor 0.75. |
| **Applying a decay factor to an original value** [5.1] | original value $\cdot$ decay factor = new value | A \$120 item decreases by 25%. Its new value is \$120 $\times$ 0.75 = \$90. |
| **Applying a decay factor to a new value** [5.1] | new value $\div$ decay factor = original value | An item has already decreased by 25% and is now worth \$180. Its original value was \$180 $\div$ 0.75 = \$240. |
| **Applying a sequence of percent changes** [5.2] | The cumulative effect of a sequence of percent changes is the product of the associated growth or decay factors. | The effect of a 25% increase followed by a 25% decrease is 1.25 $\times$ 0.75 = 0.9375.<br><br>That is, the item is now worth only 93.75% of its original value. The item's value has decreased by 6.25%. |

| | | |
|---|---|---|
| **Exponential function** [5.3] | An exponential function is a function whose $y$-values exhibit a constant percent growth (or decay). In an equation defining an exponential function, $y = ab^x$, $b > 0$, $b \neq 1$, the $x$-values variable always occurs as the exponent on the growth (decay) factor. | $y = 16 \cdot (2.1)^x$ |
| **Decay factor of an exponential function** [5.3] | If $0 < b < 1$, the function is decreasing, and $b$ is called the decay factor. | The exponential function $y = \left(\frac{1}{2}\right)^x$ has a decay factor of $\frac{1}{2}$. |
| **Growth factor of an exponential function** [5.3] | If $b > 1$, the function is increasing, and $b$ is called the growth factor. | The exponential function $y = 3^x$ has a growth factor of 3. |
| **$y$-intercept of an exponential function** [5.3] | The $y$-intercept of an exponential function $y = a \cdot b^x$ is $(0, a)$. | The graph of $y = 5 \cdot 2^x$ passes through the point $(0, 5)$. |
| **Horizontal asymptote of an exponential function** [5.3] | The line $y = 0$ is a horizontal asymptote of an exponential function $y = b^x$. | As $x$ gets smaller, the output values of $y = 3^x$ approach 0. |
| **Doubling time** [5.5] | The doubling time of an exponential function is the time it takes for an output to double. The doubling time is set by the growth factor and remains the same for all output values. | Example 2, Activity 5.5. |
| **Half-life** [5.5] | The half-life of an exponential function is the time it takes for an output to decay by one-half. The half-life is determined by the decay factor and remains the same for all output values. | Problem 10, Activity 5.5. |
| **Growth model** [5.6] | If $r$ represents the annual growth rate, the exponential function that models the quantity $P$ can be written as $P(t) = P_0(1 + r)^t$, where $P_0$ is the initial amount, $t$ represents the number of elapsed years, and $1 + r$ is the growth factor. | Example 2, Activity 5.6. |
| **Decay model** [5.6] | If $r$ represents the annual percent that decays, the exponential function that models the amount remaining can be written as $P(t) = P_0(1 - r)^t$, where $1 - r$ is the decay factor. | Example 3, Activity 5.6. |
| **Compound interest** [5.7] | The formula for compounding interest is $A = P\left(1 + \frac{r}{n}\right)^{nt}$. | Example 1, Activity 5.7; |
| **Continuous compounding** [5.7] | The formula for continuous compounding is $A = Pe^{rt}$. | Example 4, Activity 5.7; |

| | | |
|---|---|---|
| **Continuous growth at a constant percentage rate** [5.7], [5.8] | Whenever growth is continuous at a constant percentage rate, the exponential model used is $y = y_0 e^{rt}$. | Problem 10, Activity 5.7; |
| **Continuous decay at a constant percentage rate** [5.8] | Whenever decay is continuous at a constant rate, the model used is $y = y_0 e^{-rt}$. | Example 2, Activity 5.8; |
| **Logarithm** [5.10] | In the equation $y = b^x$, where $b > 0$ and $b \neq 1$, $x$ is called a logarithm or log. | For the equation $3^4 = 81$, 4 is the logarithm of 81, base 3. |
| **Notation for logarithms** [5.10] | The notation for logarithms is $\log_b x = y$, where $b$ is the base of the log, $x$ (a positive number) is the power of $b$, and $y$ is the exponent. | In the equation $\log_2 16 = 4$, 2 is the base, 4 is the log or exponent, and 16 is the power of 2. |
| **Common logarithm** [5.10] | A common logarithm is a base-10 logarithm. The notation is $\log_{10} x = \log x$. | $1000 = 10^3$. The common logarithm of $10^3$ is 3; i.e., $\log 1000 = 3$. |
| **Natural logarithm** [5.10] | A natural logarithm is a base-$e$ logarithm. The notation is $\log_e x = \ln x$. | $\log_e e^3 = \ln e^3 = 3$ |
| **Logarithmic equation** [5.10] | The logarithmic equation $y = \log_b x$ is equivalent to the exponential equation $b^y = x$. | The equations $6 = \log_4 x$ and $x = 4^6$ are equivalent. |
| **Basic properties of logarithms** [5.10] | If $b > 0$ and $b \neq 1$, $\log_b 1 = 0$, $\log_b b = 1$, and $\log_b b^n = n$. | $\log_4 1 = 0$, $\log_7 7 = 1$, $\log_6 6^4 = 4$ |
| **Logarithmic function** [5.11] | If $b > 0$ and $b \neq 1$, the logarithmic function is defined by $y = \log_b x$. | $y = \log_4 x$ |
| **Graph of the logarithmic function** [5.11] | The graph is increasing for all $x > 0$, has an $x$-intercept of $(1, 0)$ and has a vertical asymptote of $x = 0$, the $y$-axis. | |
| **Comparison of the graphs of** $f(x) = b^x$**, where** $b > 1$**, and** $g(x) = \log_b (x)$**, where** $b > 1$ [5.11] | Both graphs increase. The exponential function increases faster as $x$ increases; the log function increases slower as $x$ increases. The domain of the exponential function is the range of the log, which is all real numbers; the range of the exponential function is the domain of the log, which is the interval $(0, \infty)$. | Problem 6, Activity 5.11; |

| | | |
|---|---|---|
| If $A > 0$, $B > 0$, $b > 0$, and $b \neq 1$, then $\log_b (A \cdot B) = \log_b A + \log_b B$ [5.13] | The logarithm of a product is the sum of the logarithms. | $\log_2 (4 \cdot 8) = \log_2 (4) + \log_2 (8) = 2 + 3 = 5$ |
| If $A > 0$, $B > 0$, $b > 0$, and $b \neq 1$, then $\log_b \left(\frac{A}{B}\right) = \log_b A - \log_b B$ [5.13] | The logarithm of a quotient is the difference of the logarithms. | $\log_3 \left(\frac{81}{27}\right) = \log_3 81 - \log_3 27 = 4 - 3 = 1$ |
| If $A > 0$, $B > 0$, $b > 0$, and $b \neq 1$, then $\log_b (A + B) \neq \log_b (A) + \log_b (B)$ [5.13] | The logarithm of a sum is not the sum of the logarithms. | $\log 2 + \log 3 = 0.3010 + 0.4771 = 0.7781$ $\log (2 + 3) = \log 5 = 0.6990$ |
| If $A > 0$, $p$ is a real number, $b > 0$, and $b \neq 1$, then $\log_b A^p = p \log_b A$ [5.13] | The logarithm of a power of $A$ is the exponent times the logarithm of A. | $\log_5 x^4 = 4 \log_5 x$ $\log_3 \sqrt{x} = \frac{1}{2} \log_3 x$ |
| **Change of base formula** [5.13] | The logarithm of any positive number $x$ to any base can be found using the formula $\log_b x = \frac{\log x}{\log b}$ or $\log_b x = \frac{\ln x}{\ln b}$. | $\log_2 (2.5) = \frac{\log (2.5)}{\log 2} = 1.3219$ |

# Gateway Review

1. Due to inflation your tuition will increase 6% each year.

   a. If tuition is $300 per credit now, determine how much it will be in five years, in ten years.

   b. Calculate the average rate of change in tuition over the next five years.

   c. Calculate the average rate of change in tuition over the next ten years.

   d. If the inflation stays at 6%, approximately when will the tuition double?

2. a. Determine some of the output values for the function $f(x) = 8^x$ by completing the following table.

   | $x$ | $-1$ | $-\frac{1}{3}$ | $0$ | $1$ | $\frac{4}{3}$ | $2$ | $3$ |
   |---|---|---|---|---|---|---|---|
   | $f(x) = 8^x$ | | | | | | | |

   b. Sketch the graph of the function, $f$.

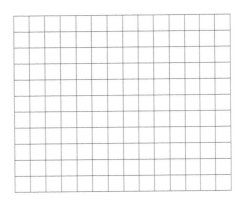

**c.** Is this function increasing or decreasing? Explain how you know this by looking at the equation of the function.

**d.** What is the domain?

**e.** What is the range?

**f.** What are the $x$- and $y$-intercepts?

**g.** Are there any asymptotes? If yes, write the equations of the asymptotes.

**h.** Compare the graph of $f$ to the graph of $g(x) = \left(\frac{1}{8}\right)^x$. What are the similarities and the differences?

**i.** In what way does the graph of $h(x) = 8^x + 5$ differ from that of $f(x) = 8^x$?

**j.** Write the equation of the function that is the inverse of the function $f(x)$.

**3.** Complete the table for each exponential function. Use a graphing calculator to check your work.

| FUNCTION | BASE, $b$ | GROWTH OR DECAY FACTOR | $x$-INTERCEPT | $y$-INTERCEPT | HORIZONTAL ASYMPTOTE | INCREASING OR DECREASING |
|---|---|---|---|---|---|---|
| $h(x) = 6^x$ | | | | | | |
| $g(x) = \left(\frac{1}{3}\right)^x$ | | | | | | |
| $p(x) = 5(2.34)^x$ | | | | | | |
| $q(x) = 3(0.78)^x$ | | | | | | |
| $r(x) = 2^x - 4$ | | | | | | |

**4.** Use a graphing calculator to help you determine the domain and range for each function.

| FUNCTION | $f(x) = 0.8^x$ | $h(x) = 6^x + 2$ | $t(x) = 3^x - 5$ | $q(x) = \log_4 x$ | $r(x) = \ln(x - 3)$ |
|---|---|---|---|---|---|
| DOMAIN | | | | | |
| RANGE | | | | | |

5. **a.** Given the following table, determine whether the given data can be approximately modeled by an exponential function. If it can, what is the growth or decay factor?

| $x$ | 0 | 1 | 2 | 3 | 4 |
|---|---|---|---|---|---|
| $y$ | 10 | 15.5 | 24 | 36 | 55.5 |

   **b.** Determine an exponential equation that models this data.

6. **a.** Your salary has increased at the rate of 1.5% annually for the past 5 years, and your boss projects this will continue for the next 5 years. You were making $15,000 annually in 2008. Complete the following table.

| 2008 | 2009 | 2010 | 2011 | 2012 | 2013 |
|---|---|---|---|---|---|
| 15,000 | | | | | |

   **b.** Write the exponential growth function that models your annual salary during this period of time. Let $x$ represent the number of years since 2008.

   **c.** If your increase in salary continues at this rate, how much will you make in 2016? Is this realistic?

   **d.** You would like to double your salary. How many years will you have to work before your salary will be twice the salary you made in 2008?

7. Complete the following tables representing exponential functions. Round calculations to two decimal places whenever necessary.

   **a.**

| $x$ | 0 | 1 | 2 | 3 | 4 |
|---|---|---|---|---|---|
| $y$ | 3.00 | 6.12 | | | |

   **b.**

| $x$ | 0 | 1 | 2 | 3 | 4 |
|---|---|---|---|---|---|
| $y$ | 4.50 | 3.15 | | | |

   **c.**

| $x$ | 0 | 1 | 2 | 3 | 4 |
|---|---|---|---|---|---|
| $y$ | $\frac{1}{4}$ | 4 | | | |

**8.** Write the equation of the exponential function that represents the data in each table in Problem 7.

**9. a.** You just inherited $5000. You can invest the money at a rate of 6.5% compounded continuously. How much will be in the bank after 8 years? Use the equation $A = A_0 e^{rt}$.

**b.** For how many years would you have to leave the money in the bank to have $12,000?

**10.** The number of multiple births (triplets or higher) in the United States between 1990 and 1999 is listed in the following table, with 0 representing the year 1990.

| NUMBER OF YEARS SINCE 1990 | 0 | 2 | 3 | 4 | 5 | 6 | 7 | 8 | 9 |
|---|---|---|---|---|---|---|---|---|---|
| NUMBER OF MULTIPLE BIRTHS | 3028 | 3883 | 4168 | 4594 | 4973 | 5939 | 6737 | 7625 | 7321 |

*Source:* National Center for Health Statistics.

**a.** Plot the data on an appropriately scaled and labeled coordinate axis.

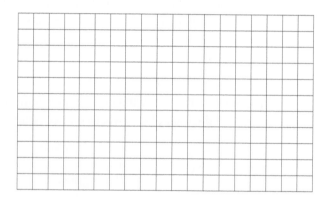

**b.** Does the scatterplot show that the data would be better modeled by a linear or an exponential model?

**c.** Use a graphing calculator to determine the exponential regression equation that best fits the multiple births data.

**d.** According to your model, what is the growth factor for the multiple births data?

**e.** Estimate the growth rate (written as a percent) in multiple births each year.

**f.** Use the regression equation to determine the predicted total number of multiple births in 2012.

**g.** Use your graphing calculator to determine the doubling time for your exponential model.

**11.** Using transformations, sketch a graph of each of the following. Determine any intercepts and asymptotes. Verify the graph using a graphing calculator.

**a.** $y = 2^x + 3$

**b.** $y = 2^{x+3}$

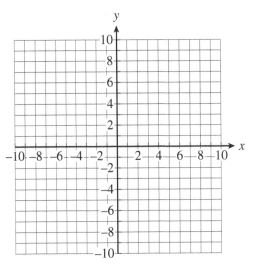

**c.** $y = 2^{-x}$

**d.** $y = -3 \cdot 2^x$

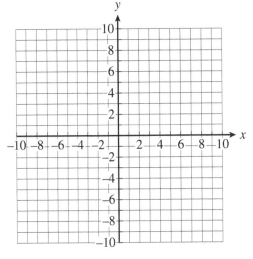

**e.** $y = e^x + 3$

**f.** $y = -3e^x$

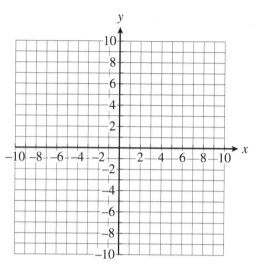

**g.** $y = 5 + 3 \ln x$

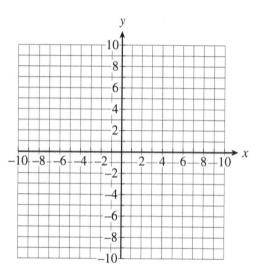

**h.** $y = \ln(x - 1)$

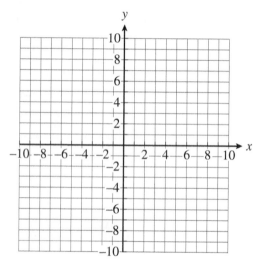

**i.** $y = -4 \log x$               **j.** $y = \ln(-x)$

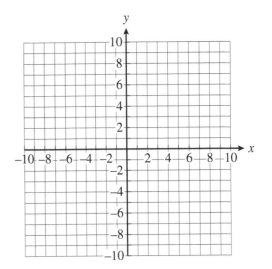

**12.** Determine the value of each of the following without using your calculator.

    **a.** $\sqrt[3]{125^2}$            **b.** $\log_3 \frac{1}{9}$            **c.** $\log_5 625$

    **d.** $\log 0.001$           **e.** $\ln e^2$

**13.** Write each equation in logarithmic form.

    **a.** $6^2 = 36$           **b.** $0.000001 = 10^{-6}$       **c.** $2^{-5} = \frac{1}{32}$

**14.** Write each equation in exponential form.

    **a.** $\log_3 81 = 4$        **b.** $\log_7 1 = 0$       **c.** $\log_{10} 0.0001 = -4$

    **d.** $\ln e = 1$           **e.** $\log_q y = b$

**15.** Solve each equation for the unknown variable.

**a.** $\log_5 x = -3$       **b.** $\log_b 256 = 4$       **c.** $\log_2 64 = y$

**d.** $\log_4 x = \dfrac{3}{2}$

**16. a.** Complete the table of values for the function $f(x) = \log_5 x$.

| x | 0.008 | 0.04 | 0.2 | 1 | 5 | 25 |
|---|---|---|---|---|---|---|
| f(x) | | | | | | |

**b.** Sketch a graph of the function.

**c.** Use your graphing calculator to check your result in parts a and b.

**d.** Determine the x-intercept.

**e.** What is the domain of the function?

**f.** What is the range?

**g.** Does the graph have a vertical or horizontal asymptote?

**h.** Use your graphing calculator to determine $f(23)$.

**i.** Use your graphing calculator to determine $x$ when $f(x) = 2.46$.

**17.** Use the change of base formula and your calculator to approximate the following.

    **a.** $\log_7 21$                                    **b.** $\log_{15} \frac{8}{9}$

**18.** Write each of the following as a sum, difference, or multiple of logarithms. Assume that $x$, $y$, and $z$ are all greater than 0.

    **a.** $\log_2 \dfrac{x^3 y}{z^{1/2}}$                              **b.** $\log \sqrt[3]{\dfrac{x^4 y^3}{z}}$

**19.** Rewrite the following as the logarithm of a single quantity.

    **a.** $\log x + \frac{1}{4}\log y - 3\log z$              **b.** $\frac{1}{3}\left(\log x - 2\log y - \log z\right)$

**20.** Solve the following algebraically.

    **a.** $3^{3+x} = 7$                                **b.** $\log_2 (4x + 9) = 4$

    **c.** $50 + 6\ln x = 85$

**21. a.** Sketch the graph of the function using the data from the given table.

| $x$ | 0.1 | 0.5 | 1 | 2 | 4 | 16 |
|---|---|---|---|---|---|---|
| $f(x)$ | −1.66 | −0.5 | 0 | .5 | 1 | 2 |

**b.** Use the table and the graphing feature of your calculator to verify that the equation that defines function $f$ is $f(x) = 0.5 \log_2 x$.

**c.** Use the function to determine the value of $f(54)$.

**d.** If $f(x) = 2.319$, determine the value of $x$.

**e.** Use your graphing calculator to verify that the function $g(x) = 4^x$ is the inverse of $f$.

**22.** The population (in millions) of New York State and Florida can be modeled by the following:

New York State:    $P_N = 18.98e^{0.0055t}$

Florida:    $P_F = 15.98e^{0.0235t}$

where $t$ represents the number of years since 2000.

**a.** Determine the population of New York and Florida in 2000 ($t = 0$).

**b.** Sketch a graph of each function on the same coordinate axes.

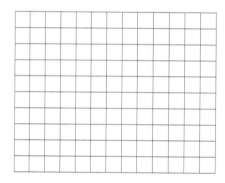

**c.** Determine graphically the year when the population of Florida will equal the population of New York State.

**d.** Determine algebraically the year when the population of Florida will first exceed 25 million.

**23.** The atmospheric pressure decreases with increasing attitude. The following data is collected during a science experiment to investigate the relationship between the height of an object above ground level and the pressure exerted on the object.

| atmospheric pressure, x (in millimeters of mercury) | 760 | 740 | 725 | 700 | 650 | 630 | 600 | 580 | 550 |
|---|---|---|---|---|---|---|---|---|---|
| height, y (in kilometers) | 0 | 0.184 | 0.328 | 0.565 | 1.079 | 1.291 | 1.634 | 1.862 | 2.235 |

**a.** Use a graphing calculator to determine a logarithmic regression model that best fits the data.

**b.** Use the log equation in part a to predict the height of the object if the atmospheric pressure is 500 millimeters of mercury.

# CHAPTER 6

# Probability Models

**ACTIVITY 6.1**
Chances Are!

**OBJECTIVES**

1. Determine relative frequencies for a collection of data.

2. Determine both theoretical and experimental probabilities.

3. Simulate an experiment and observe the law of large numbers.

4. Identify and understand the properties of probabilities.

The study of probability began with mathematical problems arising from games of chance. In 1560, Italian Gerolamo Cardano wrote a book about games of chance. This book is considered to be the first written on probability. Two French mathematicians, Blaise Pascal and Pierre de Fermat, are credited by many historians with the founding of probability theory. They exchanged ideas on probability theory in games of chance and worked together on the geometry of the die.

Although probability is most often associated with games of chance, probability is used today in a wide range of areas, including insurance, opinion polls, elections, genetics, weather forecasting, medicine, and industrial quality control.

## Relative Frequency

The following table gives the years of service of the 789 workers at High Tech Manufacturing.

| SENIORITY | LESS THAN ONE YEAR | BETWEEN ONE AND TEN YEARS | MORE THAN TEN YEARS | TOTAL |
|-----------|--------------------|---------------------------|---------------------|-------|
| Male | 82 | 361 | 47 | |
| Female | 49 | 202 | 48 | |
| **Total** | | | | |

**1. a.** Complete the table to display the total number of workers in each category.

**b.** What is the total number of males?

**c.** What is the total number of workers having between one and ten years of service?

**d.** Should the sum of the right-most column be the same as the sum of the bottom row?

Each of the numbers in the above table can be considered a frequency for that category. If you consider this frequency a fractional part of the whole workforce, it becomes a **relative frequency**. For example, the relative frequency of male workers with less than one year of experience is $\frac{82}{789} \approx 0.104 = 10.4\%$.

**2.** Calculate the relative frequency, expressed as a decimal, for each category. Record your answer in the following table.

| SENIORITY | LESS THAN ONE YEAR | BETWEEN ONE AND TEN YEARS | MORE THAN TEN YEARS | TOTAL |
|---|---|---|---|---|
| Male | 0.104 | | | |
| Female | | | | |
| **Total** | | | | |

Now consider choosing one of the 789 workers by some random process, like drawing names out of a hat. The **probability** of picking a male worker with less than one year of experience is 0.104, the relative frequency for that particular outcome. Choosing a male worker with less than one year experience is called an **event**.

**3. a.** What is the probability of choosing a female with more than ten years of experience?

 **b.** What is the probability of choosing a male?

 **c.** What is the probability of choosing a worker with less than one year of experience?

---

**DEFINITION**

$$\text{Probability of event} = \frac{\text{number of outcomes for which the event is true}}{\text{total number of equally likely possible outcomes}}$$

---

For example, the probability of choosing a male is $\frac{490}{789} \approx 0.621$. The event is "choosing a male." Of the 789 possible outcomes, 490 of the outcomes make the event true.

If $x$ represents a particular outcome, then $P(x)$ represents the probability of that outcome occurring. Therefore, the probability of choosing a male can be written as

$$P(\text{choosing a male}) \approx 0.621$$

One important assumption is necessary for this definition to hold true. All the possible outcomes must be equally likely to occur. Selecting one worker at **random** implies that each worker has the same likelihood, or probability, of being chosen.

**4. a.** If your uncle is one of the 789 workers, what is the probability that he will be chosen?

 **b.** What is the probability that the person selected works at High Tech?

 **c.** What is the probability that your aunt (who does not work at High Tech) will be chosen?

**5.** Now consider a very random experiment, rolling a typical six-sided die. Each side contains a unique number of dots, from 1 to 6.

**a.** What makes this experiment random?

**b.** What is the probability of rolling a five?

**c.** What is the probability of rolling an even number?

**d.** For this experiment, think of an event that has a probability of zero.

**e.** Complete this table for the die roll **probabilities**.

| OUTCOME | PROBABILITY |
|---------|-------------|
| 1       |             |
| 2       |             |
| 3       |             |
| 4       |             |
| 5       |             |
| 6       |             |

**f.** Letting $P(x)$ be the probability of rolling $x$ on the die, what does $P(3)$ equal?

**g.** What is the sum of all the possible probabilities for the die roll? Explain why this makes sense.

The collection of all possible single outcomes for an experiment is called a **sample space**. All the possible probabilities make up a **probability distribution**.

**6.** Consider another random experiment, flipping a coin.

**a.** To be a random process, you must use a fair coin. What do you think is meant by a fair coin?

**b.** By definition, what is the probability of getting heads on a single flip of the coin?

**c.** What is the sample space for this experiment?

> The probability definition you used to answer the questions in Problems 5 and 6 is sometimes called the **theoretical probability** of an event. Theoretical probability is determined through a study of all possible outcomes that can occur.

## Experimental Probability

Sometimes theoretical probabilities are not possible to calculate. For example, suppose you want to estimate the probability of rain today or to predict the likelihood of living past the age of 80. There is another way to define probability that depends on experimental observation.

**7.** Suppose the weather forecaster claims that there is a 60% chance of rain tonight. How do you think such a probability could be calculated?

**8. a.** If you flip a coin ten times, how many heads would you expect to get?

**b.** Would you be surprised to get ten heads in your ten flips?

**c.** How about nine heads or only one head?

**d.** Have each member of the class flip a coin ten times. Summarize the results for the entire class in the following frequency table.

| NUMBER OF HEADS | FREQUENCY |
|:---:|:---:|
| 0 | |
| 1 | |
| 2 | |
| 3 | |
| 4 | |
| 5 | |
| 6 | |
| 7 | |
| 8 | |
| 9 | |
| 10 | |

**e.** Does the probability (or frequency) distribution confirm your answers in parts a–c?

**f.** You know that the theoretical probability of getting a head on a single coin flip is $\frac{1}{2}$. For this to be true, what assumption are you making?

**9.** When you flip a coin, you should expect to get heads approximately one-half the time. Determine the relative frequency of getting a head for the class experiment in Problem 8d. Would you be surprised if the relative frequency was not close to one half?

You could use this relative frequency based on the results of the experiment to define the probability of getting a head, especially if you did not know the theoretical probability. This probability would be an **experimental probability**.

**10.** Repeat the coin-tossing experiment as a class, with each member of the class tossing the coin 20 times and recording the number of heads observed. How does the resulting relative frequency compare with the theoretical probability?

## Law of Large Numbers

Appendix

If more is better, you could be flipping coins for a long time to get a truly large number of observations. You can accomplish this by employing technology. Your calculator or a computer can be used to **simulate** the flipping of a coin a very large number of times. This can be done by randomly generating a large number of zeros and ones (ones representing heads and zeros representing tails). The probability of getting a one must be 50%. (See Appendix A for TI-83/84 Plus instructions.)

**11. a.** Use technology to simulate flipping a coin 100 times and then 500 times. Record your results in the following table. Then combine all your class-mates' results to get as many observations as you can.

| NUMBER OF FLIPS | NUMBER OF HEADS | RELATIVE FREQUENCY OF HEADS |
|---|---|---|
| 100 | | |
| 500 | | |

**b.** What conclusion can you make about the relative frequency as the number of observations increases?

In Problems 9–11, as the number of coin flips increased, the experimental probability of obtaining a head got closer to the theoretical probability of getting a head. This is usually called the **law of large numbers**.

1. An experiment is a controlled procedure that gives a set of recordable results.

2. The possible results of an experiment are called outcomes.

3. An event is a single outcome or collection of outcomes of the experiment.

4. The sample space of an experiment is the collection of all possible single outcomes of the experiment.

5. Randomly selecting an object from a collection means that all objects in the collection have an equal chance of being selected.

6. The probability of a particular event (or combination of events) measures the likelihood of that event occurring.

7. **Theoretical Probability**

$$\text{Probability of event} = \frac{\text{number of outcomes in event}}{\text{total number of equally likely possible outcomes}}$$

8. **Experimental Probability**

$$\text{Probability of event} = \frac{\text{number of observed occurrences of event}}{\text{total number of observations}}$$

9. **Law of Large Numbers**

The larger the number of observations, the closer the experimental probability of an event will get to the theoretical probability of that same event.

10. **Properties of Probabilities**

If $P(x)$ is the probability that outcome $x$ occurs, then the following special properties of probabilities must be true.

- The collection of all possible individual outcomes is called the **sample space** of $P$.
- $0 \leq P(x) \leq 1$ for all $x$ in the sample space.
- If $x$ is impossible, then $P(x) = 0$.
- If $x$ is a certainty, then $P(x) = 1$.
- The sum of the probabilities of all $x$ in the sample space must equal 1.

1. Some teens belong to the 4-H club. A random survey of 100 teens in your community yields the following results.

| | 4-H MEMBER | NON 4-H MEMBER | TOTAL |
|---|---|---|---|
| **FEMALE** | 24 | 32 | |
| **MALE** | 24 | 20 | |
| **TOTAL** | | | |

a. Complete the totals in the table.

b. Calculate the relative frequency for each category.

| | 4-H MEMBER | NON 4-H MEMBER | TOTAL |
|---|---|---|---|
| FEMALE | | | |
| MALE | | | |
| TOTAL | | | |

c. Using these relative frequencies as the basis for defining probabilities, what is the probability that a teen in your community is a 4-H member?

d. If you choose one teen at random from your community, what is the probability that he or she is a female non 4-H member?

e. Given the fact that you have already chosen a female at random, what is the probability that she is a 4-H member?

f. Given the fact that you have already chosen a male at random, what is the probability that he is a 4-H member?

g. From your results in parts e and f, would you say there are more male or female teen 4-H members in your community? Explain.

2. Twenty uniformly shaped stones are placed in a vase. Five of the stones are white, eight of the stones are gray, and the remaining stones are black. One stone is drawn at random from the vase. The outcome of this experiment is to note the color of the selected stone.

a. What is the sample space for these probabilities?

b. Make a table showing the probability of each individual outcome.

| $x$ | white | gray | black |
|---|---|---|---|
| $P(x)$ | | | |

c. Find: $P$(white), $P$(gray), $P$(black), and $P$(red).

3. If $P(x)$ is the probability of living to age $x$, interpret the statement $P(80) = 0.16$.

4. State whether you think each of the following is a theoretical or experimental probability.

a. The chance of rain tonight is 35%.

b. The probability of living past 100 years of age is 0.03.

    **c.** The probability of getting two tails on two flips of a coin is 0.25.

    **d.** The probability that the Sun will come up tomorrow is 1.

    **e.** The probability of selecting a green stone from the vase of Exercise 2 is zero.

**5.** You are blindfolded and then throw a dart at a square dartboard, as illustrating that the dart does hit the board, what is the probability that you will hit region II?

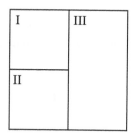

**6.** If you and your friend separately choose a number between 1 and 10 at random, what is the probability that you will choose the same number?

**7.** Which of the following tables could be probability distributions? For those that cannot be a probability distribution, give a reason.

    **a.**

| x | 1 | 2 | 3 | 4 | 5 |
|---|---|---|---|---|---|
| P(x) | 0.2 | 0.2 | 0.2 | 0.2 | 0.2 |

    **b.**

| x | 3 | 4 | 5 | 6 | 7 | 8 | 9 | 10 | 11 | 12 |
|---|---|---|---|---|---|---|---|----|----|----|
| P(x) | 0.1 | 0.15 | 0.2 | 0.25 | 0.12 | 0.1 | 0.05 | 0.02 | 0.01 | 0.01 |

    **c.**

| x | blue | green | red | white | black | gray |
|---|------|-------|-----|-------|-------|------|
| P(x) | 0.3 | 0.4 | 0.2 | −0.3 | 0.2 | 0.2 |

**8.** The spinner pictured at the right is used in a
board game.

 **a.** Assuming that it is a fair spinner, construct a table
for the probability distribution where $x$ represents
the set of individual outcomes.

| $x$ | 1 | 2 | 3 | 4 |
|---|---|---|---|---|
| $P(x)$ | | | | |

 **b.** What is the probability of getting a number greater
than 1?

 **c.** What is the probability of getting an odd number?

**9.** In your class of 28 students, there are 12 girls. Of these 12 girls, only 3 are under
16 years old. There are 13 students in class that are 16 years old or older. This information is summarized in the following table.

| | UNDER 16 | 16 OR OVER | TOTAL |
|---|---|---|---|
| **GIRLS** | 3 | | 12 |
| **BOYS** | | | |
| **TOTAL** | | 13 | 28 |

A student is selected at random.

 **a.** What is the probability that the student is a boy?

 **b.** What is the probability that the student is a girl who is also at least 16 years old?

 **c.** What is the probability that the student is under 16 years old?

**10.** You flip a coin 500 times and get 500 heads. What conclusion would you make about
this coin?

**11.** A standard deck of 52 playing cards consists of four suits: hearts, clubs, diamonds, and spades. Hearts and diamonds are red cards; clubs and spades are black cards. Each suit has 13 cards, including numbered cards ace (1) through 10 and three picture (or face) cards: the jack, the queen, and the king. There are 12 picture cards, consisting of 4 jacks, 4 queens, and 4 kings.

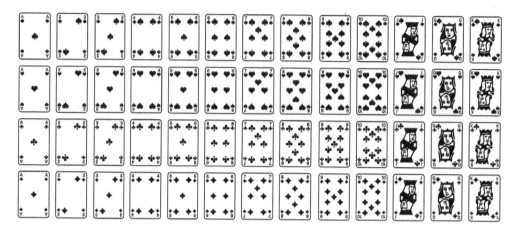

One card is randomly selected from the deck of cards. Determine the probability that the card selected is

**a.** a 10 of hearts.

**b.** a 10.

**c.** a club.

**d.** a red card.

**e.** a picture card.

**f.** a card greater than 4 and less than 7.

**g.** a diamond and a club.

**12.** In an election for senior class president at your high school, 45 seniors were polled and asked for whom they planned to vote. The results of the poll are given in the following table.

| | VOTES |
|---|---|
| Candidate A | 18 |
| Candidate B | 12 |
| Candidate C | 15 |

**a.** If one student who was polled was randomly selected, what is the probability that the student planned to vote for Candidate A?

**b.** According to the poll, estimate the probability that a senior not polled will vote for Candidate A in the election? Is this an experimental probability or a theoretical probability? Explain.

**13.** A pharmaceutical company is testing a new drug to help people lose weight. The drug is given to 300 adults. The results of the test are as follows:

| WEIGHT | NUMBER OF ADULTS |
|---|---|
| Reduced | 190 |
| Unchanged | 60 |
| Increased | 50 |

**a.** If the drug was given to an adult **not** in the testing program, estimate the probability that the person will lose weight?

**b.** Is the probability in part a experimental or theoretical?

**14.** Most individuals have seen the "taste test" between Coke and Pepsi. Can people selected at random distinguish between these drinks?

**a.** Design an experiment to determine the experimental probability that a person randomly selected will choose Pepsi over Coke when given samples of both Pepsi and Coke.

**b.** Perform the experiment in part a. Construct a table showing the results of the experiment.

**c.** Determine the experimental probability that a randomly selected person will prefer Pepsi over Coke.

**15.** Insurance companies use experimental probabilities in determining insurance premiums. Use a variety of references, such as the Internet or your family insurance agent, to gather information on this topic. Write a report on your findings. Include any graphs, numerical information, or formulas that can help demonstrate the use of experimental probabilities in determining insurance premiums.

**16.** Certain physical traits are not evenly distributed in the general population. For example, there are more right-handed than left-handed people. Conduct a survey of persons chosen at random at your high school. Ask at least 50 students the following questions:

    **1.** Are you right or left-handed?

    **2.** What color is your hair?

    **3.** What color are your eyes?

Complete the following table by filling in all of the data collected.

| HANDEDNESS | NUMBER OF PERSONS |
|------------|-------------------|
| Right-handed | |
| Left-handed | |
| **Eye Color** | **Number of Persons** |
| Brown | |
| Blue | |
| Green | |
| Other | |
| **Hair Color** | **Number of Persons** |
| Brown | |
| Blond | |
| Black | |
| Red | |

    **a.** What is the total number of students in your survey?

Using the survey results, estimate the probability that a randomly selected student in your high school

    **b.** is left-handed.

    **c.** has blue eyes.

    **d.** has brown hair.

**ACTIVITY 6.2**
Choices

**OBJECTIVES**

1. **Apply the multiplication principle of counting.**

2. **Determine the sample space for a probability distribution.**

3. **Display a sample space with a tree diagram.**

4. **Determine complementary probabilities.**

5. **Use Venn diagrams to illustrate relationships between events.**

Suppose you are looking for a new car and have narrowed your decision down to a Mustang, but can't decide on the exact color, transmission, engine, or options package. There are three sizes of engine (3.0 liters, 3.8 liters, and 4.6 liters), two transmissions (standard and automatic), five colors you like (black, silver, red, yellow, and green), and three option packages (GL, Sport, and XL). With all these possible choices, you want to know how many different Mustangs there are from which you must choose.

1. From the choices given, how many different Mustangs are possible? (Solve this any way you can. A diagram or list may help.)

In solving the Mustang problem, you might have recognized a counting shortcut. If the outcomes you wish to count consist of a sequence of choices, it is possible to apply the **multiplication principle of counting**.

For example, suppose you have three sweaters: one cotton, one wool, and one alpaca. You also have four hats, colored red, green, black, and purple. If you want to wear one sweater and one hat, how many different combinations are possible?

**Option 1:** You could simply list all the possibilities:

| | | |
|---|---|---|
| cotton + red | wool + red | alpaca + red |
| cotton + green | wool + green | alpaca + green |
| cotton + black | wool + black | alpaca + black |
| cotton + purple | wool + purple | alpaca + purple |

You could shorten the process with a **tree diagram** (and abbreviations), where each level of branching represents the next choice.

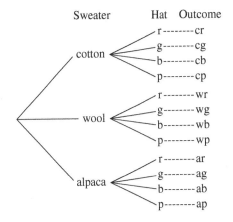

The total number of end points represents all the possibilities. Tracing each branch displays all the possible outcomes.

**Option 2:** You could use a table approach if there are only two levels of choices.

| | RED | GREEN | BLACK | PURPLE |
|---|---|---|---|---|
| **COTTON** | cr | cg | cb | cp |
| **WOOL** | wr | wg | wb | wp |
| **ALPACA** | ar | ag | ab | ap |

**Option 3:** You could multiply the 3 choices for a sweater by the 4 choices for a hat to get a total of 12 combinations. This is called the *multiplication principle of counting*.

> **The Multiplication Principle of Counting** If some choice can be made in $M$ ways and a subsequent choice can be made in $N$ ways, then there are $M$ times $N$ ways these choices can be made in succession.

2. Apply the multiplication principle to the Mustang problem to verify your answer in Problem 1.

3. **a.** You want to create an ID code for all your customers based on three characters. The first character must be a letter of the alphabet, and the second and third must each be a digit between 1 and 9, inclusive. How many such codes are there? (Use the multiplication principle.)

   **b.** Would a list or tree diagram be practical in this case?

4. **a.** Suppose you flip a penny and a dime. Determine the number of outcomes.

   **b.** Use a tree diagram to display all possible outcomes.

   **c.** Assume that each single outcome is equally likely. Use the tree diagram to help calculate probabilities. What is the probability of getting two heads?

   **d.** What is the probability of getting one head and one tail, on either coin?

   **e.** If the variable $x$ represents the number of heads, complete the table for this **probability distribution**.

| x | P(x) |
|---|------|
| 0 |      |
| 1 |      |
| 2 |      |

**f.** What must be true about the sum of the probabilities for this (and any other) probability distribution?

> The collection of all the possible single outcomes displayed by the tree diagram is the **sample space** for the probability distribution.

5. Two fair dice are rolled.

   **a.** Determine the number of possible outcomes.

   **b.** Display the sample space of all possible outcomes. You may use a tree diagram or a table. It may help to think of the dice as being different colors.

   **c.** What is the probability of getting a total of two dots on the dice (snake eyes)? That is, what is the probability of rolling a 1 on each die?

   **d.** What is the probability of rolling a total of 6 on the two dice?

   **e.** If the variable $x$ represents the total number of spots on the two dice, refer to your sample space to complete the table for this probability distribution.

| $x$ | 2 | 3 | 4 | 5 | 6 | 7 | 8 | 9 | 10 | 11 | 12 |
|-----|---|---|---|---|---|---|---|---|----|----|----|
| $P(x)$ | | | | | | | | | | | |

   **f.** What must be the sum of all probabilities?

   **g.** Are you as likely to roll a sum of 2 as you are of rolling a sum of 7? Explain.

6. To win the jackpot in a large state lottery, the winner must pick correctly all six numbers from among 1 through 54. The theoretical probability of doing this is $\frac{1}{25,827,165} \approx .0000000387$. Stated another way, a single pick has a 1 in 25,827,165

chance to win the jackpot (and even then it might be shared with other winners). The theory of probability originated out of a desire to understand games of chance. Show how the 25,827,165 is determined.

7. What is the probability of getting ten heads on ten flips of a coin?

8. Two tennis balls are randomly selected from a bag that contains one Penn, one Wilson, and one Dunlop tennis ball.

   a. If the first tennis ball picked is replaced before the second tennis ball is selected, determine the number of outcomes in the sample space.

   b. Construct a tree diagram and list the outcomes in the sample space.

   c. Determine the probability that a Penn followed by a Wilson tennis ball is the outcome.

   d. Suppose the first tennis ball picked is not replaced before the second tennis ball is selected. Determine the number of outcomes in the sample space.

**e.** Construct a tree diagram and list the outcomes in the sample space.

**f.** Determine the probability that a Penn followed by a Wilson tennis ball is the outcome.

## Complementary Events

In some situations, you are interested in determining the probability that an event A does **not** happen. The event "not A", denoted by $\overline{A}$, is called the complement of A. For example,

- The complement of success is failure.
- The complement of selected voter is Democrat is the selected voter is not a Democrat.
- The complement of a 6 is rolled is a 6 is not rolled.

Since the sum of the probabilities for all outcomes of an experiment is 1, it follows that

$$P(A) + P(\overline{A}) = 1.$$

Rewriting, you have

$$P(A) = 1 - P(\overline{A}) \text{ or } P(\overline{A}) = 1 - P(A).$$

**9. a.** A die is rolled. What is the probability that the number 6 does not show?

**b.** A card is randomly selected from a standard deck of 52 cards. What is the probability that the card is not a king?

Complementary probabilities are very useful when trying to determine the probability of "at least one." The statement that "an event happens at least once" is equivalent to "the event happens one or more times". Therefore,

$$P\left(\begin{matrix}\text{event happens}\\\text{at least once}\end{matrix}\right) = P\left(\begin{matrix}\text{event happens}\\\text{one or times}\end{matrix}\right). \qquad (1)$$

The complement of "an event happens one or more times" is "the event does not happen". Therefore,

$$P\left(\begin{matrix}\text{event happens}\\\text{one or more times}\end{matrix}\right) + P(\text{event does not happen}) = 1 \qquad (2)$$

or

$$P\left(\begin{matrix}\text{event happens}\\\text{one or more times}\end{matrix}\right) = 1 - P(\text{event does not happen}). \qquad (3)$$

Substituting the results of equation (3) into equation (1), you have the formula

$$P\left(\begin{matrix}\text{event happens}\\\text{at least once}\end{matrix}\right) = 1 - P(\text{event does not happen}).$$

10. **a.** A fair dice is rolled. What is the probability that the number is at least two?

 

**b.** Two fair die are rolled. What is the probability that the sum is at least 3?

## Venn Diagrams

Complementary events can be illustrated using Venn diagrams. These diagrams were invented by English mathematician John Venn (1834–1923) and first appeared in a book on symbolic logic in 1881. In a Venn diagram, a rectangle generally represents the sample space. The items (all possible outcomes of a particular experiment) inside the rectangle can be separated into subdivisions which are generally represented by circles. The items in a circle represent the outcomes in the sample space that make a certain event true.

For example, suppose a die is rolled. The rectangle would contain all the possible outcomes of whole numbers 1 through 6. If A represents the event that the number rolled is greater than 4, then the Venn diagram at the top of the next page represents the relationship between the sample space and the event A.

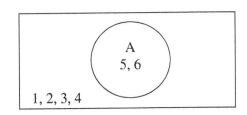

11. **a.** Determine the complement of event A in the roll-a-die experiment.

   **b.** Describe what portion of the Venn diagram above represents the complement of A.

1. The **multiplication principle of counting** says that if some choice can be made in $M$ ways and a subsequent choice can be made in $N$ ways, then there are $M$ times $N$ ways these choices can be made in succession.

2. A **tree diagram** displays all possible outcomes for a sequence of choices, one outcome for each branch of the tree.

3. The **sample space** of a probability distribution is the collection of all possible outcomes.

4. The sum of the probability that an event A will occur and the probability that the event will not occur is 1. The event "not A," denoted by $\overline{A}$, is called the complement of A. Stated symbolically,

$$P(A) + P(\overline{A}) = 1 \text{ or } P(A) = 1 - P(\overline{A}).$$

1. Phone numbers consist of a three-digit area code followed by seven digits. If the area code must have a 0 or 1 for the second digit, and neither the area code nor the seven-digit number can start with 0 or 1, how many different phone numbers are possible?

2. You have four sweaters, five pairs of pants, and three pairs of shoes. How many different combinations can you make, wearing one of each?

3. If you flip a coin ten times, how many different sequences of heads and tails are possible?

4. If you roll a die three times, how many different sequences are possible?

5. You want to order a triple-scoop ice cream cone, with a different flavor for each scoop. If there are 23 flavors available, how many different cones are possible?

6. In a single experiment, a die is tossed and a spinner with the letters A, B, and C is spun. Each letter is equally likely.

   **a.** Determine the number of possible outcomes.

   **b.** Construct a tree diagram to help determine the resulting sample space.

   **c.** Determine the probability of getting a 2 on the die *and* a B on the spinner.

   **d.** Determine the probability of getting a B.

   **e.** Determine the probability of getting a 2 or a B.

7. A computer is programmed to generate a sequence of three digits, where each digit is either 0 or 1, and each of these is equally likely to occur.

   **a.** Construct a tree diagram that shows all possible three-digit sequences of 0s and 1s.

**b.** What is the probability that a sequence will contain exactly one 0?

**c.** What is the probability that a sequence will contain at least one 0?

8. Two teams are playing a best-of-seven series. For each game there are only two possible outcomes: One team wins or the other team wins. Construct a tree diagram showing all the possible outcomes for such a series. As soon as one team wins a fourth game, the series ends (and that branch of the tree ends also).

9. You roll two fair dice. Use the sample space you recorded in Problem 5 of the activity to determine the probabilities of the following events.

   **a.** $P$(a sum of 7)

   **b.** $P$(both dice show an even number)

   **c.** $P$(one die is even, the other odd)

   **d.** $P$(one die is 1 more than the other)

   **e.** $P$(the sum is less than 6)

   **f.** $P$(the product of the two numbers on the dice is even)

10. You have decided to purchase a new computer system. After researching the cost and features of different models of computers, printers, and monitors, you have narrowed your choices to the following:

   Computer:   Dell, Compaq, and IBM
   Printer:   Epson, Hewlett-Packard
   Monitor:   Omega, Toshiba

   **a.** Determine the number of possible computer system combinations that you can purchase.

**b.** Construct a tree diagram and list the possible computer systems that can be purchased.

**c.** Determine the probability that a Dell computer is part of the system purchased. Assume that all outcomes are equally likely.

**d.** What is the probability that a Dell computer is not part of the computer system you select?

**e.** Determine the probability that an Epson printer is part of the computer package purchased.

**f.** Determine the probability that tAAhe system purchased contained an IBM computer and Omega monitor.

**11.** Two thumbtacks are dropped, one after another, onto a hard surface. Assume that the thumbtack can only land point up or point down. Let

- U represent the event that the thumbtack will land point up.
- D represent the event that the thumbtack will land point down.

**a.** Are the events U and D equally likely? Explain.


**b.** Design and conduct an experiment involving dropping thumbtacks. Use the results to determine the experimental probability that a thumbtack will land point up when dropped and the experimental probability that the thumbtack will land point down.

**ACTIVITY 6.3**
Experimenting
with Probabilities

Consider the following two probability experiments.

**Experiment 1.** You roll two fair dice. What is the probability that a 4 shows on each die?

**Experiment 2.** You pick two cards from a standard deck of 52 cards without replacing the first card before picking the second. What is the probability that the cards are both red suited?

These experiments are very similar. In each case, you are determining the probability that two events occur **together**. In Experiment 1, both dice must show a 4 for the event to be successful. In Experiment 2, both cards must be red suited for a favorable outcome to occur. The word *and* is used to indicate that both events must occur.

The word *and* is generally interpreted to mean intersection. Venn diagrams can be used to illustrate the overlap or common outcomes between two events. The shaded region in the following Venn diagram represents the outcomes that satisfy both events A and B.

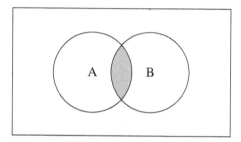

The probability question in Experiments 1 and 2 can be restated as follows:

**Experiment 1.** Determine $P$ (4 on first die and 4 on second die)

**Experiment 2.** Determine $P$ (red on first card and red on second card)

Although similar, Experiments 1 and 2 have a very important difference. These differences are investigated in Problems 1 and 2.

**1. a.** In the dice experiment, what is the probability that a 4 is rolled on the first die?

**b.** Assuming that a 4 was rolled on the first die, what is the probability that a 4 is rolled on the second die?

In the dice experiment, the outcome of a 4 on the first die has no effect on the probability of a 4 showing on the second die. In such a case, the two events are said to be **independent**.

**DEFINITION**

Events A and B are independent events if the occurrence of either event does not affect the probability of the occurrence of the other event.

**2. a.** In the card experiment, what is the probability of a red suited card on the first draw?

**b.** When calculating the probability of picking a red suited card on the second draw, you must assume that a red card was picked on the first draw. Since the first card is not returned to the deck, there are only 51 cards remaining and only 25 of these are red suited. What is the probability of picking a red card on the second draw?

**c.** Are the events *a red suited card on the first draw* and *a red suited card on the second draw* independent events? Explain.

Therefore, in the card experiment, the two events are not independent. The outcome of the first draw changes the probability of getting a red card on the second draw. In such a case, the events are said to be **dependent**.

**DEFINITION**

Events A and B are dependent events if the occurrence of either event affects the probability of the occurrence of the other event.

**3.** You draw two cards from a standard deck of 52 cards. The first card is replaced before the second card is drawn.

**a.** What is the probability that an ace is drawn on the first draw?

**b.** What is the probability that an ace is drawn on the second draw?

**c.** Are the events in parts a and b dependent or independent? Explain.

## Calculating Probabilities Involving *"and"* Statements

The probability of an outcome composed of a sequence of independent events can be determined by multiplying the probabilities of the individual events. This is formally called the **multiplication principle of probability**.

**Multiplication Principle of Probability**

The probability that two independent events both occur is equal to the product of the probabilities of the individual events. Stated symbolically, if A and B are independent events, then

$$P(A \text{ and } B) = P(A) \cdot P(B)$$

When using this formula, you must be sure that A and B are independent events.

You will now use the multiplication principle to answer the probability problem in Experiment 1.

 4. **Experiment 1.** You roll two fair dice.

   **a.** Use the multiplication formula to determine the probability that a 4 shows on each die.

   **b.  i.** How many outcomes are in the sample space for Experiment 1?

   **ii.** List the outcomes in the sample space for which the condition is satisfied.

   **iii.** Using the results from parts i and ii, determine the probability that a 4 shows on each die.

   **c.** Compare the results from parts a and b.

In most real-world applications, it is often too time-consuming or even impossible to solve probability problems by first constructing the sample space. That is one of the reasons why formulas were developed.

As you will discover in Problem 5, the multiplication formula must be adjusted if the consecutive events are dependent.

 5. **Experiment 2.** You pick two cards from a standard deck of 52 cards without replacing the first card before picking the second. What is the probability that both cards are red?

   Be careful! Recall that the events in this situation are dependent. The probability of picking a red card on the second draw is affected by not replacing the red card picked on the first draw. When the events are dependent, the multiplication formula is written as follows:

   $P(A \text{ and } B) = P(A) \cdot P(B)$ becomes
   $P(A \text{ and } B) = P(A) \cdot P(B, \text{given } A \text{ has occurred})$

   **a.** Determine $P(\text{red on first})$.

**b.** Determine $P$(red on second, given red on first, not replaced).

**c.** Determine $P$(red on first and red on second) using the modified multiplication rule.

The $P(B$, given $A$ has occurred) will be discussed further in Activity 6.4.

6. **Experiment 3.** A fair coin is tossed three times. What is the probability that the coin shows heads on all three tosses?

## Calculating Probabilities Involving "*or*" Statements

Consider the following experiment:

**Experiment 4.** Each of the numbers 1, 2, 3, 4, 5, 6, 7, 8, 9 and 10 are written on index cards. The ten cards are then put in a box and one card is randomly selected. Determine the probability that the number is odd or a number less than 5.

7. Referring to Experiment 4, let A represent the number picked is odd and B represent the number picked is less than 5.

**a.** List the outcomes in the sample space of Experiment 4.

**b.** List the outcomes that make each event A and B true.

**c.** Complete the following diagram by writing the remaining outcomes in the appropriate region of the Venn diagram.

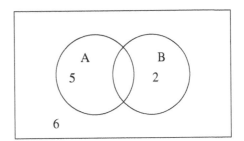

**d.** What relationship do you observe between the outcomes that make events A and B true?

**8. a.** In order for an outcome in Experiment 4 to satisfy the condition, must the number showing be both odd **and** less than 5? Explain.

**b.** What is the probability that the number is odd?

**c.** What is the probability that the number is less than 5?

In general, $P(A \text{ or } B) = P(A) + P(B)$. However, in this situation, the two events–number is odd, number is less than 5–overlap. You do not want to count the outcomes that satisfy both events twice. Therefore,

$$P(A \text{ or } B) = P(A) + P(B) - P(A \text{ and } B).$$

**d.** List the outcomes in Experiment 4 for which the number selected is both odd and less than 5. What is the probability of the number selected is both odd and less than 5?

**e.** Determine the probability that the number selected is odd or less than 5.

**9. Experiment 5.** A single card is drawn from a standard deck of 52 cards.

In parts a–d, determine the indicated probability of selecting the given cards.

**a.** $P(\text{ace})$                      **b.** $P(\text{jack})$

**c.** $P(\text{ace and jack})$            **d.** $P(\text{ace or jack})$

In Problem 9c, it is not possible for the card drawn to be both an ace and a jack. Such events are said to be **mutually exclusive**.

> DEFINITION
>
> Two events A and B are said to be **mutually exclusive** if it is not possible for both events to occur at the same time.

**10.** Construct a Venn diagram that illustrates events A and B are mutually exclusive.

**11.** With regard to Experiment 5, in which a single card is drawn from a standard deck of 52 cards,

   **i.** Determine if the following events are mutually exclusive.

   **ii.** Determine $P(A \text{ or } B)$.

   **a.** $A$: a red card, $B$: a black card

   **b.** $A$: a king, $B$: a red card

**12. Experiment 1 revisited**:  You roll two fair dice.

   **a.** What is the probability that you will get an odd number on the first die and a number greater than 2 on the second die?

    **b.** What is the probability of obtaining a sum of 10 on the two dice? Hint: The sample space for rolling two dice is 36 equally likely outcomes.

    **c.** What is the probability of rolling a sum of less than 5?

## SUMMARY
### Activity 6.3

1. Events A and B are **independent events** if the occurrence of either event does not affect the probability of the occurrence of the other event.

2. Events A and B are **dependent events** if the occurrence of either event affects the probability of the occurrence of the other event.

3. The probability that two independent events both occur is equal to the product of the probabilities of the individual events. Stated symbolically, if A and B are independent events, then

$$P(A \text{ and } B) = P(A) \cdot P(B)$$

4. If A and B are dependent events, then $P(A \text{ and } B) = P(A) \cdot P(B, \text{given } A \text{ has occurred})$.

5. Two events A and B are said to be **mutually exclusive** if it is not possible for both events to occur at the same time.

6. If A and B are mutually exclusive events, then
  **i.** $P(A \text{ and } B) = 0$
  **ii.** $P(A \text{ or } B) = P(A) + P(B)$

7. If A and B are not mutually exclusive, then

$$P(A \text{ or } B) = P(A) + P(B) - P(A \text{ and } B)$$

**EXERCISES**
**Activity 6.3**

1. One of your classmates is selected at random. Let *A* represent the event that the person selected owns a computer, and *B* represent the event that the person selected owns an iPod. Are *A* and *B* mutually exclusive events? Explain.

2. You are one of ten finalists in a radio station contest for tickets to a concert. Names of the finalists are written on index cards, placed in a hat, and a name is randomly selected. Suppose that three sets of tickets are to be given away and that a single finalist can win only one set of tickets. Are the three events of selecting the three winners from the group of finalists independent events? Explain.

3. The spinner pictured at the right is used in a board game. Assume that it is a fair spinner and that the pointer cannot land on a line. The pointer is spun twice. Assuming independence, determine the probability that the pointer lands on

   **a.** 2 both times.

   **b.** an even number first and then 4.

   **c.** an even number and then an odd number.

**4.** Suppose the pointer in Exercise 3 is spun once. What is the probability that the pointer lands on

 **a.** 2 or an even number?

 **b.** 2 or 3?

 **c.** Are the events "lands on 2" and "lands on 3" mutually exclusive? Explain.

**5.** You pick two cards from a standard deck of 52 cards. You replace the first card before picking the second.

 **a.** Determine the probability that both cards are aces.

 **b.** What is the probability that both cards are aces if the first card is not replaced before picking the second card? Compare your results to the probability in part a.

 **c.** Determine the probability that the first card is a heart and the second card is a club. Assume the first card is not replaced before picking the second card.

**6.** A young couple with three children has purchased the house next to you. How likely is the occurrence that all three children are boys? Assuming independence and the probability of a boy is $\frac{1}{2}$, determine the probability that

   **a.** all three children are boys.

   **b.** all three children are girls.

   **c.** the youngest child is a boy and the older children are girls.

**7. a.** Referring to Exercise 6, what is the probability of any specific boy-girl combination of three children?

   **b.** If a family has three boys, what is the probability that a fourth child will be a boy? Explain.

**8.** One card is drawn from a standard deck of 52 cards. Determine the probability that the card selected was

   **a.** an ace or king.

   **b.** a 10 or a red-suited card.

**c.** a club or a red card.

**d.** a face card (jack, queen, king) or a king.

9. A survey was conducted to determine the number of television sets in a household. The results are summarized in the following table.

| | NUMBER OF TELEVISION SETS | | | | |
|---|---|---|---|---|---|
| | 0 | 1 | 2 | 3 | 4 or more |
| Probability | 0.05 | 0.22 | 0.35 | 0.20 | 0.18 |

Determine each of the following:

**a.** $P(1 \text{ or } 2 \text{ sets})$

**b.** $P(1, 2, \text{ or } 3 \text{ sets})$

**c.** $P(2 \text{ or more sets})$

10. Two golf balls are randomly selected from a bag that contains 3 Titleist, 5 Top Flite, and 2 Pinnacle golf balls.

   **a.** If the first golf ball is replaced before the second golf ball is selected, determine the probability that you select a Titleist and then a Top Flite.

**b.** If the first golf ball selected is not replaced before the second ball is picked, determine the probability that you select a Titleist and then a Top Flite.

**c.** If the first golf ball is not replaced, determine the probability that both golf balls selected are Top Flite.

**d.** Suppose only one golf ball is selected from the bag. What is the probability that the ball is a Pinnacle or Titleist?

**11.** A five-question multiple-choice quiz is given in science class. Each question has four possible answers. If you randomly pick an answer for each question, determine the probability that you answer

**a.** any given question correctly.

**b.** any given question incorrectly.

**c.** all five questions correctly.

**d.** only the first two questions correctly.

**12.** There are 18 sophomores and 15 juniors in your math class. Of the 18 sophomores, 10 are male. Of the 15 juniors, 8 are male.

**a.** Complete the following table.

|  | MALES | FEMALES | TOTAL |
|---|---|---|---|
| Sophomores |  |  |  |
| Juniors |  |  |  |
| Total |  |  |  |

A student is randomly selected. Determine the probability that the student selected is

**a.** a male.

**b.** a sophomore or female.

**c.** a junior or male.

**13. a.** The style and manufacturer of automobiles in a local used car dealership is summarized in the given table. Complete the table.

|  | UNITED STATES | MODEL EUROPEAN | JAPANESE | TOTAL |
|---|---|---|---|---|
| Suv | 8 | 4 | 6 |  |
| Sedan | 13 | 11 | 15 |  |
| Hatchback | 12 | 7 | 9 |  |
| Total |  |  |  |  |

A vehicle is randomly selected. Determine the probability that the vehicle selected is

**a.** a Japanese model.

**b.** a Japanese model and a hatchback.

    **c.** a Japanese model or a hatchback.

    **d.** European made or a sedan.

**14.** Assume the probability that a person in a certain income bracket will be audited is 0.35. The tax return of a person in this income bracket is randomly selected. What is the probability that the person selected will be audited in three successive years. Assume that each year's selection of who to be audited is independent of last year's selection. Also assume that a person stays in the same income bracket for three consecutive years.

**ACTIVITY 6.4**
Conditional
Probabilities

**OBJECTIVES**

1. **Identify a conditional probability problem.**

2. **Determine conditional probabilities using the sample space or the data from a table.**

3. **Determine conditional probabilities using a formula.**

It has rained for the past three days. However, the weather forecast for tomorrow's football game is sunny and no chance of rain. You decide not to take a rain jacket, only to get drenched when there is a sudden downpour during the game.

Although not perfect, the level of accuracy of weather forecasting has increased significantly through the use of computer models. These models analyze current data and predict atmospheric conditions at some short period of time from that moment. Based on these predicted conditions, another set of atmospheric conditions are predicted. This process continues until the forecast for the day and the extended forecast for the next several days are completed.

1. **a.** What does the level of accuracy in the weather forecasting model described above depend upon?

**b.** The level of accuracy decreases as the forecasts extend several days ahead. Explain.

The accuracy of weather forecasting is based upon **conditional probabilities**; that is, the probability that one event happens, given that another event has occurred. For example, the probability that it will rain this afternoon, given that a low pressure system moved into the area this morning, is a conditional probability.

Weather forecasting is revisited in Situation 2 of Activity 6.5.

## Calculating Conditional Probabilities

How do you determine conditional probabilities? First, consider the following problem to see how the condition affects the sample space.

2. A family with two children is moving into your neighborhood.

**a.** Determine the sample space of possibilities for the gender of the first and second child using a tree diagram.

**b.** Assume that the probability of a boy and girl are each $\frac{1}{2}$. Are the outcomes in the sample space equally likely? Explain.

   **c.** What is the probability that both children are boys?

   **d.** What is the probability that both children are boys, given that the first child is a boy?

In Problem 2c, you selected outcomes from the entire sample space for which the event (both boys) was true. In Problem 2d, you are given that the first child is a boy. Therefore, the sample space is **reduced** to only include outcomes that make the given event true. The outcomes in which the first child is not a boy are neglected.

The probability that both children are boys, given that the first child is a boy, is a **conditional probability**. There is a special notation for conditional probabilities.

In general, $P(A|B)$ denotes the probability of event $A$, given that event $B$ has occurred.

In Problem 2d, the probability that both children are boys, given that the first child is a boy, is written as

$$P(\text{both boys} \mid \text{first is a boy})$$

   **3.** Referring to Problem 2, what is the probability that both children are boys, given at least one of the children is a boy?

## Calculating Conditional Probabilities Using a Formula

In general, a formula is used to calculate conditional probabilities. The following gives an intuitive justification for this formula.

   **4.** Suppose a person is selected at random in the United States. Now, let

     $A$ represent the event that the person selected is a student at the University of Virginia, and

     $B$ represent the event that the person selected is a resident of Charlottesville, VA.

     **a.** What can you say about $P(A)$ and $P(B)$? Explain.

**b.** How does the $P(A)$ in part a compare to the probability of attending the University of Virginia given that the person selected lives in Charlottesville, VA? That is, how does $P(A)$ in part a compare to $P(A|B)$? Explain.

The situation in Problem 4 can be demonstrated by the following Venn diagram. All the people who live in the United States are contained in the rectangle; all the people who attend the University of Virginia are contained in circle A; all people who live in Charlottesville, VA are in circle B.

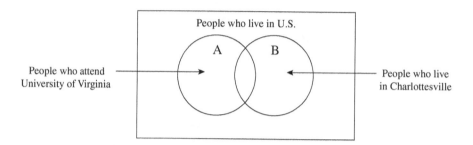

**5. a.** Describe the region that represents the new sample space, given that the person selected lives in Charlottesville.

**b.** Describe the region that represents the outcomes that satisfy the event that the person selected is a student at the University of Virginia, given the person lives in Charlottesville.

Therefore, the $P(A|B)$ should be a fraction of the number of people that are both a student at Virginia **and** live in Charlottesville divided by the number of people who live in Charlottesville. Stated symbolically,

If the outcomes for events $A$ and $B$ are equally likely, then

$$P(A|B) = \frac{n(A \text{ and } B)}{n(B)},$$

where $n(A \text{ and } B)$ represents the number of outcomes common to both events $A$ and $B$, and $n(B)$ is the number of outcomes for which event $B$ is true. Note that $n(B) \neq 0$.

**6.** In Problem 2d, you used the reduced sample space to determine the probability that the two children are both boys, given the first child is a boy. Redo the problem using the conditional probability formula. Compare the results.

**7.** A taste test is given to 200 people at a local mall. The results are summarized in the following table.

|  | PREFERS COKE | PREFERS PEPSI | TOTAL |
| --- | --- | --- | --- |
| Male | 51 | 40 | 91 |
| Female | 34 | 75 | 109 |
| Total | 85 | 115 | 200 |

If one person who participated in the taste test is randomly selected, use the data in the table to determine the probability that the person selected

**a.** prefers Coke.                                    **b.** is a male.

**c.** is a male and prefers Coke.

**d.** prefers Coke, given that a male is selected.

**e.** prefers Pepsi, given that a female is selected.

In many applications, you don't know the actual numbers, but you do know the percentages and probabilities. In such situations, the formula used to calculate conditional probabilities is

$$P(A|B) = \frac{P(A \text{ and } B)}{P(B)}, \text{ where } P(B) \neq 0.$$

The probabilities $P(A \text{ and } B)$ and $P(B)$ are determined using the original sample space.

**8.** In Europe, 88% of all households have a television and 51% of all households have a television and a VCR.

**a.** If a household in Europe is randomly selected, what is the probability that the household has a television?

**b.** Determine the probability that a randomly selected household has a television and a VCR.

**c.** What is the probability that a household has a VCR given that it has a television?

**9.** Motor vehicles sold in the United States are classified as either cars or light trucks, and as either domestic or imported. Light trucks include SUVs and minivans. The following table gives the probabilities for a randomly selected vehicle recently sold in the United States. For example, the probability of selecting a domestic light truck is 0.47.

|  | DOMESTIC | IMPORTED | TOTAL |
|---|---|---|---|
| Light truck | 0.47 | 0.07 | |
| Car | 0.33 | 0.13 | |
| Total | | | |

**a.** Complete the table.

In parts b–g, determine the probability that a randomly selected vehicle sold in the United States is

**b.** a car.

**c.** imported.

**d.** imported car.

**e.** a car or imported.

**f.** a car, given that the vehicle is imported.

**g.** light truck, given that the vehicle is domestic.

**SUMMARY**
Activity 6.4

1. The **conditional probability** of an event A is when the probability of the event A is affected by the knowledge that other events have already occurred.

2. $P(A|B)$ denotes the probability of event A, given that event B has occurred.

3. If the outcomes for events A and B are equally likely, then

$$P(A|B) = \frac{n(A \text{ and } B)}{n(B)},$$

where $n(A \text{ and } B)$ represents the number of outcomes common to both events A and B, and $n(B)$ is the number of outcomes for which event B is true. Note that $n(B) \neq 0$.

4. The formula used to calculate conditional probabilities is

$$P(A|B) = \frac{P(A \text{ and } B)}{P(B)}, \text{ where } P(B) \neq 0.$$

The probabilities $P(A \text{ and } B)$ and $P(B)$ are determined using the original sample space.

**EXERCISES**
Activity 6.4

1. A family has three children.

   a. Determine the sample space of possible outcomes for the gender of the first, second, and third child using a tree diagram.

   b. What is the probability that all three children are girls? Assume the probability of a girl and a boy are each $\frac{1}{2}$.

   **c.** What is the probability that all three children are girls, given the first two are girls?

   **d.** Does your result in part c support the argument that the events "a boy" and "a girl" are independent?

2. A card is randomly selected from a standard deck of 52 cards. Determine the probability that the card selected is

   **a.** a king.

   **b.** a king, given the card is a heart.

   **c.** a king, given the suit is black.

   **d.** a heart, given the card is a queen.

   **e.** an even number, given the card is a picture card.

3. Two fair dice are rolled one after the other. The sample space for this experiment is given in Problem 5 in Activity 6.2. Determine the probability that the sum of the dots on the dice total

   **a.** 5.

   **b.** 5, given the first die is a 2.

   **c.** 5, given the first die is 5

   **d.** 6, given the first die is even.

4. A bag contains 6 blue marbles and 4 red marbles. A marble is randomly selected from the bag. A second marble is then randomly selected without replacing the first marble.

   **a.** What is the probability that you pick a blue marble and then a red marble?

**b.** What is the probability that you pick a red marble, *given* the first marble selected is blue?

**5.** A total of 200 people were surveyed to determine which evening news they watch most frequently. The results of the survey are given in the table.

|  | ABC | NBC | CBS | OTHER | TOTAL |
|---|---|---|---|---|---|
| **MALE** | 38 | 13 | 26 | 12 | 89 |
| **FEMALE** | 32 | 37 | 29 | 13 | 111 |
| **TOTAL** | 70 | 50 | 55 | 25 | 200 |

One of the participants in the survey is randomly selected. What is the probability that the person selected watches

    **a.** CBS.

    **b.** NBC or CBS.

    **c.** ABC, given the viewer is a male.

    **d.** ABC or NBC, given the person is a female.

**6.** A child psychologist conducted a survey of 500 children in grades 4, 5, and 6 in elementary school. The aim of one of the questions in the survey was to see if boys and girls at this age had similar goals in school. They were asked whether their primary goal was to get good grades, to be popular, or to be good in sports. The results are given in the table.

|  | | GOALS | | |
|---|---|---|---|---|
|  | Grades | Popular | Sports | Total |
| Boy | 128 | 50 | 60 | 238 |
| Girl | 141 | 91 | 30 | 262 |
| Total | 269 | 141 | 90 | 500 |

A child that participated in the survey is randomly selected. Determine the probability that the child selected is

**a.** a girl.

**b.** a girl and primary goal was to be popular.

**c.** a girl, given the goal in school was to be popular.

**d.** a boy, given the goal in school was to get good grades.

7. At your high school 8.7% of students take Technology and Spanish; 68% take Technology. What is the probability that a student takes Spanish given that the student is taking Technology?

8. At a local college, 85% of incoming freshmen nursing students are female and 15% are male. Recent records show that 70% of entering female students will graduate with a BSN degree, 90% of male students will graduate with a BSN degree. An incoming freshman is selected at random.

**a.** Draw a tree diagram of the possible outcomes for freshmen nursing students.

Determine the following probabilities:

**b.** *P*(student will graduate | student is female)

**c.** *P*(student will graduate | student is male)

**d.** *P*(female and student will graduate)

**e.** *P*(student is female and not graduate)

**PROJECT
ACTIVITY 6.5**

First Serve

The following three situations illustrate how conditional probabilities are used in the problem solving process.

**Situation 1:** On each point in tennis, a player is allowed two tries to successfully serve the ball into the service box of the opponent's side of the court.

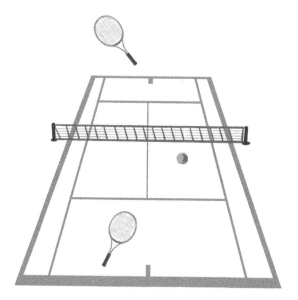

If the player is not successful in these two tries, the player automatically loses the point. This is called a double fault.

Suppose while playing in a tournament, a certain professional player gets his first serve in the service box about 75% of the time. When he gets his first serve in, he wins the point about 80% of the time. If he misses his first serve, his second serve goes in the service box about 90% of the time. When this happens, he wins the point on the second serve about 40% of the time.

  **a.** Draw a tree diagram of all the possible outcomes.

Determine each of the following probabilities

  **b.** *P*(misses first serve)

**c.** $P$(wins the point | first serve in)

**d.** $P$(loses the point | first serve in)

**e.** $P$(first serve in and wins the point)

**f.** $P$(second serve in | first serve misses)

**g.** $P$(misses the second serve)

**h.** $P$(win the point | second serve in)

**i.** $P$(lose the point | second serve in)

**j.** $P$(first serve out and second serve in and win the point)

**k.** $P$(wins the point)

The second situation is based on the introduction in Activity 6.4, which described a weather forecasting process that uses sophisticated computer models. The process is based upon conditional probabilities.

**Situation 2:** Suppose the local weather station has collected and analyzed data about the probability of precipitation in your region. The results predict that if it rains on one day, then the chance it will rain on the next day is 50%. If it is not raining, it will rain on the next day only 20% of the time.

**a.** Is the statement "If it rains on one day, then the chance it will rain on the next day is 50%." a conditional probability? Explain.

**b.** Determine $P$(does not rain next day | rains today).

**c.** If it does not rain today, what is the probability that it will rain the next day?

**d.** Determine $P$(does not rain the next day | does not rain today).

**e.** The weather forecast for today predicts a 90% chance of rain. Starting with today as the first day, the following tree diagram gives the sample space for three consecutive days of weather outcomes. Each branch of the tree indicates whether it rains (denoted by $R$) or does not rain (denoted by $N$). Complete the tree diagram.

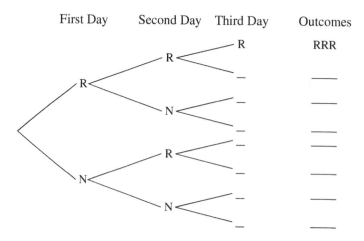

**f.** Determine the probability that it rains on all three days.

**g.** Determine the probability that it rains only on the third day.

**h.** Determine the probability that it rains on the third day.

**i.** You are given that it rains on the first day. What is the probability that it rains on the third day?

**Situation 3:** Suppose your high school basketball team is playing in a best-of-three holiday tournament against another local team.

    **a.** Construct a tree diagram to determine the sample space for this situation.

    **b.** The coach feels the team has a 50–50 chance of winning the first game against the very strong opponent. If the team wins the game, the probability of winning the next game increases to $\frac{2}{3}$. If the team loses the game, the probability of winning the next game is $\frac{1}{3}$.

      **i.** If the team wins the game, what is the probability of losing the next game?

      **ii.** If the team loses the game, what is the probability of losing the next game?

    **c.** What is the probability that the team wins the first game, but then loses the next two games?

**d.** What is the probability that the team wins the first two games?

**e.** What is the probability that the team wins the tournament, given it wins the first game?

**f.** What is the probability that the team wins the tournament?

**LAB ACTIVITY 6.6**
Colorful
Probabilities

**OBJECTIVE**

1. Solve probability problems involving M&M candies.

M&M's Milk Chocolate Candies is a recognized product throughout the world. The popular candies were first sold in the United States in 1941. According to the M&M's website, the idea for the plain chocolate candies dates back to the late 1930s. While traveling in Spain during the Spanish Civil War, Forrest Mars Sr. encountered soldiers who were eating pellets of chocolate that were covered with a hard, sugary coating to prevent them from melting. As a result of this encounter, Mr. Mars was motivated to develop a recipe for such a candy. The rest is history. Today, the M&M's characters even rival the popularity of such favorites as Mickey Mouse and Bart Simpson.

## Percentages

**1. a.** Obtain a small bag of M&M's Milk Chocolate Candies. Record the number of each color in the appropriate column of the following table.

### M&M's Milk Chocolate Candies

| COLOR | NUMBER | PERCENTAGE |
|-------|--------|------------|
| Brown | | |
| Yellow | | |
| Red | | |
| Blue | | |
| Orange | | |
| Green | | |
| Total | | |

  **b.** Determine the percentage of the candies that are red. Record your answer in the appropriate place in the table.

  **c.** Complete the percentage column in part a.

**2. a.** According to the M&M's website, 13% of their Plain M&M's Milk Chocolate Candies produced are brown, 14% are yellow, 13% are red, 24% are blue, 20% are orange, and 16% are green. Therefore, if you have a small bag of M&M's containing 50 candies, how many of each color would you expect?

  **b.** Do your results in part 1c agree with this claim?

**c.** Are you surprised to observe that there could be such large differences in the distribution of colors in your small bag of candies and the distribution of colors claimed by the company? Explain.

**3. a.** Tally each class member's number of M&M's of each color (you can now eat your M&M's) and record the class totals in the following table:

**M&M's Milk Chocolate Candies Class Totals**

| COLOR | NUMBER | PERCENTAGE |
|-------|--------|------------|
| Brown | | |
| Yellow | | |
| Red | | |
| Blue | | |
| Orange | | |
| Green | | |
| Total | | |

**b.** Using the class totals, determine the percentage of each color and record the result in the appropriate place in the table.

**c.** Now, how do the percentages in part b compare to the color distribution claimed by the M&M company? Explain why there should be less differences.

Sampling, sample sizes, and sampling techniques will be discussed in detail in Chapter 7.

## Probabilities

The percents calculated in Problem 3 are the percentages for each color in the class collection (sample). If you now want to consider the probability of selecting a red M&M from the class collection of M&M's, you treat each M&M in the class collection as a possible outcome. You are asking a question about the likelihood of a certain event (such as selecting a red M&M) occurring when you randomly pick a M&M from the entire sample space of candies in the class collection.

**4. a.** Suppose you had placed all the M&M's from the class experiment into a jar. If one candy is randomly selected, what is the probability that you will select a red M&M?

**b.** Is the probability in part a experimental or theoretical? Explain.

**5. a.** Use your results from Problem 3 to complete the following probability distribution. Let $x$ represent the color of the randomly selected candy and $P(x)$ represent the probability of selecting a candy having color $x$.

| X | BROWN | YELLOW | RED | BLUE | ORANGE | GREEN |
|---|---|---|---|---|---|---|
| P(x) | | | | | | |

**b.** What is the sum of the probabilities? Is this what you expected?

**c.** Determine the probability of selecting a blue M&M?

**d.** What is the probability of not selecting a blue M&M?

**e.** What is the probability of selecting either a yellow or orange candy?

**f.** What is the probability of selecting a candy that is a primary color?

**g.** What is the probability of selecting a purple M&M?

**EXERCISES
ACTIVITY 6.6**

In 2001, Masterfoods, the manufacturers of M&M's milk chocolate candies, decided to add another color to the standard lineup of brown, yellow, red, blue, orange, and green. In order to decide which color to add, the company asked children in nearly every country in the world to choose among purple, pink, and teal. The global winner was purple. In the United States, only 42% of those who voted picked purple. In Japan, the percentage was even lower. Only 16% voted for purple.

**1.** In Japan, the percentages of those who voted were as follows: 38% for pink, 36% for teal, and 16% for purple.

**a.** A Japanese participant in the survey is randomly selected. Determine the probability that the person voted for pink or teal. Hint: First determine if the events of voting for pink and voting for teal are mutually exclusive.

**b.** If there are two Japanese participants selected, determine the probability that both voted for purple. (First decide if the events are independent.)

**c.** What is the probability that the second person selected voted for teal, given the first person selected voted for pink? Is $P(2^{nd}$ voted for teal $|$ $1^{st}$ voted for pink$) = P(2^{nd}$ voted for teal$)$? Explain.

**d.** If three survey participants are randomly selected, what is the probability that none of the three voted for purple?

**e.** What is the probability that at least one of the three voted for purple?
Note that the statement "at least one voted for purple" is equivalent to "one or more purple votes".

2. Suppose there are 21 different candy colors available to create your own blend of candy colors. You choose to have equal numbers of teal, light blue, light purple, dark blue, and aqua green.

**a.** Your custom blend consists of 10 candies of each color. If you randomly select a candy from your custom blend, what is the probability that you will pick teal?

**b.** Suppose your custom blend consists of 100 candies of each of these colors. Does the probability in part a change?

**c.** Let $x$ represent the number of each candy in the custom blend. What is the probability that the color selected will be teal?

**ACTIVITY 6.7**
Selecting and
Rearranging
Things

**OBJECTIVES**

1. Determine the number of permutations.

2. Determine the number of combinations.

3. Recognize patterns modeled by counting techniques.

In working through the previous activities, you may have noticed there are many different varieties of counting problems. Sometimes a tree or list may be feasible to display all the possibilities. But usually the overwhelming number of possibilities makes constructing a list or tree impractical. In this activity you will explore two types of counting problems, **permutations** and **combinations**, both of which use the multiplication principle of counting.

**Permutations** are arrangements of objects, from first to last, where the order in which the objects are selected is most important.

Example 1   *You have five textbooks and wish to arrange them on your bookshelf in the usual way. In how many ways can this be done?*

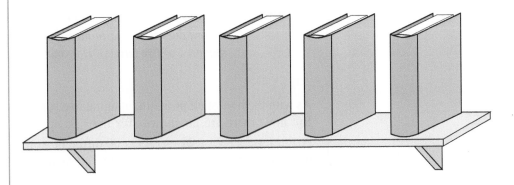

SOLUTION

Think of the five positions on the shelf, left to right. Consider how many ways the first space can be filled (5), then how many ways to fill the second space (4, since there are four books remaining), and so on. You could illustrate with a tree diagram if you wish, but a simple application of the multiplication principle will give you $5 \cdot 4 \cdot 3 \cdot 2 \cdot 1 = 120$. So there are 120 different arrangements or orderings of your five books. Equivalently, you say there are 120 *permutations* of any five objects.

1. Suppose you have seven different sweatshirts, and wish to wear a different one each day of the week. In how many ways can this be done?

2. There are 26 letters in the standard English alphabet. If you consider using all the letters to create a 26-letter word, how many different words are possible? (You will notice this is a very large number, so you will need scientific notation to give an approximate answer.)

> **Factorial Notation**
> The product of any positive integer with all smaller positive integers down to one has a special name and notation. For example, Five factorial is written as
> $5! = 5 \cdot 4 \cdot 3 \cdot 2 \cdot 1 = 120.$

**3.** Use the factorial notation on your calculator (see Appendix A) to determine 12!

*Note:* 0! is defined to be equal to one. (Check this on your calculator.) You can think of it as the number of ways to arrange zero things.

Sometimes you are interested in arrangements of only some of the objects from a larger collection. Words that are 26 letters long are a bit unrealistic, but using only five different letters might make more sense.

**Example 2**   *Suppose exactly five different letters are used to make a word (in this case a word does not have to be one found in a dictionary, but simply be a sequence of five letters). How many different words can be made?*

SOLUTION

As with the bookshelf problem, imagine five spaces, to hold each of the five letters. But now, there are 26 choices for the first space, 25 for the second, and so on. $26 \cdot 25 \cdot 24 \cdot 23 \cdot 22 = 7,893,600$ different words are possible. Notice that since there are only five letters, this is not a full factorial. These are still called permutations. There are 7,893,600 permutations of 26 objects, taken five at a time.

> **Permutations of $n$ objects taken $r$ at a time = the first $r$ factors of $n$!**
> Notation: $_nP_r = n(n-1)(n-2) \cdots (n-r+1) = \dfrac{n!}{(n-r)!}$

**4.** Redo Example 2 using the permutations formula above. Then, verify your answer by using the permutation feature on your calculator (see Appendix A).

**5.** The governor is visiting your school and you need to assign seating for 14 students. Unfortunately there are only six seats in the front row. In how many different ways can you select and arrange the six lucky students?

## Combinations

Sometimes the order in which selections are made is not important. For example, in Problem 5, if the arrangement of the six chosen students is not important, you would simply want to count how many ways a group of six students could be chosen for the first row. For this revised situation you are counting the number of combinations of 14 objects taken six at a time.

**Combinations** are collections of objects selected from a larger collection, where the order of selection is not important. The number of ways to select $r$ objects from a collection of $n$ objects is called the number of combinations of $n$ objects taken $r$ at a time.

6. In Problem 5, for each possible group of six students, how many seating arrangements are possible?

7. If you could list all 2,162,160 permutations in Problem 5, you could also group them according to the actual six students selected. Each group would have the number you determined in Problem 6. Divide accordingly to determine the number of ways to select the six students.

**Combinations of $n$ objects taken $r$ at a time:** $_nC_r = \dfrac{_nP_r}{_rP_r} = \dfrac{n!}{(n-r)!\,r!}$

8. Apply the combinations formula above to verify your answer to Problem 7.

9. From a student body of 230 students, how many different committees of four students are possible? (*Hint:* The order in which the four students are selected is not important.)

An interesting symmetrical property of combinations appears when you consider not only the objects selected from a collection, but also those left behind. Does it make sense that the number of ways to select 3 objects from a collection of 8 objects is the same as counting the number of ways to leave 5 behind?

10. Verify the above statement by computing $_8C_3$ and $_8C_5$.

Many times the most important part of the problem is determining whether or not the order of the selections is significant. In Exercise 5 of Activity 6.2, involving ordering a triple scoop ice cream cone, some people might consider the order of the scoops important. Others might not care how the three flavors are placed on the cone.

11. In each situation, determine whether you are asked to determine the number of permutations or combinations. Then do the calculation.

   a. How many ways are there to pick a starting five from a basketball team of twelve members?

**b.** How many ways are there to distribute nine different books among 15 children if no child gets more than one book?

**c.** How many ways are there to pick a subset of four different letters from the 26-letter alphabet?

**d.** How many ways can the three offices of chairman, vice chairman, and secretary be filled from a club with 25 members?

## Applications

Many variations on these basic counting techniques arise in the study of probability and computer science. Here are a couple of examples, with problems for you to try.

**Example 3**    *How many different ten-digit binary sequences (only 0s and 1s) are there with exactly seven zeros and three ones?*

SOLUTION

While the order of the binary digits is important, this counting problem is most easily solved by determining the number of combinations of ten digits taken seven at a time. Think of the ten positions for the digits, and ask: How many ways can you select seven positions for the zeros?

$$_{10}C_7 = \frac{10 \cdot 9 \cdot 8 \cdot 7 \cdot 6 \cdot 5 \cdot 4 \cdot 3 \cdot 2 \cdot 1}{(7 \cdot 6 \cdot 5 \cdot 4 \cdot 3 \cdot 2 \cdot 1) \cdot (3 \cdot 2 \cdot 1)} = \frac{10 \cdot 9 \cdot 8}{3 \cdot 2} = 120.$$

Or equivalently, how many ways can you select three positions for the ones?

$$_{10}C_3 = \frac{10 \cdot 9 \cdot 8 \cdot 7 \cdot 6 \cdot 5 \cdot 4 \cdot 3 \cdot 2 \cdot 1}{(3 \cdot 2 \cdot 1) \cdot (7 \cdot 6 \cdot 5 \cdot 4 \cdot 3 \cdot 2 \cdot 1)} = \frac{10 \cdot 9 \cdot 8}{3 \cdot 2} = 120.$$

**12.** If a coin is flipped twenty times, how many different ways are there to get exactly five heads?

**13.** What is the probability that a coin flipped twenty times will come up heads exactly five times?

**Example 4**   *How many ways are there to arrange the letters of the word SYSTEMS?*

SOLUTION

The repeated *S* makes this more difficult than a simple permutation problem. If you imagined the letters on tiles (like the game Scrabble), with the *S* tiles labeled with numbers: $S_1, S_2, S_3$, so you can tell them apart, then there would be simply 7! ways to arrange the seven tiles. But without the numbers, or tiles, the *S*'s all look the same, so you would be way over-counting the different words. Each unique word will appear 3! times, the number of ways the three *S*'s can be ordered. So if you divide out this multiplicity, you will have an accurate count:

$$\frac{7!}{3!} = 7 \cdot 6 \cdot 5 \cdot 4 = 840 \text{ truly unique words.}$$

**14.** How many different words can be formed by rearranging all the letters of the word *MIRROR*?

---

**SUMMARY
ACTIVITY 6.7**

1. **Permutations** are arrangements of objects, from first to last, where the order in which the objects are selected is most important.

2. **Factorial Notation:** $n! = n(n-1)(n-2)\cdots 3 \cdot 2 \cdot 1$

3. **Permutations of $n$ objects taken $r$ at a time** = the first $r$ factors of $n!$

   Notation: $_nP_r = n(n-1)(n-2) \cdots (n-r+1) = \dfrac{n!}{(n-r)!}$

4. **Combinations** are collections of objects selected from a larger collection, where the order of selection is not important.

5. **Combinations of $n$ objects taken $r$ at a time** = $_nC_r = \dfrac{_nP_r}{_rP_r} = \dfrac{n!}{(n-r)!r!}$

1. Compute each of the following:

   **a.** $5!$           **b.** $\dfrac{100!}{98!}$           **c.** $_9P_9$

   **d.** $_{12}P_9$        **e.** $\dfrac{_{10}P_4}{_6P_4}$        **f.** $_{12}C_5$

   **g.** $_8C_8$         **h.** $_{285}C_1$        **i.** $_8C_3 \cdot {_5}C_2$

2. How many different ways are there to arrange twelve books on a shelf?

3. How many ways are there to select a committee of five from a club with 30 members?

4. How many different four-digit numbers can be made using the digits 1, 2, 3, 4, 5, 6 if no digit can be used more than once?

5. How many ways are possible to select a president and vice president from an association with 5400 members?

6. How many different words can be made by rearranging the letters of the word *SYMMETRY*?

7. If a coin is flipped 50 times, in how many ways could there be exactly two tails?

8. A lottery ticket has 54 numbers, from which the player chooses six.

   **a.** What is the probability that all six numbers are correct, and the player wins the big jackpot?

   **b.** What is the probability that the player gets five of the six numbers correct?

**9.** A club with 46 members, of which 20 are girls, needs to form a committee of six, to be composed of the same number of boys as girls. In how many ways can this committee be selected? (*Hint:* Calculate two different numbers of combinations, then apply the multiplication principle.)

**10.** The number of combinations for any size collection makes an interesting pattern, usually called Pascal's triangle, after the French mathematician/philosopher Blaise Pascal (1623–1662). This pattern was introduced back in the exercises for Activity 1.2. Each row of the triangle has one more number than the previous row, each number the result of adding the two numbers immediately above it. The first and last numbers are always one.

   **a.** Identify the pattern and then complete the next three rows of Pascal's triangle.

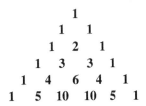

   **b.** Each row actually contains the number of combinations of $n$ objects taken $r$ at a time, where $n$ is the number of the row (starting with 0) and $r$ is the position in the row (again, starting with 0). For example, 1, 3, 3, 1 are $_3C_0$, $_3C_1$, $_3C_2$, $_3C_3$. Which number in Pascal's triangle corresponds to $_7C_4$? Verify with your calculator.

   **c.** When displayed in this form, the symmetry of the combinations is plain to see. If you know the value of $_{30}C_{18}$, what else is it equal to?

**ACTIVITY 6.8**
How Many Boys
(or Girls)?

**OBJECTIVES**

1. Recognize components of binomial experiment.

2. Calculate binomial probabilities.

In a family with five children, how unusual would it be for all the children to be boys? Or by the same token, all girls? Such questions are relevant for many families in cultures around the world, especially when one gender is favored over another.

Suppose a family does have all boys. What is the probability of such an event?

1.  Assume the birth of a boy or a girl is equally likely. What is the probability that a single child is born a boy?

2.  Now suppose a family has one boy already. What is the probability that their next child will also be a boy?

The probabilities you just determined are for a single child. You are really interested in the probability that for a family with two children, both are boys.

3.  For a family with two children, what are the possible outcomes? Provide a tree diagram or simply list the possibilities.

4.  **a.** Use the sample space in Problem 3 to determine the theoretical probability of the event that a family with two children has two boys.

    **b.** Assume that the individual outcomes of the two births are independent (i.e., the outcome of the second birth in no way depends upon the outcome of the first birth). Use the multiplication principle of probability to determine the probability that a two-child family has two boys.

5.  What is the theoretical probability of the event that a family with two children has two girls?

6.  What is the theoretical probability of the event that a family with two children has one boy and one girl?

7.  At this point, you have determined the probabilities of all the possible outcomes for a two-child family. Letting the random (independent) variable $x$ represent the number of boys in a family with two children, complete the following table for and verify the properties of the probability distribution.

    Recall: $0 \le P(x) \le 1$ for all $x$ in the sample space and the sum of the probabilities of all $x$ in the sample space must equal 1.

| x | P(x) |
|---|------|
|   |      |
|   |      |
|   |      |

Note that $P(1 \text{ boy and } 1 \text{ girl}) \neq \frac{1}{2} \cdot \frac{1}{2}$. This is because there are two ways the family could have one boy, either first born or second born. If you wanted the probability of "the first born is a boy and the second born is a girl," the probability is the product of the probabilities of independent events.

## Binomial Probability Distribution

There are many situations where each individual outcome can go one of two ways: boy or girl, head or tail, right or wrong, success or failure. Assuming the two outcomes have well defined and fixed probabilities, combinations of such outcomes define a **binomial probability distribution**. To determine an individual binomial probability, it is necessary to count how many ways an event can occur (like the two distinct ways a family with two children could have one boy).

For the moment, let's consider a different binomial (two outcome) situation, flipping a coin. Assuming fairness (head and tail equally likely, as we had assumed for boy and girl), $P(\text{head}) = P(\text{tail}) = 0.5$.

8. Consider flipping a fair coin three times. Let $x =$ the number of heads, record the sample space for this experiment (as a tree, chart or list), and fill in the table for this binomial probability distribution.

| x | P(x) |
|---|------|
|   |      |
|   |      |
|   |      |
|   |      |

9. Repeat the same process for flipping a coin four times.

| x | P(x) |
|---|------|
|   |      |
|   |      |
|   |      |
|   |      |
|   |      |

There are several shortcuts for determining the number of ways a certain number of heads can come up. In flipping a coin four times, it is not too difficult to simply list the different ways exactly two heads could result: hhtt, htht, htth, thth, thht, and hhtt. If you can agree that these are all different, and there are no more possible, then the theoretical probability of getting exactly two heads when four coins are flipped is $\frac{6}{16} = \frac{3}{8}$. (Is this what you got in Problem 9?)

But suppose you flipped a coin 100 times, or even only ten times. To determine the number of ways to get exactly five heads by listing them, or drawing a tree, would be tedious. There is, however, a formula for calculating these numbers, which are called **binomial coefficients**. They are the very same **combinations** you learned about in Activity 6.7.

**Example 1**    *Consider Problem 9, in which you flipped a coin four times. How many ways can exactly two heads occur?*

SOLUTION

This is sometimes called the "number of combinations of four things taken two at a time." There are two types of notation used, $\binom{4}{2}$ and $_4C_2$. The computation is

$$_4C_2 = \frac{4 \cdot 3 \cdot 2 \cdot 1}{(2 \cdot 1)(2 \cdot 1)} = 6.$$

The number of ways to get exactly three heads on five flips would be

$$_5C_3 = \frac{5 \cdot 4 \cdot 3 \cdot 2 \cdot 1}{(3 \cdot 2 \cdot 1)(2 \cdot 1)} = 10.$$

In general, $\binom{n}{r} = {_nC_r} = \frac{n!}{r! \cdot (n-r)!}$

$$= \frac{n(n-1)\cdots 3 \cdot 2 \cdot 1}{(r(r-1)\cdots 3 \cdot 2 \cdot 1)((n-r)(n-r-1)\cdots 3 \cdot 2 \cdot 1)}$$

This is a rather complicated formula, but binomial coefficients can be easily computed on your calculator. (See Appendix A.)

**10.** Calculate the number of ways to get exactly four heads when a coin is flipped five times, by applying the formula and by checking on your calculator.

**11.** Now determine the binomial probabilities for the number of heads when a coin is flipped five times.

| x | P(x) |
|---|------|
|   |      |
|   |      |
|   |      |
|   |      |
|   |      |
|   |      |

**12.** Experimentally, you can see if your probability distribution seems reasonable by actually flipping coins. Instead of flipping an individual coin five times, use five coins, shake them up in your cupped hands, and drop them on the table, recording the number of heads. Repeat this ten times, recording your results in a frequency table. How close are your relative frequencies to the theoretical probabilities you calculated in Problem 11?

| x | TEN REPETITIONS | | ENTIRE CLASS | |
|---|------|-----------|------|-----------|
|   | FREQ. | REL. FREQ. | FREQ. | REL. FREQ. |
|   |      |           |      |           |
|   |      |           |      |           |
|   |      |           |      |           |
|   |      |           |      |           |
|   |      |           |      |           |
|   |      |           |      |           |

**13.** Record the frequencies and relative frequencies for the entire class. Did you observe what you expected, with regard to the theoretical probabilities? Explain.

Appendix

**14.** It is also possible to simulate many repetitions of the experiment on a computer or your calculator. (See Appendix A.) Simulate flipping five coins 500 times on your calculator, by generating a list of 500 random integers between 0 and 5, from a binomial distribution. Record your results in the table, and then record the collective total for your entire class. Comment on the results, compared to your previous work.

| x | 500 REPETITIONS | | ENTIRE CLASS | |
|---|------|-----------|------|-----------|
|   | FREQ. | REL. FREQ. | FREQ. | REL. FREQ. |
|   |      |           |      |           |
|   |      |           |      |           |
|   |      |           |      |           |
|   |      |           |      |           |
|   |      |           |      |           |

**15.** It is also possible to determine any binomial probability directly from a table or your calculator. (See Appendix A.) Use your calculator to verify the theoretical probabilities you calculated in Problem 11.

In general, a binomial probability is calculated using the following formula:

$$P(x) = \binom{n}{x} p^n q^{n-x}, \text{ where}$$

> $n$ is the number of independent trials,
> $x$ is the random variable, what is being counted,
> $p$ is the probability of a success (the outcome $x$ is counting),
> $q$ is the probability of a failure (the other outcome)

For example, in the previous Problems 11–15, $n = 5$, $p = q = 0.5$. The probability of exactly three heads (successes) out of five coin flips is

$$P(3) = \binom{5}{3} 0.5^3 0.5^{5-3} = \frac{5 \cdot 4 \cdot 3 \cdot 2 \cdot 1}{(3 \cdot 2 \cdot 1) \cdot (2 \cdot 1)} 0.5^5 = 0.3125.$$

**16.** How close did your final relative frequency for three heads come to this theoretical probability?

**17. a.** Apply the formula to determine the probability that a two-child family has both boys.

**b.** Apply the formula to determine the probability that among eight children exactly five will be boys. Verify your result by finding directly with your calculator.

Because you assumed a fair coin, and the birth of a boy and girl are equally likely, the probability of a success and the probability of a failure were both 0.5. Usually these probabilities are different, as you might have guessed from the formula.

**18.** Suppose that 10% of all electrical switches are defective.

**a.** What is the probability of selecting a defective switch in a single selection?

**b.** What is the probability of selecting a good switch in a single selection?

**c.** If you select five switches, what is the probability that exactly one is defective? Apply the formula and then verify directly on your calculator.

## SUMMARY
### Activity 6.8

1. **Independent Events:** When the outcome of one event in no way affects or determines the outcome of the other event.

2. The probability that two independent events both occur is equal to the product of the individual probabilities of the events. Symbolically, if $E_1$ and $E_2$ are independent events, then $P(E_1 \text{ and } E_2) = P(E_1) \cdot P(E_2)$

3. **Binomial Coefficients:** $\dbinom{n}{r} = {}_nC_r = \dfrac{n!}{r! \cdot (n - r)!}$

$$= \dfrac{n(n - 1) \cdots 3 \cdot 2 \cdot 1}{(r(r - 1) \cdots 3 \cdot 2 \cdot 1)((n - r)(n - r - 1) \cdots 3 \cdot 2 \cdot 1)}$$

(Also called the number of combinations of $n$ things taken $r$ at a time.)

4. **Binomial Probabilities:**

When an experiment is repeated $n$ times (called $n$ trials), each trial having only two possible outcomes (success or failure), and all trials being independent, then the probability of having $x$ successes in $n$ trials is called a binomial probability, given by the formula $P(x) = \dbinom{n}{x} p^x q^{n-x}$,

where $n$ is the number of trials,

  $x$ is the random variable, what is being counted,

  $p$ is the probability of a success (the outcome $x$ is counting),

  $q$ is the probability of a failure (the other outcome)

## EXERCISES
### Activity 6.8

1. In a family with eight children, what is the probability that exactly six are boys?

2. Again with eight children, what is the probability there are at least six are boys? (*Hint:* Add the three probabilities for either six, seven, or eight boys.)

3. What is the probability that when a fair coin is flipped 20 times, there will be exactly five tails?

4. In a randomly generated sequence of 24 binary digits (0s and 1s), what is the probability that exactly half of the digits are 0?

**5.** According to the U.S. Census Bureau, 49.65% of Texas residents were male in 2000.

    **a.** If one Texan was selected at random in 2000, what is the probability he was male?

    **b.** If one Texan was selected at random in 2000, what is the probability she was female?

    **c.** Consider the experiment of selecting ten Texans at random. If you are interested in determining the probabilities of selecting $x$ males, is this a binomial probability distribution? And if so, what are the values of $n$, $p$, and $q$?

    **d.** Determine the probability that exactly two men are chosen, out of the ten people, by applying the formula. Verify by also going directly to the binomial probabilities on your calculator.

**6.** Suppose the probability of your hitting the bull's-eye on a dartboard is 0.06.

    **a.** What is the probability of getting exactly two bull's-eyes when you throw five darts?

Appendix

    **b.** Empirically verify that your probability in part a is reasonable by simulating the throwing of five darts 500 times on your calculator. (See Appendix A.) Display a histogram for your simulation, and record the relative frequencies for all the possible values of $x$, the number of bull's-eyes.

| x | REL. FREQ. |
|---|---|
|  |  |
|  |  |
|  |  |
|  |  |

    **c.** Now calculate the remaining theoretical probabilities, to see that they are close to the relative frequencies of your simulation.

| x | P(x) |
|---|---|
|  |  |
|  |  |
|  |  |
|  |  |
|  |  |
|  |  |

    **d.** About how many times might you expect to have to repeat this experiment to get five bull's-eyes on all five throws?

**7.** In taking a multiple-choice test, there are five possible answers for each problem, only one of which is correct. Assume that someone guesses randomly on all 25 problems.

    **a.** What is the probability of getting the first problem correct?

    **b.** What is the probability of getting the first problem wrong?

    **c.** What number of correct answers is needed to achieve a passing grade of 70%?

    **d.** What is the probability of getting a passing grade with the minimum number correct?

## Activities 6.1–6.8   What Have I Learned?

1. If you flip a coin 50 times and get 22 tails, should you assume that the probability of getting tails with this coin is 0.44? Explain.

2. What does the law of large numbers say about the relationship between theoretical and experimental probabilities?

3. If a random experiment consists of rolling a six-sided die ten times, how many individual outcomes make up the sample space, and what is the probability of getting all sixes?

4. Could this table represent a probability distribution? Explain.

| x | 1 | 2 | 3 | 4 | 5 |
|------|-----|-----|-----|-----|------|
| P(x) | 0.2 | 0.3 | 0.4 | 0.1 | 0.05 |

5. You shuffle a standard deck of 52 cards, and then start turning them over one at a time. The first one is a red card. So is the second card turned over. The third card turned over is also a red card. This continues so that the first 10 cards turned over are all red.

   a. What is the probability that you get 10 red cards in a row?

   b. Is the probability that the eleventh card will be black much higher than the likelihood of getting another red card? Explain.

6. If A and B are mutually exclusive events, then what is P(A and B)? Explain.

7. If A and B represent independent events, what is $P(A|B)$? Explain.

**8.** Is it possible for mutually exclusive events to be independent? Explain.

**9.** In selecting objects from a collection, the order or arrangement of the selected items is not always important. If the order is important, are you counting permutations or combinations?

**10.** In each of these counting problems, state whether you would find the number of permutations or combinations.

   **a.** In how many ways can 20 delegates be arranged in a row of 20 chairs?

   **b.** In how many ways can a committee of four be selected from a club with 235 members?

   **c.** In how many ways can the president, vice president, and treasurer be selected from an association of 2550 members?

   **d.** In how many ways can you pick three different flavors of ice cream for your sundae when there are 53 flavors from which to choose?

**11.** What are the defining characteristics of a binomial probability experiment, or distribution?

**12.** In each of these experiments, determine whether or not the probabilities are binomial probabilities. If they are, identify the values for $n$, $p$, and $q$.

   **a.** A die is rolled 20 times. What is the probability of getting $x$ even numbers?

   **b.** A pair of dice are rolled 50 times. What is the probability of getting doubles $x$ times?

   **c.** Five marbles are selected from an urn with 20 marbles (10 white and 10 black). What is the probability of selecting $x$ white marbles?

## Activities 6.1–6.8 | How Can I Practice?

1. The following table displays the annual salaries and years of education for a cross section of the population. Complete the totals for each category. Then calculate the relative frequency for each entry.

| EDUCATION | LESS THAN $20,000 | $20,000 < SALARY < $50,000 | $50,000 < SALARY < $100,000 | MORE THAN $100,000 | TOTAL |
|---|---|---|---|---|---|
| 12 years | 130 | 146 | 41 | 4 | |
| 14 years | 105 | 198 | 52 | 10 | |
| 16 years | 31 | 252 | 187 | 24 | |
| More than 16 | 6 | 161 | 241 | 60 | |
| **Total** | | | | | |

a. If an individual is selected at random, use the corresponding relative frequencies to estimate the probability that the person has:

  i. 12 years of education and makes more than $100,000.

  ii. 14 years of education and makes less than $20,000.

  iii. more than 16 years of education and makes more than $50,000.

b. Given that the individual chosen has 14 years of education, what is the probability that he or she makes more than $50,000?

c. Given that the individual chosen has 16 or more years of education, what is the probability that she or he makes more than $50,000?

2. A vase contains 35 marbles: 10 blue, 8 green, 7 yellow, 5 red, and 5 white. One marble is selected at random. Find the following probabilities.

a. *P*(red)

b. *P*(not blue)

c. *P*(green or white)

d. *P*(black)

e. *P*(not black)

**3.** If a six-sided die is rolled four times, how many different four-digit sequences are possible?

**4.** If a six-sided die is rolled three times, how many branches will be in the tree that displays the sample space?

**5.** If a coin is flipped four times, determine the probability distribution for the number of tails.

| x, THE NUMBER OF TAILS | 0 | 1 | 2 | 3 | 4 |
|---|---|---|---|---|---|
| P(x) | | | | | |

**6.** A coin is flipped and a fair die is rolled.

   **a.** Construct a tree diagram showing all the possible outcomes.

   **b.** Determine the probability that a head shows and a 2 is rolled.

   **c.** What is the probability that a tail shows or an even number is rolled?

**7.** The school's Guidance Counselor submitted a report to the School Board summarizing the percentage of students in grades 9–12 that were studying a language other than English. The results are given in the table.

| SPANISH | FRENCH | GERMAN | OTHER | NONE |
|---|---|---|---|---|
| 26% | 9% | 3% | 3% | 59% |

Determine the probability that a randomly selected student in grades $9 - 12$ is

**a.** studying Spanish          **b.** not studying French

**c.** studying French or German

8. The land area of Canada is 9,094,000 square kilometers. Of this land, 4,176,000 square kilometers is forested. A square kilometer of land in Canada is randomly selected.

  **a.** What is the probability that the selected area of land is forested?

  **b.** What is the probability that it is not forested?

9. During World War II, the British determined that the probability that a bomber was lost through enemy action on a mission over occupied Europe was 0.05.

  **a.** What is the probability that a bomber survived its mission?

  **b.** What is the probability that a bomber survived 2 missions? Assume the events are independent.

  **c.** What is the probability that a bomber returns safely after 10 missions?

10. Each of the six joints in the Challenger space shuttle's booster rocket had a 0.977 reliability. The six rocket joints worked independently.

  **a.** What does it mean that the six rocket joints work independently?

  **b.** A 0.977 reliability means that the probability of a rocket joint working successfully is 0.977. What is the probability that all six rocket booster joints work successfully?

**11.** The following table gives the number of degrees (in thousands) earned in the United States in the 2005–2006 academic year.

|  | BACHELOR'S | MASTER'S | PROFESSIONAL | DOCTORATE | TOTAL |
|---|---|---|---|---|---|
| Female | 784 | 276 | 39 | 20 | |
| Male | 559 | 197 | 44 | 25 | |
| Total | | | | | |

    **a.** Complete the table.

    **b.** If a student receiving a degree is randomly selected, what is the probability that the person selected is female?

    **c.** What is the probability that the degree recipient is a male who earned a Doctorate?

    **d.** What is the probability that the person is a female, given that the person received a Master's degree?

    **e.** What is the probability that the person selected received a bachelor's degree, given the recipient is male?

    **f.** What is the probability the person selected is a female or received a professional degree?

**12.** In a recent year, the percentage of computer games sold is summarized in the following table:

|  | GAME TYPE | | | | | |
|---|---|---|---|---|---|---|
|  | Strategy | Family and Children's | Shooters | Role Playing | Sports | Other |
| Percentage | 26.9% | 20.3% | 16.3% | 10.0% | 5.4% | 21.1% |

    **a.** What is the probability that a computer game sold was a strategy or shooters game?

    **b.** What is the probability that the computer game is not a family game?

**c.** What is the probability that the computer game sold is a strategy game, given it is not a sports game?

13. If a license plate consists of three letters (excluding I and O) followed by three digits (excluding 0 and 1), how many different plates are possible?

14. You have ten books to arrange on your bookshelf. How many different orderings of all ten books are possible?

15. There are 96 boys in the freshman class. If five boys are selected at random to form a new rock band, how many possible bands are there?

16. If the band members in the previous problem are to be assigned specific instruments (drums, bass, keyboard, guitar, and vocals), how many bands are possible?

17. How many five-digit numbers are possible, if no digit can be repeated (and 0 as the first digit is allowed)?

18. If a coin is flipped 30 times, how many possible ways could there be exactly 10 heads?

19. If a fair coin is flipped 10 times, and heads comes up every time, what is the probability that on the next flip the coin will come up tails?

20. What is the probability that in a family with 12 children, exactly half of them are boys?

21. Suppose you know 2% of all switches are defective. If two switches are used in a device:

   **a.** What is the probability that both switches are good?

   **b.** What is the probability that exactly one switch is good?

   **c.** What is the probability that at least one switch is good?

**d.** Could you also determine your answer to part c by subtracting the probability of getting two defective switches from 1?

**e.** What is the minimum number of switches that need to be selected so the probability of getting at least one good switch is greater than 0.999999?

**22.** In playing Monopoly, rolling doubles three times in a row sends you to jail.

  **a.** What is the probability of rolling three consecutive doubles?

  **b.** If you roll the dice 100 times over the course of a game, what is the probability that you will have rolled doubles, at any point, exactly three times?

# CHAPTER 6

# Summary

*The bracketed numbers following each concept indicate the activity in which the concept is discussed.*

| CONCEPT / SKILL | DESCRIPTION | EXAMPLE |
|---|---|---|
| **Relative frequency** [6.1] | Frequency of a particular value expressed as a fractional part of all possible values. | If a coin is flipped 100 times, and heads comes up 43 times, its relative frequency is 43%. |
| **Event** [6.1] | A particular outcome or result for which a probability can be defined. | The event of getting an even number when a six-sided die is rolled. |
| **Experimental probability** [6.1] | Probability of event $E = P(E)$ $$= \frac{\text{Number of observed occurrences of event}}{\text{Total number of observations}}$$ | Results of rolling a die ten times: $\{1, 4, 3, 6, 5, 2, 1, 4, 1, 5\}$ $P(\text{Even}) = \frac{4}{10} = 0.4.$ |
| **Theoretical probability** [6.1] | $$P(E) = \frac{\text{Number of outcomes in event}}{\text{Total number of equally likely possible outcomes}}$$ | In a single toss of a fair coin, $P(\text{Heads}) = \frac{1}{2} = 0.5$ |
| **Sample space** [6.1] | The collection of all possible individual outcomes. | The sample space for rolling a single die is $\{1, 2, 3, 4, 5, 6\}$. |
| **Probability properties** [6.1] | • The probability of any event is always between 0 and 1. <br><br> • The probability of an impossible event is 0. <br><br> • The probability of a certainty is 1. <br><br><br> • The sum of the probabilities of all possible outcomes in a sample space is equal to 1. | $0 \le P(E) \le 1$ <br><br> The probability of getting 7 on a single die roll is zero. <br><br> The probability of getting less than 7 on a single die roll is one. <br><br> For a single die roll, $P(1) + P(2) + P(3) + P(4) + P(5) + P(6)$ $= \frac{1}{6} + \frac{1}{6} + \frac{1}{6} + \frac{1}{6} + \frac{1}{6} + \frac{1}{6} = 1.$ |
| **Law of large numbers** [6.1] | The larger the number of observations, the closer the experimental probability of an event will get to the theoretical probability of that same event. | When a coin is flipped many times, the relative frequency of getting heads is most likely not exactly 0.5, but gets closer to 0.5 as the number of flips gets larger. |
| **Simulation** [6.1] | When some experiment or other real world situation is modeled using mathematics, and usually computers, to observe patterns and make predictions about the real world. | With a computer or calculator, flipping a coin can be simulated, to observe many more flips than could actually be done. |

| | | |
|---|---|---|
| **Multiplication principle of counting** [6.2] | If some choice can be made in $M$ ways and a subsequent choice can be made in $N$ ways, then there are $M$ times $N$ ways these two choices can be made in succession. | If you have 5 sweaters and 4 hats, there are $5 \cdot 4 = 20$ different ways for you to wear a sweater and hat. |
| **Tree diagram** [6.2] | Displays all possible outcomes for a sequence of choices, one outcome for each branch of the tree. | Tree for flipping a coin twice.<br> |
| **Independent events** [6.3] | Events $A$ and $B$ are independent events if the occurrence of either event does not affect the probability of the occurrence of the other event. | The outcomes of flipping a coin two times are independent. |
| **Dependent events** [6.3] | Events $A$ and $B$ are dependent events if the occurrence of either event affects the probability of the occurrence of the other event. | The outcomes of selecting two cards from a deck of cards without replacement are dependent. |
| **Probability of two independent events both occurring** [6.3] | The probability that two independent events both occur is equal to the product of the probabilities of the individual events. Stated symbolically, if $A$ and $B$ are independent events, then $$P(A \text{ and } B) = P(A) \cdot P(B)$$ | Selecting two cards with replacement: $P(\text{1st ace and 2nd ace})$ $= P(\text{1st ace}) \cdot P(\text{2nd ace})$ $= \dfrac{4}{52} \cdot \dfrac{4}{52} = \dfrac{1}{169}$ |
| **Probability of two dependent events both occurring** [6.3] | If $A$ and $B$ are dependent events, then $P(A \text{ and } B) = P(A) \cdot P(B,$ given $A$ has occurred). | Selecting two cards without replacement: $P(\text{1st ace and 2nd ace})$ $= P(\text{1st ace}) \cdot P\begin{pmatrix} \text{2nd ace,} \\ \text{given 1st} \\ \text{ace selected} \end{pmatrix}$ $= \dfrac{4}{52} \cdot \dfrac{3}{51} = \dfrac{1}{221}$ |
| **Mutually exclusive events** [6.3] | Two events $A$ and $B$ are said to be mutually exclusive if it is not possible for both events to occur together. | Selecting one card from a standard deck: the outcomes card is a king and card is an ace are mutually exclusive. |
| **Probabilities of mutually exclusive events** [6.3] | If $A$ and $B$ are mutually exclusive events, then<br>**i.** $P(A \text{ and } B) = 0$<br>**ii.** $P(A \text{ or } B) = P(A) + P(B)$ | **i.** a card is drawn:<br> $P(\text{ace and king}) = 0$<br>**ii.** a card is drawn:<br> $P(\text{club or heart})$<br> $= P(\text{club}) + P(\text{heart})$<br> $= \dfrac{13}{52} + \dfrac{13}{52} = \dfrac{1}{2}$ |

| | | |
|---|---|---|
| **Probability of events that are not mutually exclusive** [6.3] | If $A$ and $B$ are not mutually exclusive, then<br>$P(A \text{ or } B)$<br>$= P(A) + P(B) - P(A \text{ and } B)$ | A card is drawn:<br>$P(\text{club or ace})$<br>$= P(\text{club}) + P(\text{ace}) -$<br>$\quad P(\text{club and ace}).$<br>$= \dfrac{13}{52} + \dfrac{4}{52} - \dfrac{1}{52} = \dfrac{16}{52} = \dfrac{4}{13}$ |
| **Conditional probability** [6.4] | The **conditional probability** of an event $A$ is when the probability of the event is affected by the knowledge that other event has already occurred. $P(A|B)$ denotes the probability of event $A$, given that event $B$ has occurred. | Two fair dice are rolled. The probability that the sum of the dots on the dice is 5, given first die is a 2. |
| **Calculating conditional probabilities** [6.4] | The formula used to calculate conditional probabilities is<br>$P(A|B) = \dfrac{P(A \text{ and } B)}{P(B)}$, where<br>$P(B) \neq 0$. The probabilities $P(A \text{ and } B)$ and $P(B)$ are determined using the original sample space. | Two fair dice are rolled:<br>$P(\text{total } 5 \mid \text{first is } 2)$<br>$= \dfrac{P(\text{total } 5 \text{ and first is } 2)}{P(\text{first is } 2)}$<br>$= \dfrac{\frac{1}{36}}{\frac{6}{36}} = \dfrac{1}{6}$ |
| **Permutations** [6.7] | Arrangements of objects, from first to last, where the order in which the objects are selected is most important. | There are 6 permutations of the letters $abc$:<br>$abc, acb, bac, bca, cab, cba$ |
| **Factorial notation** [6.7] | The product of any positive integer with all smaller positive integers down to one has a special name and notation. | 6 factorial (denoted 6!) is<br>$6! = 6 \cdot 5 \cdot 4 \cdot 3 \cdot 2 \cdot 1 = 720.$ |
| **Permutations of $n$ objects taken $r$ at a time** [6.7] | The first $r$ factors of $n!$, denoted by<br>$_nP_r = n(n-1)(n-2) \cdots$<br>$(n-r+1) = \dfrac{n!}{(n-r)!}.$ | Different ways to arrange 3 books from a collection of 5 books is<br>$_5P_3 = 5 \cdot 4 \cdot 3 = 60.$ |
| **Combinations** [6.7] | Collections of objects selected from a larger collection, where the order of selection is not important. | The ways to select 6 lottery numbers are combinations, since the order of selection is not important. |
| **Combinations of $n$ objects taken $r$ at a time** [6.7] | The number of ways to select $r$ objects from a collection of $n$ objects, denoted by $_nC_r = \dfrac{_nP_r}{_rP_r} = \dfrac{n!}{(n-r)!\,r!}.$ | The number of ways of selecting a committee of 4 from a group of 20 people is<br>$_{20}C_4 = \dfrac{20 \cdot 19 \cdot 18 \cdot 17}{4 \cdot 3 \cdot 2 \cdot 1} = 4845.$ |

| The probability that two independent events both occur [6.8] | Equal to the product of the individual probabilities of the events. Symbolically, if $E_1$ and $E_2$ are independent events, then $P(E_1 \text{ and } E_2) = P(E_1) \cdot P(E_2)$ | The probability of getting heads on the first toss and tails on the second toss of a coin is $\frac{1}{2} \cdot \frac{1}{2} = \frac{1}{4}$. |
| --- | --- | --- |
| Binomial coefficients [6.8] | Another name for combinations, usually denoted by $$\binom{n}{r} = {}_nC_r.$$ | The number of ways to get 3 heads on 7 flips of a coin. $$\binom{7}{3} = {}_7C_3 = 35.$$ |
| Binomial probabilities [6.8] | When an experiment is repeated $n$ times (called $n$ trials), each trial having only two possible outcomes (success or failure), and all trials being independent, then the probability of having $x$ successes in $n$ trials is called a binomial probability, given by the formula $$P(x) = \binom{n}{x}p^x q^{n-x},$$ where $n$ is the number of trials, $x$ is the random variable, what is being counted, $p$ is the probability of a success (the outcome $x$ is counting), $q$ is the probability of a failure (the other outcome). | The probability of getting 3 heads on 7 flips of a coin is an example of a binomial probability, where $n = 7$, $x = 3$ and $p = q = 0.5$. $$P(3) = \binom{7}{3}0.5^3 \cdot 0.5^4$$ $$= \tfrac{35}{128} = 0.2734375.$$ |

# Gateway Review

1. The following table summarizes characteristics of registered voters in a small town district:

| | REPUBLICAN | DEMOCRAT | REFORM | UNAFFILIATED | TOTAL |
|---|---|---|---|---|---|
| FEMALE | 156 | 192 | 23 | 41 | 412 |
| MALE | 177 | 160 | 45 | 28 | 410 |
| TOTAL | 333 | 352 | 68 | 69 | 822 |

If one voter is selected at random, determine the following probabilities:

**a.** $P$(Democrat)

**b.** $P$(male)

**c.** $P$(female Republican)

**d.** $P$(male Reform)

**e.** $P$(not Republican)

**f.** Given the person selected is male, $P$(Reform)

2. A box of candies contains 25 red, 40 green, 30 yellow, and 50 brown candies. If one candy is selected at random, determine the following probabilities:

**a.** $P$(red)

**b.** $P$(yellow or brown)

**c.** $P$(not green)

**d.** $P$(blue)

3. A fair coin is flipped three times.
   **a.** Determine the number of outcomes.

   **b.** Construct a tree diagram to determine the sample space for this experiment.

   **c.** Let the input variable $x$ be the number of heads. Complete this table for the corresponding probability distribution.

| NUMBER OF HEADS, $x$ | $P(x)$ |
|---|---|
| 0 | |
| 1 | |
| 2 | |
| 3 | |

**4.** The six most popular colors for new cars or light trucks (including SUVs and minivans) in North America in 2005 are listed in the following table.

| | COLOR | | | | | |
|---|---|---|---|---|---|---|
| | SILVER | WHITE | GRAY | BLACK | RED | BLUE |
| PERCENT OF NEW CARS AND LIGHT TRUCKS | 18% | 17% | 15% | 11% | 11% | 12% |

A new car or light truck is randomly selected.

**a.** What is the probability that the selected vehicle is not red?

**b.** What is the probability that the selected vehicle is silver or black?

**c.** What is the probability that the selected vehicle has a color not listed in the table?

**5.** Suppose the probability that a resident of the U.S. has traveled to Canada is 0.18, to Mexico is 0.09, and to both countries is 0.04. What is the probability that a randomly selected American traveled to either Canada or Mexico?

**6.** In a recent poll, 85% of the season ticket holders for Fenway Park surveyed favored testing professional baseball players for steroids and other performance-enhancing drugs. If four season ticket holders are randomly selected, what is the probability that all four will be in favor of drug testing? Assume independence.

**7.** You live in a large city and commute to a part-time job by subway or by taxi. You take the subway 85% of the time because it costs less. You take a taxi the remaining 15% of the time. When taking the subway, you arrive at work on time 75% of the time. You make it on time 90% of the time when traveling by taxi.

**a.** What is the probability that on a given day, you took the subway and arrived on time?

**b.** What is the probability that you arrived on time, given you took a taxi?

**8.** A random sample of 200 people were asked whether they bought a new product and whether they saw an advertisement for the product before the purchase. The results are given in the table.

| | SAW ADVERTISEMENT | DID NOT SEE THE ADVERTISEMENT | TOTAL |
|---|---|---|---|
| **PURCHASED** | 105 | 20 | 125 |
| **DID NOT PURCHASE** | 15 | 60 | 75 |
| **TOTAL** | 120 | 80 | 200 |

**a.** What is the probability that a randomly selected person from the survey purchased the product?

**b.** What is the probability that a person purchased the product given the person saw the advertisement?

**c.** Does the probability in part b support the claim that advertising influences buying? Explain.

**d.** Determine $P(\text{purchase the product} \mid \text{did not see ad})$.

**9.** You have narrowed your vacation reading list to ten books. But you really only have time to read three of them. In how many ways can you choose the three books, assuming that you will also pick the order in which you will read them?

**10.** How many eight-digit serial numbers are possible if they cannot start with 0 or 1?

**11.** The portion of a city street map below shows city blocks packed with buildings. In walking from point A to point B someone needs to walk 10 city blocks. How many different ten-block walks are possible? (*Hint:* Start with a similar problem involving a shorter walk.)

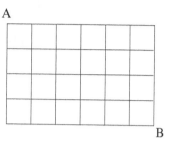

**12.** Determine the probability of getting all even numbers when a single die is rolled 12 times.

**13.** In how many ways can the letters of the word *PERMUTATION* be rearranged to form a unique word?

**14.** A family has five children, all girls. What is the probability that the next child born will be a boy?

**15.** A coin is tossed 15 times. What is the probability of exactly 10 heads?

**16.** If you know 42% of the registered voters in your county are Democrats, what is the probability of selecting 10 voters at random and getting at least eight Democrats?

# Problem Solving with Graphical and Statistical Models

**ACTIVITY 7.1**
Visualizing Trends

**OBJECTIVE**

1. Recognize how scaling of the axes of a graph can misrepresent the situation.

The overwhelming amount of data available to the American public has become an integral part of our information society. Newspapers, magazines, television news and especially the Internet provide us with data collected from a wide variety of sources. The United States Census Bureau collects a vast amount of data. For example, each month the United States Census Bureau's American Community Survey collects data from 250,000 households. The survey asks a wide range of questions about the household and each person in the household.
(See www.bls.census.gov/ACS.)

## Statistics

Statistics is the science of gathering, analyzing, and making predictions from data (numerical information). Statistics has become an indispensable tool in the study of such diverse areas as medicine and health issues, the economy, marketing, manufacturing, population trends, and the environment.

An important part of a statistical study is organizing and displaying the data collected. Throughout this textbook, you have observed how useful graphs can be for identifying patterns and trends. However, graphs can also be misleading. For example, consider the following three graphs:

**Graph I**

**Graph II**

**Graph III**

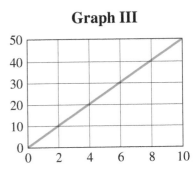

At first glance, the three graphs appear to represent the same line. However, with closer examination, the scale along the *x*- and *y*-axis is not the same. This results in the deception that the lines are identical. The lines have different slopes as shown below:

Line I: $\quad m = \dfrac{\Delta y}{\Delta x} = \dfrac{60 - 0}{20 - 0} = \dfrac{60}{20} = 3$

Line II: $\quad m = \dfrac{\Delta y}{\Delta x} = \dfrac{20 - 0}{10 - 0} = \dfrac{20}{10} = 2$

Line III: $\quad m = \dfrac{\Delta y}{\Delta x} = \dfrac{50 - 0}{10 - 0} = \dfrac{50}{10} = 5$

1. The following graphs show the performance of two stocks over the first five months of the year.

   a. Which graph appears to show the best performance? Explain.

   b. The graphs have different scales along the *y*-axis. Which scale makes the graph appear to be rising more slowly?

   As a matter of fact, the graphs in Problem 1 display the same information.

2. The following table shows the life expectancy for women in the United States for selected years in the period 1975–2000.

## Living Longer

| YEAR | 1975 | 1980 | 1985 | 1990 | 1995 | 2000 |
|---|---|---|---|---|---|---|
| WOMEN | 76.6 | 77.4 | 78.2 | 78.8 | 78.9 | 80.0 |

*Data:* U.S. Bureau of the Census

   a. Construct a line graph that makes the increase in the life expectancy from 1975–2000 appear to be relatively small.

   b. How would you change the vertical scale to make the increase seem larger?

3. The following graphs are examples of bar graphs. Bar graphs are a very popular way of displaying data in print media such as newspapers and magazines. The graphs show the increase in the use of the Internet for homework in a certain school district.

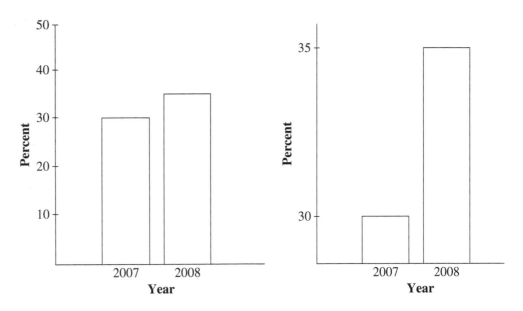

Which graph do you think best represents the increase in the use of the Internet for homework in the school district? Explain.

4. Look through your local newspaper for an article containing a line graph or bar graph. Do you think the article accurately interprets the graph? Does the scaling of the axis misrepresent the data? Explain.

A statistical study often involves a large number of data. Activity 7.2 gives additional ways of organizing and displaying data.

**ACTIVITY 7.2**

Bald Eagle
Population

**OBJECTIVES**

1. Read tables.

2. Read and interpret bar
   graphs.

3. Read and interpret circle
   graphs.

The bald eagle has been the national symbol of the United States since 1782, when its image with outspread wings was placed on the country's Great Seal. Bald eagles were in danger of becoming extinct about thirty years ago, but efforts to protect them are working. In 1999, President Clinton announced a proposal to remove this majestic bird from the list of threatened species. The bald eagle was eventually declared recovered and was delisted in July, 2007.

## Bar Graphs

The following bar graph displays the numbers of nesting bald eagle couples in the lower 48 states for the years from 1963 to 2000. The horizontal direction represents the years from 1963 to 2000. The vertical direction represents the number of nesting pairs.

*Source:* U.S. Fish and Wildlife Service

**1. a.** What was the number of nesting couples in 1963? In 1986? In 2000?

**b.** Explain how you located these numbers on the bar graph.

**2. a.** Estimate the number of nesting couples in 1982. In 1988. In 1996.

**b.** Explain how you estimated the numbers from the bar graph.

**c.** To what place value did you estimate the number of nesting couples in each case?

**d.** Compare your estimates with the estimates of some of your classmates. Briefly describe the comparisons.

**3. a.** Estimate the number of nesting couples in 1983 and 1985.

**b.** Explain how you determined your estimate from the graph.

**c.** Estimate to the nearest thousand the number of nesting couples in 1977.

**d.** From 1986 to 1998, what do the bars indicate about the growth trend in the number of eagle couples?

**4.** Use the data in the following table to create a bar graph.

| AVERAGE 2004 EARNINGS BY EDUCATIONAL ATTAINMENT FOR WORKERS 18 YEARS OF AGE AND OLDER | | | | | | |
|---|---|---|---|---|---|---|
| **EDUCATIONAL LEVEL** | Not high school graduates | High school graduates | Some college | Associate's degree | Bachelor's degree | Master's degree | All workers combined |
| **AVERAGE INCOME LEVEL** | $19,041 | $28,631 | $30,173 | $36,021 | $51,568 | $67,073 | $37,897 |

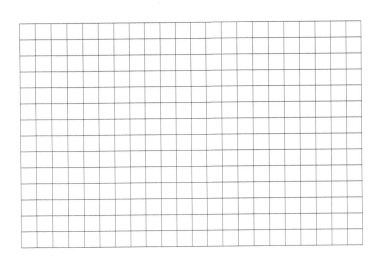

Bar graphs can be oriented either vertically or horizontally.

**5.** Approximately how many more bald eagle couples were observed in Louisiana compared to Texas in 2000?

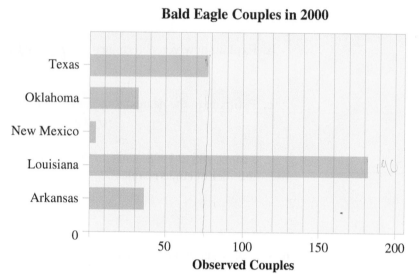

**Bald Eagle Couples in 2000**

*Source:* U.S. Fish and Wildlife Service

Bar graphs can also show paired data, such as a time series.

**6. a.** Which animal group actually saw a drop in the number of endangered and threatened species between 1995 and 2005?

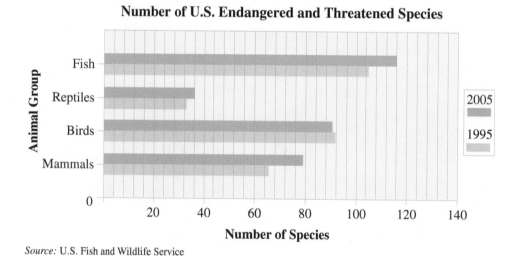

**Number of U.S. Endangered and Threatened Species**

*Source:* U.S. Fish and Wildlife Service

**b.** Which animal group showed the largest increase, and by approximately how many species?

## Circle Graphs

Circle graphs, also called pie charts, are a convenient way to display data when you are interested in showing the relative sizes of the various categories. The size of each piece ("slice" of the pie) is proportional to the percentage of the whole for that category. For example, the previous bar chart for 1995 could be displayed in the following circle graph.

### U.S. Endangered and Threatened Species — 1995

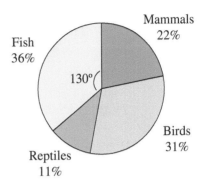

*Source:* U.S. Fish and Wildlife Service

The percent gives the relative size of each piece and the fractional part of each species type compared to the total of all four species types. For example, the total number of U.S. endangered and threatened species in 1995 was approximately 295. The number of fish species among the total of all species was about 105. The percentage of fish in the total four species was 105/295 =.3559 or 36% (rounded to the nearest whole percent). The central angle of the sector for fish is 36% of 360 degrees, or 0.36(360) = 129.6 or 130 degrees.

7. Determine the appropriate percents for each region of the world, and label each sector of the pie chart accordingly. The sectors for each category are already drawn.

### 2010 World Population

| WORLD REGION | 2010 POPULATION IN MILLIONS |
|---|---|
| Africa | 977.413 |
| Near East | 211.969 |
| Asia | 3838.247 |
| Latin America | 595.988 |
| Europe | 810.142 |
| North America | 343.546 |
| Oceania | 34.705 |

*Data:* U.S. Census Bureau

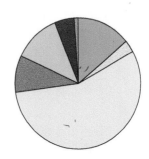

## Paired Bar Graph

The following is an example of a paired bar graph from the U.S. Census Bureau that appeared in the local newspaper.

**Age-Gender Structure of Global Population: 2002**
**The globe's population in 2002 was relatively young.**

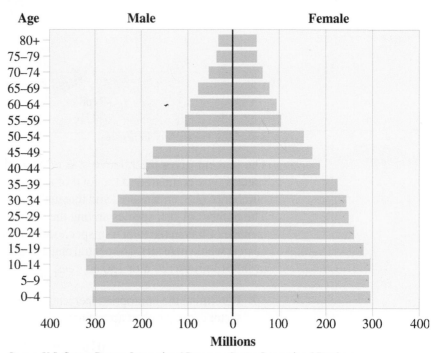

Source: U.S. Census Bureau, International Programs Center, International Database.

8. A number of conclusions can be drawn about the age-gender structure of the global population in 2002. For each of the following statements give specific data from the bar graph that either supports or refutes the claim.

   **a.** No matter what the age group, there are more females than males.

   **b.** The largest age group, regardless of gender, was 10–14-year-olds.

   **c.** Males and females were very close in number for all age groups between 40 and 59.

   **d.** The worldwide birthrate appears to have increased dramatically during the 1988–2002 period.

Stacked bar graphs are another way to show paired data. The U.S. Census Bureau projects what the world's population will look like in the coming decades, based on mathematical models, as illustrated in the stacked bar graph below.

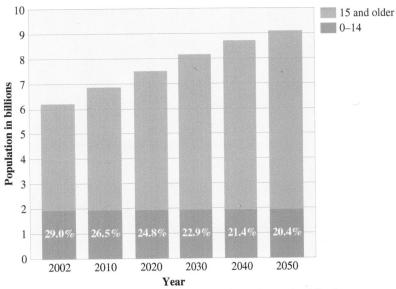

**Global Population 0–14 Years of Age Compared to Total Global Population: 2002–2050**
The percent of children across the globe is projected to decline by one-third over the next 5 decades.

*Source:* U.S. Census Bureau, International Programs Center, International Database.

9. Answer each question by referring to the stacked bar graph.

   a. What will be the increase in global population from 2002 to 2050?

   b. In 2030, what is the projected number of children between 0 and 14 years?

   c. In 2030, what is the projected number of people 15 and older?

   d. Where does the 22.9% come from, in 2030?

   e. Would you say the 0–14 population will be increasing, decreasing or staying the same over the next several decades? Explain your answer.

**SUMMARY**
**Activity 7.2**

1. A **bar graph** is a plot of data in which the number of data values falling in a category is represented by the height or length of a rectangle, or bar.

2. A **circle graph**, or pie chart, displays the relative number of data values in each category by the size of the corresponding sector, or slice.

**1.** The following chart presents the number of new and abandoned hazardous waste sites found in various regions in the United States by the 1990s.

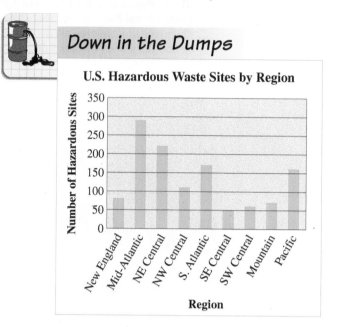

**Down in the Dumps**

**U.S. Hazardous Waste Sites by Region**

**a.** How many regions are represented in the chart?

**b.** Which region has the greatest number of hazardous waste sites? Estimate the number.

**c.** Which region has the least number of hazardous waste sites? Estimate the number.

**d.** What feature of this chart aids in estimating the number of waste sites for a given region?

**e.** Based on this data, in what region(s) would you advise someone to live (or not live)?

**f.** From the chart, estimate the total number of waste sites found in the United States by the 1990s.

2. Graph the data in the following table as a bar graph. Use the grid that follows.

| OCCUPATION | MEDIAN ANNUAL SALARY ($) |
|---|---|
| Computer engineers | 62,000 |
| Systems analysts | 52,000 |
| Database administrators | 48,000 |
| Physician assistants | 47,000 |

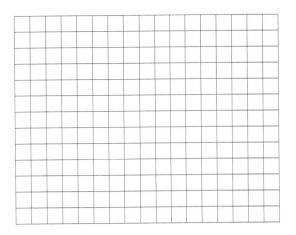

3. The following bar graph provides the annual rainfall in San Antonio, Texas, from 1934 to 2000.

When It Rains...

**Annual Precipitation Totals**
San Antonio, Texas: 1934–2000

*Source:* U.S. Weather Bureau

a. In which year(s) was there the greatest rainfall? Estimate the number of inches.

**b.** In which year(s) was there the least rainfall? Estimate the number of inches.

**c.** How many years did San Antonio have 20 to 30 inches of rain per year? Is this more or less than the number of years that San Antonio had 30 to 40 inches of rain per year? Explain.

**4.** The bar graph below shows some interesting projections for the world's population.

**Pyramids of Global Population: 2002 and 2050**
**The globe's population is expected to grow at progressively higher rates at higher ages.**

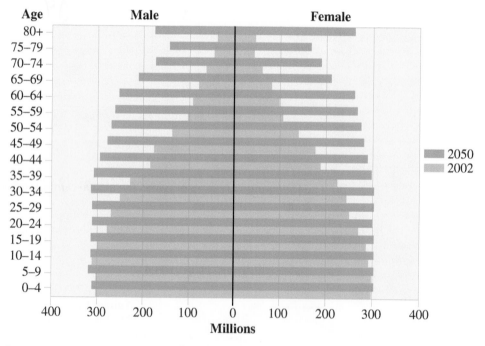

*Source:* U.S. Census Bureau, International Programs Center, International Database.

**a.** Which age group of females shows the greatest increase from 2002 to 2050, and by approximately how much?

**b.** In 2002, the age groups for males decreased in size consistently from age 10 and older. The projections for 2050 show decreases in size from age 35 to 79, but the 80+ age group shows an increase. What does this mean, compared to 2002?

**c.** In 2050, over what age groups would there be very close to the same number of women?

**d.** Which age group shows the smallest change in size between 2002 and 2050?

**5.** Use this stacked bar graph of population projections to answer the following questions.

**Global Population 15–29 Years of Age Compared to Total Global Population: 2002–2005**
**The percent of youth across the globe is projected to decline steadily over the next 50 years.**

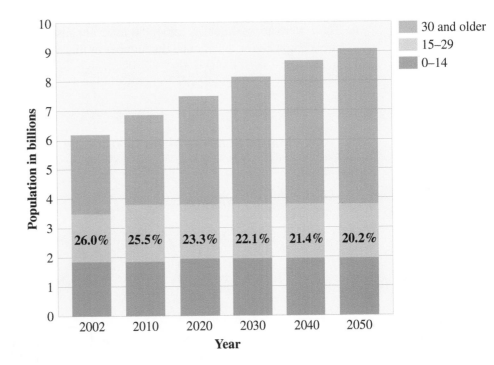

**a.** What is the projected increase in the 30 and older population between 2002 and 2050?

**b.** What was the actual population of 15–29-year-olds in 2002, and how much is it expected to change by 2050?

**c.** In light of your answer to part b, why are the percents decreasing for the 15–29-year-olds?

**d.** The 0–14-year-old population is projected to change very little through 2050. Which of the following statements provides the best explanation?

**i.** The birthrate (births per year) will level off and remain constant.

**ii.** The birthrate will actually be decreasing.

**iii.** Due to overpopulation, famine, and disease, the death rate in this age group will increase.

**iv.** It is not possible to know the individual birthrate and death rate trends, but the combined rates will result in no significant change.

**6.** There were approximately 7,964,950 male Texans 15 years or older in 2003. Use the circle graph below to estimate the number of males in each category.

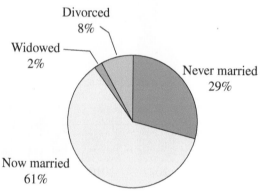

**Marital Status — Males 15 Years and Over in Texas, 2003**

Divorced 8%

Widowed 2%

Never married 29%

Now married 61%

*Source:* U.S. Census Bureau

**7.** In the late 1990's, students in grades 7 through 12 were asked about their familiarity with and use of various technologies. The results of the survey are summarized in the following table.

| TECHNOLOGY | USE DAILY |
| --- | --- |
| Computer | 44% |
| Telephone answering machine | 46% |
| VCR | 39% |
| Calculator | 67% |
| Stereo | 85% |
| Video games | 46% |

**a.** The following bar graph gives a visual display of the percentages of students that use the technologies on a daily basis.

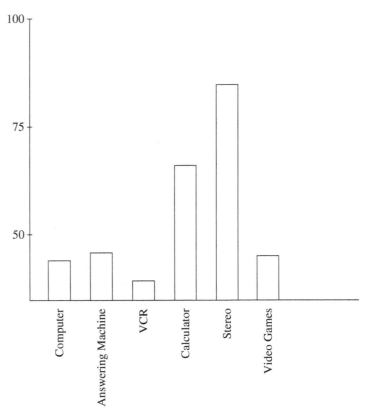

**i.** What is the actual difference in the percentages between daily calculator use and daily video game use?

**ii.** What is the impression given by the bar graph? Explain.

**iii.** How would you improve the display?

**b.** The following circle graph displays the percentages of students who use the technologies on a daily basis.

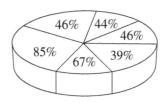

List the errors in the circle graph.

**ACTIVITY 7.3**

The Class Survey

**OBJECTIVES**

1. Organize data with frequency tables, dotplots, and histograms.

2. Organize data using stem-and-leaf plots.

Decisions that are made in business, government, education, engineering, medicine, and many other professions depend on analyzing collections of data. As a result, data analysis has become an important topic in many mathematics classes.

In this activity, you will collect and organize data from your class.

**1.** Record the requested data for your entire class.

| GENDER | NUMBER OF SIBLINGS | MILES FROM SCHOOL | TIME DOING HOMEWORK YESTERDAY (TO THE NEAREST HALF HOUR) |
|--------|--------------------|--------------------|----------------------------------------------------------|
|        |                    |                    |                                                          |
|        |                    |                    |                                                          |
|        |                    |                    |                                                          |
|        |                    |                    |                                                          |
|        |                    |                    |                                                          |
|        |                    |                    |                                                          |
|        |                    |                    |                                                          |
|        |                    |                    |                                                          |
|        |                    |                    |                                                          |

**2.** Using the data collected in Problem 1, determine the following characteristics of your entire class.

**a.** The most common number of siblings

**b.** The average number of miles from school

**c.** More females or males

**d.** The most hours studied last night

The data can be organized in several different ways to help you arrive at your answers. One visual approach is to produce a **dotplot** for each category. To illustrate, consider the following data representing the size of 20 families.

Family sizes: 4, 6, 2, 8, 3, 5, 6, 4, 7, 2, 5, 6, 4, 6, 9, 4, 7, 5, 6, 3

The data values appear on the horizontal scale of the dotplot. The number of occurrences of each data value (called the **frequency**) is recorded on the vertical scale. Each dot represents one data value.

The following frequency table for these data shows another way to organize the data.

| FAMILY SIZE | 2 | 3 | 4 | 5 | 6 | 7 | 8 | 9 |
|---|---|---|---|---|---|---|---|---|
| FREQUENCY | 2 | 2 | 4 | 3 | 5 | 2 | 1 | 1 |

3. Draw dotplots for each of the four data categories from Problem 1.

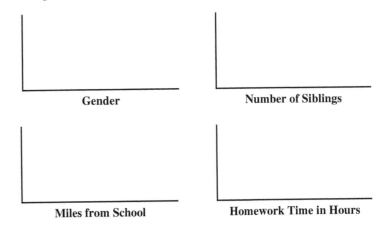

Gender                    Number of Siblings

Miles from School          Homework Time in Hours

4. Explain how you can use the dotplots to answer each of the following questions.

  a. What is the most common number of siblings?

  b. What is the average number of miles from school?

  c. Are there more girls or boys in your class?

  d. What was the most number of hours studied?

In the study of statistics, the dotplot and frequency table are usually called **frequency distributions**. They describe how the data are distributed over all possible values.

5. Looking at your dotplots in Problem 3, describe in a few sentences how the frequency distributions compare with each other visually. Note any similarities and differences.

6. Of the four frequency distributions, which one is really quite different because of the nature of the data values?

## Histograms

Histograms are statistical graphs that can be used to display a frequency distribution. The data values are located on the horizontal axis of the histogram. The frequencies are located on its vertical axis. A rectangle is constructed above each data value and its height indicates the frequency of the specific data value. Therefore, in a histogram, the column of data in a dotplot is replaced by a rectangle.

**Example 1**  *Construct a histogram of the following frequency distribution.*

| Family Size | 2 | 3 | 4 | 5 | 6 | 7 | 8 | 9 |
|---|---|---|---|---|---|---|---|---|
| Frequency | 2 | 2 | 4 | 3 | 5 | 2 | 1 | 1 |

SOLUTION

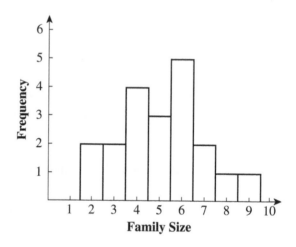

Note that the vertical scale should start at 0. The rectangles are centered at the data value and have the same width. The height of a rectangle represents the frequency of the data value.

The rectangles in a histogram should always touch.

7. Construct a histogram to show the frequency distribution from Problem 3 of the number of miles from school.

Your graphing calculator can also be used to generate a graph of a frequency distribution. Using the sample family size data in Example 1, the following **histogram** can be generated.

**8.** Use a graphing calculator to produce the histogram for the class miles from the school distribution. Refer to Appendix A for detailed instructions for the TI-83/84 plus calculator.

## Grouped Data

In the Class Survey problems, you learned that a histogram is a very useful method to display numerical data in order to visualize how individual values of data are distributed. Often, data are grouped together in order to provide information about the distribution that would be difficult to observe if the data were treated individually.

For example, suppose your mathematics teacher wants to analyze the grades on the last test for the students in his two math classes. In this situation, rather than determining the frequency for a specific test grade, such as 82, your teacher is interested in the number of 80s, as well as the number of 60s, 70s, and so forth. Therefore, the test scores are **grouped** into intervals. The interval for the number of 80s is 80–89. The frequency table for the test scores is given as follows:

| FREQUENCY INTERVAL | FREQUENCY |
| --- | --- |
| 50–59 | 2 |
| 60–69 | 6 |
| 70–79 | 16 |
| 80–89 | 18 |
| 90–100 | 8 |

Note that the **frequency intervals**, also called **classes**, for the grouped data should be of the same width. The numbers 50, 60, 70, 80 and 90 are called the **lower class limits**. The numbers 59, 69, 79, 89 are called the **upper class limits**. The difference between any two consecutive lower class (or upper class limits) is the class width. In this case, the **class width** is 10. The frequency intervals should not overlap, and each piece of data should belong to only one interval.

**9. a.** How many students are in the two courses?

**b.** How many students had a test grade in the 80s?

The grouped test scores for the students in the two mathematics sections is displayed by the following histogram:

**10.** What specific information can you gather by examining the preceding histogram?

Although you are able to easily identify the frequency of test scores within each frequency interval, the original test scores cannot be identified from the frequency table or the histogram. For example, you know that there are eight scores in the 90s, but there is no way to determine what they are. As a result, you are not able to calculate the exact values for statistical measures.

## Stem-and-Leaf Plots

A stem-and-leaf plot is a way to organize and display groups of data as well as displaying the actual data values. In a stem-and-leaf plot, each data value is split into two parts called the **stem** and the **leaf**. The *stem* is the digit or group of digits *with the greatest place value*. The remaining digits on the right of the stem form the leaf for the data value. For example, the number 517 can be split into a stem and leaf as follows:

Stem: 5     Leaf: 17

The number 517 could also be split with the stem 51 and the leaf 7. The single-digit number, 5, which can be written as 05, would have stem 0 and leaf 5.

The following example demonstrates the procedure for constructing a stem-and-leaf plot.

**Example 2**   *Construct a stem-and-leaf plot for the following test scores on a 50-point quiz:*

26 29 32 34 35 37 39 40 42 43 43 46 47 48 50 50

SOLUTION

**Step 1.** Write the data in numerical order. Although this step is not required, it makes working with the data more convenient.

The data is already in numerical order.

**Step 2.** Identify which part of the number is the *stem* and which part is the *leaf*.

Since the scores consist of two digits, use the first digit, the tens digit, as the stem and the units digit as the leaf. For example, the test score 26 has stem 2 and leaf 6.

**Step 3.** List the stems in numerical order as follows. Note that a vertical line separates the stem from the leaf.

| Stem | Leaf |
|------|------|
| 2    |      |
| 3    |      |
| 4    |      |
| 5    |      |

**Step 4.** Proceeding in numerical order, place the leaf of each data value on the right of the vertical line next to the appropriate stem. Proceed until all the leaves of the data values are displayed.

| Stem | Leaf |
|------|--------------|
| 2    | 6 9 |
| 3    | 2 4 5 7 9 |
| 4    | 0 2 3 3 6 7 8 |
| 5    | 0 0 |

**Step 5.** Determine a legend (key) to indicate how the numbers are represented by the stem and leaves.

Legend: 2 | 6 represents the number 26

Note that if the data in Example 2 is listed line by line, in groups, you have

26  29
32  34  35  37  39
40  42  43  43  46  47  48
50  50

The stem-and-leaf plot of this data reduces the repetition of the tens digits and displays the data in a more compact fashion. The stem-and-leaf plot gives the same visual display as a sideways histogram.

**11.** The test scores from the two math classes are listed below:

57  58  62  64  64  68  69  69  70  70  71  71  71  72  73  73  75  76  76  78  78
78  79  79  81  81  82  82  83  83  84  84  85  85  85  85  85  86  86  87  88  89
91  92  92  94  95  95 98  99

Construct a stem-and-leaf plot for this data. Use the tens digit for the stem and the ones digit for the leaf.

Suppose your teacher wants to analyze the test scores from each of the math classes separately. When comparing two similar collections of data, a **back-to-back stem-and-leaf plot** can be constructed.

**12.** The test scores for each math class are as follows:

Class 1: 57 58 64 69 70 70 71 72 73 73 76 78 79 82 85 85 85 88
91 92 95

Class 2: 62 64 69 71 71 75 76 78 78 79 81 81 82 83 83 84 84 85
85 86 86 87 89 92 94 95 98 99

Complete the following back-to-back stem-and-leaf plot for the two classes.

| CLASS I | | | CLASS 2 |
|---|---|---|---|
| **LEAF** | **STEM** | | **LEAF** |
| 8 7 | 5 | | |
| 9 4 | 6 | 2 4 9 | |
| | | | |
| | | | |
| | | | |

**13.** Construct a stem-and-leaf plot for the following data collected in a science experiment: 7.6 8.3 9.4 6.7 5.4 6.3 6.1 5.7 7.5 8.4 8.6 7.3 7.7 8.8 9.1

**a.** Write the data values in ascending order.

While these values have a decimal point, a stem-and-leaf plot would display these numbers without a decimal point. The legend (key) of the plot is used to show the position of decimal points in the original data.

**b.** Ignore the decimal point in the data values, and construct a stem-and-leaf plot for these numbers. Use the ones digit for the stem and the tenths digit for the leaf.

**c.** Write a legend for this plot.

SUMMARY
Activity 7.3

1. A **frequency distribution,** usually displayed in a frequency table, or visually in a dot-plot or histogram, describes how frequently each of the data values occurs.

2. A grouped histogram is useful when there is a wide range of data. In a grouped histogram, data are grouped into intervals of the same class width.

3. A stem-and-leaf organizes data by splitting each data value into two parts called the stem and leaf.

**EXERCISES**
Activity 7.3

1. A large publishing company wants to review the ages of its sales representatives. The ages of a sample of 25 sales reps are as follows:

50  42  32  35  41  44  24  46  31  47  36  32  30

44  22  47  31  56  28  37  49  28  42  38  45

Construct a histogram for the ages.

2. The scores on the last math quiz are summarized in the following frequency table.

| SCORE | 10 | 9 | 8 | 7 | 6 | 5 | 4 | 3 | 2 | 1 | 0 |
|---|---|---|---|---|---|---|---|---|---|---|---|
| FREQUENCY | 5 | 7 | 6 | 4 | 2 | 0 | 1 | 0 | 0 | 0 | 0 |

Construct a dotplot for the scores.

**3.** The frequency distribution for a collection of data is given in the following table:

| CLASS | FREQUENCY |
|---|---|
| 9.5–11.4 | 3 |
| 11.5–13.4 | 7 |
| 13.5–15.4 | 10 |
| 15.5–17.4 | 15 |
| 17.5–19.4 | 9 |
| 19.5–21.4 | 2 |

**a.** Determine the total number of data.

**b.** What is the width of each class?

**c.** If an additional class were to be added, what are its class limits?

**d.** Construct a histogram of the frequency distribution.

**4.** The following collection of data gives the weights (in pounds) of 45 male high school gym students:

105 112 115 118 125 129 130 132 135 135 137 138 138 139 141 144 145
148 148 151 154 154 156 158 158 160 161 161 162 165 166 166 169 172
174 174 176 181 184 185 192 195 206 209 218

**a.** Use this data to construct a frequency table having the first interval (class) 100–109.

| FREQUENCY INTERVAL | FREQUENCY |
|---|---|
| | |
| | |
| | |
| | |
| | |
| | |
| | |
| | |
| | |
| | |
| | |

**b.** Construct a histogram of the frequency distribution from the table above.

**5.** Construct a stem-and-leaf plot of the original data in Exercise 4. Use the hundreds and the tens digit for the stem and the ones digit for the leaf.

**6.** The scores on a 60-point exam are given in the following stem-and-leaf plot. List the original data.

| Stem | Leaf |
|------|------|
| 0 | 9 |
| 1 | 3 7 |
| 2 | 1 6 8 9 |
| 3 | 3 7 7 8 |
| 4 | 2 2 3 5 5 6 6 6 9 |
| 5 | 1 3 4 5 5 8 9 |
| 6 | 0 0 |

Legend: 1 | 3 represents 13

**7.** Subjects in a psychology study were timed while completing a certain task. Complete a stem-and-leaf plot for the following list of times (to the nearest tenth of a minute):

7.5  8.2  9.3  6.8  5.9  6.4  6.1  7.9  5.8  7.3  8.2  8.7  7.4  7.8  8.2  9.2  7.7

**ACTIVITY 7.4**
Class Survey
Continued

**OBJECTIVES**

1. Determine measures of central tendency, including the mean, median, mode and midrange.

2. Recognize symmetric and skewed frequency distributions.

3. Distinguish between percentiles and quartiles.

In Activity 7.3, The Class Survey, you worked with the following data representing the size of 20 families.

Family sizes: 4, 6, 2, 8, 3, 5, 6, 4, 7, 2, 5, 6, 4, 6, 9, 4, 7, 5, 6, 3

The frequency distribution of the data was displayed graphically using a dotplot and a histogram.

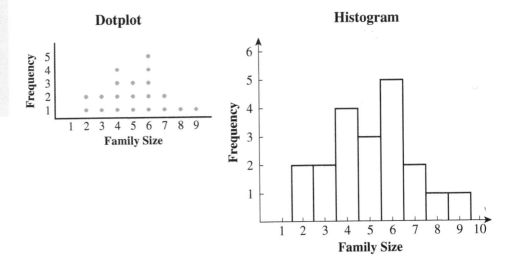

1. By observing the graphs, estimate where you think the center of the frequency distribution lies.

2. Look at the three frequency distributions with numerical data values in Problem 3 in Activity 7.3 (page 805). Estimate on each dotplot where you think the center of the frequency distribution lies. Record your estimates and compare with your classmates.

| FREQUENCY DISTRIBUTION | ESTIMATE OF THE CENTER |
|---|---|
| Siblings | |
| Miles from school | |
| Time doing homework | |

Measuring the center of a frequency distribution is a basic starting point in many statistics applications. There are several different ways to measure the center, including the mean, the median, the mode, and the midrange. Since each will result in a number near the center of the data, these statistics are said to measure the **central tendency** of a frequency distribution. The term "average" is often used to describe these measures of central tendency.

## Measures of Central Tendency

The **arithmetic mean**, or simply **mean**, is the most commonly used "average". The mean of a sample of a population is represented by the symbol $\bar{x}$, read "x bar". The mean of the entire population is represented by the Greek letter mu, $\mu$. Unless specified, you can assume that the data used in this activity represent samples.

The mean is calculated by adding the data values and dividing the sum by the number of values. The notation $\Sigma x$, read the "sum of x", is used to represent the sum of all the data. The symbol $\Sigma$ is the Greek letter sigma, used to indicate summation. The formula for calculating the mean $\bar{x}$ is

$$\bar{x} = \frac{\Sigma x}{n},$$

where $n$ represents the number of data values in the sample.

**3.** Determine the mean of the 20 family sizes in the introduction of this Activity.

A second average is the **median**. The median is in the exact middle of the numerically ordered (ranked) data. Half of the data lies above (is greater than) the median. Half of the data lies below (is less than) the median.

To calculate the median:

**Step 1.** Rank the data from the smallest to the largest (or largest to the smallest).

**Step 2.** **i.** If there is an odd number of data, the median is the number in the middle of the ranked data.

**ii.** If there is an even number of data, the median is halfway between the two middle data values. Expressed as a formula,

$$\text{median} = \frac{\text{Sum of middle data values}}{2}$$

**4.** Determine the median of the 20 family sizes in the introduction of this Activity.

The next commonly used measures of central tendencies are the **mode** and **midrange**.
- The mode is the data value that occurs most frequently.
- The midrange is the exact midpoint between the lowest and highest data values. Expressed as a formula,

$$\text{midrange} = \frac{\text{lowest value} + \text{highest value}}{2}$$

**5.** Determine the mode and midrange of the 20 family sizes.

**6. a.** Now determine the following statistics for the class survey distributions, where possible.

| DISTRIBUTION | MEAN | MEDIAN | MODE | MIDRANGE |
|---|---|---|---|---|
| Number of siblings | | | | |
| Miles from school | | | | |
| Time studying | | | | |

**b.** On your original dotplots in Problem 3, page 805, clearly mark with a vertical line each of the above statistics from the preceding table.

**c.** For each distribution, circle the statistic (mean, median, mode, midrange) that is closest to the estimate of the center that you made in Problem 2. Which type of statistic did you have in mind when you made your estimates?

**7.** Which statistic would you choose to best describe the "average" number of siblings among your classmates, and why?

**8.** Do any of these measurements of central tendency make sense for the gender distribution? Explain.

The commonly used "averages" can give very different results for the same set of data. Problem 9 demonstrates how the averages can be used to misrepresent the given situation.

**9.** A small company pays its president $200,000. The vice-president receives $150,000. There are five employees in the company: the foreman who earns $30,000; three workers, earning $25,000, $22,000, $22,000 respectively; and a secretary who earns $19,000.

**a.** Determine the mean, median, and mode income in this company.

**b.** The union representative wants to negotiate new wages for the workers. In the negotiation, should the union representative emphasize the mean, median, or mode? Explain.

**c.** Which of the three measures would the president of the company stress in the negotiations? Explain.

    **d.** Which do you think best represents this sample? Explain why in a paragraph.

    **e.** Do you think that the measure you chose in part d is always the best to use? Explain.

**10.** Which measure of central tendency is most affected by extreme data values? Explain.

**11.** Consider the following set of scores from a science test:

    10, 16, 21, 62, 62, 62, 68, 70, 71, 72, 74, 77, 78, 79, 80, 85, 88, 93

    **a.** Determine the mean, median, and mode of the science test scores.

    **b.** Which of the "averages" in part a best represents the grades on the science exam? Explain.

## Using Technology to Determine Measures of Central Tendency

Once the data are stored in your calculator, you can generate a variety of statistics for the data, including the measures of central tendency. For example, the following windows of the TI-83/84 Plus calculator result from the 20-sample family size data. Refer to Appendix A for detailed instructions for the TI-83/84 Plus calculator.

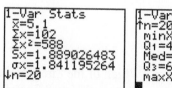

The mean $(\bar{x})$ and median (Med) are given, $n$ is the number of data values, and minX and maxX are the smallest and largest data values respectively. From these you can calculate the midrange.

**12.** Use a graphing calculator to produce the measures of central tendency for the siblings distribution from the Class Survey.

## Types of Frequency Distributions

**13. a.** The three frequency distributions pictured here have the same range of data values. What is it?

**i.**                          **ii.**                         **iii.**

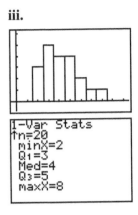

```
1-Var Stats
↑n=20
 minX=2
 Q₁=5
 Med=6.5
 Q₃=7
 maxX=8
```

```
1-Var Stats
↑n=20
 minX=2
 Q₁=4
 Med=5
 Q₃=6
 maxX=8
■
```

```
1-Var Stats
↑n=20
 minX=2
 Q₁=3
 Med=4
 Q₃=5
 maxX=8
```

**b.** Describe in your own words the visual differences among the distributions in part a.

**c.** The means for the distributions in part a are as follows:

$$\overline{x}_i = 6.0 \quad \overline{x}_{ii} = 5.0 \quad \overline{x}_{iii} = 4.2$$

Compare these to the median for each distribution.

Some distributions are symmetrical (like distribution ii in Problem 13). Others are slightly "off," as if they have been stretched to one side or the other. Distribution i is **skewed to the left**, while distribution iii is **skewed to the right**.

**14. a.** If a distribution is perfectly symmetrical, what do you think will be true about the relationship between the mean and median?

**b.** Based on your results in Problem 13, what is the relation between the mean and median of a skewed distribution?

**c.** Enter in your calculator a skewed distribution with ten data values. Record your data, sketch the histogram (or dotplot), and calculate the mean and median. Does this result help confirm your answer in part b?

## Measure of Position

Two measures of position of data within a distribution are **quartiles** and **percentiles**. Quartiles divide a set of data into four equal parts. Percentiles divide a set of data into 100 equal parts.

For a given set of data, your calculator generates the data values corresponding to the quartiles. For example, for the 20 sample family size data, the 1-Var Stats screen of the TI 83/84 Plus calculator gives the following information:

$$Q_1 = 4$$
$$\text{Med} = 5$$
$$Q_3 = 6$$

$Q_1$ represents the first quartile and has a value of 4. This means that 25% of the data has a value less than 4.

**15. a.** Explain the meaning of $Q_3 = 6$.


**b.** What is the second quartile?



Such measures are often used to make comparisons of scores of individuals when the amount of data is large. For example, suppose you scored 500 on the math portion of the Scholastic Aptitude Test (SAT). If this score is at the 80th percentile, denoted $P_{80}$, it does **not** mean that you answered 80% correct on the test. It means that 80% of the high school students who took the test scored less than you. That is, 80% of the students scored less than 500.

Determining the percentiles of a set of data will be studied in Activity 7.11.

## SUMMARY
### Activity 7.4

A **frequency distribution**, usually displayed in a frequency table, or visually in a dot-plot or histogram, describes how frequently each of the data values occurs.

There are four typical measures of the **central tendency** of a frequency distribution:

1. The **mean** is the usual average found by adding the data values and dividing by the number of values.

2. The **median** is in the exact middle of the numerically ordered data—half the data values lie above and half lie below the median. If there is an even number of data values, the median is the mean of the two middle values.

3. The **mode** is the data value that occurs most frequently.

4. The **midrange** is the exact midpoint between the lowest and highest data values.

## EXERCISES
### Activity 7.4

1. A large publishing company wants to review the ages of its sales representatives. The ages of a sample of 25 sales reps are as follows:

50  42  32  35  41  44  24  46  31  47  36  32  30

44  22  47  31  56  28  37  49  28  42  38  45

**a.** Construct a histogram for the ages.

**b.** Calculate the mean and median ages.

**c.** Determine the midrange.

**d.** Is there a mode for this distribution?

**2.** Suppose the scores of seven members of a men's golf team are 68, 62, 60, 64, 70, 66, and 72. Determine the mean, median, and midrange.

**3.** The scores on the last math quiz are summarized in the following frequency table

| SCORE | 10 | 9 | 8 | 7 | 6 | 5 | 4 | 3 | 2 | 1 | 0 |
|-------|----|---|---|---|---|---|---|---|---|---|---|
| FREQUENCY | 5 | 7 | 6 | 4 | 2 | 0 | 1 | 0 | 0 | 0 | 0 |

Calculate the mean, median, mode and midrange of this quiz distribution.

**4. a.** Create a set of ten data values whose distribution is perfectly symmetrical.

**b.** Verify that the mean, median, and midrange are identical.

**c.** Change two data values so that the resulting distribution is skewed to the left.

**d.** Predict how this will change the mean and median. Then verify by doing the calculations.

**5.** A set of data has a mean of 32.4 and a median of 38.9. Would you expect the distribution for this data to be symmetrical, skewed to the left, or skewed to the right?

6. Find a collection of at least 25 data values from a real-world source. Use your calculator to create a histogram, and calculate the four measures of central tendency.

7. The mean is the most affected by any change in the data.

   a. Determine the mean, median, mode and midrange of the following data:

$$10, 11, 12, 14, 14, 15, 16, 20$$

   b. Change the 16 to 19 in part a. Determine the mean, median, mode and midrange of the resulting set of data.

   c. Which measure of central tendency was affected by changing the 16 to 19?

   d. In addition to the mean, which measure would be affected if the 20 was changed to 19 in part a?

8. The salaries of 10 employees of a small company are listed below:

$$33,000, \quad 28,000, \quad 36,000, \quad 31,000, \quad 31,000,$$
$$68,000, \quad 29,000, \quad 32,000, \quad 86,000, \quad 34,000.$$

   a. Determine the mean, median, mode, and midrange of the 10 salaries. Verify your results using the statistics feature of the graphing calculator.

   b. Which average would the employees use to demonstrate that they were underpaid? Explain.

   c. Which average would management use if they did not want to give a raise to the employees? Explain.

9. Reports about incomes and other highly skewed distributions usually give the median rather than the mean as the measure of the "average". Explain.

10. Locate an article in a newspaper or magazine that discusses an "average".

   a. Is the average used the mean, median, or mode? Explain.

   b. Is the choice of the average used in the article appropriate for the situation? Explain.

## Activities 7.1–7.4 | What Have I Learned?

1. Bar graphs and circle graphs can be used to visualize the same collection of data. What advantage does each display have over the other?

2. Determine if the mean and median accurately represent an "average" of the following set of numbers:

   **a.** Zip codes: 12303, 13601, 7622, 52104

   **b.** Ranks of different brands of a product in a taste test: 1, 3, 5, 2

3. A small supply company employs a supervisor at $1200 a week, an inventory manager at $700 a week, six stock boys at $400 a week, and four drivers at $500 a week.

   **a.** Determine the mean and median wage.

   **b.** Which "average" best describes a typical wage at this company? Explain.

4. If a distribution is skewed to the right, then which average is generally larger, the mean or the median? Explain.

5. A county is about to impose a 4.5% property tax increase on its residents. Is the county legislature concerned about the mean or median home assessment of its residents?

## Activities 7.1–7.4    How Can I Practice?

1. The number line in the following graphic represents net exports in billions of dollars for six countries. Net exports are obtained by subtracting total imports from total exports; a negative net export means the country imported more goods than it exported.

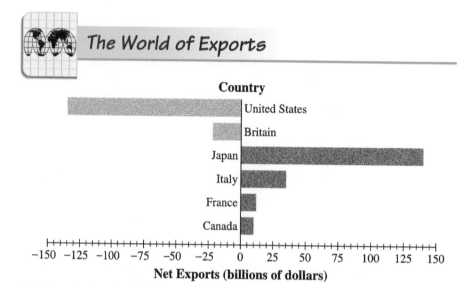

**The World of Exports**

**Country**

**Net Exports (billions of dollars)**

a. Estimate the net amount of exports for Japan. Is your answer a positive or negative integer? Explain what this number tells you about the imports and exports of Japan.

b. Estimate the net amount of exports for the United States. Is your answer a positive or negative integer? Explain what this number tells you about the imports and exports of the United States.

c. What is the difference between net exports from Japan and Italy?

d. What is the difference between the net exports from Britain and France?

e. What is the total sum of net exports for the six countries listed?

2. In the bar graphs below, a projection of world population by age groups and gender for six different regions is given as a percent of the region's population at the time.

## Population Pyramids for Regions and Selected Countries: 2002 and 2050
### In 2050, the elderly are expected to be a substantially larger part of national and regional populations.

*Source:* U.S. Census Bureau, International Programs Center, International Database.

**a.** In 2002, which region had the largest portion of its population in the 0–4-year-old age group, and what was that percent?

**b.** What is the 2050 projection for the 10–14 age group of the region you identified in part a?

**c.** In 2002, which region's 80+ age group is larger than the 75–79 age group?

In 2050, how many such regions are projected?

How could you explain this phenomenon?

**d.** In most regions, by 2050 the various age groups have become fairly equal in size, except perhaps for the oldest age groups. Which region does not appear to follow that trend?

**e.** Which two regions are projected, in 2050, to have larger populations of 60–64-year-olds than 45–49-year-olds?

**f.** In 2002, which region had pretty much equal numbers in the 0–39 and 40–80+ age groups?

**g.** In Sub-Saharan Africa, the projected size of the elderly population will remain quite small in 2050, compared to every other region. What single factor do you think might be most responsible?

3. The educational attainment of Texans 25 and older in 2003 is summarized below.

| EDUCATION | ATTAINED BY |
|---|---|
| Less than 9th grade | 1,416,434 |
| 9th to 12th grade, no diploma | 1,516,837 |
| High school graduate | 3,473,633 |
| Some college, no degree | 2,773,964 |
| Associate's degree | 778,403 |
| Bachelor's degree | 2,163,749 |
| Graduate or professional degree | 1,065,672 |

*Source:* U.S. Census Bureau

Identify each category on the circle graph.

**Education: Texans 25 years and older**

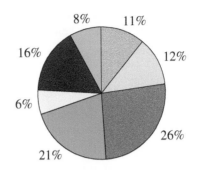

4. Wayne Gretzky scored 50% more points than anyone who ever played professional hockey. He accomplished this by playing in 280 fewer games than Gordie Howe, the second leading record holder. The number of games played by Gretzky during each season of his career are listed:

   79, 80, 80, 80, 74, 80, 80, 79, 64, 78, 73, 78, 74, 45, 81, 48, 80, 82, 82, 70

   Create a stem-and-leaf display.

5. The traveling times in minutes for 15 workers randomly chosen at High Tech Manufacturing are:

   30, 20, 15, 15, 25, 20, 35, 60, 20, 40, 10, 30, 15, 35, 20

   **a.** Create a dotplot of the frequency distribution of the traveling times.

   **b.** Determine the mean, median, mode, and midrange of the set of traveling times.

  c. Which measure best represents the set of data? Explain.

6. The body mass index (BMI) is a measure based on height and weight of a person. The BMI of randomly selected males and females are listed below:

males:      23.6, 23.4, 24.6, 26.5, 24.2, 31.0, 28.1, 26.3, 22.5, 27.9, 29.2

females:    19.6, 22.8, 20.6, 28.1, 25.5, 21.1, 27.5, 20.5, 27.9, 18.7, 29.8

  a. Determine the mean of each group of BMI measures.

  b. In general, it is believed that males weigh more than females, and males are taller than females. Do the sample means in part a support this general belief? Explain.

7. The following data is the number of cancellations on a certain commuter flight on 12 randomly selected days in the past 6 months.

$$5, \ 5, \ 6, \ 9, \ 9, \ 11, \ 12, \ 12, \ 13, \ 13, \ 13, \ 14$$

  a. Construct a dotplot of the data.

  b. Does the distribution seem skewed? Explain.

  c. Determine the mean and median of the number of cancellations.

**d.** When the data is skewed, the mean is "pulled" from the center to the direction of the skew. The median tends to remain near the center of the distribution. The following diagram illustrates the relationship between the mean and median in a distribution that is skewed to the right.

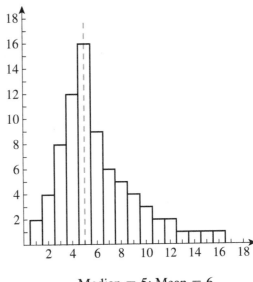

Median = 5; Mean = 6

Identify the location on the *x*-axis of the mean and median in the following distribution that is skewed to the left.

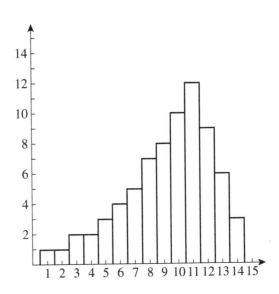

**e.** Do the results in parts b and c confirm the observation in part d?

**ACTIVITY 7.5**
Sampling a
Population

**OBJECTIVES**

1. **Know the difference between a census and a sample.**

2. **Identify the characteristics of a simple random sample.**

3. **Know what bias in a sample means.**

4. **Be able to select a simple random sample, when possible.**

5. **Identify how the size of a sample affects the result.**

Suppose you have a need to know the average weight of every adult in the United States, or the mean age of every blue crab in the Chesapeake Bay, or the median income of every household in the Commonwealth of Virginia. To determine such measures of central tendency, it is not usually practical to obtain the data for every individual in the population. If every individual in the population is measured it is called a **census**.

1. Do you think it is possible to conduct a census to determine each of the measures mentioned above? Give specific reasons for each case.

Conducting a census to determine the characteristics of an entire population is usually either too costly or time consuming. If even possible, other ways have been devised to achieve the same objective with a high degree of certainty. By taking a relatively small sample from the entire population, a great deal can be determined about that population. A **sample** consists of any portion of a population, no matter how large or small. Once a sample is chosen, this smaller collection can be measured and a central tendency can be recorded.

2. Since a sample can be of any size, how would you compare the practicality and usefulness of samples of size 1, 25 and 2 million when attempting to estimate the income of Virginia households?

The process of collecting data from some fraction of a population is called **sampling**. It allows us to learn about the entire population by studying a relatively small portion of the population. The size of the sample along with the method used to select individuals for the sample can have a big effect on the results.

3. Suppose you are interested in knowing the mean average height for everyone in your school. A census would give the exact value while a sample will result in an estimate.

   a. Assume you got a sample of size one student less than the population. How close do you think the mean height for the sample will be to the mean of the population?

   b. If you got another sample, this time with ten less students than the population, do you think this sample mean would be as close to the population mean as the sample in part a?

**c.** If you took a sample of size 100 and another sample of size 10, which sample's mean do you think will be closer to the population's mean?

In general, a larger sample size will result in a more accurate estimate of the population. But when the population is very large, larger samples will not produce significantly better results and are usually more expensive or difficult to obtain. A decision is normally made that will balance these two tendencies, not too small to sacrifice accuracy, and not too large to sacrifice cost.

As a general rule, for very large populations, a sample in the size of hundreds is normally sufficient.

To help illustrate some of these ideas you will explore some relatively small populations. The table below shows the current grades (0–100) for all the 20 students in Mr. Horton's economics class.

| ID NUMBER | LAST NAME | CURRENT GRADE |
|---|---|---|
| 1 | Adams | 78 |
| 2 | Baker | 84 |
| 3 | Cooper | 82 |
| 4 | Davenport | 95 |
| 5 | Elacqua | 71 |
| 6 | Flanagan | 83 |
| 7 | Grant | 97 |
| 8 | Haught | 65 |
| 9 | Jacobs | 80 |
| 10 | Kim | 78 |
| 11 | Lee | 67 |
| 12 | Moloney | 91 |
| 13 | Naraparaju | 69 |
| 14 | O'Brochta | 74 |
| 15 | Park | 81 |
| 16 | Reeves | 79 |
| 17 | Snider | 62 |
| 18 | Thoreson | 88 |
| 19 | Vilece | 93 |
| 20 | Whiting | 63 |

**4.** Consider this class as the entire population. In this case, a census is quite feasible. Determine both the median and mean for this population.

5. Now suppose you did not have access to all the grades, but could be given the grades for five students. In other words, you can take a sample of size five. Choose any five students you like and calculate the mean and median grade for your sample. Such measurements taken from a sample are called **statistics**. How far are your statistics from the population mean and median?

6. Now compare your statistics to those of others in your group, or even the entire class. If you found the average of all your sample means, would you expect it to be close to the population mean? Find this average and check.

7. Describe how you chose the five students for your sample, and compare your method with others in your group and/or class.

If you chose your sample by looking at the grades and then consciously (or subconsciously) tried to pick a balanced set of grades (not too high, not too low), or purposely picked all high scores or all low scores, you introduced a bias to the selection process. **Bias** simply means that some individuals are somehow favored over others in the population. This is a critically important idea when attempting to select a sample that is representative of the entire population.

There is a classic example that helps illustrate this point. In 1936, *Literary Digest* magazine conducted a survey to predict the outcome of the U.S. presidential election. They had conducted similar surveys the five previous presidential elections, and had correctly predicted the winner each time. In 1936, ten million postcards were distributed to a list of voters, generated primarily from owners of automobiles and telephones. Over two million of the postcards were returned, and on that basis the Republican governor of Kansas, Alf Landon, was predicted to beat the incumbent Democratic president, Franklin Roosevelt, by an overwhelming margin, with 57% of the popular vote. The election was actually won by Roosevelt, with over 61% of the popular vote!

8. There was a bias in this presidential election survey. What do you think could have been the cause?

## Simple Random Sample (SRS)

Many methods have been devised to select samples in a way that eliminates, or at least minimizes, any form of bias. To achieve this, the most basic idea is the random selection of the individuals in the sample. Recall from your study of probability in Chapter 6, to select randomly means every individual in the population has an equal chance of being selected. A **simple random sample** (SRS for short) is the result of a sampling method that assures every possible sample of the same size has an equal probability of being selected.

**9.** Describe a method that would ensure your sample of five students from Mr. Horton's class will be a simple random sample. Compare and discuss your method with others in your class.

**10.** Use your calculator to generate five random integers between 1 and 20. Use these numbers to identify the five students for your sample, by simply counting each student's position in the alphabetical class list.

    **a.** Suppose one of your random numbers is repeated. Since you need five different numbers, what could you do next?

    **b.** Record your five random numbers and the student associated with each number.

    **c.** What is the probability of selecting your particular sample of size five from Mr. Horton's class?

    **d.** Does the same probability apply to every possible sample of size five using this method? Why?

    **e.** Calculate the mean and median grade for your sample.

    **f.** As you did in Problem 5, use the mean and median from part e for all the samples to find the average mean and average median for your class. Compare your averages this time to what you found in Problem 5. Which are closer to the population mean and median?

In general, all the possible sample means will naturally vary, both above and below the population mean. But the average of several sample means will generally be very close to the population mean, an idea that is useful for further statistical analysis.

Random numbers are a primary tool in selecting simple random samples. There are several ways to get random numbers, in addition to using your calculator. Books of random numbers have been published (especially useful before computers became commonplace), and websites exist which provide truly random numbers, based upon physical phenomena, like the weather. (See www.random.org)

**SUMMARY**
**Activity 7.5**

1. A **census** is the result of measuring or counting every individual in a population.

2. A **sample** is the result of measuring or counting any portion of a population.

3. **Sampling** is the process of collecting a sample from a population.

4. The larger the sample size, the more accurate the estimate for the population.

5. A **bias** occurs when some individuals in a population have a greater chance of being selected for a sample than others.

6. A **statistic** is a measurement derived from a sample, usually intended to be representative of an entire population.

7. A **simple random sample** (**SRS** for short) is a sample that is selected by a method that ensures every possible sample of a given size has an equal chance of being selected.

**EXERCISES**
**Activity 7.5**

1. The following list of digits was taken from a table of random numbers.

   39 63 46 23 49 74 08 86 55 64 16 37 91 97 13 39 15 39 45 91 79 86 45 37

   59 53 50 50 40 46 92 74 78 44 52 66 73 31 93 36 55 45 26 22 35 69 08 32

   30 73 47 15 71 83 72 27 97 12 25 77 56 51 78 07 76 32 92 81 13 13 01 96

   62 88 91 26 91 25 42 40 90 25 75 20 30 91 39 41 17 31 46 06 08 91 56 30

   83 19 51 13 43 51 14 20 82 15 14 03 47 33 68 07 61 82 92 69 48 68 04 68

   70 58 37 03 61 41 04 72 67 92 84 66 90 43 24 33 01 49 39 09 86 54 59 06

   54 09 20 83 00 19 11 60 76 75 52 48 79 25 31 23 17 84 12 07 77 72 50 10

   95 83 62 25 30 91 78 58 02 10 34 36 15 22 28 33 86 99 43 32 38 68 61 67

   **a.** Since there are 20 students in Mr. Horton's class, think of each student's ID number as a two digit sequence (the ID number for Baker is 02). Start at the beginning of the table, looking at each two-digit number, and record the first eight numbers that are between 01 and 20. These give the student ID numbers. (If there is a repeated number, simply ignore the repetition.) What students would make a sample of size 8, using this table?

**b.** If you wanted a different sample, you would of course need to use different random numbers. But there is another way to use the table without bypassing so many numbers. Since there are 100 possible two digit numbers in the table (00 through 99), and 100 is a multiple of 20, each student could be assigned five numbers, their student ID plus a multiple of 20. So, for example, Jacobs would be identified by 09, 29, 49, 69 and 89. Use the first row of the table to choose a different sample of size 8, and identify the students by name.

2. In a population of 30 students, how many different samples of size six are possible?

3. **a.** Given a population with 200 members, how many different samples of size ten are possible? In words, about how large is this number?

   **b.** In a SRS, what is the probability of selecting a particular sample of size ten?

4. Out of a residential phonebook with 25,640 different entries, what is the probability that a simple random sample of size three consists of the following telephone numbers?

      {540-644-9077, 804-266-0450, 540-745-9913}

5. A sample of size 100 is to be selected from each of the following populations. In which cases do you think a simple random sample is possible? Give a reason for your answer.

   **a.** All the adult blue crabs in the Chesapeake Bay

   **b.** All the students enrolled in your school

c. All the passenger cars registered in the Commonwealth of Virginia

d. All the passenger cars on the road in Virginia on December 25th, 2008

e. All the homeless people in the United States

6. The data below (10 rows by 20 columns) gives the weights, in pounds, of 200 chickens at the Pluck poultry farm.

| 5.9 | 6.4 | 4.3 | 5.9 | 5.3 | 6.0 | 5.5 | 5.4 | 5.3 | 4.8 | 6.0 | 4.0 | 5.1 | 4.9 | 5.5 | 6.0 | 4.6 | 4.1 | 4.8 | 6.7 |
|-----|-----|-----|-----|-----|-----|-----|-----|-----|-----|-----|-----|-----|-----|-----|-----|-----|-----|-----|-----|
| 5.7 | 6.1 | 6.1 | 6.2 | 5.9 | 4.1 | 4.7 | 5.2 | 6.7 | 6.5 | 5.1 | 5.4 | 5.8 | 4.1 | 5.8 | 5.1 | 5.0 | 6.0 | 5.3 | 6.2 |
| 5.8 | 6.5 | 6.9 | 6.7 | 5.9 | 4.6 | 4.9 | 6.3 | 6.6 | 5.4 | 5.3 | 5.2 | 6.9 | 6.7 | 4.7 | 6.9 | 5.5 | 6.6 | 5.7 | 5.2 |
| 6.8 | 5.2 | 4.9 | 4.9 | 6.8 | 6.7 | 6.7 | 6.7 | 5.6 | 6.9 | 6.9 | 6.8 | 5.1 | 5.3 | 7.0 | 4.9 | 4.2 | 4.5 | 6.7 | 4.4 |
| 5.7 | 6.2 | 6.8 | 5.8 | 4.5 | 4.7 | 5.8 | 4.4 | 4.7 | 5.1 | 4.5 | 5.1 | 6.1 | 4.6 | 5.2 | 4.7 | 4.2 | 4.9 | 6.2 | 6.8 |
| 4.4 | 4.9 | 6.1 | 6.9 | 6.1 | 6.9 | 4.3 | 4.8 | 4.8 | 4.9 | 6.2 | 4.3 | 4.4 | 4.4 | 5.2 | 5.0 | 6.2 | 6.3 | 6.7 | 6.0 |
| 6.1 | 5.3 | 6.3 | 5.8 | 4.8 | 7.0 | 6.7 | 4.3 | 6.6 | 6.7 | 5.3 | 6.2 | 6.6 | 6.4 | 6.4 | 5.8 | 5.2 | 5.3 | 4.0 | 6.6 |
| 4.2 | 4.8 | 5.9 | 4.5 | 6.7 | 5.5 | 5.7 | 6.2 | 4.1 | 6.5 | 5.8 | 4.8 | 5.3 | 6.2 | 5.4 | 5.8 | 6.9 | 5.5 | 6.4 | 5.0 |
| 6.1 | 4.1 | 4.3 | 6.9 | 6.3 | 4.2 | 6.6 | 5.8 | 6.6 | 5.1 | 4.6 | 4.8 | 4.1 | 6.9 | 4.4 | 6.5 | 6.7 | 4.8 | 5.5 | 6.1 |
| 5.5 | 4.7 | 5.9 | 5.3 | 5.8 | 5.9 | 4.8 | 6.1 | 6.9 | 6.4 | 5.0 | 4.3 | 5.7 | 7.0 | 5.4 | 6.2 | 6.4 | 5.2 | 4.9 | 5.6 |

a. Generate random numbers from your calculator to select a SRS of size 10. (Use integers between 1 and 200.) Explain exactly how you chose your sample, showing your random numbers and the associated weights. Calculate the mean weight for your sample.

b. Now select a SRS of size 25 and calculate the mean weight for this sample.

c. Which of your samples do you think has a mean closer to the population mean, and why?

d. Calculate the population mean to check your answer to part c.

e. If your larger sample was closer to the population mean, that was to be expected, but was not a certainty. Hand pick ten weights that result in a sample mean further from the population mean than your size 25 sample mean.

**7.** The random numbers generated on your calculator are not quite as random as you might think. It is possible that two different calculators could generate the same random list of numbers in the same order. The random number generator (rand) used in the calculators relies on what is known as a seed value. The default seed value is 0. With each rand execution, the calculator will generate the same random number sequence for a given seed value. To obtain a different random number sequence, store any nonzero number to rand. (from http://epsstore.ti.com)

This sort of random number is called a **pseudorandom number**. For most random sampling purposes, pseudorandom numbers work fine. Truly random numbers can be generated from truly random processes, like the weather or the physical behavior of atomic particles. Such random numbers are available on the web, at sites such as www.random.org. Visit this website, generate a list of ten different random integers between 1 and 200, and report on the process that was used to generate the numbers.

## ACTIVITY 7.6
Highway Proposal
–Yes or No?

**OBJECTIVES**

1. Identify the characteristics of a well defined sample survey.

2. Know how to collect a stratified sample.

3. Identify ways in which a sample might be biased.

Opinion polls are everywhere these days, on TV and the Internet, in all print media, and at meetings of decision makers in business and government. Such polls generally attempt to measure the percentage of a population that holds a certain opinion or will make a certain decision (like for whom they plan to vote). Such a poll is an example of a **sample survey**, a methodical process of collecting a sample that is representative (hopefully) of the larger population. A simple random sample, as defined in the previous activity, results from one of several different methods that can be employed to attain an unbiased sample. In this activity you will explore different sampling methods and sources of bias.

## Highway Proposal

In your capacity as an administrative assistant for your county government, you need to assess the attitude of your community for a new highway proposal. Some people will favor the highway in the belief it will provide greater mobility and promote business. Others will argue that it will bring even more congestion and will negatively impact the environment. An opinion poll will be helpful for government leaders in making final decisions.

1. Since you have been asked to submit your preliminary report as soon as possible, there is no time to even consider a census of the 100,000 plus adult residents of your county. So you turn to one of the more convenient tools at your disposal, the phonebook. Describe a plan you could use to come up with a sample of 50 adult residents using the phone book. Do you think your method results in a simple random sample?

Even if you did truly randomize the process of selecting names from the phone book, the overall process of using a phone book is flawed. For example, will every adult resident of your community have an equal chance of being included in the sample?

2. Give several reasons why your sampling plan of using a phone book to create the sample and then calling each person in the sample is biased and will not result in a SRS of the entire population of adult residents.

One of the biggest difficulties with whatever plan you might employ in your poll, is the same as the bias created with the *Literary Digest* poll in 1936. A significant number of adult residents didn't even have a chance to be included. It is possible that all the individuals in the phonebook really are representative of the entire adult population, but you don't know that. Therefore, you have to assume there is a bias in the sampling results.

**3.** Can you think of other ways to obtain a complete list of adult residents of your county, so a true SRS could be attained?

Whatever list is used for sampling purposes, usually not the entire population, is called the **sampling frame**. The closer the sampling frame comes to the actual population, the better. At best, it should be representative of the entire population.

## Nonrespondents

The issue of **nonrespondents** also will create a bias. No matter how you select individuals for the sample, some will not answer their phone, or will refuse to participate or simply forget to return the questionnaire. That group of individuals may not be representative of the whole population, so their exclusion will definitely result in inaccurate results.

**4.** It is important for any sampling plan to include how to deal with nonrespondents. What do you think are some possibilities?

## Mean of the Sample Means

Now let's turn to a sample survey that you can do with your classmates. You may wonder how much television the students in your school watch each day. It would probably be feasible to do a census in this case, but for the sake of understanding the sampling process, let's assume it is best to take a sample. In fact, let's first limit the population to your math class.

**5.** Using a list of all students in your math class, devise and describe a plan to take a SRS of size ten. Take the poll by asking each selected student to estimate how many hours of television they watch each week, and then calculate the mean for your sample.

**6.** Now determine the mean of all the sample means from the samples in your class. Compare your sample mean to the class's mean of all the sample means.

7. Since the population (your math class) is relatively small, you can take a census to determine the population mean number of TV hours watched each week. How close is the class mean of the sample means to this population mean?

You should have discovered that the mean of all the sample means comes very close to the population mean. This basic fact of statistics is very powerful and is used to make inferences and decisions about entire populations based upon relatively small samples. This phenomenon will be studied in great detail if and when you take an elementary statistics course.

## Stratified Sampling

Now suppose you suspect there may be a real difference in boys' and girls' TV watching habits. (If you happen to be in a class with all girls, or all boys, you will need to use a different distinction, maybe based on age or ethnicity.) If there is a real difference, and your sample just happened to be almost all girls, or almost all boys, it will not be very representative of the population.

8. What is the ratio of boys in your class to the total number of students in the class (the population)? Express as a decimal number.

9. **a.** What fraction of your sample of size ten, from Problem 5, consisted of boys?

   **b.** If you round the population ratio you determined in Problem 8, is it the same as the sample ratio?

You want the ratios in Problems 8 and 9 to be nearly the same. Then your sample would be proportional to the population. But it is entirely possible your SRS could result in almost all boys, or almost all girls. To try to remove any gender bias in your sample, you could devise your sampling method to assure the sample ratio of boys and girls is the same as, or at least as close as possible to, the population ratios.

10. With a sample size of ten, how many boys should be in your sample to closely match (as close as possible) the ratio of boys to students in your class?

Once you know how many boys and how many girls need to be in your sample, you can then separate the class into two groups, called **strata**, the boys and the girls. From each group you then randomly select the required number. Such a method is called **stratified sampling**.

11. Use your result in Problem 10 to produce a stratified sample, and then calculate the mean.

## Self-selection

You will end this activity by considering one of the most prevalent types of opinion polls. Whether on the web, TV, the radio or in a print magazine or newspaper, you often are offered the chance to make your opinion known.

12. Suppose you hear on a popular TV show that the results of a phone-in poll have been completed. 83% of the callers prefer text-messaging over in-person talking. This seems like an overwhelming majority.

   a. How would you describe this method of sampling?

   b. Why do you think this sample is biased?

   c. Do you think there is a way to design this method to eliminate a bias?

The previous problem illustrates a classic form of bias, called **self-selection**. The individuals in the sample who chose to take part in the poll were motivated to do so. That motivation will most likely be more prevalent among those that hold one opinion over another. Of course, it also means everyone in the population will not have the same probability of being included, even if everyone hears of the poll. There will be some individuals with no motivation to respond, hence no likelihood of being included in the sample. Self-selection as a method may be cheap and easy to do (hence their prevalence), but as a sampling method is deeply flawed.

## SUMMARY
### Activity 7.6

1. A **sample survey** is a methodical process of collecting a sample from a larger population.

2. A **statistical experiment** consists of a well-defined process that applies statistical analysis to answer a question about some given population.

3. A **sampling plan** refers to the detailed step-by-step procedure to collect data through a specific sampling method.

4. A **sampling frame** is the collection of individuals from which a sample is drawn. It may or may not be the entire population.

5. There are several common sources of **bias** that can occur, even with a well estab-lished sampling method.

   Selected individuals for a sample may be unavailable or choose to not respond. Such **nonrespondents** do not have the same likelihood of being included, hence creating a bias.

   A sample composed of individuals that voluntarily respond, a **self-selected** sample, creates a bias since everyone in the population is not equally likely to be included.

6. A **stratified sample** results when a population is separated into two or more subgroups, called **strata**, and simple random samples are selected from each strata in proportion to the relative size of the strata.

1. Use your local phonebook to select a sample of ten people in your community.

   **a.** Precisely describe the method you used.

   **b.** Is your sample random? Explain.

2. One way to reduce the number of nonrespondents in a survey is to make face-to-face contact. This is more expensive than phoning or mailing, due to additional travel time, especially if the population is spread over a large geographic area. One method that helps reduce this expense is called **cluster sampling**. For example, to personally interview a representative sample of all residents of Virginia, a simple random sample of 500 residents would most likely be spread far and wide across the commonwealth. Creating a plan to efficiently visit 500 different locations would be a costly challenge. With cluster sampling, the plan would be to randomly select a small number of geographic regions, or clusters, and then find a fixed size SRS within each cluster.

   **a.** In designing a cluster sampling plan, what do you think would be a reasonable choice for the clusters?

   **b.** If you chose the counties of Virginia for the clusters, how many clusters would there be? (A resource for the geography of Virginia: www.virginiaplaces.org)

   **c.** If your plan is to include ten clusters, what size SRS should be selected from each cluster?

   **d.** Find a list of all the counties in Virginia and randomly select ten counties for your clusters. Describe your process. On a map of Virginia, shade in the selected counties.

   **e.** Assuming you then generate the required SRS for each cluster, in what ways might your resulting overall sample have a bias? Could a bias be fixed?

**3.** When a sample is to be drawn from a list, such as a phone directory, it is sometimes easiest to select one individual at random, and then count from that first individual a fixed number to pick the next individual. The fixed number is also randomly chosen, and is used to continue counting until the sample size is completed. Such a method is called **systematic sampling**. For example, the random number 134 might be chosen, to select the 134th individual on the list for the sample. Then if the random number 20 was chosen, the 154th individual on the list would be the next one chosen.

   **a.** With these numbers, what positions would the third, fourth and fifth chosen individual's position be?

   **b.** Suppose you desire a sample of size 50, chosen from a list of students at your school. If you randomly generate 58 for the first student chosen, and 15 for the count to the next student, what will be the positions of the second, third and fourth students chosen?

   **c.** By the time the last student is chosen, what would their position be?

   **d.** Suppose there are not that many students in your school? How could you still complete your sample of size 50 using this method?

   **e.** As long as the order of the list will in no way influence the response, as in an alphabetic listing, a representative sample will be acquired. Suppose the listing is by age. Can you think of a question and random numbers that would result in a bad sample (meaning not representative of the population)?

**4.** The principal of a high school wants to determine the "average" number of children in the families of students who attend the high school. The principal visits each classroom in the building and selects the four students who are seated closest to the corners of the classroom. The principal then asks each student how many children are in his family. Will this sampling technique result in an unbiased sample? Explain.

**5.** A **convenience sample** uses data that is easily or readily available. However, this type of sampling can be extremely biased. For example, suppose the city council wants to raise taxes in order to build a new wing on the high school. In order to obtain the opinion of the city residents on the issue, the first 50 adults leaving the local shopping mall are asked if they are in favor of raising taxes to build the new wing.

  **a.** Discuss the possible cause of a bias in the sample.

  **b.** Describe a sampling technique that would be less biased.

**6.** The student council at your high school wants to survey students about the quality of food in the school cafeteria. It is decided that students leaving the cafeteria will be given a short questionnaire. Is this method of sampling unbiased? Explain.

**7.** Your student council desires a quick and representative poll of student attitudes toward a dress code proposed by the administration. In case there are differences in opinion among students in the various grades, you recommend that a stratified sample be used. You know there are 212 seniors, 273 juniors, 255 sophomores and 320 freshmen in your high school. To get a sample of 50 students, using the four classes as your strata, what number of students from each class should be in your sample?

**8.** The Addison–Wesley Publishing Company wants you to obtain a sample of 100 students who use this textbook. Describe the procedure to obtain:

    **a.** a simple random sample.

    **b.** a stratified sample.

    **c.** a cluster sample.

    **d.** a systematic sample.

**9.** A popular magazine mailed a questionnaire to its subscribers about cars and other consumer products. Also included were a request for a voluntary contribution and a ballot for the Board of Directors. Responses were to be mailed back in envelopes that required postage. Discuss potential problems with this sampling technique.

**10.** Identify each of the following as simple random sampling, stratified sampling, systematic sampling, cluster sampling, or convenience sampling.

    **a.** Randomly select high schools from different geographic regions and survey all students at each of the chosen schools.

    **b.** Survey each 10th student who walks in the front entrance of the school.

    **c.** Obtain a list of students enrolled in a high school. Number these students and then use a random number table to obtain the sample.

**d.** Obtain a list of students enrolled at a high school. Draw a random sample from each of the freshman, sophomore, junior, and senior classes, proportional to the size of each class.

**e.** At a local tire manufacturing plant, every 20th tire coming off the assembly line is checked for defects.

**f.** Survey the first five students who enter the classroom.

**g.** Elementary school children in a large city are classified based on the neighborhood school they attend. A random sample of five elementary schools is selected. All the children from each selected school are included in the sample.

**h.** A teacher at the high school teaches five classes of Spanish. Two of the classes are chosen by the principal and all the students in those classes fill out a teacher evaluation form about that Spanish teacher.

**i.** The first 50 people entering a museum are asked if they support the city council's increase in funding for the arts.

**j.** Students in your senior class obtain the voting records for the county. You randomly select 50 Democrats, 40 Republicans, and 8 Independents. (The numbers chosen are based on the percentage of registered voters in each category in the county.) You survey them concerning their favorite candidate for County Commissioner in the upcoming fall election.

**k.** A state is divided into regions using zip codes. A random sample of 15 zip code areas is selected.

**l.** Every 10th person in line to purchase tickets to a rock concert is asked their age.

**m.** At a Key Club meeting, the names of all members are written on identical slips of paper and placed in a bowl. The names of five members are drawn. These five people will participate in face-to-face interviews with a pollster.

**n.** You are approached by a person at a local mall who asks you to answer a few questions about the security at the mall.

**o.** Numbered ping pong balls are placed in a bin. The bin is shaken. A ball is then selected from the bin.

**p.** A marketing expert for MTV is planning a survey in which 500 people will be randomly selected from each of the following age groups: 10–14, 15–19, 20–24, 25–29.

**ACTIVITY 7.7**
Statistical
Survey

**OBJECTIVE**

1. **Design and execute a statistical survey.**

Many different sampling methods were described in Activities 7.5 and 7.6. Efficiency in cost and time is usually an important factor in deciding which sampling method is appropriate. Designing a sample survey requires a well-defined, step-by-step process, as outlined below.

1. Formulate the problem and devise a plan.

   • State what you need to know.

   • Identify the population and what is to be measured.

   • Decide on an appropriate sampling method and sample size.

   • Think carefully about the exact form of all questions and responses.

2. Execute the plan.

   • Follow the plan to gather the data.

   • Specify all the details of the methodology.

3. Analyze and organize the results in a report.

   • Discuss all elements of the sampling process.

   • Interpret the results and state final conclusions.

To illustrate this process, let us return to the highway proposal situation introduced in Activity 7.6. Suppose your county executive decides that you should survey only registered voters in your community, to determine whether the majority of county residents favor a new highway proposal. You do have a complete list of registered voters, with their party affiliation (34% are Republicans, 45% are Democrats and 21% are independent). In Problems 1–3 use complete sentences to record your design for this sample survey.

1. You can save money by using a sample of size 100, instead of doing a census. Record a plan for this sample survey.

   a. State what you need to know.

   b. Identify the population that is to be measured, and the sampling frame.

   c. Which sampling method, simple random sample or stratified sample, do you think would be best? Give a reason for your choice.

2. Since you are only discussing a hypothetical sample survey, you are not actually going to execute the survey. However, describe precisely all the details of what you would need to do.

3. The report for your survey will include all the difficulties that were encountered, the actual results of the survey, how the results might be biased, and an interpretation of those results. Use your imagination to write a feasible report for this sample survey. (Hint: start by assuming you used a stratified sample, and fill in the table to help create your report.)

| RESPONSE | REPUBLICAN | DEMOCRAT | INDEPENDENT | TOTAL |
|---|---|---|---|---|
| Favors proposal | | | | |
| Doesn't favor | | | | |

In a real sample survey, the results will be subjected to more advanced statistical analysis, which include the notion of margins of error and confidence levels. For example, if you concluded that 58% of residents favor the highway proposal, the sample size would yield an error of $\pm 10\%$, at the .05 confidence level. This means that you expect the real percentage of residents favoring the proposal to be between $58 - 10 = 48\%$ and $58 + 10 = 68\%$, with a .05 probability that you are wrong. These topics are studied fully in a statistics course.

## EXERCISES
### Activity 7.7

1. Conduct your own sample survey to determine how many hours per week students at your school spend using the Internet during the week. In your sampling plan, be sure to follow the step-by-step process outlined in this activity:

   a. Formulate the problem and devise a plan.

   State what you need to know.
   Identify the population and what is to be measured.
   Decide on an appropriate sampling method and sample size.
   Think carefully about the exact form of all questions and responses.

   b. Execute the plan.

   Follow the plan to gather the data.
   Specify all the details of the methodology.

   c. Analyze and organize the results in a report.

   Discuss all elements of the sampling process.
   Interpret the results and state final conclusions.

**2.** Depending upon what sampling method you used in Exercise 1, discuss how you could have applied either stratified or systematic sampling to conduct your survey.

**3.** With a group of your classmates, come up with an issue concerning some particular population that you would like to know about.

    **a.** Clearly state the following, as a preliminary proposal.

        **i.** What you would like to find out?

        **ii.** Precisely what population would be involved?

        **iii.** How would you go about collecting a sample?

    **b.** Is your proposal feasible? (i.e., is it something you and your classmates could actually do?)

        **i.** If feasible, clear your idea with your teacher, and proceed to conduct your statistical survey. Be sure to follow all steps in the process outlined in this activity.

        **ii.** If your proposal is not feasible (or your teacher does not approve it), go back and revise the proposal, or start all over.

**ACTIVITY 7.8**
What's the
Cause?

**OBJECTIVES**

1. Understand the purpose and principles of experimental design.

2. Know when a causal relationship can be established.

3. Understand the importance of randomization, control treatments and blinding.

In Activity 2.7 Body Fat Percentage, you learned how to recognize a linear correlation between two variables. Recall that finding a correlation does not necessarily establish a cause-and-effect relationship between two variables. Problem 1 demonstrates such a situation.

1. Suppose a survey of elementary school students in your county results in the following scatterplot of reading level versus shoe size.

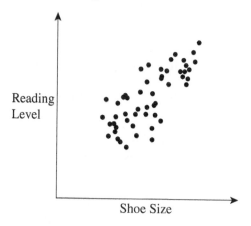

**a.** How would you describe the association between reading level and shoe size?

**b.** Based upon your response in part a, would you be willing to conclude that an increase in shoe size causes a higher reading level? Why or why not?

**c.** If your answer in part b was no, can you think of a lurking variable that might explain the correlation?

## Experimental Design

Scientists and statisticians have developed methods to determine causal relationships. **Experimental design** involves a very meticulous procedure for controlling the environment surrounding two variables. The goal is to determine whether changing one variable actually causes a change in the second variable.

2. The mathematics department at your school has started using a new computerized study program for Algebra I. After the first semester, the average scores on the midterm test were 5% higher than last year. The department chairman thinks that the computer program caused the increase in test scores.

**a.** Do you think there is enough evidence to justify this claim? Explain the reason for your answer.

**b.** What other factors might be involved, that could also result in higher scores?

    **c.** What groups of students are being compared, and how might that affect the results?

## Treatment and Control Groups

When attempting to establish a causal relationship, a good experimental design will always try to control outside variables. That means, in this example, any other influence beyond using the computer program (or not) and the test scores should be kept constant for all students, as much as is possible. For example, to better establish the chairman's claim, all Algebra I students could be divided into two groups. One group would use the computer program (or receive the **treatment**, as it is usually called). The other group would not (usually called the **control group**).

    **3.** If a control group is used for the Algebra I experiment, what outside influences (that you may have identified in Problem 2) could be controlled so they do not vary between the groups?

Another critically important aspect of a good experimental design is randomization. Recall how collecting a sample randomly is essential to assure unbiased results. In a similar way selecting members for the control group must be done randomly, to help even out any unforeseen variables that could effect the results.

    **4.** Suppose the group to receive the computer program treatment in Algebra I is selected on a voluntary basis, instead of being selected by a random process. How might this invalidate the results of the experiment?

> To summarize, a **good experimental design** will consist of a **control group** and at least one **treatment group** that will receive the treatment being studied. The selection of subjects for the groups must be **selected through a random process**.

The real point of a control group is to try to minimize the possibility that some unanticipated factor might be at least part of the cause for the results you see. If everyone receives the treatment, maybe the real cause of the improved test scores is a subtly improved test. Students may do better on the test simply because they now understand the questions. The average scores would improve, but not necessarily because of the treatment. With a control group, the improvement would be seen in both the treatment group and the control group, so there would be no reason to believe the computer program was the cause of the improved test scores.

This methodology has been used for research in the sciences for many years, credited to the psychologist Gustav Fechner in the mid-1800s. Medical research has benefited greatly, whether in testing the effectiveness and safety of new drugs or searching for new innovative treatments of dangerous diseases. A classic example of the later occurred over fifty years ago, as medical researchers were seeking a cure for polio, a devastating disease that has since been nearly defeated.

5. Dr. Jonas Salk is credited with discovering a polio vaccine. This successful discovery depended upon many years of experimentation with control groups. To further control for unseen variables, subjects in both the control group and the treatment group were not allowed to know which group they were in. This is called **blinding**.

   a. What kind of influence do you think blinding would eliminate?

   b. During the course of this lengthy experiment, many children participated. Some were treated and some were not. The treatment eventually proved to be effective in preventing the spread of polio. What ethical problem comes to mind as a result of this experiment?

You may have heard of the **placebo effect**. A placebo is a false treatment. In other words, if the treatment is a medicine that is given as a pill, a fake pill (a sugar pill) would be given to the control group so they would not know they were not given the treatment (they would think they were given the treatment). The placebo effect is the real power of the human mind/body to affect positive results without a treatment, just by believing a treatment has been received! Compare this with your answer in problem 5.a.

6. Suppose you are involved in a study to determine whether a new drug is effective in lowering blood pressure. A placebo is administered to the control group.

   a. How important is it that the control group not know they are given a placebo?

   b. Should the treatment group be allowed to know that they are given the real treatment? Why or why not?

   c. What should be done so the administrator/technician does not inadvertently tip-off the subject?

To assure that the subject does not know which group they are in, the personnel administering the treatment (or placebo) are also blinded (doesn't know which they are giving). This makes the experiment **single-blind**. To further assure there is no subjective influence among any involved parties, the evaluators are also blinded to group membership. This will make an experiment **double-blind**.

**7.** There have been cases where experimenters have influenced the results by evaluating the subjects without double-blinding. Suppose a researcher is trying to establish a new herb from the Amazon as a remedy for dry skin. The experiment is single-blind, but not double-blind. The study results in the claim that there was a remarkable improvement in skin condition. What might be wrong with this conclusion?

## Replication

It is critical that an experiment include enough participants for the results to be statistically significant. Providing a treatment to one or two individuals will prove nothing. But to truly establish a causal relationship the entire experiment must be repeatable by others. It is very possible that positive results occurred by chance. Repeating the experiment will help verify, or deny, the claim. This feature is usually called **replication**. If researchers in another laboratory can't duplicate the results independently, then the entire study is brought into question. A classic example occurred in 1989 when physicists at The University of Utah produced what they called cold fusion. Fusion is a nuclear process that produces vast amounts of energy but is very difficult to control. After many years of research it is not currently feasible as an energy source. But the claim of cold fusion (fusion that could take place very cheaply) appeared to be a breakthrough and caused quite a stir in the mass media. As it turned out no other physicists could replicate the results, so the excitement was short lived.

## SUMMARY
### Activity 7.8

1. To establish a **cause-and-effect relationship** between two variables an **experimental design** must include a **control group**, **randomization**, and be **replicable**.

   • A **control group** includes individuals that do not receive the treatment under study.

   • To be valid, assignment of members to the control and treatment groups must be done through a **random** process.

   • An experiment should include as many subjects as possible, and the results should be **replicated** with further experiments with different study groups.

2. Most good experiments are **double-blind**, meaning neither the participants (subjects and administrators) nor the evaluators know which subjects received the treatment and which are in the control group.

3. A **placebo** is a treatment having no effect (a false treatment), given to the control group so all subjects experience the same conditions.

4. Many humans will respond positively to a placebo, even though the treatment being tested is not present. This **placebo effect** could fool the researcher into thinking the treatment caused a positive result, unless a placebo is used with the control group.

1. **a.** Suppose a city passes a gun control law, and two years later the number of violent crimes increases. Can you conclude that the gun control law caused the crime rate to go up? Explain.

   **b.** If the crime rate had decreased, can you conclude that the gun control law caused the crime rate to go down? Explain.

2. A study skills company claims their SAT prep program will increase your overall SAT score by 45 points. Their claim is based upon 2350 students that completed their course, and scored on average 45 points higher than their first attempt at the SAT. Do you accept their inferred claim, that their program caused the higher scores?

3. In the 1990s a study was designed to determine if listening to Mozart's music would improve performance on an IQ test. Subjects were randomly assigned to two groups. One group listened to Mozart, the second group was not given any instructions or music. The sample mean scores on the IQ test were 119 for the Mozart group and 110 for the no instructions group. Describe how well this experiment was designed, and whether you think a causal relationship was established. How could the experiment be improved, in your opinion?

4. Over the past twenty years mathematics educators have been very busy reforming the way algebra is taught. The goal has been to improve the basic conceptual understanding required to successfully apply algebra in other courses and work. Suppose you wish to determine how well a particular reformed algebra course accomplishes this goal, compared to a traditionally taught algebra course. In other words, does taking a reformed algebra course cause a higher level of learning than the traditional course?

   **a.** Classes using the reformed course materials take a standardized algebra test. Standardized means the test has been given to many other algebra students and the mean and standard deviation are known. If the reformed class scores higher than the mean for this test, would you be able to conclude the reformed course caused the higher scores? Explain.

    **b.** Describe how you could design an experiment to better assess whether the goal is being met.

**5.** A research doctor has developed a new medication to relieve the joint swelling of arthritis. Twenty patients have volunteered to take part in an experiment to determine if the new medication is more effective than their old medication.

    **a.** Describe how this experiment should be conducted. Carefully describe how each aspect of a good experiment can be accomplished.

    **b.** How can the control group and placebo effect be managed so patients still receive some medication?

**6.** Does filling the gas tank of a car with premium gasoline result in better fuel efficiency than with regular unleaded gasoline? Design an experiment to determine whether premium gasoline causes a car to get better gas mileage.

7. Sometimes a very strong belief can influence how the results of an experiment are interpreted, hence the need for double-blinding. Many popular beliefs and superstitions have not been subject to rigorous testing with good experimental design. Dowsing is a widely held belief that the use of a forked stick (called a dowsing rod) can be used to detect underground water. The dowser holds the two ends of the forked part, leaving the main stem pointing in front. When walking along with the dowsing rod held horizontally in front, if the pointer dips down, that is interpreted to mean underground water has been detected. Many people have employed dowsers over the years to help find the best location to dig a well, for example. In attempting to prove that hidden water is causing the dowsing rod to dip the following experiment is performed. Twenty buckets are laid out in a field, half are filled with water, the other half are empty. Boards are placed over each bucket, so no one can see inside. The dowser proceeds to walk around, passing the dowsing rod over each bucket. The evaluator, who also was responsible for filling and laying out the buckets, records the reaction of the rod in each case. The dowser goes over all the buckets a second time and reconfirms the choices from the first round. The dowser has picked out twelve buckets that he claims contain water, and in fact nine of them do. This means the dowser has correctly identified the contents of 16 out of 20, or 80%, of the buckets. A pretty good score, since the expected result by randomly guessing would be 50%. Are you convinced? Explain.

8. Think of something that interests you. Try to find two variables that are related to your interests and to each other. Pose a question about how one variable might cause a change in the other variable. Design an experiment that could test this situation, being sure to address how your experiment would address all aspects of a good design. If possible, conduct the experiment and report on the results.

**ACTIVITY 7.9**
A Switch Decision

**OBJECTIVE**

1. **Measure the variability of a frequency distribution.**

Statistical analysis is useful when important decisions need to be made. The following sets of data are the result of testing two different switches that can be used in the life-support system on a submarine. Two hundred of each type of switch were placed under continuous stress until they failed, the time recorded in hours. Switch A and switch B have approximately the same means and medians, as displayed by the following histograms. (The displays are from a TI-83/84 Plus.)

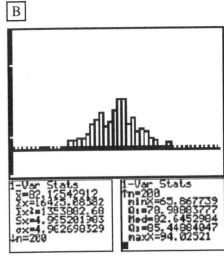

1. Verify that the means and medians for both switches are approximately the same. What does this tell you about the general shapes of the distributions?

2. Which distribution is the most spread out?

3. Which distribution is packed more closely around its center?

4. Based on these tests, which switch would you choose to use and why?

Like the central tendency of a distribution, the spread, or **variability,** of a distribution is also measured several different ways. The **range** is simply the difference between the minimum and maximum data values.

5. Determine the range for each set of switch data to the nearest hour. Do these ranges confirm your answers to Problems 2 and 3?

6. The range is of limited value in describing the variability (or spread) of a distribution. Consider these two data sets.

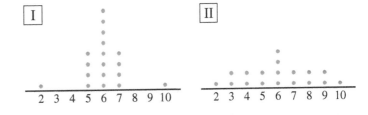

    **a.** Which distribution has greater variability?

    **b.** Calculate the range for each distribution.

    **c.** What is your conclusion about the range as a measure of variability?

## Standard Deviation

The most common measure of spread is the **standard deviation** (symbol $\sigma$, the Greek lowercase letter sigma). It measures how much the data deviates from the mean.

**7.** Calculate the mean for distributions I and II of Problem 6.

**Deviation** refers to how far a data value is from the mean. For example, if the mean is 7, then a data value of 10 is a distance of 3 from the mean, and you would say that the data value 10 has a deviation of 3 from the mean. If the data value is 4, it is still a distance of 3 from the mean, but its deviation is $-3$, indicating that it is below the mean.

**8. a.** Calculate the deviations for every data value in both distributions I and II of Problem 6. Record your results in the column having heading $x-\bar{x}$. Then add all the deviations for each distribution.

| DISTRIBUTION I | | | | DISTRIBUTION II | | |
|---|---|---|---|---|---|---|
| $x$ | $x-\bar{x}$ | $(x-\bar{x})^2$ | | $x$ | $x-\bar{x}$ | $(x-\bar{x})^2$ |
| | | | | | | |
| | | | | | | |
| | | | | | | |
| | | | | | | |
| | | | | | | |
| | | | | | | |
| | | | | | | |
| | | | | | | |
| | | | | | | |
| | | | | | | |
| | | | | | | |
| | | | | | | |
| | | | | | | |
| | | | | | | |
| | | | | | | |
| | | | | | | |
| **Total** | | | | **Total** | | |

**b.** Is the sum of the deviations, denoted by $\sum (x - \bar{x})$, a good measure of the spread of the data? Explain.

To overcome the deficiency of the total deviation, you could simply take the absolute value of each deviation. The more conventional method is to calculate the **standard deviation**. The standard deviation of a distribution involves summing the squares of the deviations, denoted by $\sum (x - \bar{x})^2$.

**9.** For each distribution, calculate the standard deviation using the following procedure.

| | Distribution I | Distribution II |
|---|---|---|
| **a.** Square each deviation in both of the tables of Problem 8 and then record your results in the column $(x - \bar{x})^2$. a. | | |
| **b.** Add the squares of all the deviations: b. | _____ | _____ |
| **c.** Divide by the number of data values: c. | _____ | _____ |
| **d.** Take the square root: d. | _____ | _____ |

In a single formula, the standard deviation is $\sigma = \sqrt{\dfrac{\sum (x - \bar{x}^2)}{n}}$, where $\sigma$ is the standard deviation, $\sum$ is short for "the sum of," $x$ is a single data value, $\bar{x}$ is the mean, and $n$ is the number of data values.

**e.** Does distribution I or distribution II have greater variability? Explain using the standard deviation of each distribution.

**10.** Verify that your standard deviations in Problem 9d agree with those in the following display, from the TI-83/84 Plus. (The TI-83/84 Plus uses $\sigma x$ for $\sigma$.)

Distribution I

```
1-Var Stats
 x̄=6
 Σx=108
 Σx²=688
 Sx=1.533929978
 σx=1.490711985
↓n=18
```

Distribution II

```
1-Var Stats
 x̄=6
 Σx=108
 Σx²=736
 Sx=2.275185836
 σx=2.211083194
↓n=18
```

**11.** What do you think a standard deviation of zero would mean?

**12. a.** Return to the testing of switches A and B. The standard deviations of each distribution are given by the calculator output screen in the introduction of the activity. Record the standard deviations here.

   **b.** Which distribution has the greater variability? Explain using the standard deviation of each distribution.

## Boxplots

Another type of statistical graph, the **boxplot**, helps you to visualize the variability of a distribution. Five statistics form a boxplot: the minimum data value, the **first quartile ($Q_1$)**, the median, the **third quartile ($Q_3$)**, and the maximum data value, in order from smallest to largest. These are often referred to as the **five-number summary** for the distribution.

Quartiles refer to values that separate the data into quarters. The lowest 25% of all the data falls between the minimum and the first quartile. The next lowest 25% of the data falls between the first quartile and the median. Hence, 75% of the data is above the first quartile.

**13. a.** How much of the data is below the third quartile?

   **b.** How much of the data is between the first and third quartiles?

The five-number summaries are displayed here for the switch A and B data.

Sometimes called box-and-whisker plots, the preceding boxplots show visually how the quartiles for the switch data compare. The box represents the middle 50% of the data. The whiskers represent the extent of the lower and upper quarters of the data.

Appendix

See Appendix A for details to obtain a boxplot using the TI-83/84 Plus calculator.

**14.** Consider the following boxplots for three distributions.

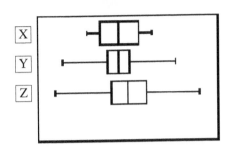

**a.** Compare the minimum, first quartile, median, third quartile, and maximum for the three distributions.

**b.** Compare the ranges for each of the three distributions.

**c.** Which distribution do you think has the least variability? Explain.

## SUMMARY
### Activity 7.9

1. The **variability** of a frequency distribution refers to how spread out the data is, away from the center.

2. The **range** of a frequency distribution is the difference between the lowest and highest data values.

3. The **deviation** of a data value is how far it is from the mean of the data set.

4. The **standard deviation** is a measure of how far all the data collectively is from the mean.

5. A **boxplot** is a graph that displays the **five-number summary** (the minimum, first quartile, median, third quartile, and maximum data value) for a distribution.

## EXERCISES
### Activity 7.9

*Do the calculations in each of the following exercises. Fill in the table as part of your calculation. Then check your work by using the statistics features of your calculator.*

**1.** Consider the following data:   5   8   2   1   7   1

Determine the standard deviation by filling in the table as part of your calculation.

| $x_i$ | $\overline{x}$ | $x - \overline{x}$ | $(x - \overline{x})^2$ |
|---|---|---|---|
|  |  |  |  |
|  |  |  |  |
|  |  |  |  |
|  |  |  |  |
|  |  |  |  |
|  |  |  |  |

2. Eight adults are surveyed and asked how many credit cards they possess. Their responses are 4, 0, 3, 1, 5, 2, 2, and 3. Determine the standard deviation for these data. Fill in the table as part of your calculation.

| $x_i$ | $\overline{x}$ | $x - \overline{x}$ | $(x - \overline{x})^2$ |
|---|---|---|---|
|  |  |  |  |
|  |  |  |  |
|  |  |  |  |
|  |  |  |  |
|  |  |  |  |
|  |  |  |  |
|  |  |  |  |
|  |  |  |  |

3. A student takes ten exams during a semester and receives the following grades: 90, 85, 97, 76, 89, 58, 82, 102, 70, and 67. Find the five-number summary.

4. In a year-long music course, you are required to attend 12 concerts. Last season, the lengths of the concerts were 92, 101, 98, 112, 80, 119, 92, 90, 116, 106, 78, and 65 minutes. Find the five-number summary for these data. Decide on a scale and draw a boxplot.

**5.** The weights, in pounds, of a group of workers are as follows:

173  123  171  175  188  120  177  160  151  169  162  128  145

140  158  132  202  162  154  180  164  166  157  171  175

Find the five-number summary for these data. Decide on a scale and draw a boxplot.

**6.** Joe DiMaggio played center field for the New York Yankees for 13 years. Mickey Mantle, who played for 18 years, succeeded him. Here is the number of home runs by DiMaggio and Mantle.

DiMaggio:   29, 46, 32, 30, 31, 30, 21, 25, 20, 39, 14, 32, 12

Mantle:      13, 23, 21, 27, 37, 52, 34, 42, 31, 40, 54, 30, 15, 35, 19, 23, 22, 18

**a.** Compute the five-number summary for each player.

|  | Min | $Q_1$ | Median | $Q_3$ | Max |
|---|---|---|---|---|---|
| DiMaggio: | _____ | _____ | _____ | _____ | _____ |
| Mantle: | _____ | _____ | _____ | _____ | _____ |

**b.** Using the same scale, draw a box-and-whisker plot for each player. (Draw one boxplot above the other.)

**c.** Discuss the similarities or differences of the two boxplots.

**7.** Given the following boxplots of three distributions, which do you think will have the smallest standard deviation?

**OBJECTIVES**

1. Identify a normal distribution.

2. List the properties of a normal curve.

3. Determine the z-score of a given numerical data value in a normal distribution.

4. Identify the properties of a standard normal curve.

5. Solve problems using the z-scores of a standardized normal curve.

The following collection of data gives the heights, in inches, of 35 randomly selected eleventh grade male students. The measurement was made to the nearest inch.

```
63  64  65  65  66  66  66  67  67  67  67  67  68  68  68  68  68  68
69  69  69  69  69  70  70  70  70  71  71  72  72  73  74  75  76
```

**1. a.** Complete the following frequency distribution.

| HEIGHT IN INCHES | NUMBER OF ELEVENTH GRADE MALES |
|---|---|
|  |  |
|  |  |
|  |  |
|  |  |
|  |  |
|  |  |
|  |  |
|  |  |
|  |  |
|  |  |
|  |  |
|  |  |
|  |  |
|  |  |

**b.** Construct a histogram from the frequency distribution in part a.

**c.** Does the distribution appear to be skewed or symmetrical? Explain.

**d.** Determine the mean, median, and mode of the given set of data. Do your results verify your conclusion in part c?

## Normal Distribution

One of the most important distributions is called the **normal distribution**. The histogram for a normal distribution has the following general shape:

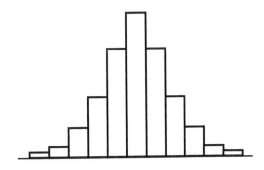

The normal distribution is important because many sets of data are normally distributed, or nearly so. Such distributions include heights and weights of males and females, measures of reading ability, intelligence quotients, scores on standardized tests, and wear-out mileage of car tires. Much of the theory in the study of statistics is based on normal distributions.

**2.** Is the distribution in Problem 1 normal? Explain.

When the histogram of a normal distribution is smoothed to form a curve, the curve is **bell-shaped**. This curve is called a **normal curve** and is used to model the normal distribution.

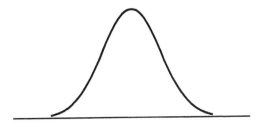

The bell can vary in size. It can be high and narrow, or short and wide. For example, each of the following graphs represents a normal curve.

Although normal curves have a variety of sizes, all normal curves have the same basic properties. Use the normal curve given in Problem 3 to help identify some of these properties.

**3.** Assume the heights of all 16-year-old males are normally distributed with mean 68 and standard deviation 2. The following normal curve represents this distribution, where $x$ represents the height in inches.

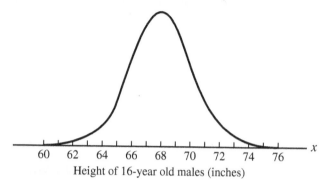

Height of 16-year old males (inches)

**a.** For what value of $x$ does the maximum or highest point of the curve occur? What does this value of $x$ correspond to in this distribution?

**b.** Each tick mark along the $x$-axis presents one inch. Locate the point on the $x$-axis that is one standard deviation greater than the mean.

**c.** If $\mu + \sigma$ represents the $x$-value that is one standard deviation greater than the mean, what does $\mu - \sigma$ represent? Locate the point on the graph.

**d.** The curve is symmetric about a vertical line through the mean $\mu$. Describe this symmetry property of the given normal curve. What is the equation of the vertical line in this situation?

**e.** Since the curve is symmetrical about the mean, what is the median and mode of the height distribution? What percentage of the data points is greater than the mean? Less than the mean?

**f.** Approximately 68% of the data values in any normal distribution fall between $\mu - \sigma$ and $\mu + \sigma$. What percent of the data values are between $\mu$ and $\mu + \sigma$?

**g.** The horizontal axis is an asymptote for every normal curve. Describe what this means.

**Summary of the properties of a normal curve:**

**1.** The curve is bell-shaped with the highest point at the mean $\mu$.

**2.** The curve is symmetrical about a vertical line $x = \mu$.

**3.** The mean, median, and mode are all equal.

**4.** 50% of the data values of the distribution are to the right of the mean $\mu$; 50% of the data values are to the left of the mean $\mu$.

**5.** Approximately 68% of the data values fall between $\mu - \sigma$ and $\mu + \sigma$; that is, 68% of the data values in the normal distribution are between $x = \mu - \sigma$ (one standard deviation less than the mean) and $x = \mu + \sigma$ (one standard deviation greater than the mean).

**6.** The normal curve model approaches the horizontal axis, but never touches or crosses the axis.

**4.** Use the following normal curves to answer parts a–d.

A

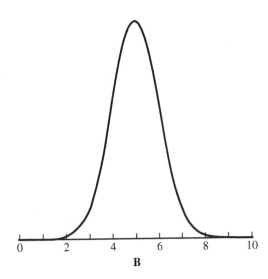

B

**a.** Determine the mean, median, and mode of each normal distribution.

**b.** One of the curves corresponds to a normal distribution with $\sigma = 3$ and the other with $\sigma = 1$. Match each curve with the correct standard deviation.

    **c.** For curve A, what value corresponds to each of the following:

        **i.** one standard deviation less than the mean, represented by $\mu - \sigma$

        **ii.** one standard deviation greater than the mean, represented by $\mu + \sigma$

    **d.** What percentage of the data in the distribution represented by curve A is between the values determined in part c?

## Standard Scores

Different normal distributions vary from each other based on the values of the mean $\mu$ and standard deviation $\sigma$. The mean $\mu$ may be located anywhere on the $x$-axis. The bell-shape may be wide or narrow, depending on the value of the standard deviation $\sigma$. But no matter how large or small the standard deviation might be, about 68% of the data values in the normal distribution will fall within one standard deviation of the mean. Therefore, the standard deviation $\sigma$ is often used as a standard unit of measurement that will allow you to compare different normal distributions.

**Standard scores,** also called $z$-scores, give the number of standard deviations that the original measurement $x$ is from the mean, $\mu$. The $z$-score formula is

$$z = \frac{x - \mu}{\sigma},$$

where    $z = z$-score,

         $x = $ given data value,

         $\mu = $ mean of the $x$-score distribution,

         $\sigma = $ standard deviation of the $x$-score distribution.

**Example 1**    *The heights of 16-year-old males are normally distributed with mean 68 inches and standard deviation 2 inches. Determine the z-score for:*

    **a.** 70 inches.

    **b.** 66 inches.

SOLUTION

    **a.** Let $x = 70$, $\mu = 68$, and $\sigma = 2$. Substituting, you have

$$z = \frac{x - \mu}{\sigma} = \frac{70 - 68}{2} = \frac{2}{2} = 1.$$

    **b.** Let $x = 66$, $\mu = 68$, and $\sigma = 2$.

$$z = \frac{x - \mu}{\sigma} = \frac{66 - 68}{2} = \frac{-2}{2} = -1$$

Therefore, in the 16-year old male height distribution with mean 68 and standard deviation 2, a height of 70 has a $z$-score of 1. This means that a height of 70 inches is one standard deviation greater than the mean of 68 inches. Similarly, a height of 66 inches has a corresponding $z$-score of $-1$. This indicates that 66 inches is one standard deviation less than the mean of 68 inches.

**5.** Determine the $z$-score for each of the following heights of 16-year-old males. Recall that this population is normally distributed with mean 68 inches and standard deviation 2 inches.

**a.** 71 inches

**b.** 74 inches

**c.** 68 inches

**d.** 64 inches

**e.** 62 inches

**6.** The mean of the normal 16-year old male height distribution is 68. The corresponding $z$-score (see Problem 5c) for 68 is 0. Will the mean of every normal distribution have a $z$-score of 0? Explain.

Data below the mean will always have negative z-scores. Data above the mean will always have positive z-scores. The mean will always have a z-score of 0.

**7.** Suppose the test scores on the last exam in the Algebra, Functions and Data Analysis course are normally distributed. The $z$-scores for some of the students in your class were:

$$1.5, 0, -1.2, -2, 1.95, 0.5.$$

**a.** List the $z$-scores of students that scored below the mean.

**b.** List the $z$-scores of students that scored above the mean.

**c.** If the mean of the exam was $\mu = 80$, did any of the students selected above have an exam score of 80? Explain.

**d.** Which $z$-score represents the student that scored the highest among the students selected above? Explain.

**e.** If the standard deviation of the exam was $\sigma = 5$, what was the actual test score for the student having $z$-score 1.95?

If the original distribution of $x$-values is normal, then the corresponding $z$-values will be normally distributed. The $z$-distribution will have a mean of $\mu = 0$ and a standard deviation of $\sigma = 1$.

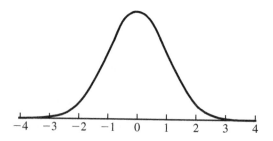

The resulting curve is called the **standard normal curve**.

**SUMMARY**
**Activity 7.10**

1. **Normal curve** is a **bell-shaped** curve that is symmetric about its mean. The mean, mode, and median in a normal distribution are the same. Each normal distribution can be modeled by a corresponding normal curve.

2. 50% of the data values of a normal distribution are greater than the mean $\mu$; 50% of the data values are less than the mean $\mu$.

3. Approximately 68% of the data values fall between $\mu - \sigma$ and $\mu + \sigma$; that is, 68% of the data values in the normal distribution are between $x = \mu - \sigma$ (one standard deviation less than the mean) and $x = \mu + \sigma$ (one standard deviation greater than the mean).

4. The normal curve model approaches the horizontal axis, but never touches or crosses the axis.

5. A normal curve can have any mean and any standard deviation; however, a **standardized normal curve** has $\mu = 0$ and $\sigma = 1$.

6. **Standard scores,** also called $z$-scores, indicate the number of standard deviations that the original measurement $x$ is from the mean $\mu$ of the normal distribution.

**7.** The z-score formula is: $z = \dfrac{x - \mu}{\sigma}$,

where     $z$ = z-score,

$x$ = given data value,

$\mu$ = mean of the x-score distribution,

$\sigma$ = standard deviation of the x-score distribution.

**8.** The mean of a normal distribution always has z-score 0. The values in any normal distribution that are below the mean have negative z-scores, those above the mean have positive z-scores.

## EXERCISES
### Activity 7.10

**1.** A normal distribution has a mean $\mu = 100$ and standard deviation $\sigma = 10$. Determine the z-score for each of the following x-values.

**a.** 110                     **b.** 125                     **c.** 100

**d.** 90                     **e.** 85

**2.** The high school Physical Education Department offers an Advanced First Aid course. The scores of the first exam were normally distributed. The z-scores for some of the students are shown below:

$$1.10,\ 1.70,\ -2.00,\ 0.00,\ -0.80,\ 1.60$$

**a.** Which of these students scored above the mean?

**b.** Which of these students had a test score equal to the mean of the exam?

**c.** Which of these students scored below the mean?

**d.** If the mean score was $\mu = 150$ with standard deviation $\sigma = 20$, what was the exam score for the student having z-score 1.70?

3. Students who drive to school are randomly selected. Each participant is asked the "arrival" time (in minutes) it takes to drive from their home, park the car, and enter the high school building. After analyzing the data, it is determined that the data is normally distributed with mean 20 minutes and standard deviation 3 minutes.

   **a.** If the arrival time is 26 minutes, determine the corresponding $z$-score.

   **b.** If the arrival time is 14 minutes, determine the corresponding $z$-score.

   **c.** If the arrival time is 20 minutes, determine the corresponding $z$-score. Is this answer to be expected? Explain.

   **d.** If the arrival time is 25 minutes, determine the corresponding $z$-score.

   **e.** If the arrival time is less than 20 minutes, is the corresponding $z$-score positive or negative?

   **f.** If the $z$-score for a certain arrival time is positive, then what can you determine about the value of the arrival time?

4. Your $z$-score on a college entrance exam is 1.3. If the $x$-scores on the exam have a mean of 480 and a standard deviation of 70 points, what is your $x$-score?

5. If a $z$-score is less than $-2$ ($z < -2$) or more than $2$ ($z > 2$), the corresponding $x$-value is considered "unusual". If $z < -3$ $or$ $z > 3$, then the corresponding $x$-value is considered "very unusual".

   **a.** Assume the white blood cell count per cubic millimeter of whole blood has a distribution that is approximately normal with mean $\mu = 7500$ and standard deviation $\sigma = 1750$. If someone had a white blood count of 3500, would that be considered unusually low?

**b.** If the red blood cell count in millions per cubic millimeter has an approximately normal distribution with mean $\mu = 4.8$ and standard deviation $\sigma = 0.3$, would a red blood count of 5.9 or higher be considered unusually high?

**6. a.** You score 680 on the mathematics portion of the SAT. If the math scores on the SAT are normally distributed with mean $\mu = 518$ and standard deviation $\sigma = 114$, determine the corresponding $z$-score for $x = 680$.

**b.** Your friend scores 27 on the ACT assessment mathematics test. If the ACT math scores are normally distributed with mean $\mu = 20.7$ and standard deviation 5.0, determine the corresponding $z$-score for $x = 27$.

**c.** Assume the tests both measure the same kind of ability. Compare the z-scores in parts a and b to determine who scored higher.

**ACTIVITY 7.11**

Part-time Jobs

Many high school students have part-time jobs after school and on weekends. Suppose the number of hours students spend working per week is approximately normally distributed, with a mean of 16 hours and a standard deviation of 4 hours. If a student is randomly selected, what is the probability that the student works between 12 and 18 hours per week? Before you can answer this question, you need to look more closely at the normal curve.

## Area Under a Normal Curve

A normal curve is used to model or represent a corresponding normal distribution. If $\mu$ and $\sigma$ represent the mean and standard deviation, respectively, of a normal distribution, then the equation of the corresponding normal curve is

$$y = \frac{e^{-\frac{1}{2}\left(\frac{x-\mu}{\sigma}\right)^2}}{\sigma\sqrt{2\pi}}.$$

1. The distribution of hours worked after school has mean $\mu = 16$ hours and standard deviation $\sigma = 4$ hours. Use a graphing calculator to graph the normal curve model for this distribution. Use the window settings Xmin = 4, Xmax = 28, Ymin = $-0.05$ and Ymax = 0.2. The screen should appear as follows:

Probability theory dictates that the area under the normal curve between two $x$-values and the $x$-axis represents a probability. The shaded area in the graph below gives the probability that a randomly selected high school student works between 12 and 18 hours per week.

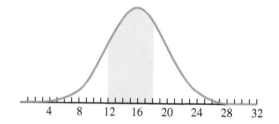

How do you calculate this area? In calculus, methods have been developed to find such areas, which can then be used to produce tables that give the areas. Later in this Activity, you will determine that the area is approximately 0.5328. This means the probability of selecting a student that works between 12 and 18 hours per week is 0.5328.

But there is still a problem. It just isn't very practical to construct a table for every possible combination of mean $\mu$ and standard deviation $\sigma$ for normal distributions. This is where the standard normal curve is so important.

## Area Under Standard Normal Curve

Before calculating areas for specific regions under a standard normal curve, your first question might be what is the total area under any normal curve?

2. The area under the normal curve corresponds to a probability. What is the total area under a normal curve? *Hint:* What is the sum of the probabilities of all possible outcomes?

In Activity 7.10, you learned that you can convert any normal distribution of original *x*-scores to a standard normal distribution of *z*-scores. Using the *z*-table (see Appendix C), you can determine the area under the standard normal curve for specific *z*-values. The *z*-table actually consists of two tables: one for negative *z*-scores and another for positive *z*-scores. The table entries give the **cumulative area from the left** of a specified *z*-score. The area corresponds to the probability that a randomly selected *z*-score is less than the specified *z*-score.

Example 1 demonstrates the process.

### Example 1

Determine the area under the standard normal curve to the left of $z = 1.00$.

SOLUTION

**Step 1.** Draw a diagram of the standard normal curve and shade the area to be determined.

**Step 2.** Determine the area of the shaded region using the appropriate *z*-table.

Since the specified *z*-score in this case is $z = 1.00 > 0$, you use the positive *z*-score table.

The *z*-column has the units and tenths value for *z*. The top row indicates the hundredths value of *z*. The table entries give the area under the standard normal curve to the left of the indicated *z*-score.

The area under the curve to the left of $z = 1.00$ is 0.8413

**Step 3.** The area under the standard normal curve to the left of $z = 1.00$ represents the probability that a *z*-value selected at random from the standard normal distribution is less than $z = 1.00$, denoted by P ($z < 1.00$).

**NOTE:** The area under the standard normal curve to the left of $z = -1.50$ can be determined in a similar fashion using the negative *z*-scores table. The area to the left of $z = -1.50$ is 0.0668.

Suppose you want to determine the area under the standard normal curve between two specific *z*-scores. The *z*-tables cannot be used directly to determine this area.

However, as Example 2 demonstrates, the table can be used in an indirect way to determine the desired area.

## Example 2

Determine the area under the standard normal curve between $z = -1.50$ and $z = 1.00$.

SOLUTION

**Step 1.** Draw a diagram.

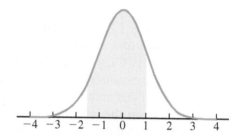

**Step 2.** Determine the area of shaded region using the $z$-tables.

The following areas can be determined directly from the table.

**i.** The area to the left of $z = -1.50$ is 0.0668.

**ii.** The area to the left of $z = 1.00$ is 0.8413.

The shaded area in the above diagram is the difference between 0.8413 and 0.0668.

The shaded area $= 0.8413 - 0.0668 = 0.7745$.

**Step 3.** Interpret the area as a probability.

The probability that a randomly selected $z$-score is between $z = -1.50$ and $z = 1.00$ is 0.7745. Symbolically,

$$P(-1.50 < z < 1.00) = 0.7745.$$

As you can see in Example 2, a diagram of the desired area is extremely helpful. The following Problems give you some practice in determining areas under the standard normal curve. All of the following information will be useful: a well labeled diagram, areas determined from the $z$-table, symmetry of the normal curve and the fact that the total area under the curve is 1.

3. For each of the following, use the $z$-table to determine the area under the standard normal curve for the given $z$-scores. Interpret your result as a probability.

   **a.** $z$ is less than $-1.15$

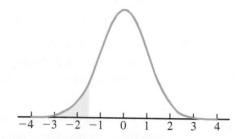

**b.** $z = -1.00$ to $z = 0.95$

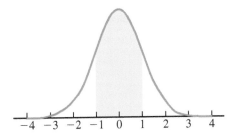

**c.** $z = 1.00$ to $z = 2.50$

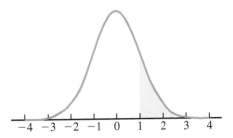

**d.** $z$ is greater than $-1.50$    HINT: The total area under the standard normal curve is 1.

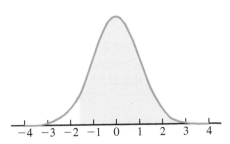

## Standardizing a Normal Curve

As you have observed, in most practical situations, the normal curve under investigation is not the standard normal curve. In general, there will not be tables of areas for these normal curves. Therefore, you can convert the original $x$-values to corresponding $z$-scores and then use the $z$-table.

For example, in the Part-time Job introductory problem, the number of hours students spent working per week is approximately normally distributed, with mean $\mu = 16$ hours and standard deviation $\sigma = 4$ hours. To determine the probability that a randomly selected student works between 12 and 18 hours per week, you first standardize the normal curve and convert $x = 12$ and $x = 18$ to its corresponding $z$-scores. Problem 4 guides you through the process.

**4. a.** Determine the $z$-score for $x = 12$ and $x = 18$ in the Part-time Job situation.

Now, the probability that a randomly selected student in the normal distribution works between 12 and 18 hours per week is equivalent to the probability that a randomly selected $z$-score in the standard normal distribution has a $z$-score between $z = -1.00$ and $z = 0.50$.

**b.** Determine the probability that a $z$-score randomly selected from the standard normal distribution is between $z = -1.00$ and $z = 0.50$.

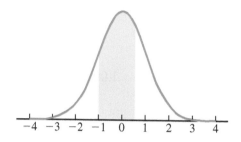

**c.** What is the probability that a randomly selected high school student works between 12 and 18 hours per week?

## Area Using Technology

A graphing calculator can be used to determine the area between two values under **any** normal curve. Besides being a more direct method, calculators often give more accurate results than the $z$-tables.

In Example 2, the $z$-table was used to determine the area under the standard normal curve between $z = -1.50$ and $z = 1.00$. The following example demonstrates how to use the TI 83/84 Plus calculator to determine this area.

**Example 3** Determine the area under the standard normal curve between $z = -1.50$ and $z = 1.00$.

SOLUTION

**Step 1.** Press 2ND, VARS to get to the distribution DISTR menu.

**Step 2.** Menu item 2, normalcdf, is used to get areas (probabilities) under a normal curve. Press 2 to select normalcdf from the menu to obtain this function on the home screen.

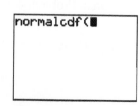

**Step 3.** Enter the following four values, separated by commas: left score, right score, mean, standard deviation.

Since $\mu = 0$ and $\sigma = 1$ for the standard normal curve, enter $-1.50$, $1.00$, $0$, $1$) and press ENTER

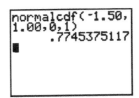

Therefore, the area is 0.7745 (rounded).

In Problem 4, you determined the probability that a randomly selected high school student works between 12 and 18 hours per week. Because you only had the $z$-table to determine areas, you had to determine the corresponding $z$-scores for $x = 12$ and $x = 18$. The normal distribution **does not** have to be standardized when using a graphing calculator to determine areas. You can enter the $x$-scores directly!

Be careful. Since you are using $x$-scores of the original normal distribution, you must enter the mean $\mu$ and standard deviation $\sigma$ of the original normal distribution.

5. **a.** Use a graphing calculator to determine the probability (area) that a randomly selected high school student works between 12 and 18 hours a week at a part-time job.

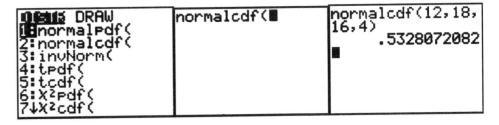

   **b.** How does your answer compare with the result in Problem 4c?

> The syntax for the normalcdf function is normalcdf($a$, $b$, $\mu$, $\sigma$), where $a$ is the left score (lower bound), $b$ is the right score (upper bound), $\mu$ is the mean and $\sigma$ is the standard deviation of the normal distribution.

## Applications

6. The time a fully changed iPod can be used on battery power is normally distributed with a mean $\mu = 8$ hours, and a standard deviation $\sigma = 0.8$ hours. What is the probability an iPod can be used on battery power for 7 to 9 hours?

**7. a.** Use the normalcdf calculator function to determine the probability an iPod battery will last between 8.5 and 10 hours.

**b.** Determine the probability an iPod battery will last more than 9 hours. Note: You want to determine $P(x > 9)$. There is no upper bound, $b$, for this problem. To determine $P(x > a)$, use a large positive number for the upper bound, at least five standard deviations above the mean. Let $b = 100$.

**c.** Determine the probability an iPod battery will last less than 6 hours. Note: You want to determine $P(x < 6)$. There is no lower bound, $a$, for this problem. To determine $P(x < b)$, use a large (in magnitude) negative number for the lower bound. Let $a = -100$.

**8.** You have just purchased a new DVD player. The warranty on the player is 2 years. If testing indicates that the lifetime of the DVD player is normally distributed with mean $\mu = 2.3$ years and standard deviation $\sigma = 0.4$ years, what is the probability that the DVD player will break down during the warranty period?

---

## SUMMARY
### Activity 7.11

**1.** A normal curve is used to model a corresponding normal distribution.

**2.** The total area under a normal curve is 1.

**3.** The area under a normal curve between $x = a$, $x = b$, and the $x$-axis represents the probability that a randomly selected $x$-value from the distribution is between $x = a$ and $x = b$.

**4.** The $z$-tables (see Appendix C) give the cumulative area under the standard normal curve to the left of a given $z$-score. If $z < 0$, use the negative $z$-score table. If $z > 0$, use the positive $z$-score table. See Example 1 on page 875.

**5.** The $z$-tables can be used indirectly to determine the area under the standard normal curve between two $z$-scores. Example 2 on page 876 demonstrates the process.

6. The normalcdf feature of the TI 83/84 Plus calculator can be used to determine the area between any two x-values under any normal curve.

Step 1. Press 2nd, VARS to get DISTR menu

Step 2. Select item 2, normalcdf to get the normalcdf function

Step 3. Enter $a$, $b$, $\mu$, $\sigma$ and press ENTER, where $a$ is the left score (lower bound), $b$ is the right score (upper bound), $\mu$ is the mean and $\sigma$ is the standard deviation of the normal distribution.

## EXERCISES
### Activity 7.11

1. For each of the following, use the z-tables to determine the area under the standard normal curve for the given z-scores. Interpret your result as a probability.

   a. $z$ less than 1.25

   b. $z$ less than $-2.45$

   c. $z = -1.95$ to $z = 1.75$

   d. $z = 0.50$ to $z = 2.30$

   e. $z$ is greater than 0.95

2. Verify your results in Exercise 1 using the normalcdf feature of a graphing calculator. Remember that the standard normal curve has mean $\mu = 0$ and standard deviation $\sigma = 1$.

   a. $z$ less than 1.25

   b. $z$ less than $-2.45$

   c. $z = -1.95$ to $z = 1.75$

   d. $z = 0.50$ to $z = 2.30$

   e. $z$ greater than 0.95

3. The scores on the National Assessment of Educational Progress 12th grade mathematics test are approximately normally distributed. The maximum score on the test is 500. The mean of the scores on a recent test was $\mu = 310$ and standard deviation $\sigma = 40$.

   a. Determine the probability that a randomly selected student who took the test had a score greater than 395. Standardize the given score and use the z-table.

  **b.** Determine the probability in part a using the normalcdf feature of a calculator. Use the given test score directly in the process.

  **c.** Compare the results in parts a and b.

4. A vending machine is designed to dispense a mean of 7.8 oz of soda into an 8 oz cup. The standard deviation of the amount of soda dispensed is 0.15 oz. Assume that the amount of soda dispensed is normally distributed.

  **a.** What is the probability that a randomly selected cup of soda has an amount less than 8 oz?

  **b.** What is the probability that a randomly selected cup of soda has an amount greater than 7.9 oz?

5. The Scholastic Aptitude Test (SAT) in mathematics is normally distributed with a mean score $\mu = 500$ and standard deviation $\sigma = 100$. Math scores are reported on a scale of 200 to 800. What is the probability that a randomly selected high school senior who took the SAT received a math score of

  **a.** more than 600?

  **b.** less than 450?

  **c.** between 650 and 750?

6. Ambulance response time is the difference between the time a call is first received by the dispatcher and the time the ambulance radios that it has arrived at the scene. In a certain city, data over a long period of time shows that response time is approximately normally distributed with mean 8.5 minutes and standard deviation 1.8 minutes. What is the probability that the response time of a randomly received emergency call will be

  **a.** between 5 and 10 minutes?

  **b.** less than 5 minutes?

  **c.** more than 10 minutes?

7. At a ski area in northern Vermont, the daytime high temperature in January is normally distributed with a mean of $\mu = 22°F$ and a standard deviation $\sigma = 10°F$. What is the probability that a randomly selected day in January will have a daytime high of

   a. greater than 45°F?

   b. between 30°F and 40°F?

   c. lower than 15°F?

8. Your sister will be graduating from college this year and is currently applying to the graduate school of business at a nearby university. Applicants are required to take the Graduate Management Aptitude Test (GMAT). Last year, the mean score for the GMAT was 472 with a standard deviation of 105. Assume the GMAT scores are normally distributed. Determine the probability that a randomly selected GMAT score is

   a. between 450 and 550.

   b. greater than 600.

9. Assume the mean life of a refrigerator (before replacement) is $\mu = 14$ years and a standard deviation of $\sigma = 2.5$ years. If the age in years at which a refrigerator is replaced is approximately normally distributed, what is the probability that the refrigerator will be

   a. replaced in less than 5 years?

   b. replaced between 10 and 12 years?

   c. be kept for more than 12 years?

10. A popular restaurant does not take reservations. As a result, there is usually a waiting time before you can be seated. Assume the waiting time before being seated is normally distributed with a mean of $\mu = 19$ minutes and a standard deviation of $\sigma = 4$ minutes. What is the probability that the waiting time will exceed 25 minutes?

**ACTIVITY 7.12**
Who Did Better?

**OBJECTIVES**

1. Compare different $x$-values in a normal distribution using $z$-scores.

2. Determine the percent of data between any two values of the normal distribution.

3. Determine the percentile of a given $x$-score in a normal distribution.

4. Compare different $x$-values using percentiles.

4. Determine $x$-value given its percentile in a normal distribution.

You and your friend are enrolled in two different sections of the Algebra, Functions and Data Analysis course. Recently, different midterm tests were given in each section. Since the high school has large class sizes, the test scores in both sections are approximately normally distributed. In your section, the mean was 80 and your score was 92. In your friend's section, the mean was 71 and her score was 83. Is it possible to determine who did better?

1. Since your test score of 92 is higher than your friend's test score of 83, can you claim that you did better on your exam than she did on her exam?

The absolute comparison of the test scores does not tell you how well each of you did with respect to the other students in the class.

2. a. Determine the difference between your test score and the mean of the test scores for your class.

   b. Determine the difference between your friend's test score and the mean for her class.

   c. How do the differences in parts a and b compare?

The result in part c does not indicate that you each did equally well on the respective midterm exams. Comparing just the means does not take into account the spread of the distribution of test scores.

The mean is the base value for comparison. However, to answer the question "Who Did Better?" more accurately, you need to know how far the scores are from the mean. This means you must take into account both the mean $\mu$ and the standard deviation $\sigma$ of the normal distribution. This can be accomplished by comparing the corresponding $z$-scores.

3. a. The standard deviation of the test scores in your section was $\sigma = 6.7$. Determine the corresponding $z$-score for your test score of $x = 92$. Recall that the mean $\mu = 80$.

   b. The standard deviation of test scores in your friend's section was $\sigma = 6.1$. Determine the corresponding $z$-score of your friend's grade of 83. Recall that the mean $\mu = 71$.

**c.** Did you or your friend do better on their midterm test? Explain.

## Percentages

When asking a question like

"What part of the entire math class scored between 85 and 90 on the midterm test?",

you often answer with a percentage. For example, 16% of the class scored between 85 and 90.

A probability number, such as 0.16, is used to answer the question

"What is the likelihood that a randomly selected student from your class scored between 85 and 90?"

The numbers 16% and 0.16 have the same value, but the orientation of the situation and the questions asked are different. So whether you want a percentage or a probability depends upon how the question is asked.

The good news is that the area under the normal curve between $x = 85$ and $x = 90$ is a graphical representation of **both percentage and probability**. The shaded area in the graph below answers both percentage and probability questions above.

**4. a.** Determine the percent of students in your math class that scored between 85 and 90 on the midterm test. The percentage is the shaded area in the graph. Recall that the mean of the test scores was $\mu = 80$ and standard deviation $\sigma = 6.7$.

**b.** What is the probability that a randomly selected student in your class scored between 85 and 90 on the midterm test?

**5.** Determine the percentage of students in your class that failed the test, that is, received a grade below 65?

## Percentiles

Suppose you want to know how you stand among all the students in your class who took the midterm test. You could determine the $z$-score corresponding to each test score and then compare. However, it is more common to use **percentiles**. A percentile is the percentage of test scores that are less than a given $x$-score. That is, the percentile corresponding to an $x$-score is the area under the normal curve to the left of the $x$-score.

For example, your classmate received an 84 on the midterm test. The percentage of students who received a grade less than 84 is the classmate's percentile, or relative position, in the class. This percentage is represented by the following shaded area.

Using the normalcdf feature of the TI 83/84 Plus calculator, enter 0, 84, 80, 6.7) and press [ENTER]. Your screen should appear as follows:

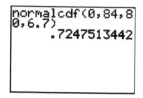

Since 72% of the class scored less than 84, your classmate is at the 72nd percentile, denoted by $P_{72}$.

Note that the $z$-table gives the area under the standard normal curve to the left of a given $z$-score. Since this area can be interpreted as the percentage of scores less than the specific $z$-score, the table values in the $z$-tables are actually percentiles.

**6.** Another student in your class received a grade of 75. What is her percentile?

Recall that your friend received a grade of 83 on the midterm math test in a different section. In Problem 3, $z$-scores were used to compare your test score of 92 (test statistics: $\mu = 80$, $\sigma = 6.7$) with your friend's test score of 83 (test statistics: $\mu = 71$, $\sigma = 6.1$). In general, percentiles are used for this type of situation to compare scores and determine who did better.

**7. a.** What is your percentile among students in your class who took the midterm exam?

**b.** What is your friend's percentile among students in her class who took the midterm exam?

**c.** Who did better? Explain.

## Percentile to x-score

Suppose you wanted to determine what test score in your section represented the 80th percentile, denoted $P_{80}$. This situation is represented below.

The invNorm function of the TI-83/84 plus can be used to determine the corresponding $x$-score for a given percentile.

First, press $\boxed{\text{2ND}}$, $\boxed{\text{VARS}}$ to get to the distribution $\boxed{\text{DISTR}}$ menu.

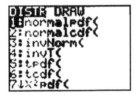

Menu item 3, invNorm, is used to determine the $x$-score that corresponds to a given percentile. Select invNorm from the menu to obtain this function on the home screen.

To get the $x$-score at the 80th percentile for the exam, enter 0.80, 80, 6.7 and press ENTER.

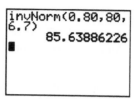

The 80th percentile, denoted by $P_{80}$, is 86 (rounded).

> In general, to get the $x$-score for the $k$th percentile, $P_k$, use the invNorm function as follows:
>
> $$P_k = \text{invNorm}\left(\frac{k}{100}, \mu, \sigma\right),$$
>
> where $\mu$ is the mean and $\sigma$ is the standard deviation of the distribution.

**8.** In your section, what grade did a student receive if she is in the 90th percentile?

## Additional Applications

**9.** In a national survey, it was determined that the number of hours high school students watch television per year is approximately normally distributed. If the mean is $\mu = 1500$ hours, and the standard deviation is $\sigma = 100$ hours, determine the percentage of students that watch television

    **a.** less than 1600 hours per year.

    **b.** more than 1700 hours per year.

    **c.** between 1400 and 1650 hours per year.

**10.** Suppose an engineering school honor's program will only accept high school seniors with a mathematics Scholastic Aptitude Test (SAT) score in the top 10% (above the 90th percentile). The SAT scores in math are normally distributed with mean $\mu = 500$ and standard deviation $\sigma = 100$. What is the minimum SAT score in math for acceptance into the program?

**SUMMARY**
Activity 7.12

1. The corresponding $z$-scores of $x$-scores can be used to compare the relative position of $x$-scores from two different distributions.

2. The area under the normal curve between two $x$-scores is a graphical representation of both percentage and probability.

3. The percentile corresponding to a given $x$-score gives the relative position of the $x$-value in the distribution.

4. The percentile is the percentage of $x$-values that are less than a given $x$-score. For example, if $x = 85$ presents the 90th percentile, denoted by $P_{90}$, then 90% of the $x$-values in the distribution are less than $x = 85$. Any score greater than 85 is in the top 10% of the distribution.

5. Using the normalcdf feature of the TI 83/84 Plus calculator, the percentile for a given $x$-value can be determined by entering $-9999, x, \mu, \sigma)$ and pressing ENTER.

6. The percentile corresponding to an $x$-score is the area under the normal curve to the left of the $x$-score. Therefore, the table values in the $z$-tables represent percentiles.

7. To obtain the $x$-score of the $k$th percentile, $P_k$,

   **Step 1.** Press 2nd, VARS to get DISTR menu

   **Step 2.** Select item 3, invNorm to get the invNorm function

   **Step 3.** Enter $\dfrac{k}{100}, \mu, \sigma)$ and press ENTER.

**EXERCISES**
Activity 7.12

1. **a.** In the 2004 Olympics, Austra Skujyte of Lithuania had an impressive throw of 16.4 meters in the Shot Put competition of the women's heptathlon. If the Shot Put event had a mean of 13.29 meters and a standard deviation of 1.24 meters, determine the corresponding $z$-score for 16.4.

   **b.** Caroline Kluft won the long jump in the women's heptathlon with a jump of 6.78 meters. If $\mu = 6.16$ meters and $\sigma = 0.23$ meters for the long jump event, determine the corresponding $z$-score for 6.78.

   **c.** Who did better? Explain.

2. You will be attending college in the fall. At a recent visit to the campus to take placement exams, you scored 82 in English and 86 in math. The college reported that the English exam had a mean of 72 and a standard deviation of 8. The mean of the math exam was 68, with a standard deviation of 12. On which exam did you do better?

3. **a.** What is your percentile on the English exam in Exercise 2?

   **b.** What is your percentile on the math placement exam in Exercise 2?

4. The Environmental Protection Agency (EPA) fuel economy estimates for car models recently tested had a mean of 24.5 mpg and a standard deviation of 6.1 mpg for highway driving. Assume the gas mileage was normally distributed.

   **a.** About what percent of the cars should get between 35 and 40 mpg?

   **b.** About what percent of the cars should get more than 30 mpg?

5. The cholesterol levels of adult American women are approximately normally distributed with a mean of 188 mg/dL and a standard deviation of 24 mg/dL.

   **a.** What percent of adult women do you expect to have a cholesterol level between 140 and 160 mg/dL?

   **b.** What percent of adult women do you expect to have a cholesterol level of more than 200 mg/dL?

6. The Dutch are among the tallest people in the world. The mean height of Dutch men is approximately 6 feet, with a standard deviation of about 3.12 inches. What percentage of all Dutch men will be over 6 feet 6 inches tall? Assume that height is normally distributed.

7. Assume the distribution of ages for licensed drivers has a mean of 44.5 years and a standard deviation of 17.1 years. If the distribution of ages is normally distributed, determine the percentage of drivers that are

   **a.** between the ages of 18 and 25.          **b.** younger than 21 years of age.

**c.** between the ages of 30 and 55.        **d.** older than 65 years of age.

**8.** In a recent American College Test (ACT), students had a mean reading score of 21.3 and a standard deviation of 6.0. Assume the scores are normally distributed.

  **a.** Determine the percent of students having ACT scores between 18 and 22.

  **b.** What is a student's percentile for a ACT score of 24?

  **c.** What score on the ACT corresponds to the 90th percentile?

**9.** Scores of high school seniors on the SAT exams are normally distributed with mean $\mu = 1026$ and standard deviation $\sigma = 209$.

  **a.** What percent of seniors score at least 800?

  **b.** What percent of seniors score greater than 1200?

  **c.** A senior scores 1250 on the SAT exam. What is his percentile among the high school seniors that took the exam?

  **d.** What SAT score corresponds to the 80th percentile?

**10.** Scores on an IQ test are normally distributed with a mean $\mu = 100$ and standard deviation $\sigma = 15$. The organization MENSA requires an IQ score of 130 or higher for membership.

  **a.** What percent of individuals taking the test qualify for membership?

  **b.** You score a 120 on the IQ test. What is your percentile among those individuals who took the test?

**11.** Women's heights are normally distributed with mean 63.6 inches and standard deviation 2.5 inches. A social organization for tall people requires that women must be at least 70 inches tall.

  **a.** What percentage of women meets the requirement?

  **b.** If your older sister is 6 feet tall, what is her percentile?

12. The standard normal distribution has mean $\mu = 0$ and standard deviation $\sigma = 1$. Determine the $z$-score corresponding to

   a. the 90th percentile.                    b. the 99th percentile.

13. In order to increase sales, the manufacturer of an expensive computer game wants to advertise an impressive guarantee period. The guarantee policy would require a full refund of the purchase price if the computer control system fails during the guarantee period. According to product testing results, the computer game's life is normally distributed with mean $\mu = 30$ months and standard deviation $\sigma = 4$ months.

   a. What percentage of the computer games sold will fail in less than 28 months?

   b. If the guarantee period was 28 months, what percentage of computer games could be returned for a full refund of the purchase price?

   c. If the guarantee period was 18 months, what percentage of the computer games could be returned for a full refund?

   d. A guarantee period of 18 months is not impressive enough. The company calculates that they can meet their projected profit if no more than 7% of the computer games are returned for a full refund. That is, if no more than 7% of the computer games lasts fewer months than the guarantee period. Determine the number of months for the guarantee period.

What Have I Learned?

1. A voluntary response sample (or self-selected sample) is one in which individuals decide to be included in the sample. Will such a sampling technique result in a biased example? Explain.

2. You want to determine the average family size of households in Virginia. You collect data consisting of the number of siblings from students in your high school. Regardless of the sampling technique used, is the sample representative of all households in the state?

3. Determine if the following sampling techniques result in a random sampling. Explain why or why not.

   a. Your teacher obtains a sample by selecting the first six students entering the classroom.

   b. Your math classroom consists of 30 students in six different rows. Your teacher rolls a die to determine a row, then rolls the die again to select a particular student in the row. This process is repeated until a sample of 6 students is obtained.

4. Which do you think has more variation: the IQ scores of 20 randomly selected graduating college seniors or the IQ scores of 20 randomly selected adults entering the local mall? Explain.

5. Does adding the same number to each value of a set of data affect the measure of variability for that set of data?

6. Which distribution has greater variability?

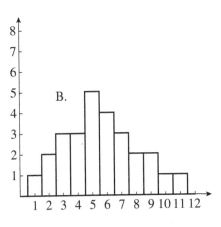

**7. a.** Use a graphing calculator to determine the mean and standard deviation of the following two data sets:

| Data 1 | 9.14 | 8.14 | 8.74 | 8.77 | 9.26 | 8.10 | 6.13 | 3.10 | 9.13 | 7.26 | 4.74 |
|--------|------|------|------|------|------|------|------|------|------|------|------|
| Data 2 | 6.58 | 5.76 | 7.71 | 8.84 | 8.47 | 7.04 | 5.25 | 5.56 | 7.91 | 6.89 | 12.50 |

**b.** Construct a stem-and-leaf plot of each distribution and compare the shapes of the distribution.

**8.** For a given data set, is the second quartile, $Q_2$, always the same as the median of the data? Explain.

**9.** Does the following histogram represent a distribution that is approximately normal? Explain.

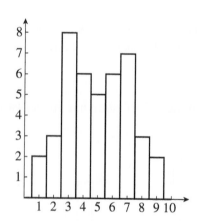

**10.** Identify the following distributions as skewed to the left, normal, or skewed to the right.

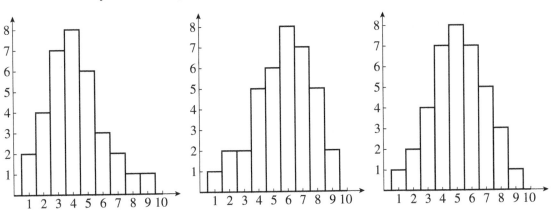

**11.** A value from a large data set has a corresponding $z$-score of $-2$. Is the data value greater than or less than the mean of the data set?

**12.** For a standard normal distribution:

**a.** What is the mean $\mu$ and standard deviation $\sigma$ of the distribution?

**b.** Determine the positive $z$-score that is two standard deviation from the mean on the $z$-axis.

**c.** Determine the percentage of $z$-scores that are within 1 standard deviation of the mean. That is, the percentage of $z$-scores between $z = -1$ and $z = 1$?

**d.** What is the probability that a randomly selected $z$-score is greater than $z = 3$?

**e.** If $P(z < a) = 0.4500$, determine the value of $a$.

**13.** Heights of males are normally distributed. If the heights ($x$-values) are measured in units of inches, what are the units for the $z$-scores that correspond to specific heights?

**1.** Consider the following data: 12, 8, 9, 10, 12, 9

Determine the standard deviation by filling in the table as part of your calculation.

| $x$ | $\bar{x}$ | $x - \bar{x}$ | $(x - \bar{x})^2$ |
| --- | --- | --- | --- |
| | | | |
| | | | |
| | | | |
| | | | |
| | | | |
| | | | |

**2.** The following speeds of 21 cars are recorded as they pass a concealed marker on an interstate highway that has a legal speed limit of 65 mph: 73, 67, 69, 65, 64, 77, 59, 74, 71, 67, 70, 58, 67, 69, 71, 70, 69, 64, 85, 67, and 64. Determine the five-number summary and produce the boxplot.

**3.** The management of Disney World would like to determine the amount of waiting time for the rides at Space Mountain. The following data represents a random sample of waiting times in minutes (rounded to the nearest half-minute):

4.0  5.5  9.5  5.0  13.5  6.5  8.5  9.0  9.5  12.0  8.0  7.5

**a.** What is the mean waiting time for the ride?

**b.** What is the standard deviation?

**c.** Assuming the waiting time is approximately normally distributed, estimate the probability that a randomly selected person will wait longer than 10 minutes. Use the mean and standard deviation in parts a and b for the mean and standard deviation of the distribution of the population of waiting times.

**d.** Estimate the percentage of persons waiting less than 5 minutes to ride the roller-coaster.

4. Sandy Allen is the world's tallest woman having a height of 91.25 inches (7 feet, 7.25 inches). The heights of adult females are normally distributed with mean $\mu = 63.6$ inches and a standard deviation $\sigma = 2.5$ inches.

**a.** Determine the $z$-score corresponding to Sandy Allen's height.

**b.** An event having a probability of 0.000000001 or less is considered to be extremely improbable. What is the probability that a randomly selected female has a height of greater than 6 feet, 6 inches?

5. Two companies market batteries that are designed for MP3 players. Company 1 claims a mean battery life of 11 hours. Company 2 promotions advertise a mean battery life of 12 hours.

**a.** Before deciding which brand to purchase, explain why you would also like to know the standard deviation of the battery lifespans.

**b.** If the standard deviation for the battery produced by Company 1 is 1.5 hours, what is the probability that the battery will last at least 8 hours?

**c.** If the standard deviation for the battery manufactured by Company 2 is 2 hours, what is the probability that the battery will last at least 8 hours?

**d.** Which battery would you purchase? Explain.

6. A recent survey of 300 high school students was conducted during a certain week in February, 2007 to determine the number of hours of TV watched during the week. The mean of the data collected was $\mu = 3.66$ hours and a standard deviation of $\sigma = 4.93$ hours.

   a. Assuming that the number of hours of TV watched was normally distributed, estimate the percentage of high school students that watch between 5 and 10 hours of TV per week.

   b. What percentage of high school students is expected to watch more than 10 hours of TV per week?

7. The number of minutes that a certain flight arrives late at O'Hare Airport in Chicago is normally distributed with mean $\mu = 8.4$ minutes and a standard deviation $\sigma = 2.8$ minutes.

   a. What percentage of the flights on this route is between 5 and 10 minutes late?

   b. What percentage of the flights are less than 5 minutes late?

   c. What percentage of the flights are more than 10 minutes late?

8. The actual amount in a half-gallon container of a certain brand of apple juice is normally distributed with mean $\mu = 65$ ounces and standard deviation $\sigma = 0.35$ ounce.

   a. What percentage of the juice containers contain between 64 and 66 ounces?

   b. What percentage of containers has more than 65 ounces of juice?

9. A study of adult male weights indicated that the weights are normally distributed with mean $\mu = 181$ pounds and standard deviation $\sigma = 20$ pounds.

   a. Based on the study, what percentage of adult males weigh more than 200 pounds?

   b. What is the probability that a randomly selected adult male weighs less than 175 pounds?

   c. What weight corresponds to the 80th percentile? Explain what this means in the context of this situation?

**10.** Women's heights are normally distributed with mean $\mu = 63.0$ inches and standard deviation $\sigma = 2.5$ inches.

    **a.** Determine the height that corresponds to the 10th percentile.

    **b.** Determine the height that corresponds to the 90th percentile.

**11.** Many high school seniors take the ACT as part of the admission requirement to colleges. ACT scores are reported on a scale of 1 to 36. In recent years, ACT scores have been approximately normally distributed with a mean $\mu = 20.9$ and standard deviation $\sigma = 4.8$.

    **a.** What percentage of the ACT scores is between 25 and 30?

    **b.** Your friend scores a 28 on the ACT. What is your friend's percentile?

    **c.** What ACT score corresponds to the 90th percentile?

    **d.** What ACT score corresponds to the 30th percentile?

**12.** A tire manufacturer wants to establish a mileage guarantee on a new model tire. Test results on the wear-life of the tire show a mean $\mu = 45,000$ miles and standard deviation $\sigma = 3,000$ miles.

    **a.** If the guaranteed mileage was 35,000 miles, what percentage of the tires would have to be replaced? That is, what percentage of tires would "wear out" in less than 35,000 miles?

    **b.** The tire company wants to set the guaranteed mileage so that no more than 5% of the tires will have to be replaced. Determine the guaranteed mileage.

**13.** Assume human body temperatures are normally distributed with mean $\mu = 98.20°F$ and standard deviation $\sigma = 0.62°F$. If a hospital uses $100.6°F$ as the lowest temperature to be considered a fever, what percentage of normal and healthy people would be considered to have a fever? Is this reasonable? Explain.

# Summary

*The bracketed numbers following each concept indicate the activity in which the concept is discussed.*

| CONCEPT / SKILL | DESCRIPTION | EXAMPLE |
|---|---|---|
| **Line graph** [7.1] | When data points are plotted and connected with line segments to better show a trend. | |
| **Bar graph** [7.1], [7.2] | A plot of data where the number of data values falling in a category is represented by the height or length of a rectangle, or bar. | |
| **Circle graph** [7.2] | Displays the relative number of data values in each category by the size of the corresponding sector, or slice. | |
| **Stacked bar graph** [7.2] | When paired data separates a bar into two parts, to show relative sizes for each category. | |
| **Frequency table** [7.3] | A table that displays the number of times (the frequency) a data value occurs. | |
| **Dot plot** [7.3] | The frequency is measured on the vertical scale, one dot for each data value. | |
| **Histogram** [7.3] | Displays the frequency of each category of data, with each rectangle's height giving the frequency. | |

| | | |
|---|---|---|
| **Frequency distribution** [7.3] | Any collection of data that has been organized, according to how frequently each data value occurs, in a table or graph. | |
| **Measures of the central tendency of a frequency distribution** [7.4] | An indication, or measurement, of the approximate location of the center or middle of a collection of data. | Mean, median, mode, and midrange are all different ways of measuring the center. |
| **Mean** [7.4] | The usual average found by adding the data values and dividing by the number of values. | The mean of $\{1, 3, 4, 8, 10\}$ is $(1 + 3 + 4 + 8 + 10)/5 = 5.2$. |
| **Median** [7.4] | The exact middle of the numerically ordered data, half the data values lie above and half lie below the median. (If there is an even number of data values, the median is the mean of the two middle values.) | The median of $\{1, 3, 4, 8, 10\}$ is 4. |
| **Mode** [7.4] | The data value that occurs most frequently. | The mode of $\{1, 3, 3, 3, 5, 7, 7\}$ is 3. |
| **Midrange** [7.4] | The exact midpoint between the lowest and highest data values. | The midrange of $\{1, 3, 4, 8, 10\}$ is $(1 + 10)/2 = 5.5$. |
| **Simple random sample (SRS)** [7.5] | A sample that is selected where every possible sample of a given size has an equal chance of being selected. | |
| **Bias in a sample** [7.5], [7.6] | When some individuals in a population have a greater chance of being selected for a sample than others. | |
| **Sampling plan** [7.5], [7.6], [7.7] | A detailed step-by-step procedure to collect data through a specific sampling method. | |
| **Stratified sample** [7.6] | When a population is separated into two or more strata, with a SRS selected from each, proportional to the relative size of each strata. | |
| **Experimental Design** [7.8] | To establish a cause-and-effect relationship between two variables through control, randomization and replication. | |
| **Control group** [7.8] | The individuals in an experiment that do not receive the treatment. | |

| | | |
|---|---|---|
| **Double-blind** [7.8] | Desirable in a good experiment, when all individuals involved in the study, subjects, administrators and evaluators, have no knowledge of which subjects are receiving the treatment. | |
| **Placebo-effect** [7.8] | When a human responds positively to a false treatment (normally in the control group). | |
| **Variability of a frequency distribution** [7.9] | Refers to how spread out the data is, away from the center. | $\{1, 4, 7, 13, 25, 34\}$ has greater variability than $\{3, 3, 3, 4, 4, 5\}$. |
| **Range of a frequency distribution** [7.9] | The difference between the minimum and maximum data values. | The range of $\{1, 3, 4, 8, 10\}$ is $10 - 1 = 9$. |
| **Deviation of a data value** [7.9] | Refers to how far a data value is from the mean. | In the data set $\{1, 3, 4, 8, 10\}$, the deviation of 10 is $10 - 5.2 = 4.8$. |
| **Standard deviation** [7.9] | A measure of how far all the data collectively is from the mean. A standard deviation of zero means all the data is the same number (the mean), there is no variation. | $$\sigma = \sqrt{\frac{\sum (x - \bar{x})^2}{n}}$$ For $\{1, 3, 4, 8, 10\}$, $\sigma \approx 3.31$. |
| **Five-number summary for a distribution** [7.9] | The minimum, first quartile, median, third quartile, and maximum data value, for a distribution. | 1-Var Stats<br>↑n=20<br>minX=18<br>Q1=19<br>Med=21<br>Q3=26<br>maxX=35 |
| **Boxplot** [7.9] | A graph that displays the five-number summary for a distribution. | |
| **Standard normal curve (distribution)** [7.10] | A bell-shaped curve representing a normal distribution with $\mu = 0$ and $\sigma = 1$. | |
| **Standard (z) scores** [7.10] | The number of standard deviations a data value is from the mean of normal distribution. | $z = \dfrac{x - \mu}{\sigma}$, where $x =$ data value, $\mu =$ mean, $\sigma =$ standard deviation |

| **Area under a normal curve represents probability** [7.11], [7.12] | The probability that a randomly selected data value from a normal distribution is between $a$ and $b$ is the same as the area under the normal curve for $a < x < b$. | Given a normal distribution with $\mu = 8$ and $\sigma = 3$, $$P(5 < x < 8) =$$ 0.68, the area under the normal curve between 5 and 11. |
|---|---|---|

1. The weights, in pounds, of a group of workers are as follows:

| 173 | 123 | 171 | 175 | 188 | 120 | 177 | 160 | 151 | 169 |
|-----|-----|-----|-----|-----|-----|-----|-----|-----|-----|
| 162 | 128 | 145 | 140 | 158 | 132 | 202 | 162 | 154 | 180 |
| 164 | 166 | 157 | 171 | 175 |     |     |     |     |     |

   Determine the mean, standard deviation, and five-number summary for these data. Decide on a scale and draw a boxplot. Check your answers with your calculator.

2. **a.** Determine the mean, median, mode, and midrange for this collection of class test scores:

| 88 | 82 | 97 | 76 | 79 | 92 | 65 | 84 | 79 |
|----|----|----|----|----|----|----|----|----|
| 90 | 75 | 82 | 78 | 77 | 93 | 88 | 95 | 73 |
| 69 | 89 | 93 | 78 | 60 | 95 | 88 | 72 | 80 |
| 94 | 88 | 74 |    |    |    |    |    |    |

   **b.** From these measures of central tendency, would you guess that the distribution is symmetrical, skewed to the left, or skewed to the right? Check your answer by displaying the histogram and/or boxplot on your grapher.

3. The ages of 10 randomly selected NASCAR drivers are listed.
   33, 48, 41, 29, 40, 48, 44, 42, 49, 28

   **a.** Determine the mean age of the 10 drivers.

   **b.** Determine the median age.

   **c.** Determine the mode, if it exists.

   **d.** Determine the midrange of the ages of the 10 drivers.

**e.** Determine the standard deviation of the ages of the 10 NASCAR drivers.

**f.** Verify your results in parts a–d using a graphing calculator.

4. A company is receiving complaints from customers about the amount of time waiting on hold when attempting to contact customer service. A sample of 40 customers are randomly selected and the amount of time on hold when calling customer service is recorded (in minutes).

| | | | | | | | |
|-----|-----|-----|-----|-----|-----|-----|------|
| 0.5 | 4.6 | 5.5 | 6.3 | 6.8 | 7.8 | 8.9 | 10.1 |
| 1.6 | 4.6 | 5.6 | 6.3 | 6.9 | 8.0 | 9.2 | 10.5 |
| 3.2 | 4.9 | 6.0 | 6.4 | 7.0 | 8.3 | 9.3 | 10.6 |
| 3.7 | 5.1 | 6.0 | 6.5 | 7.2 | 8.6 | 9.4 | 11.0 |
| 4.3 | 5.3 | 6.2 | 6.5 | 7.5 | 8.6 | 9.7 | 11.3 |

**a.** Using 0–1.9 as the first class width, construct a histogram of the data.

**b.** Describe the shape of the distribution.

**c.** Determine the mean of the sample.

**d.** Determine the standard deviation.

**e.** Assume the distribution of the amount of waiting time is approximately normal. Use the mean and standard deviation of the sample in parts c and d to estimate the mean and standard deviation of the distribution of all waiting times. Estimate the probability that a randomly selected call to customer service will be on hold more than 5 minutes.

5. A cereal manufacturer wants to ensure that its 16-ounce boxes of cereal are not underweight. To help prevent underweight boxes, the company sets the packaging machine so that the mean weight is 16.3 ounces. Based on their experience, the weight of the amount of cereal in each box is normally distributed with standard deviation 0.2 ounces.

   a. What percentage of the filled cereal boxes weigh less than 16 ounces?

   b. What percentage of the filled cereal boxes weigh between 16 and 16.3 ounces?

   c. What percentage of the filled boxes weigh more than 16.3 ounces?

6. Scores on the verbal test Scholastic Aptitude Test (SAT) are normally distributed with mean $\mu = 504$ and standard deviation $\sigma = 111$. How high must a student score in order to be in the top 10% of all students taking the SAT?

7. The combined scores (math and verbal) of high school seniors on the SAT exam are normally distributed with mean $\mu = 1026$ and standard deviation $\sigma = 209$.

   a. What is the probability that a randomly selected student who took the test had a combined score of at least 820?

   b. What percentage of all students who take the SAT have combined scores between 720 and 820?

   c. What score represents the 95th percentile on the SAT?

8. Scores on the Wechsler Adult Intelligence Scale are approximately normally distributed with mean $\mu = 100$ and standard deviation $\sigma = 15$.

   a. How high must a score be to be in the top 20%?
      HINT. Determine the score that represents the 80th percentile.

   b. What scores are in the lowest 10%?

9. A study of weekly salaries at High Tech Manufacturing indicated that weekly salaries are normally distributed with mean $\mu = \$725$ and standard deviation $\sigma = \$45$.

   a. What percentage of employees' salaries was less than $685?

**b.** What is the probability that a randomly selected employee at High Tech has a weekly salary greater than $800?

**c.** What salary represents the 75th percentile? Explain what this means in the context of this situation.

10. One study suggests that the systolic blood pressure of adult males is approximately normally distributed with mean $\mu = 118$ and standard deviation $\sigma = 10.5$.

   **a.** Determine the pressure level that corresponds to the 5th percentile.

   **b.** Determine the pressure level that corresponds to the 95th percentile.

11. Many colleges require their applicants for admission to take the SAT. SAT scores are reported on a scale of 400 to 1600. Recently, SAT scores have been approximately normally distributed with mean $\mu = 998$ and standard deviation $\sigma = 202$.

   **a.** What percentage of the SAT scores is between 1200 and 1400?

   **b.** You score a 1250 on the SAT. What is your percentile?

   **c.** What SAT score corresponds to the 80th percentile?

   **d.** What SAT score corresponds to the 25th percentile?

12. According to a study of the length of time it takes to play a major league baseball game (see MLB.com), the time it takes to play a game is approximately normally distributed with mean $\mu = 2$ hours, 50 minutes and standard deviation $\sigma = 21$ minutes (rounded).

   **a.** What percentage of major league baseball games take more than 3 hours?

   **b.** What percentage of games take less than 2 hours, 30 minutes?

13. Birth weights in the United States are normally distributed with a mean $\mu = 3420$ grams and standard deviation $\sigma = 495$ grams. Newborns weighing less than 2405 grams represent what percentage of the newborn population?

# Problem Solving with Financial Models

**ACTIVITY 8.1**
Income and
Expenses

**OBJECTIVE**

1. Solve problems involving personal finances.

You are starting your first job in Syracuse, New York as a salesperson at a sporting goods store. Your income consists of a base salary of $8.00 per hour, with time and a half for more than 40 hours per week and double time for holidays. You also receive a 3% commission on total sales.

1. Based on a 5-day week, 8-hour day, and 52-week year, determine your annual gross base salary.

2. You are paid biweekly. What is your gross base salary per pay period?

> **Example 1** *If the Social Security tax is 6.2% of gross income, determine the amount of your Social Security deduction (6.2% = 0.062) in each pay period.*
>
> SOLUTION
>
> $0.062(640) = 39.68$    The amount of the Social Security deduction is $39.68.

3. **a.** If Medicare is 1.45% of gross income, determine your Medicare deduction (1.45% = 0.0145) in each pay period.

   **b.** Use the tax tables on the following three pages to find the federal and state biweekly deductions for a single person earning $640 biweekly and claiming zero for withholding allowances.

   **c.** Union dues of ten dollars per pay period are also deducted. Determine the total of all deductions in each pay period.

# SINGLE Persons—BIWEEKLY Payroll Period
## (For Wages Paid in 2005)

| If the wages are— | | And the number of withholding allowances claimed is— | | | | | | | | | | |
|---|---|---|---|---|---|---|---|---|---|---|---|---|
| At least | But less than | 0 | 1 | 2 | 3 | 4 | 5 | 6 | 7 | 8 | 9 | 10 |
| | | The amount of income tax to be withheld is— | | | | | | | | | | |
| $0 | $105 | $0 | $0 | $0 | $0 | $0 | $0 | $0 | $0 | $0 | $0 | $0 |
| 105 | 110 | 1 | 0 | 0 | 0 | 0 | 0 | 0 | 0 | 0 | 0 | 0 |
| 110 | 115 | 1 | 0 | 0 | 0 | 0 | 0 | 0 | 0 | 0 | 0 | 0 |
| 115 | 120 | 2 | 0 | 0 | 0 | 0 | 0 | 0 | 0 | 0 | 0 | 0 |
| 120 | 125 | 2 | 0 | 0 | 0 | 0 | 0 | 0 | 0 | 0 | 0 | 0 |
| 125 | 130 | 3 | 0 | 0 | 0 | 0 | 0 | 0 | 0 | 0 | 0 | 0 |
| 130 | 135 | 3 | 0 | 0 | 0 | 0 | 0 | 0 | 0 | 0 | 0 | 0 |
| 135 | 140 | 4 | 0 | 0 | 0 | 0 | 0 | 0 | 0 | 0 | 0 | 0 |
| 140 | 145 | 4 | 0 | 0 | 0 | 0 | 0 | 0 | 0 | 0 | 0 | 0 |
| 145 | 150 | 5 | 0 | 0 | 0 | 0 | 0 | 0 | 0 | 0 | 0 | 0 |
| 150 | 155 | 5 | 0 | 0 | 0 | 0 | 0 | 0 | 0 | 0 | 0 | 0 |
| 155 | 160 | 6 | 0 | 0 | 0 | 0 | 0 | 0 | 0 | 0 | 0 | 0 |
| 160 | 165 | 6 | 0 | 0 | 0 | 0 | 0 | 0 | 0 | 0 | 0 | 0 |
| 165 | 170 | 7 | 0 | 0 | 0 | 0 | 0 | 0 | 0 | 0 | 0 | 0 |
| 170 | 175 | 7 | 0 | 0 | 0 | 0 | 0 | 0 | 0 | 0 | 0 | 0 |
| 175 | 180 | 8 | 0 | 0 | 0 | 0 | 0 | 0 | 0 | 0 | 0 | 0 |
| 180 | 185 | 8 | 0 | 0 | 0 | 0 | 0 | 0 | 0 | 0 | 0 | 0 |
| 185 | 190 | 9 | 0 | 0 | 0 | 0 | 0 | 0 | 0 | 0 | 0 | 0 |
| 190 | 195 | 9 | 0 | 0 | 0 | 0 | 0 | 0 | 0 | 0 | 0 | 0 |
| 195 | 200 | 10 | 0 | 0 | 0 | 0 | 0 | 0 | 0 | 0 | 0 | 0 |
| 200 | 205 | 10 | 0 | 0 | 0 | 0 | 0 | 0 | 0 | 0 | 0 | 0 |
| 205 | 210 | 11 | 0 | 0 | 0 | 0 | 0 | 0 | 0 | 0 | 0 | 0 |
| 210 | 215 | 11 | 0 | 0 | 0 | 0 | 0 | 0 | 0 | 0 | 0 | 0 |
| 215 | 220 | 12 | 0 | 0 | 0 | 0 | 0 | 0 | 0 | 0 | 0 | 0 |
| 220 | 225 | 12 | 0 | 0 | 0 | 0 | 0 | 0 | 0 | 0 | 0 | 0 |
| 225 | 230 | 13 | 0 | 0 | 0 | 0 | 0 | 0 | 0 | 0 | 0 | 0 |
| 230 | 235 | 13 | 1 | 0 | 0 | 0 | 0 | 0 | 0 | 0 | 0 | 0 |
| 235 | 240 | 14 | 1 | 0 | 0 | 0 | 0 | 0 | 0 | 0 | 0 | 0 |
| 240 | 245 | 14 | 2 | 0 | 0 | 0 | 0 | 0 | 0 | 0 | 0 | 0 |
| 245 | 250 | 15 | 2 | 0 | 0 | 0 | 0 | 0 | 0 | 0 | 0 | 0 |
| 250 | 260 | 15 | 3 | 0 | 0 | 0 | 0 | 0 | 0 | 0 | 0 | 0 |
| 260 | 270 | 16 | 4 | 0 | 0 | 0 | 0 | 0 | 0 | 0 | 0 | 0 |
| 270 | 280 | 17 | 5 | 0 | 0 | 0 | 0 | 0 | 0 | 0 | 0 | 0 |
| 280 | 290 | 18 | 6 | 0 | 0 | 0 | 0 | 0 | 0 | 0 | 0 | 0 |
| 290 | 300 | 19 | 7 | 0 | 0 | 0 | 0 | 0 | 0 | 0 | 0 | 0 |
| 300 | 310 | 20 | 8 | 0 | 0 | 0 | 0 | 0 | 0 | 0 | 0 | 0 |
| 310 | 320 | 21 | 9 | 0 | 0 | 0 | 0 | 0 | 0 | 0 | 0 | 0 |
| 320 | 330 | 22 | 11 | 0 | 0 | 0 | 0 | 0 | 0 | 0 | 0 | 0 |
| 330 | 340 | 23 | 11 | 0 | 0 | 0 | 0 | 0 | 0 | 0 | 0 | 0 |
| 340 | 350 | 24 | 12 | 0 | 0 | 0 | 0 | 0 | 0 | 0 | 0 | 0 |
| 350 | 360 | 25 | 13 | 1 | 0 | 0 | 0 | 0 | 0 | 0 | 0 | 0 |
| 360 | 370 | 26 | 14 | 2 | 0 | 0 | 0 | 0 | 0 | 0 | 0 | 0 |
| 370 | 380 | 27 | 15 | 3 | 0 | 0 | 0 | 0 | 0 | 0 | 0 | 0 |
| 380 | 390 | 29 | 16 | 4 | 0 | 0 | 0 | 0 | 0 | 0 | 0 | 0 |
| 390 | 400 | 30 | 17 | 5 | 0 | 0 | 0 | 0 | 0 | 0 | 0 | 0 |
| 400 | 410 | 32 | 18 | 6 | 0 | 0 | 0 | 0 | 0 | 0 | 0 | 0 |
| 410 | 420 | 33 | 19 | 7 | 0 | 0 | 0 | 0 | 0 | 0 | 0 | 0 |
| 420 | 430 | 35 | 20 | 8 | 0 | 0 | 0 | 0 | 0 | 0 | 0 | 0 |
| 430 | 440 | 36 | 21 | 9 | 0 | 0 | 0 | 0 | 0 | 0 | 0 | 0 |
| 440 | 450 | 38 | 22 | 10 | 0 | 0 | 0 | 0 | 0 | 0 | 0 | 0 |
| 450 | 460 | 39 | 23 | 11 | 0 | 0 | 0 | 0 | 0 | 0 | 0 | 0 |
| 460 | 470 | 41 | 24 | 12 | 0 | 0 | 0 | 0 | 0 | 0 | 0 | 0 |
| 470 | 480 | 42 | 25 | 13 | 0 | 0 | 0 | 0 | 0 | 0 | 0 | 0 |
| 480 | 490 | 44 | 26 | 14 | 1 | 0 | 0 | 0 | 0 | 0 | 0 | 0 |
| 490 | 500 | 45 | 27 | 15 | 2 | 0 | 0 | 0 | 0 | 0 | 0 | 0 |
| 500 | 520 | 47 | 29 | 16 | 4 | 0 | 0 | 0 | 0 | 0 | 0 | 0 |
| 520 | 540 | 50 | 32 | 18 | 6 | 0 | 0 | 0 | 0 | 0 | 0 | 0 |
| 540 | 560 | 53 | 35 | 20 | 8 | 0 | 0 | 0 | 0 | 0 | 0 | 0 |
| 560 | 580 | 56 | 38 | 22 | 10 | 0 | 0 | 0 | 0 | 0 | 0 | 0 |
| 580 | 600 | 59 | 41 | 24 | 12 | 0 | 0 | 0 | 0 | 0 | 0 | 0 |
| 600 | 620 | 62 | 44 | 26 | 14 | 2 | 0 | 0 | 0 | 0 | 0 | 0 |
| 620 | 640 | 65 | 47 | 29 | 16 | 4 | 0 | 0 | 0 | 0 | 0 | 0 |
| 640 | 660 | 68 | 50 | 32 | 18 | 6 | 0 | 0 | 0 | 0 | 0 | 0 |
| 660 | 680 | 71 | 53 | 35 | 20 | 8 | 0 | 0 | 0 | 0 | 0 | 0 |
| 680 | 700 | 74 | 56 | 38 | 22 | 10 | 0 | 0 | 0 | 0 | 0 | 0 |
| 700 | 720 | 77 | 59 | 41 | 24 | 12 | 0 | 0 | 0 | 0 | 0 | 0 |
| 720 | 740 | 80 | 62 | 44 | 26 | 14 | 1 | 0 | 0 | 0 | 0 | 0 |
| 740 | 760 | 83 | 65 | 47 | 28 | 16 | 3 | 0 | 0 | 0 | 0 | 0 |
| 760 | 780 | 86 | 68 | 50 | 31 | 18 | 5 | 0 | 0 | 0 | 0 | 0 |
| 780 | 800 | 89 | 71 | 53 | 34 | 20 | 7 | 0 | 0 | 0 | 0 | 0 |

## SINGLE Persons—BIWEEKLY Payroll Period
### (For Wages Paid in 2005)

| If the wages are— | | And the number of withholding allowances claimed is— | | | | | | | | | | |
|---|---|---|---|---|---|---|---|---|---|---|---|---|
| At least | But less than | 0 | 1 | 2 | 3 | 4 | 5 | 6 | 7 | 8 | 9 | 10 |
| | | The amount of income tax to be withheld is— | | | | | | | | | | |
| $800 | $820 | $92 | $74 | $56 | $37 | $22 | $0 | $0 | $0 | $0 | $0 | $0 |
| 820 | 840 | 95 | 77 | 59 | 40 | 24 | 11 | 0 | 0 | 0 | 0 | 0 |
| 840 | 860 | 98 | 80 | 62 | 43 | 26 | 13 | 1 | 0 | 0 | 0 | 0 |
| 860 | 880 | 101 | 83 | 65 | 46 | 28 | 15 | 3 | 0 | 0 | 0 | 0 |
| 880 | 900 | 104 | 86 | 68 | 49 | 31 | 17 | 5 | 0 | 0 | 0 | 0 |
| 900 | 920 | 107 | 89 | 71 | 52 | 34 | 19 | 7 | 0 | 0 | 0 | 0 |
| 920 | 940 | 110 | 92 | 74 | 55 | 37 | 21 | 9 | 0 | 0 | 0 | 0 |
| 940 | 960 | 113 | 95 | 77 | 58 | 40 | 23 | 11 | 0 | 0 | 0 | 0 |
| 960 | 980 | 116 | 98 | 80 | 61 | 43 | 25 | 13 | 1 | 0 | 0 | 0 |
| 980 | 1,000 | 119 | 101 | 83 | 64 | 46 | 27 | 15 | 3 | 0 | 0 | 0 |
| 1,000 | 1,050 | 122 | 104 | 86 | 67 | 49 | 30 | 17 | 5 | 0 | 0 | 0 |
| 1,050 | 1,040 | 125 | 107 | 89 | 70 | 52 | 33 | 19 | 7 | 0 | 0 | 0 |
| 1,040 | 1,060 | 128 | 110 | 92 | 73 | 55 | 36 | 21 | 9 | 0 | 0 | 0 |
| 1,060 | 1,080 | 131 | 113 | 95 | 76 | 58 | 39 | 23 | 11 | 0 | 0 | 0 |
| 1,080 | 1,100 | 134 | 116 | 98 | 79 | 61 | 42 | 25 | 13 | 0 | 0 | 0 |
| 1,100 | 1,120 | 137 | 119 | 101 | 82 | 64 | 45 | 27 | 15 | 2 | 0 | 0 |
| 1,120 | 1,140 | 140 | 122 | 104 | 85 | 67 | 48 | 30 | 17 | 4 | 0 | 0 |
| 1,140 | 1,160 | 143 | 125 | 107 | 88 | 70 | 51 | 33 | 19 | 6 | 0 | 0 |
| 1,160 | 1,180 | 146 | 128 | 110 | 91 | 73 | 54 | 36 | 21 | 8 | 0 | 0 |
| 1,180 | 1,200 | 149 | 131 | 113 | 94 | 76 | 57 | 39 | 23 | 10 | 0 | 0 |
| 1,200 | 1,220 | 152 | 134 | 116 | 97 | 79 | 60 | 42 | 25 | 12 | 0 | 0 |
| 1,220 | 1,240 | 157 | 137 | 119 | 100 | 82 | 63 | 45 | 27 | 14 | 2 | 0 |
| 1,240 | 1,260 | 162 | 140 | 122 | 103 | 85 | 66 | 48 | 29 | 16 | 4 | 0 |
| 1,260 | 1,280 | 167 | 143 | 125 | 106 | 88 | 69 | 51 | 32 | 18 | 6 | 0 |
| 1,280 | 1,300 | 172 | 146 | 128 | 109 | 91 | 72 | 54 | 35 | 20 | 8 | 0 |
| 1,300 | 1,320 | 177 | 149 | 131 | 112 | 94 | 75 | 57 | 38 | 22 | 10 | 0 |
| 1,320 | 1,340 | 182 | 152 | 134 | 115 | 97 | 78 | 60 | 41 | 24 | 12 | 0 |
| 1,340 | 1,360 | 187 | 157 | 137 | 118 | 100 | 81 | 63 | 44 | 26 | 14 | 2 |
| 1,360 | 1,380 | 192 | 162 | 140 | 121 | 103 | 84 | 66 | 47 | 29 | 16 | 4 |
| 1,380 | 1,400 | 197 | 167 | 143 | 124 | 106 | 87 | 69 | 50 | 32 | 18 | 6 |
| 1,400 | 1,420 | 202 | 172 | 146 | 127 | 109 | 90 | 72 | 53 | 35 | 20 | 8 |
| 1,420 | 1,440 | 207 | 177 | 149 | 130 | 112 | 93 | 75 | 56 | 38 | 22 | 10 |
| 1,440 | 1,460 | 212 | 182 | 152 | 133 | 115 | 96 | 78 | 59 | 41 | 24 | 12 |
| 1,460 | 1,480 | 217 | 187 | 156 | 136 | 118 | 99 | 81 | 62 | 44 | 26 | 14 |
| 1,480 | 1,500 | 222 | 192 | 161 | 139 | 121 | 102 | 84 | 65 | 47 | 28 | 16 |
| 1,500 | 1,520 | 227 | 197 | 166 | 142 | 124 | 105 | 87 | 68 | 50 | 31 | 18 |
| 1,520 | 1,540 | 232 | 202 | 171 | 145 | 127 | 108 | 90 | 71 | 53 | 34 | 20 |
| 1,540 | 1,560 | 237 | 207 | 176 | 148 | 130 | 111 | 93 | 74 | 56 | 37 | 22 |
| 1,560 | 1,580 | 242 | 212 | 181 | 151 | 133 | 114 | 96 | 77 | 59 | 40 | 24 |
| 1,580 | 1,600 | 247 | 217 | 186 | 155 | 136 | 117 | 99 | 80 | 62 | 43 | 26 |
| 1,600 | 1,620 | 252 | 222 | 191 | 160 | 139 | 120 | 102 | 83 | 65 | 46 | 28 |
| 1,620 | 1,640 | 257 | 227 | 196 | 165 | 142 | 123 | 105 | 86 | 68 | 49 | 31 |
| 1,640 | 1,660 | 262 | 232 | 201 | 170 | 145 | 126 | 108 | 89 | 71 | 52 | 34 |
| 1,660 | 1,680 | 267 | 237 | 206 | 175 | 148 | 129 | 111 | 92 | 74 | 55 | 37 |
| 1,680 | 1,700 | 272 | 242 | 211 | 180 | 151 | 132 | 114 | 95 | 77 | 58 | 40 |
| 1,700 | 1,720 | 277 | 247 | 216 | 185 | 154 | 135 | 117 | 98 | 80 | 61 | 43 |
| 1,720 | 1,740 | 282 | 252 | 221 | 190 | 159 | 138 | 120 | 101 | 83 | 64 | 46 |
| 1,740 | 1,760 | 287 | 257 | 226 | 195 | 164 | 141 | 123 | 104 | 86 | 67 | 49 |
| 1,760 | 1,780 | 292 | 262 | 231 | 200 | 169 | 144 | 126 | 107 | 89 | 70 | 52 |
| 1,780 | 1,800 | 297 | 267 | 236 | 205 | 174 | 147 | 129 | 110 | 92 | 73 | 55 |
| 1,800 | 1,820 | 302 | 272 | 241 | 210 | 179 | 150 | 132 | 113 | 95 | 76 | 58 |
| 1,820 | 1,840 | 307 | 277 | 246 | 215 | 184 | 153 | 135 | 116 | 98 | 79 | 61 |
| 1,840 | 1,860 | 312 | 282 | 251 | 220 | 189 | 158 | 138 | 119 | 101 | 82 | 64 |
| 1,860 | 1,880 | 317 | 287 | 256 | 225 | 194 | 163 | 141 | 122 | 104 | 85 | 67 |
| 1,880 | 1,900 | 322 | 292 | 261 | 230 | 199 | 168 | 144 | 125 | 107 | 88 | 70 |
| 1,900 | 1,920 | 327 | 297 | 266 | 235 | 204 | 173 | 147 | 128 | 110 | 91 | 73 |
| 1,920 | 1,940 | 332 | 302 | 271 | 240 | 209 | 178 | 150 | 131 | 113 | 94 | 76 |
| 1,940 | 1,960 | 337 | 307 | 276 | 245 | 214 | 183 | 153 | 134 | 116 | 97 | 79 |
| 1,960 | 1,980 | 342 | 312 | 281 | 250 | 219 | 188 | 158 | 137 | 119 | 100 | 82 |
| 1,980 | 2,000 | 347 | 317 | 286 | 255 | 224 | 193 | 163 | 140 | 122 | 103 | 85 |
| 2,000 | 2,020 | 352 | 322 | 291 | 260 | 229 | 198 | 168 | 143 | 125 | 106 | 88 |
| 2,020 | 2,040 | 357 | 327 | 296 | 265 | 234 | 203 | 173 | 146 | 128 | 109 | 91 |
| 2,040 | 2,060 | 362 | 332 | 301 | 270 | 239 | 208 | 178 | 149 | 131 | 112 | 94 |
| 2,060 | 2,080 | 367 | 337 | 306 | 275 | 244 | 213 | 183 | 152 | 134 | 115 | 97 |
| 2,080 | 2,100 | 372 | 342 | 311 | 280 | 249 | 218 | 188 | 157 | 137 | 118 | 100 |

## New York State Tax Table

**T-4**

Method I

Table II

**NY STATE Income Tax**

**SINGLE**

**BIWEEKLY** Payroll Period

| WAGES | | EXEMPTIONS CLAIMED | | | | | | | | | | 10 |
| At Least | But Less Than | 0 | 1 | 2 | 3 | 4 | 5 | 6 | 7 | 8 | 9 | or more |
| | | TAX TO BE WITHHELD | | | | | | | | | | |
| $0 | $200 | $0.00 | | | | | | | | | | |
| 200 | 210 | 0.00 | | | | | | | | | | |
| 210 | 220 | 0.00 | | | | | | | | | | |
| 220 | 230 | 0.00 | $0.00 | | | | | | | | | |
| 230 | 240 | 0.00 | 0.00 | | | | | | | | | |
| 240 | 250 | 0.00 | 0.00 | | | | | | | | | |
| 250 | 260 | 0.00 | 0.00 | | | | | | | | | |
| 260 | 270 | 0.00 | 0.00 | $0.00 | | | | | | | | |
| 270 | 280 | 0.30 | 0.00 | 0.00 | | | | | | | | |
| 280 | 290 | 0.70 | 0.00 | 0.00 | | | | | | | | |
| 290 | 300 | 1.10 | 0.00 | 0.00 | | | | | | | | |
| 300 | 320 | 1.70 | 0.10 | 0.00 | $0.00 | | | | | | | |
| 320 | 340 | 2.50 | 0.90 | 0.00 | 0.00 | | | | | | | |
| 340 | 360 | 3.30 | 1.70 | 0.20 | 0.00 | $0.00 | | | | | | |
| 360 | 380 | 4.10 | 2.50 | 1.00 | 0.00 | 0.00 | | | | | | |
| 380 | 400 | 4.90 | 3.30 | 1.80 | 0.30 | 0.00 | $0.00 | | | | | |
| 400 | 420 | 5.70 | 4.10 | 2.60 | 1.10 | 0.00 | 0.00 | | | | | |
| 420 | 440 | 6.50 | 4.90 | 3.40 | 1.90 | 0.30 | 0.00 | $0.00 | | | | |
| 440 | 460 | 7.30 | 5.70 | 4.20 | 2.70 | 1.10 | 0.00 | 0.00 | $0.00 | | | |
| 460 | 480 | 8.10 | 6.50 | 5.00 | 3.50 | 1.90 | 0.40 | 0.00 | 0.00 | | | |
| 480 | 500 | 8.90 | 7.30 | 5.80 | 4.30 | 2.70 | 1.20 | 0.00 | 0.00 | $0.00 | | |
| 500 | 520 | 9.70 | 8.10 | 6.60 | 5.10 | 3.50 | 2.00 | 0.40 | 0.00 | 0.00 | | |
| 520 | 540 | 10.50 | 8.90 | 7.40 | 5.90 | 4.30 | 2.80 | 1.20 | 0.00 | 0.00 | $0.00 | |
| 540 | 560 | 11.30 | 9.70 | 8.20 | 6.70 | 5.10 | 3.60 | 2.00 | 0.50 | 0.00 | 0.00 | |
| 560 | 580 | 12.10 | 10.50 | 9.00 | 7.50 | 5.90 | 4.40 | 2.80 | 1.30 | 0.00 | 0.00 | $0.00 |
| 580 | 600 | 12.90 | 11.30 | 9.80 | 8.30 | 6.70 | 5.20 | 3.60 | 2.10 | 0.60 | 0.00 | 0.00 |
| 600 | 620 | 13.80 | 12.10 | 10.60 | 9.10 | 7.50 | 6.00 | 4.40 | 2.90 | 1.40 | 0.00 | 0.00 |
| 620 | 640 | 14.70 | 13.00 | 11.40 | 9.90 | 8.30 | 6.80 | 5.20 | 3.70 | 2.20 | 0.60 | 0.00 |
| 640 | 660 | 15.60 | 13.90 | 12.20 | 10.70 | 9.10 | 7.60 | 6.00 | 4.50 | 3.00 | 1.40 | 0.00 |
| 660 | 680 | 16.50 | 14.80 | 13.10 | 11.50 | 9.90 | 8.40 | 6.80 | 5.30 | 3.80 | 2.20 | 0.70 |
| 680 | 700 | 17.40 | 15.70 | 14.00 | 12.30 | 10.70 | 9.20 | 7.60 | 6.10 | 4.60 | 3.00 | 1.50 |
| 700 | 720 | 18.50 | 16.60 | 14.90 | 13.10 | 11.50 | 10.00 | 8.40 | 6.90 | 5.40 | 3.80 | 2.30 |
| 720 | 740 | 19.50 | 17.50 | 15.80 | 14.00 | 12.30 | 10.80 | 9.20 | 7.70 | 6.20 | 4.60 | 3.10 |
| 740 | 760 | 20.60 | 18.60 | 16.70 | 14.90 | 13.20 | 11.60 | 10.00 | 8.50 | 7.00 | 5.40 | 3.90 |
| 760 | 780 | 21.60 | 19.60 | 17.60 | 15.80 | 14.10 | 12.40 | 10.80 | 9.30 | 7.80 | 6.20 | 4.70 |
| 780 | 800 | 22.80 | 20.70 | 18.60 | 16.70 | 15.00 | 13.30 | 11.60 | 10.10 | 8.60 | 7.00 | 5.50 |
| 800 | 820 | 24.00 | 21.70 | 19.70 | 17.70 | 15.90 | 14.20 | 12.50 | 10.90 | 9.40 | 7.80 | 6.30 |
| 820 | 840 | 25.20 | 22.90 | 20.70 | 18.70 | 16.80 | 15.10 | 13.40 | 11.70 | 10.20 | 8.60 | 7.10 |
| 840 | 860 | 26.40 | 24.10 | 21.80 | 19.80 | 17.80 | 16.00 | 14.30 | 12.50 | 11.00 | 9.40 | 7.90 |
| 860 | 880 | 27.50 | 25.30 | 23.00 | 20.80 | 18.80 | 16.90 | 15.20 | 13.40 | 11.80 | 10.20 | 8.70 |
| 880 | 900 | 28.70 | 26.50 | 24.20 | 21.90 | 19.90 | 17.80 | 16.10 | 14.30 | 12.60 | 11.00 | 9.50 |
| 900 | 920 | 29.90 | 27.60 | 25.40 | 23.10 | 20.90 | 18.90 | 17.00 | 15.20 | 13.50 | 11.80 | 10.30 |
| 920 | 940 | 31.10 | 28.80 | 26.50 | 24.30 | 22.00 | 19.90 | 17.90 | 16.10 | 14.40 | 12.70 | 11.10 |
| 940 | 960 | 32.30 | 30.00 | 27.70 | 25.50 | 23.20 | 21.00 | 19.00 | 17.00 | 15.30 | 13.60 | 11.90 |
| 960 | 980 | 33.40 | 31.20 | 28.90 | 26.60 | 24.40 | 22.10 | 20.00 | 18.00 | 16.20 | 14.50 | 12.70 |
| 980 | 1,000 | 34.60 | 32.40 | 30.10 | 27.80 | 25.50 | 23.30 | 21.10 | 19.00 | 17.10 | 15.40 | 13.60 |
| 1,000 | 1,020 | 35.80 | 33.50 | 31.30 | 29.00 | 26.70 | 24.50 | 22.20 | 20.10 | 18.10 | 16.30 | 14.50 |
| 1,020 | 1,040 | 37.00 | 34.70 | 32.40 | 30.20 | 27.90 | 25.60 | 23.40 | 21.10 | 19.10 | 17.20 | 15.40 |
| 1,040 | 1,060 | 38.30 | 35.90 | 33.60 | 31.40 | 29.10 | 26.80 | 24.50 | 22.30 | 20.20 | 18.20 | 16.30 |
| 1,060 | 1,080 | 39.60 | 37.10 | 34.80 | 32.50 | 30.30 | 28.00 | 25.70 | 23.50 | 21.20 | 19.20 | 17.20 |
| 1,080 | 1,100 | 41.00 | 38.40 | 36.00 | 33.70 | 31.40 | 29.20 | 26.90 | 24.60 | 22.40 | 20.30 | 18.20 |
| 1,100 | 1,120 | 42.40 | 39.80 | 37.20 | 34.90 | 32.60 | 30.40 | 28.10 | 25.80 | 23.50 | 21.30 | 19.30 |
| 1,120 | 1,140 | 43.80 | 41.10 | 38.50 | 36.10 | 33.80 | 31.50 | 29.30 | 27.00 | 24.70 | 22.50 | 20.30 |
| 1,140 | 1,160 | 45.10 | 42.50 | 39.90 | 37.30 | 35.00 | 32.70 | 30.40 | 28.20 | 25.90 | 23.60 | 21.40 |
| 1,160 | 1,180 | 46.50 | 43.90 | 41.20 | 38.60 | 36.20 | 33.90 | 31.60 | 29.40 | 27.10 | 24.80 | 22.50 |
| 1,180 | 1,200 | 47.90 | 45.20 | 42.60 | 40.00 | 37.30 | 35.10 | 32.80 | 30.50 | 28.30 | 26.00 | 23.70 |
| 1,200 | 1,220 | 49.20 | 46.60 | 44.00 | 41.30 | 38.70 | 36.30 | 34.00 | 31.70 | 29.40 | 27.20 | 24.90 |
| 1,220 | 1,240 | 50.60 | 48.00 | 45.30 | 42.70 | 40.10 | 37.40 | 35.20 | 32.90 | 30.60 | 28.40 | 26.10 |
| 1,240 | 1,260 | 52.00 | 49.30 | 46.70 | 44.10 | 41.40 | 38.80 | 36.30 | 34.10 | 31.80 | 29.50 | 27.30 |
| 1,260 | 1,280 | 53.30 | 50.70 | 48.10 | 45.40 | 42.80 | 40.20 | 37.50 | 35.30 | 33.00 | 30.70 | 28.40 |
| 1,280 | 1,300 | 54.70 | 52.10 | 49.50 | 46.80 | 44.20 | 41.50 | 38.90 | 36.40 | 34.20 | 31.90 | 29.60 |
| 1,300 | 3,460 | 6.85% (.0685) of the excess over $1,300 plus: | | | | | | | | | | |
| | | 55.40 | 52.80 | 50.10 | 47.50 | 44.90 | 42.20 | 39.60 | 37.00 | 34.80 | 32.50 | 30.20 |
| $3,460 & OVER | | Use Method II, "Exact Calculation Method," on page T-13 of this booklet | | | | | | | | | | |

**d.** What is your net base salary per pay period?

**4.** During the first pay period of a certain month, you work 10 days. Two of these days are holidays (HOL). During the second pay period, you work 10 days, and on four occasions you work overtime (OT), accumulating $2\frac{1}{4}$, $4\frac{2}{3}$, $5\frac{1}{2}$, and $3\frac{3}{4}$ hours overtime. Calculate your net pay for these pay periods by filling in the accompanying table.

**Reminder:** Use 6.2% (6.2% = 0.062) for Social Security, 1.45% (1.45% = 0.0145) for Medicare, and the tables for federal and state taxes. Don't forget the union dues.

| Where Does It All Go? | FIRST PAY PERIOD | SECOND PAY PERIOD |
|---|---|---|
| Gross Base ($) | | |
| Gross OT/Hol. ($) | | |
| Total Gross ($) | | |
| Federal Income Tax ($) | | |
| State Income Tax ($) | | |
| Social Security Tax ($) | | |
| Medicare ($) | | |
| Union Dues ($) | | |
| Total Net ($) | | |

**5.** You sell $10,000 worth of merchandise during each pay period this month.

**a.** What is your total commission (3% = 0.03)?

**b.** Your commission is paid to you in a separate paycheck. Calculate your take-home pay for commission for this month. (Remember that federal and state

**c.** What is your total take-home pay for the month in Problem 4, including commission?

**6. a.** You want to purchase a new TV that costs $549 plus 7% sales tax. You plan to save your overtime pay to purchase the TV outright and not pay monthly installments on the bill. Estimate the number of hours you need to work to yield enough net overtime pay to purchase the TV.

(Use 3% = 0.03 state income tax and 13% = 0.13 federal income tax, plus 6.2% = 0.062 Soc. Sec. and 1.45% = 0.0145 Medicare.)

**b.** Your overtime hours for the month in Problem 4 are a reasonable estimate of the hours you work each month. How many months of saving will it take for you to purchase the TV?

**7.** You are trying not to go any further into debt, and you want to pay off some of your debts. Each month you analyze how you spend your money and categorize your expenses under the following headings: (1) household, (2) medical, (3) entertainment, (4) loans, (5) insurance, (6) personal, and (7) miscellaneous.

You recorded the actual expenses you incurred for a previous month in the following list. The number in parentheses indicates the category of the expense.

car payment (4), $125
car insurance (5), $72
parking (7), $50
bowling (3), $60
shoes (6), $43
dentist (2), $30
groceries (1), $150
credit-card debt (4), $50
bank charges (7), $7
gas/car (7), $80

rent (1), $300
utilities (1), $140
movies (3), $20
towels (1), $22
student loan (4), $60
film (7), $5
savings (6), $100
medicines (2), $47
clothes (6), $110
restaurant/fast food (3), $80

**a.** If computers are accessible, create a spreadsheet; otherwise, use the accompanying table to group the information. List the given expenses in the appropriate columns in the table.

## Life by the Numbers

| HOUSEHOLD (1) | MEDICAL (2) | ENTERTAINMENT (3) | LOANS (4) | INSURANCE (5) | PERSONAL (6) | MISC. (7) |
|---|---|---|---|---|---|---|
|  |  |  |  |  |  |  |
|  |  |  |  |  |  |  |
|  |  |  |  |  |  |  |
|  |  |  |  |  |  |  |
| **Totals:** |  |  |  |  |  |  |
|  |  |  |  |  |  |  |

**b.** Do you think that the expenses you incurred this month will be consistent with the month in part a? Explain.

**c.** What are your total expenses for the month?

**d.** Will you have enough income to cover your expenses this month? Explain.

**e.** You are considering a move to another apartment that has two bedrooms. How much more do you think you can afford to pay, based on your calculated income and expenses? Will the move be possible?

**ACTIVITY 8.2**

Time Is Money
Revisited

**OBJECTIVES**

1. Distinguish between simple and compound interest.

2. Apply the compound interest formula to determine the future value of a lump-sum investment earning compound interest.

3. Determine the future value using technology.

4. Determine the effective interest rate.

5. Apply the present value formula in a given situation involving compound interest.

6. Determine the present value using technology.

**1. a.** Suppose $10,000 is deposited in a bank at 6.5% annual interest. What is the interest earned after one year?

**b.** Suppose you left the money in the account for 10 years. Can the total amount of interest on your investment be calculated by multiplying your answer in part a by 10? What assumption are you making if you said yes?

Recall from Activity 5.7, Time is Money, that for **simple interest** on an investment, the interest earned during the first period does not earn interest for the rest of the life of the investment. Therefore, at 6.5% simple annual interest, an investment of $10,000 would earn a total interest of $10,000(0.065)(10) = \$6,500$.

The interest paid on savings accounts in most banks is **compound interest**. The interest earned for each period is added to the previous principal before the next interest calculation is made. Simply stated, interest earns interest.

For example, if you deposit $10,000 in the bank at 6.5%, the balance after one year is

$$10,000 + 0.065(10,000) = 10,000 + 650 = 10,650.$$

The interest, $650, earned during the year becomes part of the new balance. At the end of the second year, your balance is

$$10,650 + 0.065(10,650) = 10,650 + 692.25 = 11,342.25.$$

Note that you made interest on the original deposit, plus interest on the first year's interest. In this situation, we say that interest is compounded. Usually, the compounding occurs at fixed intervals (typically at the end of every year, quarter, month, or day). In this example, interest is compounded annually.

If interest is compounded, then the current balance is given by the formula

$$A = P\left(1 + \tfrac{r}{n}\right)^{nt},$$

where A is the current balance or compound amount in the account,
   P is the principal (the original amount deposited),
   r is the annual interest rate (in decimal form),
   n is the number of times per year that interest is compounded, and
   t is the time in years the money has been invested.

The given formula for the compound amount A is called the **compound interest formula**.

Example 1   *You invest $2000 at 8% compounded quarterly. How much money do you have after five years?*

SOLUTION

The principal is $2000; so $P = 2000$. The annual interest rate is 8%; so $r = 0.08$. Interest is compounded quarterly; that is, four times per year, so $n = 4$. The money is invested for five years; so $t = 5$. Substituting numbers for the variables in the preceding formula, you have

$$A = 2000(1 + \tfrac{0.08}{4})^{4 \cdot 5} = \$2971.89.$$

The amount $A = \$2971.90$ in Example 1 is called the **future value** of the investment.

**2. a.** Suppose you deposit $10,000 in an account that has a 6.5% annual interest rate and whose interest is compounded annually ($n = 1$). Substitute the appropriate values for the variables into the compound interest formula to verify that the balance $A$ at the end of the second year is $11,342.25.

**b.** Suppose you deposit the $10,000 into an account that has the same interest rate of 6.5%, with compounding quarterly ($n = 4$) rather than annually ($n = 1$). Write a new formula for your balance, $A$, as a function of time.

**c.** What would be your balance after 5 years?

**d.** Now deposit your $10,000 into a 6.5% account with *monthly* compounding ($n = 12$). Use your graphing calculator and the appropriate formula to determine your balance after 5 years.

## Future Value Using Technology

Your TI-83/84 Plus graphing calculator has several built-in functions to help you solve many of the finance problems encountered in this chapter. To access the finance applications menu, press (APPS) , followed by (ENTER).

Next, press (ENTER) to select option 1: TVM Solver... The following screen will appear

where the time-value-of-money (TVM) variables represent the following:

N = total number of compounding periods;

I% = r, where r% is the annual interest rate;

PV = present value (amount invested or principal);

PMT = payment;

FV = future value;

P/Y = number of payments per year;

C/Y = number of compounding periods per year;

PMT:END = payment due at the end of the period); and

PMT:BEGIN = payment due at the beginning of the period).

**Example 2** *Determine the future value of $2000 invested at 8% compounded quarterly for five years (see Example 1).*

SOLUTION

Use the up and down arrow keys to enter the following information

$$N = 20, I\% = 8, PV = -2000, PMT = 0, P/Y = 4, C/Y = 4$$

The value of N is 20 because 5 years × 4 periods/year = 20 compounding periods. The present value is entered as a negative value since it is a cash outflow; 0 is entered for PMT to specify no payments; P/Y and C/Y are set to 4 to indicate 4 periods/year. Now, arrow up to FV to highlight FV=■ and press (ALPHA) followed by (ENTER) to select [SOLVE]. The future value appears next to ■FV.

Therefore, after five years the investment will grow to $2971.89.

3. When you were born, your parents invested the cash gifts that they received from friends and relatives into a certificate of deposit (CD). Cash gifts received on birthdays were also added to this account. Currently, there is a total balance of $4500. If this money were invested into an account at 6% compounded semiannually, use your graphing calculator to determine the future value in seven years.

## Effective Annual Yield

4. **a.** Determine the interest earned on an investment of $1200 at 10% simple annual interest for one year.

**b.** Determine the interest earned on an investment of $1200 at 10% compounded monthly for one year.

**c.** Which investment option earned more? Is this what you expected? Why?

**d.** The interest in part b is what percent of the $1200 investment?

The annual interest rate of 10.47% is called the **effective annual yield** of an investment at 10% compounded monthly. Most financial institutions refer to the effective annual yield as the **annual percentage yield** (**APY**). The effective interest yield can be determined using several different methods. Example 3 demonstrates the use of the graphing calculator.

**Example 3** *Determine the annual percentage yield (APY) on an investment of $1200 at 10% annual interest compounded monthly.*

SOLUTION

Press (APPS), followed by (ENTER). Use ↓ to select option C:▶Eff(.

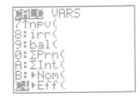

Press (ENTER) to select the Eff option. Enter the annual interest rate 10 (for 10%), followed by a comma, followed by the number of compounding periods 12. Press (ENTER) and the effective annual rate will appear on the screen.

Therefore, the APY is 10.47%.

**5.** Your local credit union is offering a one-year certificate of deposit (CD) at an annual interest rate of 5.25% compounded daily. Determine the APY.

## Present Value

A local bank is offering a 60-month CD at a rate of 5.70% APY compounded monthly. How much must be invested now in the CD to accumulate $6000 at the end of five years?

In previous problems, the amount to be invested, called the **present value**, was known and you needed to determine the future value. In this problem, the **future value** (amount needed in the future) is known and you must determine the present value.

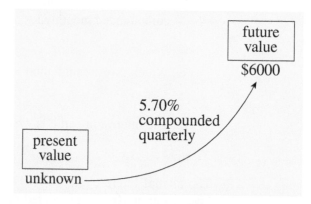

A formula for the present value can be determined by solving the compound interest formula for the principal $P$ (present value).

**6. a.** Solve the compound interest formula $A = P\left(1 + \dfrac{r}{n}\right)^{nt}$ for $P$. Replace the amount accumulated, $A$, with the future value $FV$ and the principal $P$ with the present value $PV$. The new formula is called the **present value formula**. Check your result with the formula given in the Activity 8.2 Summary.

**b.** Use the present value formula from part a to determine how much must be invested now (present value $PV$) in the 60-month CD at 5.70% APY compounded monthly in order to have $6000 at the end of five years.

The present value for a known future value can also be determined using the graphing calculator.

**Example 4**    *Determine how much money must be invested now (present value) at 6.5% APY compounded daily if $5000 is due in three years.*

SOLUTION

Using the TI-83/84 Plus TVM SOLVER, enter the following values:

$$N = 1095, I\% = 6.5, PMT = 0, FV = 5000, P/Y = 365, C/Y = 365$$

*Note:* You can input 3*365 for the value of N and the calculator will determine the product, 1095.

Now, arrow up to PV and press (ALPHA) followed by (ENTER) to select [SOLVE]. The screen should appear as follows:

```
N=1095
I%=6.5
▪PV=-4114.24▪717
PMT=0
FV=5000
P/Y=365
C/Y=365
PMT:END BEGIN
```

Therefore, $4114.24 must be invested now in order for the investment to accumulate to $5000 in three years.

7. Use the TVM feature of the TI-83/84 Plus to determine how much must be invested now in a 60-month CD at 5.70% APY compounded monthly in order to have $6000 at the end of five years. How does your answer compare to your result in Problem 6b?

## SUMMARY
### Activity 8.2

1. Compound interest is interest paid on interest as well as the principal.

2. The compound amount, also called future value, is the total amount of compound interest and principal at the end of the investment.

3. The compound amount (future value) can be calculated using the compound interest formula:

$$A = P(1 + \tfrac{r}{n})^{nt},$$

where    $A$ is the compound amount, or future value, in the account,
$P$ is the principal (the original amount deposited),
$r$ is the annual interest rate (annual percentage rate in decimal form),
$n$ is the number of times per year that interest is compounded, and
$t$ is the time in years the money has been invested.

4. The compound amount (future value) can be calculated using the TVM Solver feature of the TI-83/84 Plus graphing calculator.

5. Effective interest rate on an investment (called annual percentage yield or APY) is the true rate of return on an investment.

6. Present value (or principal) is the amount that must be invested now at compound interest to reach a given future value.

**7.** Present value formula is

$$PV = \frac{FV}{(1 + \frac{r}{n})^{nt}},$$

where     *PV* is present value (principal),
           *FV* is future value (amount accumulated),
           *r* is the annual interest rate (annual percentage rate in decimal form),
           *n* is the number of times per year that interest is compounded, and
           *t* is the time in years the money has been invested.

## EXERCISES
### Activity 8.2

**1.** Your freshman high school class had a total of $1200 from fund-raisers during the year. To help pay for a class trip at the end of your senior year, the class deposits the money into a 30-month CD paying 4.2% interest compounded monthly.

    **a.** Determine the amount the class will receive after 30 months.

    **b.** How much interest did the class earn on the investment?

**2. a.** You have just graduated from high school and received $1500 in gifts from family and friends. You also received scholarships in the amount of $800. If you deposit the total amount received into a 24-month CD at 5.5% compounded daily, how much will you receive at the end of 24 months?

    **b.** How much interest did you earn on the investment?

**3.** You started a new job and received a $2000 signing bonus. In order to save for a new car, you decide to deposit the money into an account earning 6.75% compounded monthly. How much will you have saved after five years?

**4.** Determine the effective annual yield for $100 invested for one year at 6.75% compounded monthly.

**5.** An advertisement in the local newspaper claims that the APY on a CD that paid 4.5% interest compounded quarterly was 4.58%. Is this claim accurate?

**6. a.** You are the beneficiary of a trust fund established by your grandparents 21 years ago, when you were born. The original amount of the fund was $15,000. If the money earned interest at the rate of 6% compounded annually, what is the current amount in the fund?

**b.** How much money would be in the fund if it had been invested at 6% compounded monthly?

**7.** The parents of a child have just received a large inheritance and want to put a portion of the money into a college fund. They estimate that they will need $75,000 in 12 years. If they invest the money at 7% annual interest compounded quarterly, how much should they deposit into the fund?

**8.** You have two investment options:

Option 1: Invest $10,000 at 10% compounded semiannually.

Option 2: Invest $10,000 at 9.5% compounded daily.

Which option has the greater return after five years?

**9.** When you graduate from law school in four years, you estimate that you will need $20,000 to set up a law office.

**a.** How much money must you invest now at 9% interest compounded quarterly to achieve this goal?

**b.** How much interest will you have earned on your investment?

**10.** You are a member of the town planning board. The town intends to pay off a $4,000,000 bond issue that comes due in 6 years. How much must the town set aside now in order to accumulate the necessary amount of money? Assume the money is invested in an account that earns 8% compounded quarterly.

**11.** Your car is for sale. You have received two offers:

Offer 1: The first buyer offers you $6000. He wants to pay you $2000 now, $2000 in six months, and $2000 in one year.

Offer 2: The second buyer offers to pay you $5600 in cash now.

**a.** What is the present value of offer 1? Assume you can earn 10% interest compounded monthly on your money.

**b.** Which offer is the better deal? Explain.

**ACTIVITY 8.3**
Saving for
Retirement

**OBJECTIVES**

1. Distinguish between an ordinary annuity and an annuity due.

2. Determine the future value of an ordinary annuity using a formula.

3. Determine the future value of an annuity due using technology.

4. Determine the present value of an ordinary annuity using technology.

5. Solve problems involving annuities.

You have a discussion in your business class regarding a retirement plan, including Social Security, company pension plans, 401(k) accounts, and individual accounts such as Roth IRA. Your business teacher asks you to determine how much money will accumulate for retirement if you deposit $500 each year at 6% interest compounded annually for the next 40 years.

So far, you have dealt with problems that involve the future value of a lump-sum investment or payment. To answer your teacher's question, you need to determine the future value of payments of $500 per year. If the payment for each period is fixed, and the compound interest rate is fixed over a specified amount of time, the payment is called an **annuity payment**. Such accounts are called **annuities**. Note that the number of annuity payments made each year will be the same as the number of compounding periods each year.

Before you answer your teacher's question, you need to investigate how an annuity grows over time.

1. A deposit of $1000 is made at the end of every six months (semiannually) for two years at 8% annual interest compounded semiannually.

   a. Determine the amount in the account at the end of the first six-month period.

   b. Determine the amount in the account at the end of the second six-month period. Note that the period interest rate is $8\% \div 2 = 4\%$.

   c. Enter your results from parts a and b into the following table. Then complete the table.

| PERIOD | END-OF-PERIOD VALUE IN THE ACCOUNT |
|--------|-----------------------------------|
| 1 | |
| 2 | |
| 3 | |
| 4 | |

   d. What is the future value of the annuity described in part a in two years?

In Problem 1, the payment is made at the end of each period. Such an annuity is called an **ordinary annuity**. If the payment is made at the beginning of each period, the annuity is called an **annuity due**. Therefore, the first annuity payment in an annuity due will earn interest. The difference in the future value of an ordinary annuity and an annuity due is one additional period's worth of interest for the length of the loan period.

**2.** Suppose the $1000 annuity payment in Problem 1 is made at the beginning of every six months for two years at 8% compounded semiannually.

**a.** Determine the amount in the account at the end of period 1.

**b.** Determine the amount in the account at the end of period 2.

**c.** Record your results from part a and b into the following table. Then complete the table.

| PERIOD | END-OF-PERIOD VALUE IN THE ACCOUNT |
|---|---|
| 1 | |
| 2 | |
| 3 | |
| 4 | |

**d.** What is the future value of this annuity due account at the end of two years?

**e.** Compare the future value of the ordinary annuity in Problem 1d to your result in Problem 2d. Is this what you expected?

## Future Value of an Annuity

The future value of an annuity is the total accumulation of the payments and interest earned. The formulas to determine the future value of an annuity are:

Future Value of an Ordinary Annuity

$$FV = P \cdot \frac{(1 + i)^n - 1}{i}$$

Future Value of an Annuity Due

$$FV = P \cdot \frac{(1 + i)^n - 1}{i} \cdot (1 + i),$$

where  $FV$ = future value,
$P$ = annuity payment,
$i$ = interest rate per period (written as a decimal), and
$n$ = total number of periods.

**3.** Consider the ordinary annuity in Problem 1: A deposit of $1000 made at the end of every six months for two years at 8% annual interest compounded semi-annually.

**a.** Determine the interest rate-per-period and the number of periods.

**b.** Use the appropriate formula above to determine the future value of this annuity.

You may be wondering if the TVM Solver feature of your graphing calculator can be used to determine the future value. The answer is yes.

**4.** Redo Problem 3 using the TI-83/84 Plus graphing calculator.

**a.** Enter the values for the TVM Solver variables into the calculator.

**Be careful.** The value for I% is the annual interest rate; the PMT (payment) value is entered as a negative number since the payment is a cash outflow. Since the annuity is ordinary, the payment is made at the end of the period. Therefore, the END *must* be highlighted. Simply move the cursor to END and press (ENTER) .

**b.** Determine the future value of the annuity. How does your result compare to the answer in Problem 3b using a formula?

**5. a.** Suppose $1000 is deposited at the beginning of every six months for two years at 8% compounded semiannually. Determine the future value of this annuity by using the appropriate formula.

**b.** Redo Problem 4a using the TVM calculator application.

**c.** Compare the result with the future value of the ordinary annuity in Problem 2d.

**6.** You are now ready to answer your business teacher's question: How much money will accumulate if you deposit $500 at the beginning of each year for 40 years at 6% compounded annually?

## Present Value of an Annuity

One of the requirements in your business class is to write a report describing your retirement plans. You estimate that you will need $20,000 a year at the beginning of each year for 20 years to supplement your pension and Social Security during retirement. How much money (lump sum) will you need at the time of retirement so that you can make the $20,000 annual payment for 20 years? You assume that the lump-sum amount needed will earn 5% annual interest compounded annually during the payout period.

Until now, you have considered annuities in which you start with a zero balance. Then, by making equal annuity payments for a given period of time at compound interest, a future value or accumulation is reached. This new situation starts with a lump-sum amount (unknown) so that equal payments ($20,000 per year) can be made over a specified time (20 years).

The starting lump-sum amount will earn interest (5% compounded annually) while annuity payments are being made. However, the starting amount will continue to decline to a zero balance at the end of 20 years. The lump sum that must be present in the beginning is called the **present value of an annuity**.

DEFINITION

The **present value of an annuity** is a lump sum that is put into a fund in order for the fund to payout a specified regular payment for a specified amount of time.

7. Now, let us review the details of the problem just given.

As part of your retirement plan, you want to set up an annuity in which a regular payment of $20,000 is made at the end of each year. You need to determine how much money must be deposited (present value), in order to make the annuity payment for 20 years. Assume the money is earning 5% compounded annually.

a. What is the annuity payment? What is the number of payments?

b. What is the annual interest rate?

c. What is the future value?

d. Is the annuity ordinary or due?

e. Use the TVM feature of your graphing calculator to determine the present value of the annuity.

Formulas to determine the present value of an annuity are given in Exercise 8 of this activity.

## Applications

8. Your business teacher asks the class to consider the following retirement plans. Assume that the money is invested at 7% compounded annually and that all annuities are ordinary. If the annuity payments stop, the money will continue in the account at 7% compounded annually.

Plan 1:   Invest $500 per year for 25 years and then stop the payments.

Plan 2:   Wait to invest for 15 years, and then invest $500 per year for 25 years.

a. Determine the total accumulation of money for retirement plan 1 over the next 40 years.

**b.** Determine the total accumulation of money for plan 2 over the next 40 years.

**c.** Which retirement plan results in the largest accumulation? Does this seem reasonable? Why?

9. Your parents began depositing $500 at the beginning of each year into a college fund. The fund paid 8% annual interest compounded annually for the first 10 years. For the last eight years, your parents have increased the payments to $1000 per year, but the interest has dropped to 6% interest compounded annually. Determine the amount of money in the college fund after 18 years.

---

## SUMMARY
### Activity 8.3

1. An **annuity** is the payment (or receipt) of equal cash payments per period for a given period of time.

2. **Ordinary annuity** is an annuity in which the payments are made at the end of the period.

3. **Annuity due** is an annuity in which the payments are made at the beginning.

4. **Future value** of an annuity is the total accumulation of the payments and interest earned.

5. Future value of an ordinary annuity

$$FV = P \cdot \frac{(1 + i)^n - 1}{i}$$

Future value of an annuity due

$$FV = P \cdot \frac{(1 + i)^n - 1}{i} \cdot (1 + i),$$

where $FV$ = future value,
$P$ = annuity payment,
$i$ = interest rate per period (written as a decimal), and
$n$ = total number of periods.

6. A **present value** of an annuity is a lump sum that is put into a fund in order for the fund to pay out a specified regular payment for a specified amount of time.

7. The future value (and present value) of an annuity can be determined using the TVM solver feature of the TI-83/84 Plus graphing calculator.

1. A college fund is established in which $100 is deposited at the end of every month at 6% per year compounded monthly. If the account started when you were five years old, how much will be in the account when you turn 18?

2. After making a $1500 down payment on a truck, you paid $210 per month for 36 months for a loan. The interest rate for the loan was 10.5% compounded monthly.

   a. What was the amount of the loan?

   b. What was the original cost of the truck?

3. As part of your retirement plan, at the beginning of each year you want to invest $2000 into an IRA. If you plan to retire in 25 years, how much will be in the IRA if it earns 8% compounded annually?

4. At your current place of employment, you have $100,000 in a retirement account. Since you are beginning work at a new company, you plan to roll over the $100,000 into a new account earning 7.5% per year compounded quarterly. You plan to deposit an additional $2000 at the end of each quarter into a second account until you retire. The second account also pays 7.5% per year compounded quarterly.

   a. If you plan to retire in 20 years, what amount of money will be in the first retirement account?

   b. How much money will be in the second retirement account?

5. The winner of the $2,000,000 state lottery will receive 20 payments of $100,000 per year. The payments are to be made as follows:

   1. The first payment of $100,000 is to be made immediately.

   2. The next 19 payments of $100,000 will be made at the end of each year.

   Determine the amount of money that the state needs to have on deposit in order to make the payments. Assume that the balance on deposit will earn 5% per year compounded annually.

6. As part of your retirement plan, you have decided to deposit $2500 at the beginning of each year into an account paying 5.5% interest compounded annually.

   a. How much will be in the account after 10 years?

**ACTIVITY 8.4**

Buy or Lease?

**OBJECTIVES**

1. Determine the amortization payment on a loan using a formula.

2. Determine the amortization payment on a loan using technology.

3. Solve problems involving repaying a loan or liquidating a sum of money by amortization model.

You are interested in purchasing a new car. You have decided to buy a 2008 Honda Accord for $20,995. The credit union requires a 10% down payment and will finance the balance with an 8% interest loan for 36 months. The sales tax in your city is 7%, and the license and title charges are $80.

**1. a.** What is the total purchase price of the car including tax, license, and title?

**b.** What is the amount of the down payment?

**c.** What is the total amount of the car loan?

Many large-sum loans, such as business loans for new equipment, home mortgages, and car loans are repaid through amortization. Generally, a loan is repaid by a series of equal periodic payments over a specific period of time. Each payment typically includes an amount for interest and a principal reduction (amortization).

When amortizing a loan, the original amount of the loan is known (present value). Since amortization is actually an application of an annuity, you can use a variation of the present value formula for annuities (see Exercise 8 in Activity 8.3) to develop a new formula for determining the amortization payment. Assume the payments are made at the end of each period (ordinary annuity).

## Calculating Amortization Payments by Formula

The formula to determine the amount of the payment, *Amt*, is

$$Amt = PV \cdot \frac{i}{1 - (1 + i)^{-n}} \text{ or, equivalently}$$

$$Amt = PV \cdot \frac{i}{1 - \dfrac{1}{(1 + i)^n}},$$

where:

$Amt$ = amortization payment,
$PV$ = amount of loan (present value),
$i$ = interest rate per period, and
$n$ = number of periods.

Example 1 *What monthly amortization payment at 12% interest is required to pay off an $8000 loan in two years?*

SOLUTION

To use the amortization formula, you need to first determine the interest rate per period and the number of periods *n*.

$$n = 2 \text{ years} \times 12 \text{ periods per year} = 24$$

$$i = \frac{12\%}{12} = 1\% \text{ or } 0.01$$

Now, substituting 8000 for *PV*, 24 for *n*, and 0.01 for *i*, you have

$$Amt = PV \cdot \frac{i}{1 - (1 + i)^{-n}}$$

$$= 8{,}000 \cdot \frac{0.01}{1 - (1 + 0.01)^{-24}}$$

$$= 8{,}000 \cdot \frac{0.01}{1 - (1.01)^{-24}}.$$

Using your graphing calculator to perform the calculations, the screen should appear as follows:

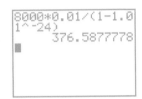

```
8000*0.01/(1-1.0
1^-24)
          376.5877778
■
```

Therefore, the monthly amortization payment is $376.59.

**2.** Determine the monthly amortization payment on your car loan in Problem 1c using the amortization payment formula.

**3.** Redo Problem 2 using the TMV Solver feature of your graphing calculator. How does the calculator result compare to the answer obtained by the formula in Problem 2?

## College Fund

Your parents and grandparents have been contributing to your college fund for many years. The fund currently has a total of $16,000. The decision has been made to amortize (liquidate) that amount so you will receive equal monthly payments over the next four years of college. At the end of the four years, there will be no funds in the account. If the single college account earns 6% annual interest, how much money will you receive each month?

**4. a.** What is the number of payments?

**b.** What is the annual interest rate?

**c.** What is the present value of the annuity?

**d.** Assume that payments will be made at the beginning of each month. Use your graphing calculator to determine the monthly payment.

## Leasing a Car

Rather than purchasing the car, you have the option of **leasing.** The car dealership salesperson explains to you that a lease is an agreement in which you make equal monthly payments for a specific period of time. At the end of this period, you return the car to the leasing dealer. You do not have ownership of the car and, therefore, have no equity or asset at the end of the leasing period. You have the option of purchasing the car at a predetermined price. There can be end-of-lease termination fees as well as charges for excess mileage or damage.

She gives you the following advertisement that the dealership just placed in the local newspaper:

---

### Lease a 2008 Honda Accord

**for only $249 per month for 36 months**

**WITH NO SECURITY DEPOSIT**

$2500 at signing plus tax, license, and title with approved credit

---

**5. a.** What is the leasing monthly payment?

**b.** How does the monthly leasing payment compare to the monthly purchase payment determined in Problem 2?

Since the monthly leasing payment is much lower than the monthly amortization payment, it seems like you are getting more for your money. Rather than comparing the monthly payments, you decide to compare the total cost of purchasing (Problem 6) to the total cost of leasing the car (Problem 7).

**6. a.** What is the down payment if you purchase the car?

**b.** If the monthly amortization payment is $635.82 (see Problem 2), what is the total of the loan payments?

**c.** Your down payment could have earned interest if you did not purchase the car. If your money currently earns 4% compounded annually in a savings account, how much interest would have been earned in the three-year period?

**d.** Since you own the car after the loan is paid off, you have equity in the car. You search the Internet and discover that the 2006 Honda Accord should depreciate about $1850 dollars per year. What is the value of the car at the end of the loan?

**e.** Using parts a–d, determine the total cost of purchasing the car.

**7. a.** What is the down payment and security deposit if you lease the car?

**b.** If the monthly leasing payment is $249, what is the total of the lease payments?

**c.** How much interest is lost if the amount in part a had been deposited at 4% compounded annually for three years?

**d.** Assume there are no end-of-lease termination fees or charges for excess mileage or damage. If a full refund of the security deposit (if any) is made, what is the total cost of leasing?

**8.** Is it better to purchase or lease your new car? Explain.

## SUMMARY
### Activity 8.4

1. **Amortization** is the process of repaying a loan by a series of equal periodic payments over a specific period of time. Amortization can also be used to liquidate a fund down to a zero balance.

2. The **amortization payment** can also be determined using the following formula:

$$Amt = PV \cdot \frac{i}{1 - (1 + i)^{-n}} \text{ or, equivalently}$$

$$Amt = PV \cdot \frac{i}{1 - \dfrac{1}{(1 + i)^{n}}}$$

where    $Amt$ = amortization payment,
             $PV$ = amount of loan,
             $i$ = interest rate per period, and
             $n$ = number of periods.

1. You borrow $5000 from the credit union to purchase a car. You agree to repay the loan in 36 equal monthly payments. The credit union charges 12% per year compounded monthly.

   a. What is the monthly payment? Use the amortization formula and then verify your result using your graphing calculator.

   b. How much interest was charged for the loan?

2. You buy a new high-definition (HD) TV for $3000 and finance the purchase at 14% interest compounded monthly for 24 months.

   a. What is the monthly payment?

   b. What was the total finance charge?

3. You have two options to finance $22,500 for a new truck:

   Option 1:   0% financing for 48 months
   Option 2:   A $3000 rebate

   If you choose the rebate, you can obtain a loan for the balance at 8.5% compounded annually for 48 months.

   a. If you choose option 1, what is the monthly payment?

   b. If you choose option 2, what is the monthly payment?

   c. Which option should you choose? Explain.

4. The outstanding balance on your credit card is $4000. The bank issuing the credit card is charging 18.5% per year compounded monthly. You decide you must pay off the balance before you get married in 18 months. If you make equal monthly payments for the next 18 months, determine the monthly payment. Assume no additional charges are made.

5. You make a profit of $30,000 on the sale of your small business. You deposit the money into an account paying 7.2% interest compounded annually. You want to make equal annual withdrawals from the account over the next five years. At the end of the five years, there will be no funds in the account.

   a. Determine the amount of each withdrawal. Assume the withdrawal is made at the beginning of each year.

   b. Determine the amount of each withdrawal if the money must last 10 years.

6. Find a lease advertisement in your local newspaper for a lease offer on a vehicle you would like to own. Obtain the information necessary to determine whether it is better to lease or purchase the vehicle. Use your local dealership, banks, and the Internet. Submit a report of your findings and conclusions.

**ACTIVITY 8.5**

Buy Now,
Pay Later

**OBJECTIVES**

1. Determine the amount financed, the installment price, and the finance charge of an installment loan.

2. Determine the installment payment.

3. Determine the annual percentage rate (APR) using the APR formula and using a table.

4. Determine the unearned interest on a loan if paid before it is due.

5. Determine the interest on a credit card account using the average daily balance method.

Significant price cuts have recently taken place in the cost of high-definition televisions. You have decided that now is the time to take the plunge. After researching the features of different types of HD TVs, including LCD, plasma, rear-projection, and picture-tube, you have selected a 50-inch HD plasma TV at a cost of $4000.

The electronics store salesperson informs you that the store is offering a 36-month installment plan to finance the TV. You are interested and discuss the details of the plan with the salesperson.

## Closed-End Installment Loan

The installment loan that is being offered by the electronics store is an example of **closed-end installment loan**. You repay the amount borrowed plus interest in equal payments (usually monthly) over a certain period of time. Such loans are commonly used to purchase furniture, appliances, and computers. The length of the loans can vary from a few months to several years.

1. The store requires no down payment. The salesperson tells you that you can finance the HD plasma TV with 36 monthly payments of $132.86.

    a. Determine the total amount paid. This total is called the **installment price**.

    b. Determine the finance charge (interest) of the installment loan. Remember that the monthly payment includes payment of interest as well as repayment of some of the amount borrowed (principal).

## Annual Percentage Rate (APR)

You are wondering about the interest rate being charged on the TV loan. The results from Problem 2 can be used to demonstrate a hidden cost when borrowing money on an installment plan.

2. a. Suppose you borrowed $1000 for a year and had an interest charge of $100. If you repaid the amount borrowed plus interest at the end of the year, what is the annual interest rate on the loan?

    b. Suppose you paid the amount borrowed plus interest on a 12-month installment plan, what is the monthly payment?

In Problem 2a, you would have the use of the $1000 for the entire year. In part b, you are losing the use of some of the $1000 since you are using some of it to pay $91.67

each month. Therefore, when paying a loan on an installment plan, the actual interest rate charged is more than 10% (the actual rate charged if you paid off the loan at the end of the year). The true annual interest rate charged is called the **annual percentage rate (APR)**.

> DEFINITION
>
> The **annual percentage rate (APR)** is the true rate of interest charged for the loan.

The APR can be calculated using the formula:

$$APR = \frac{72i}{3P(n+1) + i(n-1)},$$

where
   APR = annual percentage rate,
   $i$    = interest (finance) charge on the loan,
   $P$    = principal or amount borrowed, and
   $n$    = number of months of the loan.

**3. a.** In Problem 2, $1000 was borrowed at an interest rate of 10%. If the loan is paid off in 12 monthly payments and $100 interest was charged, determine the APR using the APR formula.

**b.** Verify your result in part a using the TVM Solver feature of the TI-83 Plus graphing calculator. Your screen should appear as follows:

**4.** Let us return to your TV loan. You are borrowing $4000 to purchase a HD plasma TV using a 36-month installment plan. Determine the annual percentage rate (APR) using the APR formula. Round your answer to the nearest whole percent. Recall that the interest charge was $782.96 (see Problem 1b).

In 1969, congress passed the **Truth in Lending Act**. This legislation required the lender to provide the borrower with the finance charge and APR of the loan. In order to help lending institutions and businesses to provide this information, the Federal Reserve Board has published APR tables. A portion of one of these tables appears in Table 8.1.

The following Example demonstrates the process for using APR Table 8.1 to determine the APR for a loan.

## Table 8.1
## Interest per $100 of Amount Financed

| NUMBER OF MONTHLY PAYMENTS | APR (ANNUAL PERCENTAGE RATE) | | | | | | | | | | | |
|---|---|---|---|---|---|---|---|---|---|---|---|---|
| | 10.00% | 10.50% | 11.00% | 11.50% | 12.00% | 12.50% | 13.00% | 13.50% | 14.00% | 14.50% | 15.00% | 15.50% |
| 1 | 0.83 | 0.87 | 0.92 | 0.96 | 1.00 | 1.04 | 1.08 | 1.12 | 1.17 | 1.21 | 1.25 | 1.29 |
| 2 | 1.25 | 1.31 | 1.38 | 1.44 | 1.50 | 1.57 | 1.63 | 1.69 | 1.75 | 1.82 | 1.88 | 1.94 |
| 3 | 1.67 | 1.76 | 1.84 | 1.92 | 2.01 | 2.09 | 2.17 | 2.26 | 2.34 | 2.43 | 2.51 | 2.59 |
| 4 | 2.09 | 2.20 | 2.30 | 2.41 | 2.51 | 2.62 | 2.72 | 2.83 | 2.93 | 3.04 | 3.14 | 3.25 |
| 5 | 2.51 | 2.64 | 2.77 | 2.89 | 3.02 | 3.15 | 3.27 | 3.40 | 3.53 | 3.65 | 3.78 | 3.91 |
| 6 | 2.94 | 3.08 | 3.23 | 3.38 | 3.53 | 3.68 | 3.83 | 3.97 | 4.12 | 4.27 | 4.42 | 4.57 |
| 7 | 3.36 | 3.53 | 3.70 | 3.87 | 4.04 | 4.21 | 4.38 | 4.55 | 4.72 | 4.89 | 5.06 | 5.23 |
| 8 | 3.79 | 3.98 | 4.17 | 4.36 | 4.55 | 4.74 | 4.94 | 5.13 | 5.32 | 5.51 | 5.71 | 5.90 |
| 9 | 4.21 | 4.43 | 4.64 | 4.85 | 5.07 | 5.28 | 5.49 | 5.71 | 5.92 | 6.14 | 6.35 | 6.57 |
| 10 | 4.64 | 4.88 | 5.11 | 5.35 | 5.58 | 5.82 | 6.05 | 6.29 | 6.53 | 6.77 | 7.00 | 7.24 |
| 11 | 5.07 | 5.33 | 5.58 | 5.84 | 6.10 | 6.36 | 6.62 | 6.88 | 7.14 | 7.40 | 7.66 | 7.92 |
| 12 | 5.50 | 5.78 | 6.06 | 6.34 | 6.62 | 6.90 | 7.18 | 7.46 | 7.74 | 8.03 | 8.31 | 8.59 |
| 13 | 5.93 | 6.23 | 6.53 | 6.84 | 7.14 | 7.44 | 7.75 | 8.05 | 8.36 | 8.66 | 8.97 | 9.27 |
| 14 | 6.36 | 6.69 | 7.01 | 7.34 | 7.66 | 7.99 | 8.31 | 8.64 | 8.97 | 9.30 | 9.63 | 9.96 |
| 15 | 6.80 | 7.14 | 7.49 | 7.84 | 8.19 | 8.53 | 8.88 | 9.23 | 9.59 | 9.94 | 10.29 | 10.64 |
| 16 | 7.23 | 7.60 | 7.97 | 8.34 | 8.71 | 9.08 | 9.46 | 9.83 | 10.20 | 10.58 | 10.95 | 11.33 |
| 17 | 7.67 | 8.06 | 8.45 | 8.84 | 9.24 | 9.63 | 10.03 | 10.44 | 10.82 | 11.22 | 11.62 | 12.02 |
| 18 | 8.10 | 8.52 | 8.93 | 9.35 | 9.77 | 10.19 | 10.61 | 11.03 | 11.45 | 11.87 | 12.29 | 12.72 |
| 19 | 8.54 | 8.98 | 9.42 | 9.86 | 10.30 | 10.74 | 11.18 | 11.63 | 12.07 | 12.52 | 12.97 | 13.41 |
| 20 | 8.98 | 9.44 | 9.90 | 10.37 | 10.83 | 11.30 | 11.76 | 12.23 | 12.70 | 13.17 | 13.64 | 14.11 |
| 21 | 9.42 | 9.90 | 10.39 | 10.88 | 11.36 | 11.85 | 12.34 | 12.84 | 13.33 | 13.82 | 14.32 | 14.82 |
| 22 | 9.86 | 10.37 | 10.88 | 11.39 | 11.90 | 12.41 | 12.93 | 13.44 | 13.96 | 14.48 | 15.00 | 15.52 |
| 23 | 10.30 | 10.84 | 11.37 | 11.90 | 12.44 | 12.97 | 13.51 | 14.05 | 14.59 | 15.14 | 15.68 | 16.23 |
| 24 | 10.75 | 11.30 | 11.86 | 12.42 | 12.98 | 13.54 | 14.10 | 14.66 | 15.23 | 15.80 | 16.37 | 16.94 |
| 25 | 11.19 | 11.77 | 12.35 | 12.93 | 13.52 | 14.10 | 14.69 | 15.28 | 15.87 | 16.46 | 17.06 | 17.65 |
| 26 | 11.64 | 12.24 | 12.85 | 13.45 | 14.06 | 14.67 | 15.28 | 15.89 | 16.51 | 17.13 | 17.75 | 18.37 |
| 27 | 12.09 | 12.71 | 13.34 | 13.97 | 14.60 | 15.24 | 15.87 | 16.51 | 17.15 | 17.80 | 18.44 | 19.09 |
| 28 | 12.53 | 13.18 | 13.84 | 14.49 | 15.15 | 15.81 | 16.47 | 17.13 | 17.80 | 18.47 | 19.14 | 19.81 |
| 29 | 12.98 | 13.66 | 14.33 | 15.01 | 15.70 | 16.38 | 17.07 | 17.75 | 18.45 | 19.14 | 19.83 | 20.53 |
| 30 | 13.43 | 14.13 | 14.83 | 15.54 | 16.24 | 16.95 | 17.66 | 18.38 | 19.10 | 19.81 | 20.54 | 21.26 |
| 31 | 13.89 | 14.61 | 15.33 | 16.06 | 16.79 | 17.53 | 18.27 | 19.00 | 19.75 | 20.49 | 21.24 | 21.99 |
| 32 | 14.34 | 15.09 | 15.84 | 16.59 | 17.35 | 18.11 | 18.87 | 19.63 | 20.40 | 21.17 | 21.95 | 22.72 |
| 33 | 14.79 | 15.57 | 16.34 | 17.12 | 17.90 | 18.69 | 19.47 | 20.26 | 21.06 | 21.85 | 22.65 | 23.46 |

**Table 8.1** *(continued)*
**Interest per $100 of Amount Financed**

| NUMBER OF MONTHLY PAYMENTS | APR (ANNUAL PERCENTAGE RATE) | | | | | | | | | | | |
|---|---|---|---|---|---|---|---|---|---|---|---|---|
| | 16.00% | 16.50% | 17.00% | 17.50% | 18.00% | 18.50% | 19.00% | 19.50% | 20.00% | 20.50% | 21.00% | 21.50% |
| 1 | 1.33 | 1.37 | 1.42 | 1.46 | 1.50 | 1.54 | 1.58 | 1.62 | 1.67 | 1.71 | 1.75 | 1.79 |
| 2 | 2.00 | 2.07 | 2.13 | 2.17 | 2.26 | 2.32 | 2.38 | 2.44 | 2.51 | 2.57 | 2.63 | 2.70 |
| 3 | 2.68 | 2.76 | 2.85 | 2.93 | 3.01 | 3.10 | 3.18 | 3.27 | 3.35 | 3.44 | 3.52 | 3.60 |
| 4 | 3.36 | 3.46 | 3.57 | 3.67 | 3.78 | 3.88 | 3.99 | 4.10 | 4.20 | 4.31 | 4.41 | 4.52 |
| 5 | 4.04 | 4.16 | 4.29 | 4.42 | 4.54 | 4.67 | 4.80 | 4.93 | 5.06 | 5.18 | 5.31 | 5.44 |
| 6 | 4.72 | 4.87 | 5.02 | 5.17 | 5.32 | 5.46 | 5.61 | 5.76 | 5.91 | 6.06 | 6.21 | 6.36 |
| 7 | 5.40 | 5.58 | 5.75 | 5.92 | 6.09 | 6.26 | 6.43 | 6.60 | 6.78 | 6.95 | 7.12 | 7.29 |
| 8 | 6.09 | 6.29 | 6.48 | 6.67 | 6.87 | 7.06 | 7.26 | 7.45 | 7.64 | 7.84 | 8.03 | 8.23 |
| 9 | 6.78 | 7.00 | 7.22 | 7.43 | 7.65 | 7.87 | 8.08 | 8.30 | 8.52 | 8.73 | 8.95 | 9.17 |
| 10 | 7.48 | 7.72 | 7.96 | 8.19 | 8.43 | 8.67 | 8.91 | 9.15 | 9.39 | 9.63 | 9.88 | 10.12 |
| 11 | 8.18 | 8.44 | 8.70 | 8.96 | 9.22 | 9.49 | 9.75 | 10.01 | 10.28 | 10.54 | 10.80 | 11.07 |
| 12 | 8.88 | 9.16 | 9.45 | 9.73 | 10.02 | 10.30 | 10.59 | 10.87 | 11.16 | 11.45 | 11.74 | 12.02 |
| 13 | 9.28 | 9.89 | 10.20 | 10.50 | 10.81 | 11.12 | 11.43 | 11.74 | 12.05 | 12.36 | 12.67 | 12.99 |
| 14 | 10.29 | 10.67 | 10.95 | 11.28 | 11.61 | 11.95 | 12.28 | 12.61 | 12.95 | 13.28 | 13.62 | 13.95 |
| 15 | 11.00 | 11.35 | 11.71 | 12.06 | 12.42 | 12.77 | 13.13 | 13.49 | 13.85 | 14.21 | 14.57 | 14.93 |
| 16 | 11.71 | 12.09 | 12.46 | 12.84 | 13.22 | 13.60 | 13.99 | 14.37 | 14.75 | 15.13 | 15.52 | 15.90 |
| 17 | 12.42 | 12.83 | 13.23 | 13.63 | 14.04 | 14.44 | 14.85 | 16.25 | 15.66 | 16.07 | 16.48 | 16.89 |
| 18 | 13.14 | 13.57 | 13.99 | 14.42 | 14.85 | 15.28 | 15.71 | 16.14 | 16.57 | 17.01 | 17.44 | 17.88 |
| 19 | 13.86 | 14.31 | 14.76 | 15.22 | 15.67 | 16.12 | 16.58 | 17.03 | 17.49 | 17.95 | 18.41 | 18.87 |
| 20 | 14.59 | 15.06 | 15.54 | 16.01 | 16.49 | 16.97 | 17.45 | 17.93 | 18.41 | 18.90 | 19.38 | 19.87 |
| 21 | 15.31 | 15.81 | 16.31 | 16.81 | 17.32 | 17.82 | 18.33 | 18.83 | 19.34 | 19.85 | 20.36 | 20.87 |
| 22 | 16.04 | 16.57 | 17.09 | 17.62 | 18.15 | 18.68 | 19.21 | 19.74 | 20.27 | 20.81 | 21.34 | 21.88 |
| 23 | 16.78 | 17.32 | 17.88 | 18.43 | 18.98 | 19.54 | 20.09 | 20.65 | 21.21 | 21.77 | 22.33 | 22.90 |
| 24 | 17.51 | 18.09 | 18.66 | 19.24 | 19.82 | 20.40 | 20.98 | 21.56 | 22.15 | 22.74 | 23.33 | 23.92 |
| 25 | 18.25 | 18.85 | 19.45 | 20.05 | 20.66 | 21.27 | 21.87 | 22.48 | 23.10 | 23.71 | 24.32 | 24.94 |
| 26 | 18.99 | 19.62 | 20.24 | 20.87 | 21.50 | 22.14 | 22.77 | 23.41 | 24.04 | 24.68 | 25.33 | 25.97 |
| 27 | 19.74 | 20.39 | 21.04 | 21.69 | 22.35 | 23.01 | 23.67 | 24.33 | 25.00 | 25.67 | 26.34 | 27.01 |
| 28 | 20.48 | 21.16 | 21.84 | 22.52 | 23.20 | 23.89 | 2.458 | 25.27 | 25.96 | 26.65 | 27.35 | 28.05 |
| 29 | 21.23 | 21.94 | 22.64 | 23.35 | 24.06 | 24.27 | 25.49 | 26.20 | 26.92 | 27.64 | 28.37 | 29.09 |
| 30 | 21.99 | 22.72 | 23.45 | 24.18 | 24.92 | 25.66 | 26.40 | 27.14 | 27.89 | 28.64 | 29.39 | 30.14 |
| 31 | 22.71 | 23.50 | 24.26 | 25.02 | 25.78 | 26.55 | 27.32 | 28.09 | 28.86 | 29.64 | 30.42 | 31.20 |
| 32 | 23.50 | 24.28 | 25.07 | 25.86 | 26.65 | 27.44 | 28.24 | 29.04 | 29.84 | 30.64 | 31.45 | 32.26 |
| 33 | 24.26 | 25.07 | 25.88 | 26.70 | 27.52 | 28.34 | 29.16 | 29.99 | 30.82 | 31.65 | 32.49 | 33.33 |

**Table 8.1** (*continued*)
**Interest per $100 of Amount Financed**

| NUMBER OF MONTHLY PAYMENTS | APR (ANNUAL PERCENTAGE RATE) | | | | | | | | | | | |
|---|---|---|---|---|---|---|---|---|---|---|---|---|
| | 10.00% | 10.50% | 11.00% | 11.50% | 12.00% | 12.50% | 13.00% | 13.50% | 14.00% | 14.50% | 15.00% | 15.50% |
| 34 | 15.25 | 16.05 | 16.85 | 17.64 | 18.46 | 19.27 | 20.08 | 20.90 | 21.72 | 22.54 | 23.37 | 24.19 |
| 35 | 15.70 | 16.53 | 17.35 | 18.18 | 19.01 | 19.85 | 20.69 | 21.53 | 22.38 | 23.23 | 24.08 | 24.94 |
| 36 | 16.16 | 17.01 | 17.86 | 18.71 | 19.57 | 20.43 | 21.30 | 22.17 | 23.04 | 23.92 | 24.80 | 25.68 |
| 37 | 16.62 | 17.49 | 18.37 | 19.25 | 20.13 | 21.02 | 21.91 | 22.81 | 23.70 | 24.69 | 25.51 | 26.42 |
| 38 | 17.08 | 17.98 | 18.88 | 19.78 | 20.69 | 21.61 | 22.52 | 23.45 | 24.37 | 25.30 | 26.24 | 27.17 |
| 39 | 17.54 | 18.46 | 19.39 | 20.32 | 21.26 | 22.20 | 23.14 | 24.09 | 25.04 | 26.90 | 26.96 | 27.92 |
| 40 | 18.00 | 18.95 | 19.90 | 20.86 | 21.82 | 22.79 | 23.76 | 24.73 | 25.71 | 26.70 | 27.69 | 28.68 |
| 41 | 18.47 | 19.44 | 20.42 | 21.40 | 22.39 | 23.38 | 24.38 | 25.38 | 26.39 | 27.40 | 28.41 | 29.44 |
| 42 | 18.93 | 19.93 | 20.93 | 21.94 | 22.96 | 23.98 | 25.00 | 26.03 | 27.06 | 28.10 | 29.15 | 30.19 |
| 43 | 19.40 | 20.42 | 21.45 | 22.49 | 23.53 | 24.57 | 25.62 | 26.68 | 27.74 | 28.81 | 29.88 | 20.96 |
| 44 | 19.86 | 20.91 | 21.97 | 23.03 | 24.10 | 25.17 | 26.25 | 27.33 | 28.42 | 29.52 | 30.62 | 31.72 |
| 45 | 20.33 | 21.41 | 22.49 | 23.58 | 24.67 | 25.77 | 26.88 | 27.99 | 29.11 | 30.23 | 31.36 | 32.49 |
| 46 | 20.80 | 21.90 | 23.01 | 24.13 | 25.25 | 26.37 | 27.51 | 28.65 | 29.79 | 30.94 | 32.10 | 33.26 |
| 47 | 21.27 | 22.40 | 23.53 | 24.68 | 25.82 | 26.98 | 28.14 | 29.31 | 30.48 | 31.66 | 32.84 | 34.03 |
| 48 | 21.74 | 22.90 | 24.06 | 25.23 | 26.40 | 27.58 | 28.77 | 29.97 | 31.17 | 32.37 | 33.59 | 34.81 |
| 49 | 22.21 | 23.39 | 24.58 | 25.78 | 26.98 | 28.19 | 29.41 | 30.63 | 13.86 | 33.09 | 34.34 | 35.59 |
| 50 | 22.69 | 23.89 | 25.11 | 26.33 | 27.56 | 28.80 | 30.04 | 31.29 | 32.55 | 33.82 | 35.09 | 36.37 |
| 51 | 23.16 | 24.40 | 25.64 | 26.89 | 28.15 | 29.41 | 30.68 | 31.96 | 33.25 | 34.54 | 35.84 | 37.15 |
| 52 | 23.64 | 24.90 | 26.17 | 27.45 | 28.73 | 30.02 | 31.32 | 32.63 | 33.95 | 35.27 | 36.60 | 37.94 |
| 53 | 24.11 | 25.40 | 26.70 | 28.00 | 29.32 | 30.64 | 31.97 | 33.30 | 34.65 | 36.00 | 37.36 | 38.72 |
| 54 | 24.59 | 25.91 | 27.23 | 28.56 | 29.91 | 31.25 | 32.61 | 33.98 | 35.35 | 36.73 | 38.12 | 39.52 |
| 55 | 25.07 | 26.41 | 27.77 | 29.13 | 30.50 | 31.87 | 33.26 | 34.65 | 36.05 | 37.46 | 38.88 | 40.31 |
| 56 | 25.55 | 26.92 | 28.30 | 29.69 | 31.09 | 32.49 | 33.91 | 35.33 | 36.76 | 38.20 | 39.65 | 41.11 |
| 57 | 26.03 | 27.43 | 28.84 | 30.25 | 31.68 | 33.11 | 34.56 | 36.01 | 37.47 | 38.94 | 40.42 | 41.91 |
| 58 | 26.51 | 27.94 | 29.37 | 30.82 | 32.27 | 33.74 | 35.21 | 36.69 | 38.18 | 39.68 | 41.19 | 42.71 |
| 59 | 27.00 | 28.45 | 29.91 | 31.39 | 32.87 | 34.36 | 35.86 | 37.37 | 38.89 | 40.42 | 41.96 | 43.51 |
| 60 | 27.48 | 28.96 | 30.45 | 31.96 | 33.47 | 34.99 | 36.52 | 38.06 | 39.61 | 41.17 | 42.74 | 44.32 |

**Table 8.1** *(continued)*
**Interest per $100 of Amount Financed**

| NUMBER OF MONTHLY PAYMENTS | APR (ANNUAL PERCENTAGE RATE) | | | | | | | | | | | |
|---|---|---|---|---|---|---|---|---|---|---|---|---|
| | 16.00% | 16.50% | 17.00% | 17.50% | 18.00% | 18.50% | 19.00% | 19.50% | 20.00% | 20.50% | 21.00% | 21.50% |
| 34 | 25.03 | 25.86 | 26.70 | 27.54 | 28.38 | 29.24 | 30.09 | 30.95 | 31.80 | 32.67 | 33.53 | 34.40 |
| 35 | 25.79 | 26.66 | 27.52 | 28.39 | 29.27 | 30.14 | 31.02 | 31.91 | 32.79 | 33.68 | 34.58 | 35.47 |
| 36 | 26.57 | 27.46 | 28.35 | 29.25 | 30.15 | 31.05 | 31.96 | 32.87 | 33.79 | 34.71 | 35.63 | 36.56 |
| 37 | 27.34 | 28.26 | 29.18 | 30.10 | 31.03 | 31.97 | 32.90 | 33.84 | 34.79 | 35.74 | 36.69 | 37.64 |
| 38 | 28.11 | 29.06 | 30.01 | 30.96 | 31.92 | 32.88 | 33.85 | 34.82 | 35.79 | 36.77 | 37.75 | 38.73 |
| 39 | 28.89 | 29.87 | 30.85 | 31.83 | 32.81 | 33.80 | 34.80 | 35.80 | 36.80 | 37.81 | 38.82 | 39.83 |
| 40 | 29.68 | 30.68 | 31.68 | 32.69 | 33.71 | 34.73 | 35.75 | 36.78 | 37.81 | 38.85 | 39.69 | 40.93 |
| 41 | 30.46 | 31.49 | 32.52 | 33.56 | 34.51 | 35.66 | 36.71 | 37.77 | 38.83 | 39.89 | 40.96 | 42.04 |
| 42 | 31.25 | 32.31 | 33.37 | 34.44 | 35.51 | 36.59 | 37.67 | 38.76 | 39.85 | 40.95 | 42.05 | 43.15 |
| 43 | 32.04 | 33.13 | 34.22 | 35.31 | 36.42 | 37.52 | 38.63 | 39.75 | 40.87 | 42.00 | 43.13 | 44.27 |
| 44 | 32.83 | 33.95 | 35.07 | 36.19 | 37.33 | 38.46 | 39.60 | 40.75 | 41.90 | 43.06 | 44.22 | 45.39 |
| 45 | 33.63 | 34.77 | 35.92 | 37.08 | 38.24 | 39.41 | 40.58 | 41.75 | 42.94 | 44.13 | 45.32 | 46.52 |
| 46 | 34.43 | 35.60 | 36.78 | 37.96 | 39.16 | 40.35 | 41.55 | 42.76 | 43.98 | 45.20 | 46.42 | 47.65 |
| 47 | 35.23 | 36.43 | 37.64 | 38.86 | 40.08 | 41.30 | 42.54 | 43.77 | 45.02 | 46.27 | 47.53 | 48.79 |
| 48 | 36.03 | 37.27 | 38.50 | 39.75 | 41.00 | 42.26 | 43.52 | 44.79 | 46.07 | 47.35 | 48.64 | 49.93 |
| 49 | 36.84 | 38.10 | 39.37 | 40.65 | 41.93 | 43.22 | 44.51 | 45.81 | 47.12 | 48.43 | 49.75 | 51.08 |
| 50 | 37.65 | 38.94 | 40.24 | 41.55 | 42.86 | 44.18 | 45.50 | 46.83 | 48.17 | 49.52 | 50.87 | 52.23 |
| 51 | 38.46 | 39.79 | 41.11 | 42.45 | 43.79 | 45.14 | 46.50 | 47.86 | 49.23 | 50.61 | 51.99 | 53.38 |
| 52 | 39.28 | 40.63 | 41.99 | 43.36 | 44.73 | 46.11 | 47.50 | 48.89 | 50.30 | 51.71 | 53.12 | 54.55 |
| 53 | 40.10 | 41.48 | 42.87 | 44.27 | 45.67 | 47.08 | 48.50 | 49.93 | 51.37 | 52.81 | 54.26 | 55.71 |
| 54 | 40.92 | 42.33 | 43.75 | 45.18 | 46.62 | 48.06 | 49.51 | 50.97 | 52.44 | 53.91 | 55.39 | 56.88 |
| 55 | 41.74 | 43.19 | 44.64 | 16.10 | 47.57 | 49.04 | 50.52 | 52.02 | 53.52 | 55.02 | 56.54 | 58.08 |
| 56 | 42.57 | 44.05 | 45.53 | 47.02 | 48.52 | 50.03 | 51.54 | 53.06 | 54.60 | 56.14 | 57.68 | 59.24 |
| 57 | 43.40 | 44.91 | 46.42 | 47.94 | 49.47 | 51.01 | 52.56 | 54.12 | 55.68 | 57.25 | 58.84 | 60.43 |
| 58 | 44.23 | 45.77 | 47.32 | 48.87 | 50.43 | 52.00 | 53.58 | 55.17 | 56.77 | 58.38 | 59.99 | 61.62 |
| 59 | 45.07 | 46.64 | 48.21 | 49.80 | 51.39 | 53.00 | 54.61 | 56.23 | 57.87 | 59.51 | 61.15 | 62.81 |
| 60 | 45.91 | 47.51 | 49.12 | 50.73 | 52.36 | 54.00 | 55.64 | 57.30 | 58.96 | 60.64 | 62.32 | 64.01 |

**Example 1**    *In Problems 2 and 3, you financed $1000 for a year and agreed to repay the loan with 12 monthly payments of $91.67. The interest charge was $100. Use the APR Table 8.1 to determine the annual percentage rate (APR).*

SOLUTION

**Step 1.**    Determine the total finance charge (interest) on the loan. The finance charge is given as $100.

**Step 2.**    Determine the finance charge per $100 of the amount financed.

$$\frac{\text{finance charge}}{\text{amount financed}} \cdot 100 = \frac{100}{1000} \cdot 100 = 10$$

Therefore, you pay $10 for each $100 being financed.

**Step 3.**    Using APR Table 8.1, determine the row for the given number of payments (12) and then move across to locate the number nearest to 10. Next, move to the top of the column to determine the APR of the loan.

Therefore, the APR is 18%

5. Redo Problem 4 (TV loan) using APR Table 8.1. How does your answer compare to the APR determined in Problem 4?

## Calculating Monthly Installment Payment

If you know the APR and the number of monthly payments, the APR Table 8.1 can be used to determine the monthly payment.

6. Suppose the salesperson at a competing electronics store offers the same model 50-inch HD plasma TV, but at a lower price of $3800. With no down payment required, you can borrow $3800 at 14% APR for 32 months.

a.  Use the APR Table 8.1 to determine the finance charge per $100 financed.

b.  Determine the total finance charge of the loan. Note that if you divide the table value of 20.40 by 100, you get the finance charge for $1 borrowed. Multiplying this number by the amount financed will give the total finance charge of the $3800 loan.

c.  What is the total of the amount financed and finance charge for the HD plasma TV at this competing store?

**d.** What is the monthly payment on the loan?

Using the TVM Solve feature, where N = 32, I% = 14, PV = 3800, FV = 0, P/Y = 12, C/Y = 12, PMT: END, you obtain $142.98 for the monthly payment.

**e.** Complete the following table to summarize the information you have calculated for each of the installment plans to purchase the 50-inch HD plasma TV.

|  | INSTALLMENT PLAN I | INSTALLMENT PLAN 2 AT COMPETING STORE |
|---|---|---|
| PURCHASE PRICE |  |  |
| DOWN PAYMENT |  |  |
| MONTHLY PAYMENT |  |  |
| NUMBER OF MONTHLY PAYMENTS |  |  |
| APR |  |  |
| FINANCE CHARGE |  |  |
| TOTAL COST |  |  |

**f.** Which installment plan represents the better deal? Explain.

## Paying an Installment Loan Before It Is Due

You purchase the HD plasma TV at the second electronics store (installment plan 2). Recall from Problem 6b that the total finance charge for plan 2 is $775.20. Suppose you pay the first 20 payments and then decide to pay off the loan. Would you have to pay the total finance charge of $775.20?

The answer is no. You are entitled to a finance charge rebate. At the time of the loan pay off, the lender must return any unearned interest that is saved by paying off the loan early.

The most commonly used method to determine the unearned interest is the **actuarial method**.

The actuarial method formula is
$$u = \frac{npv}{100 + v},$$
where
$u$ = unearned interest,
$n$ = number of remaining monthly payments,
$p$ = monthly payment, and
$v$ = value from the APR table that corresponds to the APR for the number of remaining payments.

**7.** Recall that your monthly payments for the 32-month installment plan 2 to purchase the HD plasma TV is $142.98.

**a.** If you pay off the loan after 20 payments, how many payments remain?

**b.** Determine the value $v$ in the actuarial method formula. *Hint:* Using the APR table, find the intersection of the number of remaining payments now (12) with the APR column headed by the loan APR (14%).

**c.** Substitute the appropriate values for $n$, $p$, and $v$ into the actuarial formula to determine the unearned interest $u$.

**d.** Determine the total amount due to pay off the loan after 20 payments.

## Open-end Installment Loans

You are enjoying your new HD plasma TV. You purchase a $450 cabinet to contain the TV equipment and store your large collection of DVDs. You charge the cabinet on your credit card.

Use of a credit card to purchase goods is a type of **open-end installment loan**. Rather than making fixed equal payments over a specific period time, you make variable monthly payments. There is generally no specific period of time to pay off the loan. As a matter of fact, you can actually borrow additional monies to purchase merchandise while you still have unpaid loans in the account.

Interest rates for open-ended accounts are generally given as annual rates. The interest on most open-end accounts is calculated using the **average daily balance method**. In this method, a balance is determined for each day of the billing period and then the total is divided by the number of days in that billing period. This gives an average of all the daily balances.

The following example demonstrates the process:

Example 2   *The balance on your credit card on March 1, the billing date, is $242.50. The following transactions were made during the month of March.*

| March 6  | Payment             | $50.00 |
|----------|---------------------|--------|
| March 15 | Charge: clothing    | 37.00  |
| March 20 | Charge: car tire    | 85.00  |
| March 25 | Charge: music CDs   | 41.50  |

Determine the balance due on April 1.

SOLUTION

**i.** Determine the average daily balance for the month of March.

**Step 1.**   Determine the balance due for each transaction date:

March 1     242.50
March 6     $242.50 - 50.00 = 192.50$

|            |                             |
|------------|-----------------------------|
| March 15   | $192.50 + 37.00 = 229.50$   |
| March 20   | $229.50 + 85.00 = 314.50$   |
| March 25   | $314.50 + 41.50 = 356.00$   |

**Step 2.** Determine the number of days that the balance did not change between each transaction.

| March 1–March 5   | 5 |
|-------------------|---|
| March 6–March 14  | 9 |
| March 15–March 19 | 5 |
| March 20–March 24 | 5 |
| March 25–March 31 | 7 |

**Step 3.** Multiply the balance due times the number of days it did not change.

$5(242.50) = 1212.50$
$9(192.50) = 1732.50$
$5(229.50) = 1147.50$
$5(314.50) = 1572.50$
$7(356.00) = 2492.00$

**Step 4.** Determine the sum of the products in step 3 and divide by the number of days in the billing cycle (month).

$$\frac{1212.50 + 1732.50 + 1147.50 + 1572.50 + 2492.00}{31} = \$263.13$$

Therefore, the average daily balance is $263.13.

  **ii.** Determine the finance charge for the month. Assume that the interest rate is 1.25% per month. The finance charge is

$$0.0125 \times 263.13 = 3.29$$

  **iii.** Determine the balance due on April 1.

$$\text{finance charge} + \text{balance} = 3.29 + 356 = \$359.29$$

---

**SUMMARY**
Activity 8.5

1. A **closed-end installment** loan is one in which you pay a fixed amount of money for a specified number of payments.

2. The **finance charge** is the total amount of money that the borrower must pay for its use.

3. The **finance charge** is the amount borrowed subtracted from the total monthly payments.

4. The **annual percentage rate (APR)** is the true rate of interest charged for the loan.

5. The APR can be calculated using the following formula

$$\text{APR} = \frac{72i}{3P(n + 1) + i(n - 1)},$$

where APR = annual percentage rate,
       $i$ = interest (finance) charge on the loan,
      $P$ = principal or amount borrowed, and
      $n$ = number of months of the loan.

The APR can also be calculated using Table 8.1 or the TVM Solver on the TI-83/84 Plus.

6. The **installment payment** is the amount that is paid (including interest) in regular payments.

7. The total **installment price** is the down payment plus the total of monthly payments.

8. An **open-end installment loan** is one in which you make variable payments each month.

9. The **actuarial method** is used to determine the amount of the unearned interest of an installment loan if it is paid off before it is done. The actuarial method formula is

$$u = \frac{npv}{100 + v}, \text{ where}$$

$u$ = unearned interest,
$n$ = number of remaining monthly payments,
$p$ = monthly payment, and
$v$ = value from the APR table that corresponds to the APR for the number of remaining payments.

10. The interest on most credit card accounts is calculated using the **average daily balance method** (see Example 2).

## EXERCISES
### Activity 8.5

1. You purchased a new laptop computer for $1200. You pay a 5% down payment and $55 per month on a 24-month purchase plan.

   a. What is the amount of the down payment?

   b. Determine the amount financed.

   c. Determine the total finance charge.

   d. Use the APR formula to determine the annual percentage rate to the nearest half percent.

   e. Use the TVM Solver feature of the TI-83/84 Plus to verify your result in part d.

2. You want to finance a used truck for $8000. The dealership requires a $1000 down payment and offers a 36-month installment plan to finance the balance. If your monthly payment is $235, use APR Table 8.1 to determine the APR. Verify your result using the calculator.

3. The senior class is planning a fund-raiser to purchase a new refrigerator for a local daycare center. The refrigerator's total cost is $950. In order to finance the purchase, the appliance store requires a 10% down payment, with the balance being financed with a 24-month installment plan having an APR of 10.5%.

   a. What is the amount of the down payment?

   b. What is the amount to be financed?

   c. Determine the finance charge. Use the APR table.

   d. Determine the monthly payment. Verify using the TVM Solver.

4. Your friend bought a new sport utility vehicle for $34,000. She received $8000 on her trade-in and used that money as a down payment. She financed the vehicle at 10% APR over 48 months. She received a bonus check at work and paid off the loan after making the 30th payment.

   a. Determine the total interest that would have been paid if she had made all 48 payments.

   b. What were her monthly payments?

   c. How many payments are left?

   d. Use the actuarial method formula to determine the amount of unearned interest.

   e. Determine the total amount due to pay off the loan after 30 payments.

### ACTIVITY 8.6
Home Sweet
Home

**OBJECTIVES**

1. Determine the amount of the down payment and points in a mortgage.

2. Determine the monthly mortgage payment using a table.

3. Determine the total interest on a mortgage.

4. Prepare a partial amortization schedule of a mortgage.

5. Determine if borrowers qualify for a mortgage.

You are the loan officer at a bank. You specialize in long-term loans, called mortgages, in which property is used as security for a debt. A young couple, recently married, has decided to purchase a townhouse at a negotiated price of $120,000. They have applied for a conventional mortgage from your bank. Because the townhouse is older, the bank is requiring a 20% down payment. A special interest mortgage loan of 5.5% is being offered.

The bank is also requiring 2 points for their loan at the time of closing (the final step in the sale process). You explain to the couple that charging points enables the bank to reduce the amount of interest on the mortgage loan, and therefore will reduce the amount of monthly payment.

1. Determine the amount of the down payment. This amount is paid to the seller at closing.

2. **a.** If the couple agrees to pay the premium for private mortgage insurance (PMI), the bank can lend up to 95% of the value of the property. What would be the down payment if the bank required a 5% down payment?

   **b.** Assuming they agree to purchasing the PMI, what is the amount to be mortgaged?

   **c.** A point is 1% of the amount to be borrowed. Determine the amount of the points. This amount is paid to the bank at closing.

## Calculating the Monthly Mortgage Payment

In Activity 8.4, you learned that amortization is a special type of annuity in which a large loan is paid off with equal periodic payments over a period of time. Mortgages are loans that are paid off using amortization. The amount of the mortgage is actually the present value of an annuity.

The amount of the monthly mortgage payments can be calculated by using a table. Since mortgages often run for a period of 5 to 30 years, there is a special present value table in which the periods are listed in years. Also, since mortgage loans involve large sums of money, the table values represent the monthly payment per $1000 of mortgage.

Example 1 illustrates the procedure to calculate the monthly mortgage payment using Table 8.2 on page 950.

Example 1   *Determine the monthly payment and total interest on a $250,000 mortgage at 7.5% for 20 years.*

SOLUTION

**Step 1.**   Divide the amount to be mortgaged by 1000. This gives the number of thousands of dollars to be mortgaged.

$$\frac{250,000}{1000} = 250$$

**Step 2.**  Using Table 8.2, locate the table value, monthly payment per $1000 financed, at the intersection of the number of years row (20) and annual interest rate column (7.5%).

Table value is 8.06.

**Step 3.**  Multiply the amount to be mortgaged (step 1) by the table value (step 2) to determine the monthly mortgage payment.

$$250 \cdot 8.06 = \$2015$$

Using Table 8.2, the monthly mortgage payment in Example 1 is $2015. The TVM Solver feature of your TI-83/84 Plus can be used to determine the monthly mortgage payment. Let N = 240, I% = 7.5, PV = 250,000, FV = 0, P/Y = C/Y = 12, PMT:END, you obtain PMT = –2013.98. Your screen should appear as follows:

```
N=240
I%=7.5
PV=250000
■PMT=-2013.9829…
FV=0
P/Y=12
C/Y=12
PMT:END BEGIN
```

Note that there is a small difference between the results obtained from the graphing calculator and the result using the mortgage table. This is a result of rounding numbers in the calculations.

**3. a.**  Recall from Problem 2c that the couple is applying for a mortgage amount of $114,000 at 5.5% APR. Determine the monthly payment for a 30-year mortgage.

**b.**  What is the total interest paid? Use the monthly payment obtained by the TVM Solver.

**4. a.**  The couple would like to compare the monthly payment and total interest paid for different lengths of time, in years. Complete the following table:

| $114,000 MORTGAGE AT 5.5% ANNUAL INTEREST | | |
|---|---|---|
| LENGTH OF MORTGAGE | MONTHLY PAYMENT | TOTAL INTEREST |
| 15 | | |
| 20 | | |
| 25 | | |
| 30 | | |

**Table 8.2**
**Monthly Payments per $1000 of Mortgage** (including principal and interest)

| INTEREST RATE (%) | 5 YEARS | 10 YEARS | 15 YEARS | 20 YEARS | 25 YEARS | 30 YEARS | 35 YEARS | 40 YEARS |
|---|---|---|---|---|---|---|---|---|
| 5 | 18.88 | 10.61 | 7.91 | 6.60 | 5.85 | 5.37 | 5.05 | 4.83 |
| $5\frac{1}{4}$ | 18.99 | 10.73 | 8.04 | 6.74 | 6.00 | 5.53 | 5.21 | 4.99 |
| $5\frac{1}{2}$ | 79.11 | 10.86 | 8.18 | 6.88 | 6.15 | 5.68 | 5.38 | 5.16 |
| $5\frac{3}{4}$ | 19.22 | 10.98 | 8.31 | 7.03 | 6.30 | 5.84 | 5.54 | 5.33 |
| 6 | 19.34 | 11.11 | 8.44 | 7.17 | 6.45 | 6.00 | 5.71 | 5.51 |
| $6\frac{1}{4}$ | 19.45 | 11.23 | 8.58 | 7.31 | 6.60 | 6.16 | 5.88 | 5.68 |
| $6\frac{1}{2}$ | 19.57 | 11.36 | 8.72 | 7.46 | 6.76 | 6.33 | 6.05 | 5.86 |
| $6\frac{3}{4}$ | 19.69 | 11.49 | 8.85 | 7.61 | 6.91 | 6.49 | 6.22 | 6.04 |
| 7 | 19.81 | 11.62 | 8.99 | 7.76 | 7.07 | 6.66 | 6.39 | 6.22 |
| $7\frac{1}{4}$ | 19.92 | 11.75 | 9.13 | 7.91 | 7.23 | 6.83 | 6.57 | 6.40 |
| $7\frac{1}{2}$ | 20.04 | 11.88 | 9.28 | 8.06 | 7.39 | 7.00 | 6.75 | 6.59 |
| $7\frac{3}{4}$ | 20.16 | 12.01 | 9.42 | 8.21 | 7.56 | 7.17 | 6.93 | 6.77 |
| 8 | 20.28 | 12.14 | 9.56 | 8.37 | 7.72 | 7.34 | 7.11 | 6.96 |
| $8\frac{1}{4}$ | 20.40 | 12.27 | 9.71 | 8.53 | 7.89 | 7.52 | 7.29 | 7.15 |
| $8\frac{1}{2}$ | 20.52 | 12.40 | 9.85 | 8.68 | 8.06 | 7.69 | 7.47 | 7.34 |
| $8\frac{3}{4}$ | 20.64 | 12.54 | 10.00 | 8.84 | 8.23 | 7.87 | 7.66 | 7.53 |
| 9 | 20.76 | 12.67 | 10.15 | 9.00 | 8.40 | 8.05 | 7.84 | 7.72 |
| $9\frac{1}{4}$ | 20.88 | 12.81 | 10.30 | 9.16 | 8.57 | 8.23 | 8.03 | 7.91 |
| $9\frac{1}{2}$ | 21.01 | 12.94 | 10.45 | 9.33 | 8.74 | 8.41 | 8.22 | 8.11 |
| $9\frac{3}{4}$ | 21.13 | 13.08 | 10.60 | 9.49 | 8.92 | 8.60 | 8.41 | 8.30 |
| 10 | 21.25 | 13.22 | 10.75 | 9.66 | 9.09 | 8.78 | 8.60 | 8.50 |
| $10\frac{1}{4}$ | 21.38 | 13.36 | 10.90 | 9.82 | 9.27 | 8.97 | 8.79 | 8.69 |
| $10\frac{1}{2}$ | 21.50 | 13.50 | 11.06 | 9.99 | 9.45 | 9.15 | 8.99 | 8.89 |
| $10\frac{3}{4}$ | 21.62 | 13.64 | 11.21 | 10.16 | 9.63 | 9.34 | 9.18 | 9.09 |
| 11 | 21.75 | 13.78 | 11.37 | 10.33 | 9.81 | 9.53 | 9.37 | 9.29 |
| $11\frac{1}{4}$ | 21.87 | 13.92 | 11.53 | 10.50 | 9.99 | 9.72 | 9.57 | 9.49 |
| $11\frac{1}{2}$ | 22.00 | 14.06 | 11.69 | 10.67 | 10.17 | 9.91 | 9.77 | 9.69 |
| $11\frac{3}{4}$ | 22.12 | 14.21 | 11.85 | 10.84 | 10.35 | 10.10 | 9.96 | 9.89 |
| 12 | 22.25 | 14.35 | 12.01 | 11.02 | 10.54 | 10.29 | 10.16 | 10.09 |
| $12\frac{1}{4}$ | 22.38 | 14.50 | 12.17 | 11.19 | 10.72 | 10.48 | 10.36 | 10.29 |
| $12\frac{1}{2}$ | 22.50 | 14.64 | 12.33 | 11.37 | 10.91 | 10.68 | 10.56 | 10.49 |
| $12\frac{3}{4}$ | 22.63 | 14.79 | 12.49 | 11.54 | 11.10 | 10.87 | 10.76 | 10.70 |
| 13 | 22.76 | 14.94 | 12.66 | 11.72 | 11.28 | 11.07 | 10.96 | 10.90 |
| $13\frac{1}{4}$ | 22.89 | 15.08 | 12.82 | 11.90 | 11.47 | 11.26 | 11.16 | 11.10 |
| $13\frac{1}{2}$ | 23.01 | 15.23 | 12.99 | 12.08 | 11.66 | 11.46 | 11.36 | 11.31 |
| $13\frac{3}{4}$ | 23.14 | 15.38 | 13.15 | 12.26 | 11.85 | 11.66 | 11.56 | 11.51 |
| 14 | 23.27 | 15.53 | 13.32 | 12.44 | 12.04 | 11.85 | 11.76 | 11.72 |

**b.** What is the effect on the monthly payment and total interest paid as the length of the mortgage increases?

## Amortization Schedule

The couple decides on a 30-year mortgage in order to have the lowest monthly payments. You explain to them that the monthly payment is applied to pay interest on the loan and to reduce the amount owed. The couple asks you if the $647.28 monthly payment is divided equally between reducing the amount owed (principal) and paying the interest. They are surprised that this is not the case.

**Example 2** *The calculated monthly payment for the couple's 30-year $114,000 mortgage at 5.5% annual interest is $647.28 (using TVM). Determine the outstanding balance at the start of the second month.*

SOLUTION

**Step 1.** Determine the amount of interest in the first month using $i = Prt$ where $P$ is the outstanding balance of the loan for given month, $r$ is the annual interest rate (fixed at 5.5%) and $t$ is time (fixed at 1/12).

For the first payment, $P = 114{,}000$, $r = 0.055$, $t = \frac{1}{12}$

$$i = Prt = 114{,}000(0.055)(\tfrac{1}{12}) = 522.50$$

**Step 2.** Determine the portion of the payment used to reduce the amount of the principal by subtracting the amount of interest owed (from step 1) from the monthly payment.

$$647.28 - 522.50 = 124.78$$

**Step 3.** Calculate the outstanding balance for the next month by subtracting the amount to reduce the principal (step 2) from the outstanding balance of the current month.

$$114{,}000 - 124.78 = \$113{,}875.22$$

**5. a.** Repeat steps 1–3 in Example 2 to complete the following table:

| PAYMENT NUMBER | MONTHLY PAYMENT | INTEREST | AMOUNT USED TO REDUCE PRINCIPLE | END-OF-MONTH BALANCE OF LOAN |
|---|---|---|---|---|
| 1 | $647.28 | $522.50 | $124.78 | $113,875.22 |
| 2 | | | | |
| 3 | | | | |
| 4 | | | | |

**b.** Using the results in part a, determine whether each of the following gradually increases, gradually decreases, or remains the same, as monthly payments are made over the years.

    **i.** monthly payment      _____

    **ii.** interest      _____

    **iii.** amount that reduces principal      _____

    **iv.** end-of-month balance      _____

The table in Problem 5a is a partial **amortization schedule** for the first four payments. An amortization schedule for the entire loan would require 360 lines. (Why?) Therefore, such schedules are usually done by computer spreadsheet programs and calculator websites on the Internet. For example, see the monthly mortgage payment site at www.hsh.com.

## Qualifying for a Mortgage

An important responsibility of a mortgage loan officer is to determine the borrower's ability to repay the loan. To determine if the couple is qualified for the mortgage, you obtain the following information:

| | |
|---|---|
| Couple's combined gross annual income | $60,000 |
| Estimated annual property taxes on house | $ 2200 |
| Annual house insurance | $ 670 |

**6. a.** Determine the total monthly housing expenses by adding the monthly mortgage payment and the monthly expenses for property taxes and house insurance.

**b.** Determine the couple's combined gross monthly income.

Most lenders of conventional loans use the qualifying rule that the monthly housing expenses should not be more than 28% of the monthly gross income. The ratio

$$\frac{\text{monthly housing expense}}{\text{monthly gross income}}$$

is called the **housing expense ratio**.

**7. a.** Using the results in Problem 6, determine the housing expense ratio for the couple applying for the loan.

**b.** Do they qualify for the loan?

8. The couple has just closed on the townhouse. Determine the total cost of the house by summing the down payment, the principal, the interest, and the points.

There are usually many other expenses every home buyer needs to pay when purchasing a house. These expenses include the cost of a lawyer, loan application fees, state and local real estate taxes, and title search fees.

## SUMMARY
### Activity 8.6

1. A **mortgage** is a long-term loan in which the property is used as security for the debt.

2. **Amortization** is a special type of annuity in which a large loan is paid off with equal regular payments over a specified time.

3. The monthly mortgage payment can be determined by using a table (see Example 1) or the TVM Solver feature of the TI-83 Plus graphing calculator.

4. An **amortization schedule** is a list containing the payment number, payment on the interest, payment on the principal, and balance of the loan.

5. A borrower qualifies for a mortgage if the **monthly housing expense** is no more than 28% of the monthly gross income.

## EXERCISES
### Activity 8.6

1. A house is purchased at a selling price of $285,000. The bank requires a 15% down payment. The current mortgage rate is 6.5%.

   a. Determine the amount of the down payment.

   b. What is the amount to be financed?

   c. What is the monthly payment for a 20-year mortgage on the amount in part b?

    **d.** What is the total interest paid?

2. A friend of yours is buying a new condominium for $210,000. A 20% deposit is required. In order to obtain a 5.75% mortgage rate, they must pay 2 points at the time of the closing.

    **a.** What is the amount of the down payment?

    **b.** What is the amount to be financed?

    **c.** What is the cost of the 2 points?

    **d.** What is the monthly payment for a 30-year mortgage on the amount in part b?

    **e.** What is the total interest paid?

3. **a.** How much money in interest would your friend save in mortgaging the condominium in Problem 2 if he obtained a 20-year mortgage?

    **b.** By how much would his monthly payments increase if he chose the 20-year mortgage?

4. The monthly payment for a 30-year, $185,000 conventional mortgage at 6.75% is $1199.91.

    **a.** Determine the amount of interest in the first payment.

    **b.** How much of the first payment is applied to the principal?

    **c.** What is the outstanding balance at the start of the second month of the loan?

5. You are looking for a mortgage to purchase a house selling for $300,000. You have gathered the following information about mortgage offers at two local banks:

First Bank: 10% down payment, an interest rate of 5.75%, a 30-year conventional mortgage, and 2 points to be paid at the time of closing

Second Bank: 20% down payment, an interest rate of 6.5%, a 25-year conventional mortgage, and no points

   **a.** Determine the total cost of the house if the first bank is selected.

   **b.** What is the total cost of the house if the mortgage offer from the second bank is chosen?

   **c.** Based on the results from parts a and b, which bank should you select? Explain.

6. For new homeowners, banks often require that 1/12 of the estimated property taxes and house insurance premiums be included in the monthly payment. Each month, the taxes and insurance portions of the payment are deposited into a type of savings account called an **escrow account**. The bank pays the property taxes and insurance premiums when they are due.

   A new townhouse is purchased with a mortgage of $95,000 at 6.75% for 30 years.

   **a.** What is the monthly payment needed to pay principal and interest?

   **b.** If the property taxes are $2100 per year and the insurance premium is $675.70, what amount must be added to the monthly payment?

   **c.** Determine the total monthly payment (called PITI payment) for principal, interest, taxes, and insurance.

7. You have sold your current house for a profit of $65,000 and have just received $30,000 from your grandparents' estate. Your offer of $310,000 on a new house has been accepted.

**a.** You plan to make a large down payment, including the monies from the sale of your old house, the estate, and $15,000 from savings. What will be the amount of your down payment?

**b.** What is the amount you will be financing?

**c.** The lender has offered a 30-year mortgage at 5.65% with no points. The estimated property tax is $4500 and hazard insurance costs $1200. Determine the PITI Payment.

**8.** You have enough money saved for the down payment for a new home. The monthly mortgage payment will be $850.40. All that is left is whether you qualify for the mortgage. Your annual gross earnings are $45,000. The estimated annual property taxes on the home are $1500 and the annual house insurance is $350.

**a.** Determine your total housing monthly expenses including the monthly mortgage payment and the property taxes and the insurance.

**b.** Determine your combined gross monthly income.

**c.** Determine your housing expense ratio.

**d.** Do you qualify for the loan?

**PROJECT ACTIVITY 8.7**

Which Is the Best Option?

**OBJECTIVE**

1. Use the financial models developed in this chapter to solve problems.

Each of the following problems presents a financial situation in which you must select the best option. Work with a group and be prepared to give an oral presentation of your findings to the class. The presentation should include visual displays showing any tables, equations, or graphs used in the problem solving process.

1. You are 25 years old and begin to work for a large company that offers you two different retirement options.

   **Option 1**: You will be paid a lump sum of $20,000 for each year you work for the company.

   **Option 2**: The company will deposit $10,000 annually into an account that will pay you 12% compounded monthly. When you retire, the money will be given to you.

   Which option is the best? Explain.

2. Congratulations! You have just won $50,000 in the state lottery. You decide to invest half of the money into a savings account, in order to start your own business when you graduate from college. You have three investment options:

   **Option 1**: Open a savings account that pays 6.5% simple interest.

   **Option 2**: Open a savings account that pays 3% compounded annually.

   **Option 3**: Open a savings account that pays 2.7% compounded daily.

   Which option will result in having the most money in six years? Explain.

3. You have just purchased a new computer at a local electronics store for $2400. You have two options to pay off the purchase:

   **Option 1**: Apply for a store credit card and make payments of $150 per month until paid off. Assume you will make no additional purchases using the card and that there is no annual fee. The interest on the card is 1.5% per month. Payment is due at the beginning of each month.

   **Option 2**: Apply for a fixed installment loan of $2,400 at 6.55% APR for two years.

   Which is the best option? Explain.

## Activities 8.1–8.7   What Have I Learned?

1. You invest $1000 at 4% compounded annually.

   a. Use the simple interest formula to determine the amount accumulated after three years.

   b. Use the compound interest formula to determine the amount after three years.

2. Which option would result in a greater return on your investment?

   **Option 1:**  Invest at 10% interest compounded quarterly.

   **Option 2:**  Invest at 10% interest compounded monthly.

   Explain.

3. If you invest $100 every month for five years, will you earn more interest if you made the payments at the beginning of each month or at the end of each month? Explain.

4. Banking regulations require that the effective interest rate (APR for loans, APY for deposits) be stated on all loan or investment contracts. Explain why.

5. A recent promotion for a credit card made the following introductory offer:

   • 0% fixed APR on all purchases and balance transfers for the first 12-month period

   • a low 8.5% APR thereafter

   However, if the minimum payment is not received by the due date on the billing statement or if the outstanding balance exceeds your credit limit, then your interest rate becomes a so-called default rate of 24.99%.

   a. What is the interest for the month on an average daily balance of $8000 at 8.5% APR?

**b.** What is the interest for the month on an average daily balance of $8000 at 24.99% APR?

**c.** How much more did you pay in the month at the default rate of 24.99% APR?

6. For a mortgage having a given amount and interest rate,
   **a.** What happens to the total amount of interest paid if the number of years of the mortgage increases?

   **b.** What happens to the monthly payments as the number of years increase?

## Activities 8.1–8.7    How Can I Practice?

1. You just started a new job and received a $5000 bonus. You decide to invest this money so that you can purchase a new car in four years. Your local credit union offers a CD paying 6% annual interest compounded semiannually. How much money will you have at the end of four years?

2. You are a freshman in high school and plan to attend the local community college in four years. Your father said he would pay for your college tuition, fees, and books for the first year. You estimate that $4500 will be needed to cover these expenses. Your father has done some research and has decided on a four-year CD with an interest rate of 4.65% compounded monthly. How much will he have to invest now to have $4500 in 48 months?

3. You plan to start a consulting business for computer networking. You deposit $200 at the beginning of each month into an account paying 4.75% compounded monthly.

   a. How much will be in the account after five years?

   b. How much interest was earned?

4. You notice the following advertisement in the local newspaper:

   > A 24-foot motorboat for sale
   > price of $30,000; $6000 down
   > and $555 per month for 60 months

   a. Determine the total finance charge.

   b. What is the APR of the loan?

5. You are ready to purchase your first home. This home sells for $160,000. You must put a 10% down payment and you are required to pay 3 points at the time of closing. The conventional mortgage will be for 30 years at an interest rate of 6.5%. You wonder if you can afford this home.

   a. Determine the amount of the down payment.

**b.** What is the amount of the mortgage?

**c.** Determine the cost of the 3 points.

**d.** Determine the monthly mortgage payment.

**e.** What is the total cost of the house including the down payment and points?

**f.** What is the total interest that you will pay over the life of the loan?

**g.** Determine how much of the first payment on the loan is applied to the principal.

Summary

*The bracketed numbers following each concept indicate the activity in which the concept is discussed.*

| CONCEPT / SKILL | DESCRIPTION | EXAMPLE |
|---|---|---|
| **Compound amount** [8.2] | The compound amount, also called future value, is the total amount of principal and compound interest at the end of an investment. | The compound amount of a $1000 investment at 6% interest compounded annually for two years: |

| | | |
|---|---|---|
| | | Original principal $1000.00 |
| | | Interest first year +60.00 |
| | | Balance after first year 1060.00 |
| | | Interest (.06 × 1060) +63.60 |
| | | Balance after 2 years $1123.60 |

| CONCEPT / SKILL | DESCRIPTION | EXAMPLE |
|---|---|---|
| **Calculating compound amount (future value) using the compound interest formula** [8.2] | The compound interest formula is $A = P\left(1 + \frac{r}{n}\right)^{nt}$, where $A$ is the compound amount, $P$ is the principal, $r$ is the annual interest rate (decimal form), $n$ is the number of compounding periods per year, and $t$ the number of years money invested. | See Example 1 in Activity 8.2. |
| **Calculating compound amount (future value) using technology** [8.2] | The TI-83 Plus graphing calculator has a finance applications feature (TVM Solver). | See Example 2 in Activity 8.2. |
| **The annual percentage yield (APY) or effective interest rate** [8.2] | The APY is the true rate of return on an investment. One method to calculate the APY is the Eff( feature of the TI-83 Plus. | See Example 3 in Activity 8.2. |
| **Calculating the present value of a compound amount (future value) using a formula** [8.2] | Present value is the amount that must be invested now at a compound interest to reach a given future value. The present value formula is $$PV = \frac{FV}{\left(1 + \frac{r}{n}\right)^{nt}}.$$ | The amount that must be invested now in order to have $6000 in five years, at 5.7% compounded monthly is $$P = \frac{6000}{\left(1 + \frac{0.057}{12}\right)^{5 \cdot 12}}$$ $$= \frac{6000}{(1 + 0.00475)^{60}}$$ $$= \$4515.13.$$ |
| **Calculating the present value using technology** [8.2] | The present value for a given future value of an investment can be calculated using the TVM Solver feature of the TI-83 Plus. | See Example 4 in Activity 8.2. |

| Calculating the future value of an ordinary annuity using a formula [8.3] | An annuity is the payment (or receipt) of equal cash payments per period for a given period of time. For an ordinary annuity, the payments are made at the end of each period. The future value of ordinary annuity formula is $$FV = P \cdot \frac{(1+i)^n - 1}{i},$$ where $FV$ is future value, $P$ is annuity payment, $i$ is interest rate per period (written as a decimal), and $n$ is total number of periods. | The future value of a deposit of \$1000 made at the end of every six months for two years at 8% compounded semiannually is $$FV = 1000 \cdot \frac{(1+.04)^4 - 1}{0.04}$$ $$= \$4246.46.$$ |
| --- | --- | --- |
| Calculating the future value of an annuity due using a formula [8.3] | For an annuity due, the payments are made at the beginning of each period. The future value of an annuity due formula is $$FV = P \cdot \frac{(1+i)^n - 1}{i} \cdot (1+i)$$ | The future value of a deposit of \$1000 made at the beginning of every six months for two years at 8% compounded semi-annually is $$FV = \frac{1000(1+0.04)^4 - 1}{0.04}(1+0.04)$$ $$= \$4416.32.$$ |
| Calculating the future value of an annuity using technology [8.3] | The future value of an ordinary annuity or annuity due can be calculated using the TVM Solver feature of the TI-83 Plus graphing calculator. | What is the future value of an ordinary annuity of \$500 per month, for three years, at 10% compounded monthly? Using N = 36, I% = 10, PMT = −500, PV = 0, P/Y = C/Y = 12, PMT:END, you have FV = 20890.91 |
| Calculating the present value of an annuity using technology [8.3] | The present value of annuity is a lump sum that is deposited now to yield a pay-out of equal periodic payments for a given time. Present value can be calculated using the TVM Solver feature of TI-83 Plus. | How much must be deposited now, at 6% compounded annually, to yield an annuity payment of \$5000 at the end of each year, for five years? Using N = 5, I% = 6, PMT = −5000, FV = 0, P/Y = C/Y = 1, PMT:END, PV = 21061.82. |

| | | |
|---|---|---|
| **Calculating the amortization payment by formula** [8.4] | Amortization is repaying a loan by a series of equal periodic payments over a specified period of time. The amount Amt of the amortization payment can be calculated using the formula $$\text{Amt} = PV \cdot \frac{i}{1 - (1 + i)^{-n}}$$ or, equivalently $$Amt = PV \cdot \frac{i}{1 - \dfrac{1}{(1 + i)^{n}}},$$ where Amt is amortization payment, $PV$ is amount of loan, $i$ is interest rate | per period, and $n$ is number of periods. See Example 1 in Activity 8.4. |
| **Calculating the amount of the equal period payments to amortize (liquidate) a lump sum with equal periodic payments over specified period of time** [8.4] | The TVM Solver feature of the TI-83/84 Plus graphing calculator can be used to determine the amount of the payments to liquidate a lump sum. | What payment is required at the end of each month, at 8% interest compounded monthly, to liquidate $2000 in two years? Using N = 24, I% = 8 PV = 2000, FV = 0, P/Y = C/Y = 12, PMT:END, you obtain PMT = $-90.45$. |
| **Finance charge** [8.5] | The finance charge on an installment loan is the total amount that the borrower must pay for its use. | The finance charge on an installment loan of $2000 with 24 monthly payments of $95 is the total amount of payments minus the amount financed: $$24(95) - 2000 = \$280$$ |
| **Annual percentage rate (APR)** [8.5] | The APR is the true rate of interest charged for the loan. The APR formula is $$\text{APR} = \frac{72i}{3P(n + 1) + i(n - 1)},$$ where APR is annual percentage rate, $i$ is interest (finance) charge on the loan, $P$ is principal or amount borrowed, and $n$ is number of months of the loan. | The APR on a 12-month installment loan of $1000 having finance charge of $100 is $$\text{APR} = \frac{72(100)}{3(1000)(12 + 1) + 100(12 - 1)}$$ $$= \frac{7200}{39000 + 1.1}$$ $$= 0.18 \text{ or } 18\%.$$ |
| **Calculating the APR using tables** [8.5] | The APR of a loan can be determined using APR Table 8.1 in Activity 8.5. | See Example 1 in Activity 8.5. |
| **Calculating the monthly installment payment using tables** [8.5] | If you know the APR and the number of monthly payments, the APR Table 8.1 can be used to determine the monthly payment. | See Problem 6, parts a–d, in Activity 8.5. |

| | | |
|---|---|---|
| **The amount of unearned interest when an installment loan is paid off before it is due** [8.5] | The unearned interest can be determined by the actuarial method formula $$u = \frac{npv}{100 + v},$$ where $u$ is unearned interest, $n$ is number of remaining monthly payments, $p$ is monthly payment, and $v$ is value from the APR table that corresponds to the APR for the number of remaining payments. | See Problem 7, parts a–c, in Activity 8.5. The answer in part c is: Let $n = 12$, $p = 142.98$. $v = 7.74$, $$u = \frac{npv}{100 + v}$$ $$= \frac{12(142.98)(7.74)}{100 + 7.74}$$ $$= \$123.26$$ |
| **Interest on an open-ended installment loan, such as a credit card** [8.5] | The interest on most credit card accounts is calculated using the average daily balance method. | See Example 2 in Activity 8.5. |
| **Calculating the monthly mortgage payment using a table** [8.6] | The monthly mortgage payment can be determined using Table 8.2. | See Example 1 in Activity 8.6. |
| **Calculating the monthly mortgage payment using technology** [8.6] | The TVM Solver feature of the TI-83/84 Plus can be used to determine the monthly mortgage payment. | What is the monthly payment on a $200,000 mortgage at 5.5% APR for 25 years? Let N = 300, I% = 5.5, PV = 200,000, FV = 0, P/Y = C/Y = 12, PMT:END, you obtain PMT = $-1228.17$ |
| **Amortization schedule** [8.6] | An amortization schedule displays, for given monthly payment, the amount of interest paid and the amount used to reduce principal. | See Example 2 in Activity 8.6 for a partial amortization schedule. |
| **Housing expense ratio** [8.6] | A borrower qualifies for a mortgage if the monthly housing expenses do not exceed 28% of the borrower's monthly gross income. The housing expense ratio is $$\frac{\text{monthly housing expense}}{\text{monthly gross income}}.$$ | The housing expense ratio for borrowers having $910 monthly housing expenses and $4800 monthly gross income is $\frac{910}{4800} = 0.190 = 19\% < 28\%$. The borrower qualifies. |

# Gateway Review

1.  If $100 is invested in a bank in the year the *Declaration of Independence* was signed, how much would it be worth in the year 2010? Assume the investment earned 3.5% compounded monthly.

2.  You deposit $2000 at the start of each year in a Roth IRA that earns 6.85% compounded annually. After 10 years, you stop making payments, but the money in the account continues to earn interest.

    **a.** Determine the amount in the Roth IRA after 10 years.

    **b.** If you withdraw the money 10 years after you stopped making payments, how much money did you receive?

3.  Your older brother and his wife just had a baby boy. They want to establish a college fund for their son. If they decide to deposit $2000 at the beginning of each year at 4.5% compounded annually, how much money will be in the fund after 18 years?

4.  Your parents are planning to retire and want to set aside a lump sum, earning 6.5% compounded quarterly, in order to have a pay out of $5000 per quarter for 20 years. What lump sum should your parents put aside when they retire? Assume payments are made at the beginning of each quarter.

5.  **a.** You are 20 years old. What lump sum of money must be invested today at 5.75% compounded monthly in order for the investment to have a value of $1,000,000 at age 55?

    **b.** If you started now, how much would your monthly payments be in an ordinary annuity at 5.75% compounded monthly in order to accumulate $1,000,000 at age 55?

6.  You need to finance $27,000 in order to purchase a 4-by-4 truck. The dealer offers you the option of 0% financing for 60 months or a $4500 rebate.

    **a.** What is the monthly payment if you choose the 0% financing?

**b.** If you choose the rebate, you can finance the balance for 60 months at 8% compounded monthly. What is the monthly payment? Assume payments are made at the end of each month.

**c.** Which option is the best? Explain.

7. Your passion is flying remote control model airplanes. You find the ultimate plane in a hobby shop for $675. The terms of the sale include a down payment of $175 and 12 monthly payments of $44.83.

   **a.** Determine the total amount paid or the installment price.

   **b.** Determine the finance charge of the installment loan.

   **c.** Use the formula and determine the APR.

8. You are going to college in the fall. You have just heard from your roommate who asks you to bring the stereo system for the dorm room. You find the perfect system for $1750. You have to put 25% down and you can pay the balance in 18 equal installments. The clerk tells you that you will pay a total finance charge of $112. You wonder if that is a good rate and if you can afford the monthly payments.

   **a.** How much is the down payment?

   **b.** What is the total amount financed including the finance charge?

   **c.** What is the monthly payment on the loan?

   **d.** Use the formula and determine the APR.

9. A house is selling for $250,000. The bank requires a 15% down payment, but no points. The current fixed mortgage rate is 5.75%.

   a. Determine the amount of the down payment.

   b. What is the amount of the mortgage?

   c. If a 25-year mortgage is obtained, what is the monthly mortgage payment?

   d. What is the total interest that will be paid on the loan?

   e. How much of the first payment on the loan is applied to principal?

**APPENDIX A**

# The TI-83/84 Plus Graphing Calculator

A BASIC PRIMER FOR NECESSARY FEATURES AND ROUTINES

CONTENTS

## Getting Started with the TI-83/84 Plus
## Family of Calculators

### ON-OFF

To turn on the TI-83/84 Plus, press the $\boxed{\text{ON}}$ key. To turn off the calculator, press $\boxed{\text{2nd}}$ and then $\boxed{\text{ON}}$.

Most keys on the calculator have multiple purposes. The number or symbolic function/command written directly on the key is accessed by simply pressing the key. The symbolic function/commands written above each key are accessed with the aid of the $\boxed{\text{2nd}}$ and $\boxed{\text{ALPHA}}$ keys. The command above and to the left is color coded to match the $\boxed{\text{2nd}}$ key. That command is accessed by first pressing the $\boxed{\text{2nd}}$ key and then pressing the key itself. Similarly, the command above and to the right is color coded to match the $\boxed{\text{ALPHA}}$ key and is accessed by first pressing the $\boxed{\text{ALPHA}}$ key and then pressing the key itself.

### Contrast

To adjust the contrast on your screen, press and release the $\boxed{\text{2nd}}$ key and hold $\boxed{\blacktriangle}$ to darken and $\boxed{\blacktriangledown}$ to lighten.

### Mode

The $\boxed{\text{MODE}}$ key controls many calculator settings. The activated settings are highlighted. For most of your work in this course, the settings in the left-hand column should be highlighted.

To change a setting, move the cursor to the desired setting and press $\boxed{\text{ENTER}}$.

## The Home Screen

The home screen is used for calculations.

You may return to the home screen at any time by using the QUIT command. This command is accessed by pressing (2nd) (MODE). All calculations in the home screen are subject to the order of operations.

Enter all expressions as you would write them. Always observe the order of operations. Once you have typed the expression, press (ENTER) to obtain the simplified result. Before you press (ENTER), you may edit your expression by using the arrow keys, the delete command (DEL), and the insert command (2nd) (DEL).

Three keys of special note are the reciprocal key (X⁻¹), the caret key (^), and the negative key ((-)).

Typing a number and then pressing the reciprocal command key (X⁻¹) will give the reciprocal of the number. The reciprocal of a nonzero number, $n$, is $\frac{1}{n}$. As noted in the screen below, when performing an operation on a fraction, the fraction MUST be enclosed in parentheses before accessing this command.

The caret key (^) is used to raise numbers to powers

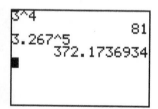

The negative key ((-)) on the bottom of the keyboard is different from the subtraction key (-). They cannot be used interchangeably. The negative key is used to change the sign of a single number or symbol; it will not perform a subtraction operation. If you mistakenly use the negative key in attempting to subtract, you will likely obtain an ERROR message.

A table of keys and their functions follows.

| KEY | FUNCTION DESCRIPTION |
| --- | --- |
| ON | Turns calculator on or off. |
| CLEAR | Clears the current line on the text screen. |
| ENTER | Executes a command. |
| (−) | Calculates the additive inverse. |
| MODE | Displays current operating settings. |
| DEL | Deletes the character at the cursor. |
| ^ | Symbol used for exponentiation. |
| ANS | Storage location of the last answer, or calculation. |
| ENTRY | Retrieves the previously executed expression. |

### ANS and ENTRY

The last two commands in the table can be real time savers. The result of your last calculation is always stored in a memory location known as ANS. It is accessed by pressing [2nd] [(−)] or it can be automatically accessed by pressing any operation button.

Suppose you want to evaluate $12.5\sqrt{1 + 0.5 \cdot (0.55)^2}$. It could be evaluated in one expression and checked with a series of calculations using ANS.

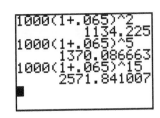

After you have keyed in an expression and pressed [ENTER], you cannot move the cursor back up to edit or recalculate this expression. This is where the ENTRY ([2nd] [ENTER]) command is used. The ENTRY command retrieves the previous expression and places the cursor at the end of the expression. You can use the left and right arrow keys to move the cursor to any location in the expression that you wish to modify.

Suppose you want to evaluate the compound interest expression $P\left(1 + \frac{r}{n}\right)^{nt}$, where $P$ is the principal, $r$ is the interest rate, $n$ is the number of compounding periods annually, and $t$ is the number of years, when $P = \$1000$, $r = 6.5\%$, $n = 1$, and $t = 2, 5$, and $15$ years.

Using the ENTRY command, this expression would be entered once and edited twice.

Note that there are many last expressions stored in the ENTRY memory location. You can repeat the ENTRY command as many times as you want to retrieve a previously entered expression.

## Functions and Graphing

### "Y =" Menu

Functions of the form $y = f(x)$ can be entered into the TI-83/84 Plus using the "Y ="menu. To access the "Y =" menu press the (Y=) key. Type the expression $f(x)$ after $Y_1$ using the (X,T,θ,n) key for the variable $x$ and press (ENTER).

For example, enter the function $f(x) = 3x^5 - 4x + 1$.

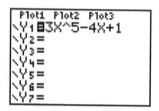

Note the = sign after $Y_1$ is highlighted. This indicates that the function $Y_1$ is active and will be graphed when the graphing command is executed and will be included in your table when the table command is executed. The highlighting may be turned on or off by using the arrow keys to move the cursor to the = symbol and then pressing (ENTER). Notice in the screen below that $Y_1$ has been deactivated and will not be graphed nor appear in a table.

Once the function is entered in the Y = menu, function values may be evaluated in the home screen.

For example, given $f(x) = 3x^5 - 4x + 1$, evaluate $f(4)$. In the home screen, press (VARS).

Move the cursor to Y-VARS and press (ENTER).

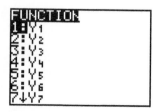

Press (ENTER) again to select Y₁. Y₁ now appears in the home screen.

To evaluate $f(4)$, press (　) (4) (　) after Y₁ and press (ENTER).

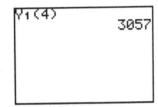

## Tables of Values

If you are interested in viewing several $y$-values for the same function, you may want to construct a table.

Before constructing the table, make sure the function appears in the "Y =" menu with its "=" highlighted. You may also want to deactivate or clear any functions that you do not need to see in your table. Next, you will need to check the settings in the Table Setup menu. To do this, use the TBLSET command ((2nd) (WINDOW)).

As shown in the screen above, the default setting for the table highlights the Auto options for both the independent ($x$) and dependent ($y$) variables. Choosing this option will display ordered pairs of the function with equally spaced $x$-values. TblStart is the first $x$-value to be displayed, and here is assigned the value $-2$. ΔTbl represents the equal spacing between consecutive $x$-values, and here is assigned the value 0.5. The TABLE command ((2nd) (GRAPH)) brings up the table displayed in the screen below.

Use the (▲) and (▼) keys to view other values in the table.

If the input values of interest are not evenly spaced, you may want to choose the ask mode for the independent variable from the Table Setup menu.

The resulting table is blank, but you can fill it by choosing any values you like for $x$ and pressing (ENTER) after each.

 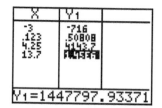

Note that the number of digits shown in the $y$- is limited by the table width, but if you want more digits, move the cursor to the desired output and more digits appear at the bottom of the screen.

## Graphing a Function

Once a function is entered in the "Y =" menu and activated it can be displayed and analyzed. For this discussion, we will use the function $f(x) = -x^2 + 10x + 12$. Enter this as $Y_1$, making sure to use the negation key ((−)) and not the subtraction key (−).

## The Viewing Window

The viewing window is the portion of the rectangular coordinate system that is displayed when you graph a function.

Xmin defines the left edge of the window.

Xmax defines the right edge of the window.

Xscl defines the distance between horizontal tick marks.

Ymin defines the bottom edge of the window.

Ymax defines the top edge of the window.

Yscl defines the distance between vertical tick marks.

In the standard viewing window, $Xmin = -10$, $Xmax = 10$, $Xscl = 1$, $Ymin = -10$, $Ymax = 10$, and $Yscl = 1$.

To select the standard viewing window, press (ZOOM) and (6).

You will view the following:

Is this an accurate and or complete picture of your function, or is the window giving you a misleading impression? You may want to use your table function to view the $y$-values for $x = -10$ to $10$.

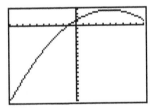

The table indicates that the minimum $y$-value on the interval from $x = -10$ to $x = 10$ is $-188$ and the maximum $y$-value is $37$. Press (WINDOW) and reset the settings to approximately the following;

Xmin $= -10$, Xmax $= 10$, Xscl $= 1$, Ymin $= -190$, Ymax $= 40$, Yscl $= 10$

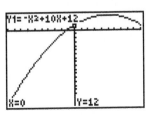

The new graph gives us a much more complete picture of the behavior of the function for $-10 \le x \le 10$.

The coordinates of specific points on the curve can be viewed by activating the trace feature. While in the graph window, press (TRACE). The function equation will be displayed at the top of the screen, a flashing cursor will appear on the curve at the middle of the screen, and the coordinates of the cursor location will be displayed at the bottom of the screen.

The left arrow key, ◀, will move the cursor toward smaller $x$-values. The right arrow key, ▶, will move the cursor toward larger $x$-values. If the cursor reaches the edge of the window and you continue to move the cursor, the window will adjust automatically.

## Zoom Menu

The Zoom menu offers several options for changing the window very quickly.

The features of each of the commands are summarized in the following table:

| ZOOM COMMAND | DESCRIPTION |
|---|---|
| 1: ZBox | Draws a box to define the viewing window. |
| 2: Zoom In | Magnifies the graph near the cursor. |
| 3: Zoom Out | Increases the viewing window around the cursor. |
| 4: ZDecimal | Sets a window so that Xscl and Yscl are 0.1. |
| 5: ZSquare | Sets equal size pixels on the $x$ and $y$ axes. |
| 6: ZStandard | Sets the window to standard settings. |
| 7: ZTrig | Sets built-in trig window variables. |
| 8: ZInteger | Sets integer values on the $x$ and $y$ axes. |
| 9: ZoomStat | Sets window based on the current values in the stat lists. |
| 0: ZoomFit | Replots graph to include the max and min output values for the current Xmin and Xmax. |

## Solving Equations Graphically

### The Intersection Method

This method is based on the fact that solutions to the equation $f(x) = g(x)$ are values of $x$ that produce the same $y$-values for the functions $f$ and $g$. Graphically, these are the $x$-coordinates of the intersection points of $y = f(x)$ and $y = g(x)$.

The following procedure illustrates how to use the intersection method to solve $x^3 + 3 = 3x$ graphically:

Step 1.  Enter the left-hand side of the equation as $Y_1$ in the "Y =" editor and the right-hand side as $Y_2$. Select the standard viewing window.

Step 2.  Examine the graphs to determine the number of intersection points.

You may need a couple of windows to be certain of the number of intersection points.

Step 3.  Access the Calculate menu by pushing (2nd) (TRACE), then choose option 5: intersect.

The cursor will appear on the first curve in the center of the window.

Step 4.  Move the cursor close to the desired intersection point and press (ENTER).

The cursor will now jump vertically to the other curve.

Step 5.  Repeat step 4 for the second curve.

Step 6.  To use the cursor's current location as your guess, press (ENTER) in response to the question on the screen that asks Guess? If you want to move to a better guess value, do so before you press (ENTER).

The coordinates of the intersection point appear below the word Intersection

The *x*-coordinate is a solution to the equation.

If there are other intersection points, repeat the process as necessary.

## Determining the Zeros of a Function

Graph the function and size the window so the *x*-intercept is visible.
For example: The zero of $y = x^3 + 2x^2 - x - 5$ is visible in the standard window, between $x = 1$ and $x = 2$. To determine the zero approximately, follow these steps.

1. Press (2nd) [CALC] to go to the CALCULATE menu, then select 2:zero.

2. Move the cursor on the graph until it is clearly to the left of the *x*-intercept, then press enter.

3. Move the cursor on the graph until it is clearly to the right of the *x*-intercept, then press enter.

4. For the guess you can simply press (ENTER). (If you move the cursor outside of the [left,right] interval you will get an error message).

The zero is $x \approx 1.3744$.

If there are more zeros, each must be determined separately by following the same procedure.

## Alternative Method to Determine a Zero

If the constant function $y = 0$ is entered as a second function, the zeros can be found by using the intersection method discussed previously.

## Determining the Linear Regression Equation for a Set of Data

**Example:**

| x | y |
|---|---|
| 2 | 2 |
| 3 | 5 |
| 4 | 3 |
| 5 | 7 |
| 6 | 9 |

Enter the data into the calculator as follows:

1. Press (STAT) and choose EDIT.

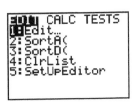

2. The TI-83/84 Plus has six built-in lists, L1, L2, . . . , L6. If there is data in L1, clear the list as follows:

   **a.** Use the arrows to place the cursor on L1 at the top of the list. Press (CLEAR) followed by (ENTER), followed by the down arrow.

   **b.** Follow the same procedure to clear L2 if necessary.

   **c.** Enter the *x*-values into L1 and the *y*-values into L2.

To see a scatterplot of the data proceed as follows.

1. STAT PLOT is the 2nd function of the (Y=) key. You must press (2nd) before pressing (Y=) to access the STAT PLOT menu.

2. Select Plot 1 and make sure that Plots 2 and 3 are Off. The screen shown below will appear. Select On and then choose the scatterplot option (first icon) on the Type line. Confirm that your *x* and *y* values are stored, respectively, in $L_1$ and $L_2$. The symbols $L_1$ and $L_2$ are 2nd functions of the (1) and (2) keys, respectively. Finally, select the small square as the mark that will be used to plot each point.

3. Press (Y=) and clear or deselect any functions currently stored.

4. To display the scatterplot, have the calculator determine an appropriate window by pressing (ZOOM) and then (9) (ZoomStat).

*The following instructions will calculate the linear regression equation and store it in $Y_1$.*

1. Press (STAT) and right arrow to highlight CALC.

2. Choose 4: LinReg($ax + b$). LinReg($ax + b$) will be pasted to the home screen. To tell the calculator where the data is, press (2nd) and (1) (for L1), then (,), then (2nd) and (2) (for L2) because the $x$ list and $y$ list are stored in $L_1$ and $L_2$ respectively. The display looks like this:

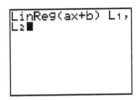

3. Press (,) and then press (VARS).

4. Right arrow to highlight Y-VARS.

**5.** Choose 1, FUNCTION.

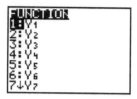

**6.** Choose 1 for $Y_1$ (or 2 for $Y_2$, etc.).

**7.** Press (ENTER).

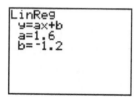

The linear regression equation for this data is $y = 1.6x - 1.2$.

**8.** To display the regression line, press (GRAPH).

**9.** Press the (Y=) key to view the equation.

## Determining the Correlation Coefficient and Residuals

**10.** If the correlation coefficient, r, does not appear with the linear regression equation, as in step 7 on page A-16, press (2nd) and (9) (CATALOG), scroll down to select DiagnosticOn, press (ENTER) twice. This will allow you to see r whenever you find a linear regression equation.

**11.** Whenever a regression equation is calculated, the residuals are automatically stored in a list. To see the residuals, go to (STAT) (EDIT) and highlight L3 at the top of the list. Press (2nd) (DEL) (for INSERT) which will open a new list. At the flashing cursor, press (2nd) (STAT) (for LIST) and scroll down to select RESID. Press (ENTER) twice and the list of residuals will appear.

## Histograms, Boxplots, and Statistics

### Entering a Collection of Data

Press (STAT), then choose (EDIT). You will see a table with heading L1, L2, L3, (L is for List). If there is a list of numbers already stored under L1, move the cursor to the L1 heading, then press (CLEAR) and (ENTER). When the list is empty start entering the data one number at a time. If you wish to store more than one set of data values, simply repeat the process for any of list L2 through L6.

**Example:**

| COLLECTION OF DATA | | | | |
|---|---|---|---|---|
| 18 | 20 | 19 | 23 | 20 |
| 19 | 25 | 21 | 18 | 27 |
| 20 | 35 | 23 | 19 | 21 |
| 28 | 18 | 21 | 28 | 33 |

**1.** Press (STAT) and choose (EDIT).

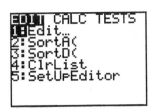

2. To enter one variable data, you will need only one list.

   a. If there is data in L1, clear the list.

   b. Enter the data into L1.

## Calculating One-Variable Statistics

Press STAT, then choose CALC. From the calculate menu, press ENTER to choose the one-variable statistics. When you see 1-Var Stats on your home screen, enter the name of the list where your data is stored (the second function of 1 through 6).

1. To calculate the one variable statistics using the example data in L1, press STAT, highlight CALC, then choose option 1: 1-Var Stats.

2. When 1-Var Stats appears on the home screen, enter 2nd and 1 (for L1). The following basic statistics appear. Scroll down to see the second screen.

The statistics you should note are:

mean, $\bar{x}$ = 22.8

standard deviation, $\sigma_x$ = 4.874423043

number of data values, $n = 20$

median, med = 21

## Creating a Histogram for One-Variable Data

**1.** Using the example data in L1, press ⟨2nd⟩ and ⟨Y=⟩ to get the STAT PLOT menu. Choose any of Plot1, Plot2, or Plot3, making sure the two you *don't* choose are Off.

**2.** In the plot menu, highlight and select On, histogram type of plot, L1 for the Xlist, and 1 for the Freq, as shown:

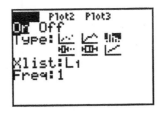

**3.** To see a histogram, press ⟨ZOOM⟩ and choose option 9: ZoomStat. The following histogram shows the domain of the distribution, grouping data values into classes.

**4.** To show the histogram where each rectangle represents one data value, press ⟨WINDOW⟩ and set Xscl to 1, then press ⟨GRAPH⟩.

**5.** Pressing ⟨TRACE⟩ allows you to see the frequency for each data value.

## Creating a Boxplot for One-Variable Data

**1.** In the plot menu, highlight and select On, boxplot type of plot, L1 for the Xlist, and 1 for the Freq, as shown below:

**2.** To see a boxplot, press (ZOOM) and choose option 9: ZoomStat.

**3.** Pressing (TRACE) allows you to see the five-number summary for this distribution.

## Factorials, Permutations, and Combinations (or Binomial Coefficients)

All are found by selecting the probability menu.

Press (MATH) and choose the PRB menu.

**1.** To calculate ten factorial, enter the integer followed by (MATH), choose the PRB menu, and select option 4: !, then (ENTER).

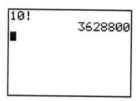

**2.** To calculate the number of permutations of ten things taken four at a time, enter 10 followed by (MATH), choose the PRB menu, and select option 2: nPr, followed by 4, then (ENTER).

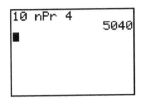

**3.** To calculate the number of combinations of ten things taken four at a time, or the binomial coefficient $\begin{pmatrix} 10 \\ 4 \end{pmatrix}$, enter 10 followed by (MATH), choose the PRB menu, and select option 3: nCr, followed by 4, then (ENTER).

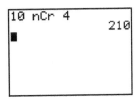

## Generating a List of Random Numbers

**1.** Press (STAT) and choose (EDIT).

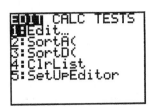

**2.** Clear list L1 and highlight the L1 heading. Press (MATH), choose the PRB menu, and select option 5: randInt(.

**3.** To randomly generate integers between 0 and 1, enter this domain, followed by the quantity of numbers desired, separated by commas. The following command generates a list of 50 zeros and ones. (Note that the command is too long to fit on the screen at once.)

4. To quickly add the numbers in a list, from the home screen, press (2nd) and (STAT) (for LIST), choose the MATH menu, and select option 5: sum(. Enter the name of the list, L1, and the sum will be displayed, as shown.

In this example, 22 of the 50 integers were ones.

## Binomial Probabilities

### Simulation of a Binomial Experiment

Example: Tossing a fair coin five times and recording the number of heads, 0 through 5.

To generate a random integer from a binomial distribution, with 5 trials and probability of success 0.5, press (MATH) and choose the PRB menu, and select option 7: randBin(, (ENTER) followed by 5, 0.5) (ENTER).

 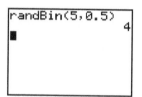

In this case a number between 0 and 5 (the number of heads) will be generated.

To generate a list of such random numbers, to create a simulation, a third number is included after the probability of success, the number of simulations. If not included, as in the previous example, the default is one simulation.

To simulate this experiment 500 times, storing the results in a list, start by pressing (STAT), select EDIT, and highlight the name of a list (L1 in this example) and press (CLEAR) and (ENTER) to empty L1. Highlight L1 again and press (MATH), choose the PRB menu, select option 7: randBin(, (ENTER) followed by 5, 0.5, 500) (ENTER). After a short while, the 500 randomly generated results will appear in L1.

The results can best be seen by generating a histogram for the list of data in L1. (Refer to Creating a Histogram for One-Variable Data on page A-19). The following window settings will allow you to trace the histogram and record the frequency for each possible number of heads (successes).

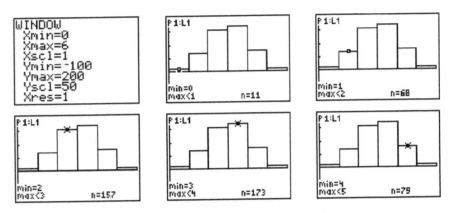

## Calculating Binomial Probabilities

A single binomial probability can be quickly determined by using the probability distribution feature on the TI-83/84 Plus. To find the probability of getting 3 heads when a fair coin is tossed 5 times ($n = 5$, $p = 0.5$, $x = 3$), in the home screen, press (2nd) and (VARS) and select option 0:binompdf(, followed by 5, 0.5, 3) (ENTER), to get the exact theoretical probability.

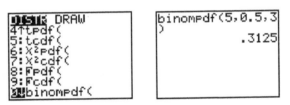

## Determining the Area under a Normal Distribution Curve

To determine the area under the normal curve between $x = 12$ and $x = 18$, where $\mu = 16$ and $\sigma = 4$:

**1.** Press (2nd), (VARS) to get to the distribution (DISTR) menu.

**2.** Menu item 2, normalcdf, is used to get areas (probabilities) under a normal curve. Press 2 to select normalcdf from the menu to paste the function to the home screen.

**3.** Enter the following four values, separated by commas: left boundary, right boundary, mean, standard deviation.

Enter: 12, 18, 16, 4) and press (ENTER)

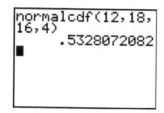

Therefore, $P(12 < x < 18) \approx 0.5328$

If the area extends indefinitely to the right or left, such as in finding $P(x < 12)$ or $P(x > 18)$, then a left or right score at least 5 standard deviations from the mean is used.

```
normalcdf(-4,12,
16,4)
        .1586549725
normalcdf(18,36,
16,4)
        .3085372451
```

Therefore, $P(x < 12) \approx 0.1587$ and $P(x > 18) \approx 0.3085$.

If the area under a standard normal curve is desired, only the left and right boundaries need to be entered, in which case the calculator assumes $\mu = 0$ and $\sigma = 1$.

```
normalcdf(-1.5,1
.0)
        .7745375117
```

Therefore, $P(-1.5 < z < 1.0) \approx 0.7745$

## Determining a Boundary Value, Given the Area under a Normal Distribution Curve

**1.** Select item 3:invNorm( from the DISTR menu.

**2.** After the invNorm( function appears in the home screen, enter the area under the curve, which is to the left of the desired cut-off value, followed by the mean and standard deviation.

For example, to find $k$ so that $P(x < k) = 0.75$, where $\mu = 16$ and $\sigma = 4$,

Enter: 0.75, 16, 4) and press ENTER

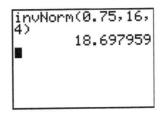

```
invNorm(0.75,16,
4)
        18.697959
■
```

Therefore, $P(x < 18.70) \approx 0.75$

## APPENDIX B

# Metric–U.S. Conversions

### Length

1 meter = 3.28 feet
1 meter = 1.094 yards
1 centimeter = 0.394 inches
1 kilometer = 0.6214 miles

1 foot = 0.305 meters
1 yard = 0.914 meters
1 inch = 2.54 centimeters
1 mile = 1.6093 kilometers

### Temperature

Celsius (C) to Fahrenheit (F)
$F = \frac{9}{5}C + 32$
Fahrenheit (F) to Celsius (C)
$C = \frac{5}{9}(F - 32)$

### Weight

1 gram = 0.03527 ounces
1 kilogram = 2.205 pounds
1 gram = 0.002205 pounds

1 ounce = 28.35 grams
1 pound = 0.454 kilograms
1 pound = 454 grams

### Volume

1 liter = 1.057 quarts
1 liter = 0.2642 gallons

1 quart = 0.946 liters
1 gallon = 3.785 liters

# U.S. System of Measurement

### Length

1 foot = 12 inches
1 yard = 3 feet
1 mile = 5280 feet

### Weight

1 pound = 16 ounces
1 ton = 2000 pounds

### Volume

1 cup = 8 fluid ounces
1 pint = 2 cups
1 quart = 2 pints
1 gallon = 4 quarts

# Metric System of Measurement

### Length

1 kilometer (km) = 1000 meters (m)
1 hectometer (hm) = 100 m
1 dekameter (dam) = 10 m

1 decimeter (dm) = $\frac{1}{10}$ m = 0.1 m
1 centimeter (cm) = $\frac{1}{100}$ m = 0.01 m
1 millimeter (mm) = $\frac{1}{1000}$ m = 0.001 m

### Mass

1 kilogram (kg) = 1000 grams (g)
1 hectogram (hg) = 100 g
1 dekagram (dag) = 10 g

1 decigram (dg) = $\frac{1}{10}$ g = 0.1 g
1 centigram (cg) = $\frac{1}{100}$ g = 0.01 g
1 milligram (mg) = $\frac{1}{1000}$ g = 0.001 g

### Volume

1 kiloliter (kl) = 1000 liters (L)
1 hectoliter (hl) = 100 g
1 dekaliter (dal) = 10 g

1 deciliter (dl) = $\frac{1}{10}$ L = 0.1 L
1 centiliter (cl) = $\frac{1}{100}$ L = 0.01 L
1 milliliter (ml) = $\frac{1}{1000}$ L = 0.001 L

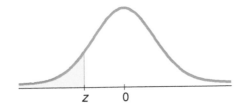

# NEGATIVE *z* Scores

| TABLE C | Standard Normal (z) Distribution: Cumulative Area from the LEFT | | | | | | | | | |
|---|---|---|---|---|---|---|---|---|---|---|
| z | .00 | .01 | .02 | .03 | .04 | .05 | .06 | .07 | .08 | .09 |
| −3.50 and lower | .0001 | | | | | | | | | |
| −3.4 | .0003 | .0003 | .0003 | .0003 | .0003 | .0003 | .0003 | .0003 | .0003 | .0002 |
| −3.3 | .0005 | .0005 | .0005 | .0004 | .0004 | .0004 | .0004 | .0004 | .0004 | .0003 |
| −3.2 | .0007 | .0007 | .0006 | .0006 | .0006 | .0006 | .0006 | .0005 | .0005 | .0005 |
| −3.1 | .0010 | .0009 | .0009 | .0009 | .0008 | .0008 | .0008 | .0008 | .0007 | .0007 |
| −3.0 | .0013 | .0013 | .0013 | .0012 | .0012 | .0011 | .0011 | .0011 | .0010 | .0010 |
| −2.9 | .0019 | .0018 | .0018 | .0017 | .0016 | .0016 | .0015 | .0015 | .0014 | .0014 |
| −2.8 | .0026 | .0025 | .0024 | .0023 | .0023 | .0022 | .0021 | .0021 | .0020 | .0019 |
| −2.7 | .0035 | .0034 | .0033 | .0032 | .0031 | .0030 | .0029 | .0028 | .0027 | .0026 |
| −2.6 | .0047 | .0045 | .0044 | .0043 | .0041 | .0040 | .0039 | .0038 | .0037 | .0036 |
| −2.5 | .0062 | .0060 | .0059 | .0057 | .0055 | .0054 | .0052 | .0051 | .0049 | .0048 |
| −2.4 | .0082 | .0080 | .0078 | .0075 | .0073 | .0071 | .0069 | .0068 | .0066 | .0064 |
| −2.3 | .0107 | .0104 | .0102 | .0099 | .0096 | .0094 | .0091 | .0089 | .0087 | .0084 |
| −2.2 | .0139 | .0136 | .0132 | .0129 | .0125 | .0122 | .0119 | .0116 | .0113 | .0110 |
| −2.1 | .0179 | .0174 | .0170 | .0166 | .0162 | .0158 | .0154 | .0150 | .0146 | .0143 |
| −2.0 | .0228 | .0222 | .0217 | .0212 | .0207 | .0202 | .0197 | .0192 | .0188 | .0183 |
| −1.9 | .0287 | .0281 | .0274 | .0268 | .0262 | .0256 | .0250 | .0244 | .0239 | .0233 |
| −1.8 | .0359 | .0351 | .0344 | .0336 | .0329 | .0322 | .0314 | .0307 | .0301 | .0294 |
| −1.7 | .0446 | .0436 | .0427 | .0418 | .0409 | .0401 | .0392 | .0384 | .0375 | .0367 |
| −1.6 | .0548 | .0537 | .0526 | .0516 | .0505 | .0495 | .0485 | .0475 | .0465 | .0455 |
| −1.5 | .0668 | .0655 | .0643 | .0630 | .0618 | .0606 | .0594 | .0582 | .0571 | .0559 |
| −1.4 | .0808 | .0793 | .0778 | .0764 | .0749 | .0735 | .0721 | .0708 | .0694 | .0681 |
| −1.3 | .0968 | .0951 | .0934 | .0918 | .0901 | .0885 | .0869 | .0853 | .0838 | .0823 |
| −1.2 | .1151 | .1131 | .1112 | .1093 | .1075 | .1056 | .1038 | .1020 | .1003 | .0985 |
| −1.1 | .1357 | .1335 | .1314 | .1292 | .1271 | .1251 | .1230 | .1210 | .1190 | .1170 |
| −1.0 | .1587 | .1562 | .1539 | .1515 | .1492 | .1469 | .1446 | .1423 | .1401 | .1379 |
| −0.9 | .1841 | .1814 | .1788 | .1762 | .1736 | .1711 | .1685 | .1660 | .1635 | .1611 |
| −0.8 | .2119 | .2090 | .2061 | .2033 | .2005 | .1977 | .1949 | .1922 | .1894 | .1867 |
| −0.7 | .2420 | .2389 | .2358 | .2327 | .2296 | .2266 | .2236 | .2206 | .2177 | .2148 |
| −0.6 | .2743 | .2709 | .2676 | .2643 | .2611 | .2578 | .2546 | .2514 | .2483 | .2451 |
| −0.5 | .3085 | .3050 | .3015 | .2981 | .2946 | .2912 | .2877 | .2843 | .2810 | .2776 |
| −0.4 | .3446 | .3409 | .3372 | .3336 | .3300 | .3264 | .3228 | .3192 | .3156 | .3121 |
| −0.3 | .3821 | .3783 | .3745 | .3707 | .3669 | .3632 | .3594 | .3557 | .3520 | .3483 |
| −0.2 | .4207 | .4168 | .4129 | .4090 | .4052 | .4013 | .3974 | .3936 | .3897 | .3859 |
| −0.1 | .4602 | .4562 | .4522 | .4483 | .4443 | .4404 | .4364 | .4325 | .4286 | .4247 |
| −0.0 | .5000 | .4960 | .4920 | .4880 | .4840 | .4801 | .4761 | .4721 | .4681 | .4641 |

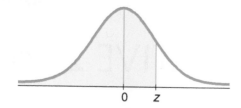

# POSITIVE z Scores

| TABLE C | Standard Normal (z) Distribution: Cumulative Area from the LEFT | | | | | | | | | |
|---|---|---|---|---|---|---|---|---|---|---|
| z | .00 | .01 | .02 | .03 | .04 | .05 | .06 | .07 | .08 | .09 |
| 0.0 | .5000 | .5040 | .5080 | .5120 | .5160 | .5199 | .5239 | .5279 | .5319 | .5359 |
| 0.1 | .5398 | .5438 | .5478 | .5517 | .5557 | .5596 | .5636 | .5675 | .5714 | .5753 |
| 0.2 | .5793 | .5832 | .5871 | .5910 | .5948 | .5987 | .6026 | .6064 | .6103 | .6141 |
| 0.3 | .6179 | .6217 | .6255 | .6293 | .6331 | .6368 | .6406 | .6443 | .6480 | .6517 |
| 0.4 | .6554 | .6591 | .6628 | .6664 | .6700 | .6736 | .6772 | .6808 | .6844 | .6879 |
| 0.5 | .6915 | .6950 | .6985 | .7019 | .7054 | .7088 | .7123 | .7157 | .7190 | .7224 |
| 0.6 | .7257 | .7291 | .7324 | .7357 | .7389 | .7422 | .7454 | .7486 | .7517 | .7549 |
| 0.7 | .7580 | .7611 | .7642 | .7673 | .7704 | .7734 | .7764 | .7794 | .7823 | .7852 |
| 0.8 | .7881 | .7910 | .7939 | .7967 | .7995 | .8023 | .8051 | .8078 | .8106 | .8133 |
| 0.9 | .8159 | .8186 | .8212 | .8238 | .8264 | .8289 | .8315 | .8340 | .8365 | .8389 |
| 1.0 | .8413 | .8438 | .8461 | .8485 | .8508 | .8531 | .8554 | .8577 | .8599 | .8621 |
| 1.1 | .8643 | .8665 | .8686 | .8708 | .8729 | .8749 | .8770 | .8790 | .8810 | .8830 |
| 1.2 | .8849 | .8869 | .8888 | .8907 | .8925 | .8944 | .8962 | .8980 | .8997 | .9015 |
| 1.3 | .9032 | .9049 | .9066 | .9082 | .9099 | .9115 | .9131 | .9147 | .9162 | .9177 |
| 1.4 | .9192 | .9207 | .9222 | .9236 | .9251 | .9265 | .9279 | .9292 | .9306 | .9319 |
| 1.5 | .9332 | .9345 | .9357 | .9370 | .9382 | .9394 | .9406 | .9418 | .9429 | .9441 |
| 1.6 | .9452 | .9463 | .9474 | .9484 | .9495 | .9505 | .9515 | .9525 | .9535 | .9545 |
| 1.7 | .9554 | .9564 | .9573 | .9582 | .9591 | .9599 | .9608 | .9616 | .9625 | .9633 |
| 1.8 | .9641 | .9649 | .9656 | .9664 | .9671 | .9678 | .9686 | .9693 | .9699 | .9706 |
| 1.9 | .9713 | .9719 | .9726 | .9732 | .9738 | .9744 | .9750 | .9756 | .9761 | .9767 |
| 2.0 | .9772 | .9778 | .9783 | .9788 | .9793 | .9798 | .9803 | .9808 | .9812 | .9817 |
| 2.1 | .9821 | .9826 | .9830 | .9834 | .9838 | .9842 | .9846 | .9850 | .9854 | .9857 |
| 2.2 | .9861 | .9864 | .9868 | .9871 | .9875 | .9878 | .9881 | .9884 | .9887 | .9890 |
| 2.3 | .9893 | .9896 | .9898 | .9901 | .9904 | .9906 | .9909 | .9911 | .9913 | .9916 |
| 2.4 | .9918 | .9920 | .9922 | .9925 | .9927 | .9929 | .9931 | .9932 | .9934 | .9936 |
| 2.5 | .9938 | .9940 | .9941 | .9943 | .9945 | .9946 | .9948 | .9949 | .9951 | .9952 |
| 2.6 | .9953 | .9955 | .9956 | .9957 | .9959 | .9960 | .9961 | .9962 | .9963 | .9964 |
| 2.7 | .9965 | .9966 | .9967 | .9968 | .9969 | .9970 | .9971 | .9972 | .9973 | .9974 |
| 2.8 | .9974 | .9975 | .9976 | .9977 | .9977 | .9978 | .9979 | .9979 | .9980 | .9981 |
| 2.9 | .9981 | .9982 | .9982 | .9983 | .9984 | .9984 | .9985 | .9985 | .9986 | .9986 |
| 3.0 | .9987 | .9987 | .9987 | .9988 | .9988 | .9989 | .9989 | .9989 | .9990 | .9990 |
| 3.1 | .9990 | .9991 | .9991 | .9991 | .9992 | .9992 | .9992 | .9992 | .9993 | .9993 |
| 3.2 | .9993 | .9993 | .9994 | .9994 | .9994 | .9994 | .9994 | .9995 | .9995 | .9995 |
| 3.3 | .9995 | .9995 | .9995 | .9996 | .9996 | .9996 | .9996 | .9996 | .9996 | .9997 |
| 3.4 | .9997 | .9997 | .9997 | .9997 | .9997 | .9997 | .9997 | .9997 | .9997 | .9998 |
| 3.50 and up | .9999 | | | | | | | | | |

# APPENDIX D

## Glossary of Geometric Formulas

Perimeter and Area of a Triangle, and Sum of Measures of the Angles

$$P = a + b + c$$
$$A = \tfrac{1}{2}bh$$
$$A + B + C = 180°$$

Pythagorean Theorem

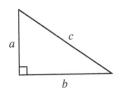

$$a^2 + b^2 = c^2$$

Perimeter and Area of a Rectangle

$$P = 2l + 2w$$
$$A = lw$$

Perimeter and Area of a Square

$$P = 4s$$
$$A = s^2$$

Area of a Trapezoid

$$A = \tfrac{1}{2}h(b_1 + b_2)$$

Circumference and Area of a Circle

$$C = 2\pi r$$
$$A = \pi r^2$$

Volume and Surface Area of a Rectangular Solid

$$V = lwh$$
$$SA = 2lw + 2lh + 2wh$$

Volume and Surface Area of a Sphere

$$V = \tfrac{4}{3}\pi r^3$$
$$SA = 4\pi r^2$$

Volume and Surface Area of a Right Circular Cylinder

$$V = \pi r^2 h$$
$$SA = 2\pi r^2 + 2\pi rh$$

Volume and Surface Area of a Right Circular Cone

$$V = \tfrac{1}{3}\pi r^2 h$$
$$SA = \pi r^2 + \pi rl$$

# Interval Notation

$(a, b) = a < x < b$     $(-\infty, a) = x < a$

$(a, b] = a < x \leq b$     $(-\infty, a] = x \leq a$

$[a, b) = a \leq x < b$     $(a, \infty) = x > a$

$[a, b] = a \leq x \leq b$     $[a, \infty) = x \geq a$

# Glossary of Functions

| Constant Function | Linear Function | Quadratic Function | Cubic Function |
|---|---|---|---|
| $f(x) = b$ | $f(x) = mx + b$ | $f(x) = ax^2 + bx + c,$ $a \neq 0$ | $f(x) = x^3$ |

Piecewise Linear Function     Absolute Value Function     Exponential Function     Exponential Function

$$f(x) = \begin{cases} ax + b, & x \leq r \\ cx + d, & x > r \end{cases}$$     $f(x) = |ax + b|$     $f(x) = ab^x$ $a > 0, b > 1$     $f(x) = ab^x$ $a > 0, 0 < b < 1$

Logarithmic Function     Logarithmic Function

$f(x) = a(\log_b x)$     $f(x) = a(\log_b x)$
$a > 0, b > 1$     $0 < b < 1, a > 0$

# Index

A-38   INDEX